TT 78-52029/04

A Revised Handbook
to the
FLORA OF CEYLON

VOLUME IV

Sponsored jointly by the
University of Peradeniya,
Department of Agriculture, Peradeniya, Sri Lanka
and the Smithsonian Institution,
Washington, D.C., U.S.A.

General Editor
M.D. DASSANAYAKE

Editorial Board
M.D. DASSANAYAKE and F.R. FOSBERG

Published for the Smithsonian Institution, and the
National Science Foundation, Washington, D.C.,
by Amerind Publishing Co. Pvt. Ltd., New Delhi
1983

January 1983

Published for the Smithsonian Institution, pursuant to an agreement with the National Science Foundation, Washington, D.C., by Amerind Publishing Co. Pvt. Ltd., 66 Janpath, New Delhi 110001

Printed at Oxonian Press Pvt. Ltd., Faridabad, India

FOREWORD

The Handbook to the Flora of Ceylon, by Henry Trimen, published in 1893–1900, was in its time, one of the most comprehensive and outstanding floras available for any comparable tropical areas. In 1931 A.H.G. Alston added a volume of additions, updating, and corrections to the original five volumes. These six volumes for many years served their purpose very well.

However, the original Handbook was published in a very small edition, and the paper on which it was printed, as was usually the case at the time, was very poor and has deteriorated very badly. Hence the Handbook has for years been absolutely unobtainable, and there are very few copies available even in libraries in Ceylon. Furthermore, botanical science has made substantial progress since the Handbook appeared, and many of Trimen's taxonomic and nomenclatural conclusions are now outdated. Also, with more thorough botanical exploration, new plants have been found to be members of the Ceylon flora. Hence, a new edition of this magnificent work was long overdue.

For quite a number of years Professor B.A. Abeywickrama had in mind a revision of Trimen's Handbook. But heavier and heavier administrative duties consumed his time and there was little opportunity for work on the Ceylon Flora, though he did produce, in 1959, on updated Checklist of the Ceylon Flora, which has been most useful to botanists.

Fortuitously, in 1967, the Smithsonian Institution initiated a number of research projects in Ceylon, in cooperation with Ceylonese institutions and scientists. These included an investigation of several problems in plant ecology, with which Prof. Abeywickrama was associated as Co-Principal Investigator. These projects were financed by the Smithsonian using U.S. excess foreign currency under the provisions of Public Law 480.

While we were discussing the ecological investigations, Prof. Abeywickrama wondered if it might not be possible to initiate, using PL-480 support, a project for the revision of Trimen's Handbook to the Flora of Ceylon. I offered to work up a cooperative proposal and submit it to the Smithsonian Special Foreign Currency Program.

This was duly done, approved, and a year's tentative budget authorized. The project was started under the joint auspices of the Smithsonian Institution, the Ceylon Department of Agriculture and the University of Ceylon. I was appointed Principal Investigator. Co-Principal Investigators are Prof. B.A. Abeywickrama, Dr. J.W.L. Peiris, Mr. D.M.A. Jayaweera, Prof. M.D. Dassanayake, and Mr. K.L.D. Amaratunga. The plan was to enlist the cooperation of botanists, from wherever available, who were preferably experts in particular families represented in the Ceylon flora. These monographers would be given a period of field work in Ceylon, an opportunity to study the specimens in the Ceylon National Herbarium, in the Royal Botanic Gardens, Peradeniya, with expenses met by the Smithsonian Institution. In return, they would provide updated manuscripts of their families for the revised Handbook, which would then be published by the University of Ceylon, with Smithsonian financing.

This enterprise was initiated in February, 1968, and has been continued without interruption since that date. Quarters for the work, herbarium and library, and other facilities have been furnished by the Division of Systematic Botany of the Department of Agriculture, Peradeniya and by the Botany Department, Faculty of Science, University of Ceylon, Peradeniya. We have enjoyed the cooperation of the U.S. Embassy, Colombo, various Ceylon government departments and agencies, especially the Wildlife Department and the Forest Department, and of many plantations and individuals in all parts of Ceylon, too numerous to enumerate.

Special thanks must be offered to Professor Dieter Mueller-Dombois, of the Botany Department, University of Hawaii, who was for two years Principal Field Investigator for the plant ecology project, and who, on top of his duties in that capacity, supervised the activities of the flora project staff, facilitated the work of the visiting botanists, and acted as finance officer of the project. Without his help, the flora project could not have got started.

Special thanks are also offered to Dr. Marie-Hélène Sachet, Research Botanist, Smithsonian Institution, who, though in no official capacity in the Project, has carried much of the administrative burden, at a sacrifice of her own work. The members of the Flora Project staff at Peradeniya directed by Mr. F.H. Popham, Smithsonian Representative in Ceylon, also deserve great credit for their willing and enthusiastic assistance to the visitors, handling and processing of specimens, typing of labels and manuscripts, and keeping the Project's work going.

The materials on which the flora revisions are based are the visiting botanists' own collections, the herbarium at Peradeniya, personal collections of Mr. K.L.D. Amaratunga and the late Mr. Thomas B. Worthington of Kandy, and materials housed in various foreign herbaria, especially those of Kew, British Museum, and the Indian National Herbarium, Calcutta for the use of which we are grateful to those in charge. A large amount of valuable material was amassed as vouchers for the ecological observations mentioned above and has been utilised by the flora project botanists. Sets of the specimens collected under the auspices of the Smithsonian projects are deposited and permanently available in the U.S. National Herbarium and the Ceylon National Herbarium, Peradeniya. Partial sets are also being deposited in several other Ceylon institutions and in a number of herbaria with tropical interests in other parts of the world.

The resulting revised treatments of the families are to be published, as material accumulates, in volumes of convenient size, without regard to the order of families. Those families, previously published in fascicles 1 and 2, are to be republished, in revised form, in the new format, as manuscripts are received from the authors. An editorial format has been suggested by us, but the content of each revision and the taxonomic conclusions are those of the various authors. An attempt has been made to have the nomenclature in accord with International Code of Botanical Nomenclature, but the application of the Code is, again, the final responsibility of the authors.

A comprehensive index to these volumes will be prepared and published as a separate volume.

It is hoped that, after the Handbook treatments are published, simplified versions can be prepared, suitable for lower school use and for the use of non-botanists.

We also have the hope that the new Handbook will stimulate active interest in the plant resources of Ceylon. Above all, it is hoped that this interest will bring about the establishment of more national parks and nature reserves in all parts of Ceylon, in order that the remarkable Ceylon flora may still have a suitable range of habitats in which to live. By this means, only, the species will be able to survive for the use and pleasure of many future generations of Ceylonese and of visitors from other parts of the world. Without a great increase in such reserves, at the present rate of deforestation and bringing land under agriculture, very many species will surely become extinct in the near future, as some probably already have.

F.R. FOSBERG,
Botanist, Emeritus,
Smithsonian Institution,
Washington, D.C., U.S.A.

CONTENTS

A Revised Handbook
to the
FLORA OF CEYLON

VOLUME IV

ANACARDIACEAE

(by Willem Meijer*)

Type genus: *Anacardium* L.

Trees or shrubs. Leaves in general spirally arranged, simple, trifoliate or imparipinnate. Stipules absent. Bark often resinuous. Flowers in terminal or axillary panicles or in inflorescences more or less like corymbs or rarely spikes, bisexual or unisexual, usually regular, (3–) 5 (–6)-merous, small. Sepals free or connate. Petals free or adnate at base, imbricate or valvate. Stamens (3)– 5–10, inserted on a disk, sometimes reduced to staminodes; anthers 2-celled, usually with filaments attached in the middle, cells longitudinally dehiscent. Disk annular, often lobed. Ovary 1 or more rarely 4–5 per flower, 1-celled (rarely 5-celled), cells with one ovule; styles 1–5, free or connate; ovule pendulous, anatropous, often with a long funiculus. Fruit a drupe with usually one seed, and with a resinuous mesocarp, one-celled, rarely 5-celled. Seed with nuclear endosperm, persistent as a thin layer or wholly absorbed; embryo large, cotyledons plane-convex or flat.

A family mostly distributed in tropical lowlands all over the world, with about 55 genera and 500 species; 6 genera and 18 species in Ceylon, the genera all with the Indo-Malesian type of distribution; the genus *Semecarpus* richly developed in the wet zone (and with some species common in the wet and intermediate zone) up to about 6000 ft altitude; *Campnosperma* and *Mangifera* each with a local endemic species; *Spondias pinnata* and *Lannea coromandelica* of wide occurrence in the Indo-Malesian area; *Buchanania* and *Nothopegia* each with one species in India and Ceylon. The largest timber trees in this family are *Mangifera zeylanica*, a species of the low country in the dry as well as wet zones, and *Campnosperma zeylanica*. *Lannea coromandelica* and *Spondias pinnata* are the only genera with pinnately compound leaves, widely planted in the lowlands of the wet zone and deciduous trees in the dry zone, and *Spondias* with a special variety (or species?) in the dry zone.

The family is most closely related to the Burseraceae and chemically characterised by the occurrence of toxic resins often turning black on exposure, especially in *Semecarpus* but also to a lesser extent in *Nothopegia* and *Campnosperma*, never with a turpentine smell as in the Burseraceae.

*University of Kentucky and Missouri Bot. Garden, U.S.A.

1

Species of this family are in general recognised by local people from characters of bole and leaves and some keys based on this are given below.

KEY TO THE GENERA

(adapted from Alston in Trimen, Handb. Fl. Ceylon 6: 59. 1931)

1 Carpels 5, distinct, only one fertile; stamens 10; leaves simple...........**1. Buchanania**
1 Carpels united
 2 Ovary 1-celled; leaves simple or pinnate
  3 Leaves pinnate; petals 4; stamens 4–8; styles 4..........................**7. Lannea**
  3 Leaves simple; flowers not completely 4-merous
   4 Styles 3..**5. Semecarpus**
   4 Style 1
    5 Petals 3; stamens 6..**2. Campnosperma**
    5 Petals 4–5; stamens 4–10
     6 Petals 4; stamens 4...**6. Nothopegia**
     6 Petals 5
      7 stamens 5–8..**3. Mangifera**
      7 stamens 8–10..**4. Anacardium**
 2 Ovary 5-celled; leaves pinnate; leaflets with marginal veins...............**8. Spondias**

Taxonomically by far the most difficult genus in this family is *Semecarpus*. There is considerable confusion between the treatments in Trimen's Flora Part I and VI and I had to go back to Hooker's revision in Fl. Br. Ind. and carefully select in the Kew Herbarium types for each species among the various Thwaites sheets marked C(eylon) P(lants). The treatment of this genus by me is still provisional, but with further large scale collecting the true taxonomic distinctions, distribution and ecology of the various species can be more firmly established.

Since most species of Anacardiaceae do not flower and fruit all year round it is desirable to make use of vegetative characters for identification of trees in the field and to use characters of flowers and fruits as further diagnostic evidence. The following field key to genera and species might be useful.

FIELD KEY TO THE GENERA

1 Leaves pinnately compound
 2 Leaflets with marginal vein; ovary 4–5-celled; bark not scaly, shallowly fissured......
 ....**8. Spondias**
 2 Leaflets without marginal vein; ovary 1-celled; bark blackish, scaly or smooth........
 ....**7. Lannea**
1 Leaves simple
 3 Cultivated tree in villages. Leaf blades when small almost as long as broad, the larger twice as long as broad, 10–20 cm long, broadly obovate, with bluntish somewhat retuse apex and rounded to slightly auriculate base; lateral nerves crowded near the base, about 8–14 pairs, sunken at upper face, furcated towards the margin and anastomosing there. Fruit a kidney-shaped nut seated on a pear-shaped, fleshy stalk.......
 ....**4. Anacardium**

3 Wild tree of forests—other combination of characters
   4 Inner bark and leaf stalks with resin which colours black soon or slowly after exposure
      5 Leaves narrowly lanceolate-oblong, more or less in 2 rows, apex rounded or shortly
         acuminate, tertiary nerves and veins slender but clearly visible as whitish lines on
         the inner face. Fruit a depressed-globose drupe..................... **6. Nothopegia**
      5 Leaves with different nervation. Fruits with a fleshy stalk............ **5. Semecarpus**
   4 No black resin
      6 Leaves more or less crowded at the end of the shoots, elliptic-oblong or obovate-
         oval, margin recurved, apex often retuse, lower face with minute reddish scales. Fruit
         a drupe, pointed at apex..................................... **2. Campnosperma**
      6 Leaves different
         7 Leaves rather thin, oblong or lanceolate-oblong, apex acute or obtuse and retuse
            base rounded, lateral veins furcated far beyond the margin. Flowers with 10 sta-
            mens and 5 distinct carpels of which only one develops. Fruit a pyriform-ovoid
            drupe about 1 cm long, somewhat compressed................... **1. Buchanania**
         7 Leaves more pointed at apex or more thick-coriaceous; flowers with 5–8 stamens
            of which only one is fertile. Carpel one, fruit a drupe with a fibrous compressed
            stone, 3.5 cm or 10–12 cm long, ovoid, compressed................. **3. Mangifera**

1. BUCHANANIA

Spreng., J. Bot. (Schrader) 2: 234. 1800; Roxb., Pl. Corom. 3: 79. t. 282. 1819.
Type species: *Buchanania lanzan* Spreng.

Trees with simple leaves in spirals. Flowers near twig apices in axillary
panicles, bisexual. Calyx deeply divided in 5 imbricate lobes, persistent. Petals
5, imbricate, oblong, recurved. Stamens 10, inserted outside the annular 5-
lobed disk. Carpels 5, distinct, only one perfect, the rest barren. Ovule with
basal funicle. Fruit a small drupe, somewhat compressed.

A genus with about 25 species in Indo-Malesia and Tropical Australia. Six
species in the Flora of India.

Buchanania axillaris (Desr.) Ramamoorthy in Saldanha & Nicolson, Fl.
Hassan Distr. 374. 1976. Type: Koenig collection (BM).

Mangifera axillaris Desr. in Lam., Enc. 3: 697. 1792.
Buchanania angustifolia Roxb., Pl. Corom. 3, t. 262. 1820; Thw., Enum. Pl.
   Zeyl. 78. 1838; Wight, Ic. Pl. Ind. Or. t. 101. 1839; Hook. f., Fl. Br. Ind.
   2: 3. 1876; Trimen, Handb. Fl. Ceylon 2: 3, 6. 1893; Gamble, Fl. Pres.
   Madras 1: 184. 1915; Alston in Trimen, Handb. Fl. Ceylon 6: 59. 1931.
Buchanania intermedia Wight, Ic. Pl. Ind. Or. t. 81. 1839.

Medium-sized tree with rough deeply fissured bark and greyish-brown
moderately hard wood. Twigs glabrous. Leaves rather thin, coriaceous; stalk
12–20 mm long, stout; blade about 10–15 cm long, oblong or lanceolate-oblong; apex acute or obtuse and retuse, base rounded or slightly decurrent into
the stalk; lateral nerves curved, 10–12, raised on both faces, furcate beyond
the margin, tertiary nerves near the midrib parallel with the laterals, dissolved

into a marginal network halfway, marginal veins reticulate, more clearly raised on the lower face, dissolved into blind endings. Panicles shorter than the
leaves, about (–10) 3–5 cm long. Flowers nearly sessile, about 5 mm in diameter. Sepals orbicular, glabrous. Petals oblong-oval. Ovary pilose; style
short. Drupe black, pyriform-ovoid, about 1 cm in diameter.

D i s t r. Ceylon, Southern India.

V e r n. Common name given by Alston (l.c.), Kiri-palu (S, Lewis).

N o t e. The kernels of the seeds called "sara pappu" in Tamil are edible
according to Gamble (l.c.). This could give more credibility to the assertion
by Alston (l.c. 60) that this species was introduced from India and planted by
Indra at Kelaniya as related by the Rajavaliya.

S p e c i m e n s E x a m i n e d. JAFFNA DISTRICT: Jaffna, *Gardner
C.P. 471* (PDA, K). KANDY DISTRICT: Hantane, 2000 ft, *Gardner 185*
(BM). BADULLA DISTRICT: Puwakgahawa, road to Haputale, 3000 ft,
Worthington 4856 (BM). MONERAGALA DISTRICT: Wellawaya, 700 ft,
Worthington 4641 (BM). LOCALITY UNKNOWN: *s. coll. C.P. 471*, fl. (BM);
s. coll. C.P. 471, fr. (BM).

2. CAMPNOSPERMA

Thw., Kew J. Bot. 6: 65. 1854, nom. cons. Type species: *Campnosperma zeylanicum* Thw.

Buchanania Roxb. p.p.
Coelopyrum Jack in Mal. Misc. II. Part VII. 65. 1822, see Van Steenis, Fl.
    Mal. Bull. 3: 74. 1948.

Trees; twigs with terminalioid branching. Leaves spirally arranged, simple,
entire. Flowers very small, greenish-yellow, physiologically unisexual, in axillary racemes, 3–(–4)-merous; female inflorescences less branched than the
male. Stamens 6–(–8), sterile in female flowers. Ovary 1-celled; stigma
sessile, with large dilated lobes. Fruit a drupe, ovoid, with a bony stone containing a curved seed.

A genus of 10 species, mostly in Malesia, a few in tropical Africa, one in
tropical America.

Campnosperma zeylanicum Thw., Kew J. Bot. 6: 65. 1854; Thw., Enum. Pl.
Zeyl. 78. 1858; Beddome, Fl. Sylv. t. 168. 1871; Hook. f., Fl. Br. Ind. 2: 41.
1867; Engler, Mon. Phan. 4: 318. 1883; Alston in Trimen, Handb. Fl. Ceylon
6: 63. 1931; Worthington, Ceylon Trees 164. 1959. Type: *C.P. 246* (BM).

Moderate to large-sized tree. Bole with inner bark red-brown, layered.
Twigs with conspicuous leaf-scars, young parts with dark brown scales. Leaves
crowded near apex of stem, stalk about 1 cm long; blade rather coriaceous,

elliptic-oblong with base gradually narrowed and decurrent along the stalk, apex rounded or slightly retuse; sizes very different, 10–20 cm long, 3–9 cm broad, strongly reduced near the inflorescences; upper surface of leaves drying darker brown, more shining than the lower. Lateral nerves 20–25 pairs, very crowded near the base of the blade, almost at right angle with the midrib, archingly connected and diminishing beyond a marginal network of tertiary nerves from which a wavy intermediate nerve descends towards the midrib, and connected with an iso-diametric network of tertiary nerves between the lateral veins of same pattern fading in endings in the tertiary network; all the tertiary nerves and veins rather prominently raised and visible on both leaf faces. Lower face of blade papillose and covered with scattered rufous scales. Inflorescences axillary, spicate, 4–6 cm long (female). Peduncle 2–3 cm. Axis of inflorescence smooth. Pedicels of flowers about 1–2 mm. Calyx lobes triangular, about 1 mm, persistent around the young fruit. Corolla lobes tongue-shaped. Stamens shorter than the petals, rather long-persistent, visible around young fruits. Young fruit inside a low-rimmed disk. Fruit about 1.5 cm long, apiculate, pulpy, purple.

D i s t r. Endemic in Ceylon.

E c o l. Flowering March–April. A typical tree of the lowland dipterocarp forest and the wet zone in and around Sinharaja Forest and the other remaining forests S.W. of the Peak Sanctuary. Probably one of the most promising economic endemic trees of Ceylon. Species of this genus in Malaya and Borneo are known as rather fast-growing. Nothing known about growth rate in Ceylon.

U s e s. The timber is considered to be an ideal tea-box wood (Lewis, 1902), and the tree is well known by Ceylon foresters and timber loggers under its local name, but so far no attempts have been made to plant it, not even in the Botanic Garden.

V e r n. Aridda (S).

S p e c i m e n s E x a m i n e d. GALLE DISTRICT: Kanneliya Forest Reserve, April 1970, fl., *Balakrishnan 617* (PDA, US); Nakiadeniya, *Worthington 2343, 5238* (PDA); Deddiyagala Forest Reserve, *Worthington 2522* (BM); Kottawa, *Meijer 274* (PDA, US); Hiniduma, 1000 ft, *Worthington 2343, 2266* (BM). RATNAPURA DISTRICT: Ratnapura, near swimming pool, 100 ft, *Worthington 2123* (BM); Gilimale Forest Reserve, 200 ft, *Worthington 6460* (BM), *Meijer 407* (PDA, US); Pelmadulla, about 10 miles E. of Ratnapura, *Worthington 6436* (BM); Sinharaja Forest, *Schmid-Hollinger 63* (PDA, US). EXACT LOCALITIES UNKNOWN: *s. coll. C.P. 246* (PDA); Hewesse, Sinharaja, Kuruwita Korale, written on labels on *C.P. 246*, one of which could be selected as the type in case one locality could be given for one collection. Alston (l.c. 6: 63) mentions Bambarabotuva and the base of Adam's Peak from Pelmadulla to Kitulgala (F. Lewis).

3. MANGIFERA

L., Sp. Pl. 200. 1753. Type species: *Mangifera indica* L.

Large trees, leaves in spirals crowded at end of shoots, simple, stalked, coriaceous. Stipules absent. Panicles terminal and in the upper leaf-axils; flowers male, female or bisexual on the same tree, 4–6 merous (5-merous in the Ceylon species). Calyx free, imbricate. Petals larger than the calyx, imbricate. Disk 5-lobed. Stamens 5–8, only one fertile, the others barren and reduced in size, inserted within the disk. Ovary 1-celled with one ovule; style one, lateral. Fruit a drupe with a fibrous compressed stone.

About 40 species in the Indo-Malesian area. One species endemic in Ceylon. *M. indica*, the edible cultivated common mango, introduced and in cultivation.

KEY TO THE SPECIES

1 Panicle and calyx more or less hairy. Leaves rather thin, acuminate at apex. Fruits 6–10 cm long...**1. M. indica**
1 Panicle and calyx glabrous. Leaves thick, coriaceous, obtuse or shortly acuminate. Fruits about 3–4 cm long..**2. M. zeylanica**

1. Mangifera indica L., Sp. Pl. 200. 1753; Hook. f., Fl. Br. Ind. 2: 13. 1876; Trimen, Handb. Fl. Ceylon 1: 318. 1893; Worthington, Ceylon Trees 152. 1959. Type: specimen 276.1 (LINN).

Medium to large-sized tree 8–30 m high, cultivated for its fruits. Leaves oblong-lanceolate, 10–32 × 2–10 cm; lateral nerves 12–25, prominent on lower face, tertiary nerves and veins reticulate. Young leaves pendulous, purplish. Panicles 6–40 cm, in general hairy. Stalks 2–4 mm. Sepals ovoid-oblong, hairy, 2–3 mm. Petals ovoid-oblong, c. 3–5 mm, white, later on often tinged with purple, with yellow or purple veins. Fertile stamen as long as the corolla. Staminodes very short. Fruits ovoid to ellipsoid, with oblique base, 10–20 cm long. Sarcocarp yellow or ochre.

D i s t r. Widely cultivated in the tropics.

E c o l. A tree widely planted in the village gardens in the lower wet and montane zone up to about 600 m altitude.

V e r n. Amba (S); Manga (T); Mango (E).

S p e c i m e n s E x a m i n e d. KANDY DISTRICT: Kadugannawa, *Worthington 1439* (K); Dolosbage, *Worthington 1846* (K). GALLE DISTRICT: Hiniduma, *Worthington 2254* (K). PUTTALAM DISTRICT: Wilpattu National Park, Moderagam Aru stream, *Mueller-Dombois 6808210* (PDA, US). BADULLA DISTRICT: Road from Bibile to Mahiyangana, scattered, not uncommon, 4 June 1971, fl., *Kostermans 24407* (PDA, US).

2. Mangifera zeylanica (Blume) Hook. f., Fl. Br. Ind. 2: 16. 1876; Engler, Mon. Phan. 4: 204. 1883; Trimen, Handb. Fl. Ceylon 1: 317. 1893; Worthington, Ceylon Trees 153. 1959. Type: Thwaites *2614* (K, PDA).

Buchanania? *zeylanica* Blume, Ann. Mus. Bot. Lugduno-Batavum 1: 185. 1850.

Large tree; bark rather rough, slightly cracked-fissured, brownish-grey, with dispersed corky lenticels. Inner bark orange-brown, sapwood white. Twigs glabrous, angular when young. Leaf stalks 1–2 cm long. Leaf blades coriaceous, 7–13 (in saplings upto 20) cm long, lanceolate or ovate-oblong, tapering towards the base, apex rounded or retuse, in saplings acute, midrib raised on both faces; lateral nerves 7–10 pairs, prominently raised on lower face; tertiary nerves in a network between the laterals visible on both faces; veins reticulate and with fading endings slightly more prominent on the lower than on the upper face. Panicles glabrous, terminal. Sepals ovate, obtuse, glabrous. Petals twice as long as the sepals, obtuse, clawed, reflexed; barren stamens reduced to short tabulate processes. Fruit 3–4 cm long, ovoid.

D i s t r. Endemic.
E c o l. A tree of the lowlands in moist and dry regions, up to 3000 ft. Flowering February, March and November.
U s e s. Timber said to be suitable for tea-boxes (Lewis, 1902). Fruit said to be edible though unpalatable.
S p e c i m e n s E x a m i n e d. PUTTALAM DISTRICT: Wilpattu National Park, between Etambagaha and Dangaha-Uraniya in Plot W 32, *Wirawan 1077, 1077a* (PDA, US), *Mueller-Dombois 69042813* (PDA, US). ANURADHAPURA DISTRICT: Habarana, *Worthington 5178* (K). TRINCOMALEE DISTRICT: Kantalai-Trincomalee Road, *Worthington 1290* (K); Horawapotana Road, *Worthington 4515* (K). BATTICALOA DISTRICT: Batticaloa, *Worthington 6302* (K), *Meijer 128* (PDA, US). AMPARAI DISTRICT: Inginiyagala, Gal Oya National Park, *Meijer 160* (PDA, US). RATNAPURA DISTRICT: Bambarabotuwa Forest Reserve, *Meijer 434* (PDA, US); Ratnapura, Gilimale Forest Reserve, *Worthington 4831* (K). GALLE DISTRICT: Batapola-Galle, *Worthington 373, 2463* (BM). KANDY DISTRICT: Hantane, *Worthington 254* (BM); Dolosbage, S.W. of Kandy, *Worthington 1918* (BM). WITHOUT EXACT LOCALITY: Road Bibile-Mahiyangane, 4 June 1971, *Kostermans 24410* (PDA, US).

4. ANACARDIUM

L., Sp. Pl. 383. 1753. Type species: *Anacardium occidentale* L.

Tree, bole with pinkish-brown inner bark with whitish latex (turning black?). Leaves spirally arranged, simple, petioled, margin entire. Flowers in terminal panicles, polygamous (male and bisexual), 5-merous. Stamens 7–10, connate into a tube, only one or two fertile, the other ones reduced in size and barren. Filament adnate to the disk. Ovary 1-celled, sessile, 1-ovuled; style lateral, subulate. Fruit indehiscent, kidney-shaped, on a fleshy, swollen, obconical pedicel.

A genus of 15 species in Tropical America, one widely cultivated in all tropical countries as a fruit tree.

Anacardium occidentale L., Sp. Pl. 383. 1753; Engler, Mon. Phan. 4: 219. 1883; Alston in Trimen, Handb. Fl. Ceylon 6: 60. 1931; Gamble, Fl. Pres. Madras 1: 185. 1935; Worthington, Ceylon Trees 154. 1959. Type: Rheede, Hort. Mal. 3: 65. t. 54. 1682.

A small tree. Young parts glabrous. Leaves somewhat crowded on twig-apices, stalks 1–2 cm long, blades 6–15 × 5–8 cm, coriaceous, obovate-oblong; apex rounded to retuse, base cuneate. Lateral nerves 8–10 pairs, curved, diminished and connected with tertiary nerves near the margin, some almost forked, raised on lower face, tertiary nerves with widespread stronger nerves along the laterals stretching halfway the distance between those, and connected with a rather dense prominent isodiametric network of tertiary nerves surrounding masses of branched but blind-ending veins. Panicles or corymbs 15–20 cm long, twigs appressed, greyish, hairy. Flowers crowded along (2) 4–5 cm long ultimate branches, in the axils of 3 mm long, ovate-lanceolate, acuminate, short, hairy bracts. Pedicels 2–5 mm, pubescent. Calyx segments 2–3 (5) mm with some pubescence on outer face. Petals at first white, soon turning red, ligulate, often halfway reflexed, about 1–1.4 cm, apex acute. Stamens in male flowers 8–11 mm, in bisexual 6–7 mm; staminodes 2–4 mm. Ovary obovoid or obcordate. Fruit pedicel yellow, 3–7.5 cm, fruit dark brown, 2.5–3 cm.

D i s t r. Tropical America, introduced into S.E. Asia by the Portuguese. In Ceylon in low country in the wet as well as the dry zone. Naturalized in the dry zone (?).

V e r n. Caju (S); Montin-kai (T); Cashew-nut (E).

N o t e s. Leaves edible when young. Resin from the nut can cause poisonous infective skin reactions. Stem supposed to yield gum in some cases.

S p e c i m e n s E x a m i n e d. PUTTALAM DISTRICT: Wilpattu National Park, Kali Villu Bungalow, *Mueller-Dombois & Balakrishnan 69042601* (PDA, US), *Cooray 70020206R* (PDA, US). BATTICALOA DISTRICT: Valachchenai, *Meijer* and *Balakrishnan 129* (PDA, US). COLOMBO DISTRICT: Jaela-Gampha Road, *Comanor 1022* (PDA, US). RATNAPURA DISTRICT: Ratnapura, near Resthouse, *Comanor 1132* (PDA, US).

5. SEMECARPUS

L. f., Suppl. Pl. 285. 1781. Type species: *Semecarpus anacardium* L. f.

Trees or rarely shrubs. Inner bark with black-drying juice which causes skin irritation to people allergic to it. Leaves in spirals, simple, coriaceous, entire, lower surface often lighter and more dull coloured than the upper. Tertiary nerves near the midrib often partly parallel with lateral nerves as intermediate nerves. Flowers in terminal or axillary panicles, small, polygamous or dioecious, the male usually smaller; calyx 5-lobed, lobes deciduous; petals 5, imbricate; stamens 5, inserted at base of disk, in female flowers smaller; anthers medifixed, in female flowers empty; disk broad, annular, faintly lobed; ovary (absent in male flowers) 1-celled with one pendulous ovule; styles 3, stigmas lobed; drupe more or less compressed, obliquely ovoid, with a thick fleshy receptacle.

A genus with about 60 species in the Indo-Malesian region and Australia.

All 11–12 species in Ceylon are endemic and known under the local name Badulla. Discrimination of species is rather difficult. As a consequence plants distributed under certain numbers by Thwaites in his Ceylon Plants series do not always belong to the same species and interpretation of types in relation with the first description of a species appears very essential in this genus in order to avoid confusion. Most species have only been collected with fruits or as sterile specimens. There is still great need for complete flowering collections.

KEY TO THE SPECIES

1 Leaves thick, coriaceous, base slightly peltate........................**2. S. subpeltata**
1 Leaves not peltate
  2 Twigs and often also the lower face of the midrib and leaves hairy, leaf blades oblong, gradually acuminate at apex, lateral nerves 11–15 pairs, archingly connected near the margin (including the less hairy *S. thwaitesii* Hook. f.)...............**3. S. pubescens**
  2 Twigs not hairy
    3 Leaf blades oblong-obovate, margin whitish, base slightly auricled, inflorescence on the stem; shrub...**1. S. marginata**
    3 Leaf margin not whitish or base not auricled, inflorescence not on the stem
      4 Leaf blades 10–15 cm long, broadly obovate, with rounded apex, base slightly auricled, stalks very short..**4. S. obovata**
      4 Leaf blades different
        5 Leaf blades elliptic, small, 5–9 cm long, apex rounded, sharply acuminate, or retuse, base decurrent into the 10–15 mm long stalk, lateral nerves 9–10 pairs, rather prominent on the lower face, but hardly more so than the reticulate nerves, which are partly stretched parallel with the laterals and join near the margin, upper face of leaf drying blackish-brown, lower reddish-brown..............**11. S. parvifolia**
        5 Leaves longer or with different nervation
          6 Leaf blades rather long (15–23 cm), thin, elliptic-oblong, apex long-acuminate, base rounded, lateral nerves 8–10 pairs, prominently raised on the lower face, tertiary nerves and veins widely reticulate.....................**9. S. acuminata**
          6 Leaf blades smaller or more thick, coriaceous
            7 Leaf blades thick, base cuneate to rounded, stalks rather short (up to 1.5 cm)

8 Leaf apex rounded or retuse. Lateral nerves (6) 8–10 pairs, prominent on both faces
....**6. S. coriacea**
8 Leaf apex shortly acuminate. Lateral nerves 10–15 pairs................**5. S. moonii**
7 Leaf blades thinner, stalks longer
9 Leaf stalks without separate corky base. Drupe oblique...............**8. S. gardneri**
9 Leaf stalks with a separate corky base, often lighter coloured and cracked when dried.
Drupe not oblique.
10 Leaf stalks (4) 6–24 mm long, channelled over its whole length. Blades obovate-
oblong. Lateral nerves 5–8 (12) pairs........................**10. S. nigro-viridis**
10 Leaf stalks 2.5–8 cm long, channelled only halfway. Blades elliptic-oblong. Lateral
nerves 8–14 pairs...**7. S. walkeri**

1. Semecarpus marginata Thw., Enum. Pl. Zeyl. 77. 1858; Trimen, Handb.
Fl. Ceylon 1: 319. 1893; Alston in Trimen, Handb. Fl. Ceylon 6: 45. 1931;
Hook. f., Fl. Br. Ind. 2: 32. 1876; Engler, Mon. Phan. 4: 476. 1883. Type:
Ratnapura, *C.P. 2677* (K, isotype; PDA, US).

A small treelet or unbranched shrub, 1.8–2.5 m high. Leaves closely
placed, very large, blades 20–40 cm long, obovate-lanceolate, tapering to a
narrow but cordate base; apex sharply acuminate; margin bordered by a thick
intramarginal vein, outside which is a semi-transparent, stiff, strong, parch-
ment-like, horny, reflexed border with a sharp-cutting edge, glabrous on both
sides, very stiff and coriaceous; lateral nerves about 18–20 pairs, almost at
right angles with the midrib, archingly connected beyond the margin, tertiary
nerves wide-reticulate, veins reticulate, branched with blind endings very well
visible on the lower face. Petiole very short and thick, transversely wrinkled.
Flowering panicles in male inflorescences 7.5–10 cm long, much branched,
coming off in clusters from the old wood of the stem for its whole length.
Flowers small, about 5 mm long, on slender articulate pedicels. Calyx glabrous, lobes broadly triangular, acute. Petals oval, spreading, obtuse. Drupe
small, about 10 mm long, when dry striate, red. Receptacle as long as the
drupe or only 5 mm long, pear-shaped, brilliant crimson.

D i s t r. As reported by Trimen, "a rare plant of the moist zone".
Endemic.

N o t e. It is very unlike the rest of the species in habit: the horny border
to the leaves is also very remarkable. The receptacle of the fruit is sweet and
edible.

S p e c i m e n s E x a m i n e d. RATNAPURA DISTRICT: Kukulawa
Vihare Kande, *Waas 276* (PDA, US); Ratnapura, Peak Gardens, *s. coll. C.P.
2677* (K, PDA); hill 1 mile Southeast of Ayagama off main road to Kalawana,
Theobald and *Krahulik 2796* (PDA); Veddagala, 16 March 1881, *s. coll. s.n.*
(PDA); near small stream by margin of rain forest SE of Depedene, *Bremer
882* (PDA, US); Gilimale Forest Reserve, *Sohmer, Waas* and *Eliezer 8777,
8811* (PDA, US), *Huber 495* (PDA, US), *Jayasuriya* and *Bandaranaike 1873*
(PDA, US); Sri Palabaddala IBP Plot, *Waas 416* (PDA, US); Adam's Peak,

N.E. of Carney, *Davidse* and *Sumithraarachchi 8720* (PDA, US); Rasagala, N. of Dotalugala Forest, *Sohmer & Waas 10483* (PDA, US). KEGALLE DISTRICT: Kitulgala, *Sohmer & Waas 10563* (PDA, US). GALLE DISTRICT: near Galle, December 1853, *s. coll. C.P. 2677* (PDA; same number as the type!)—so called var. b. *hirsuta* of Thwaites, leaves stiff-hairy beneath. LOCALITY UNKNOWN: Pitakande, *J.M. de Silva s.n.* (PDA).

2. Semecarpus subpeltata Thw., Enum. Pl. Zeyl. 75. 1858; Hook. f., Fl. Br. Ind. 2: 33. 1876; Engler, Mon. Phan. 4: 476. 1883; Trimen, Handb. Fl. Ceylon 1: 320. 1893; Alston in Trimen, Handb. Fl. Ceylon 6: 62. 1931; Worthington, Ceylon Trees 162. 1959. Type: Sinharaja Forest, 1861, *C.P. 3004* (K, isotype PDA).

Small or medium-sized tree. Inner bark instantly turning black after exposure. Twigs glabrous. Young leaves pendulous, red. Leaf stalks about 2.5–3.5 cm long, thick, grooved in dry state; blades thick, coriaceous, very large, 20–40 cm, lanceolate-oblong; base rounded and slightly peltate; apex contracted, acuminate; lateral nerves 12–14 pairs, curved along the margin and connected. Tertiary nerves wide, reticulate except for some descending towards the midrib; veins vaguely visible. Inflorescences from axils of fallen leaves, panicles 15–25 cm, with spreading branches; flowers sessile; drupe much depressed, 3 cm long by 12 cm wide, slightly compressed, striped receptacle large, broad, cupped, 2 cm wide.

D i s t r. Lowland forests of the wet zone. Endemic.

E c o l. Flowering in March.

S p e c i m e n s   E x a m i n e d. RATNAPURA DISTRICT: Sinharaja Forest, *s. coll. C.P. 3004*, type (K, PDA). KALUTARA DISTRICT: Morapitiya Forest Reserve, *Meijer 467* (PDA, US). GALLE DISTRICT: Kottawa, *Worthington 630* (BM); Nakiyadeniya Forest Reserve, *Worthington 5252* (BM), *Worthington 367* (K); Kanneliya Forest Reserve, *Worthington 5260* (K).

3. Semecarpus pubescens Thw., Enum. Pl. Zeyl. 77. 1858; Hook. f., Fl. Br. Ind. 2: 31. 1876; Engler, Mon. Phan. 4: 475. 1883; Trimen, Handb. Fl. Ceylon 1: 320. 1893; Alston in Trimen, Handb. Fl. Ceylon 6: 62. 1931; Worthington, Ceylon Trees 161. 1959. Type: Ratnapura, March 1846, *C.P. 231* (K, isotype PDA).

Small tree; branches and young parts densely tomentose; leaf stalk about 2 cm; blades densely pubescent, 12–20 cm (up to 50 cm in saplings), narrowly oblong-lanceolate, rounded at base; apex acuminate; upper surface soft-hairy on midrib; lateral nerves and the large tertiary nerves about 20 pairs, curved and diminishing near margin, intermediate tertiary nerves 1–3 between adjacent laterals, halfway to the margin dissolved in a wide network of tertiary nerves and rather prominent veins. Inflorescence lax; panicles 20–35 cm, slightly branched, more or less hairy. Calyx glabrous, 3 mm long. Petals veiny, 1.5 mm long. Drupe small, 12 mm, ovoid, purplish red; receptacle short (3 mm).

D i s t r. Moist low country. Endemic.

N o t e. A slightly less hairy form described as var. *thwaitesii* Engl., Mon. Phan. 4: 476. 1883, Syn. *S. thwaitesii* Hook. f. in Fl. Br. Ind. 2: 31. 1878, based on *C.P. 3886* from Morawake Korale, probably falls within the normal variation of this species.

S p e c i m e n s E x a m i n e d. RATNAPURA DISTRICT: *s. coll. C.P. 231* (K, PDA); Gilimale Forest Reserve, *Worthington 3182, 6496* (K), *Jayasuriya & Burtt 1128* (PDA, US), *Gunatilleke & Meijer 1360* (PDA, US), Mile 6, Culvert 17, *Sohmer, Waas & Eliezer 8790* (PDA, US); Palabaddale, *Sumithraarachchi & Foster 1822* (PDA, US); Adam's Peak Sanctuary, *Meijer 500* (PDA, US); Delgoda, *J. Lewis s.n.* (PDA). GALLE DISTRICT: Hiniduma Kande, *Bernardi 15457, 15473* (PDA, US). A specimen sent in 1908 to US, No. *163* from PDA, can be considered as a paratype (US).

4. Semecarpus obovata Moon, Cat. 22. 1824; Engler, Mon. Phan. 4: 495. 1883; Thw., Enum. Pl. Zeyl. 77. 1858; Hook. f., Fl. Br. Ind. 2: 32. 1878; Trimen, Handb. Fl. Ceylon 1: 321. 1893. Type: Galle District, *C.P. 3339* (K, isotype PDA).

Medium-sized tree. Bark smooth, whitish, twigs glabrous. Leaves almost sessile; blades very stiff, coriaceous, 10–15 cm long, broadly obovate; base rounded, slightly auricled; apex rounded; lateral nerves 8–10 pairs; tertiary nerves partly intermediate near the midrib, reticulate with the veins, very prominent on lower face. Panicles terminal, about 15 cm long; peduncles glabrous. Flowers 10 mm long. Drupe 12 mm, oblong-ovoid, pointed; receptacle narrower than the drupe.

D i s t r. Only known from the wet zone, apparently very rare. Not seen by any botanist since Thwaites' collection. Not seen in the field by me (W.M.).

E c o l. Flowering September–October.

S p e c i m e n s E x a m i n e d. GALLE DISTRICT: *s. coll. C.P. 3339* (PDA). RATNAPURA DISTRICT: Ratnapura, *Moon C.P. 3339* (K, PDA).

5. Semecarpus moonii Thw., Enum. Pl. Zeyl. 77. 1858; Engler, Mon. Phan. 4: 495. 1883; Hook. f., Fl. Br. Ind. 2: 32. 1876; Trimen, Handb. Fl. Ceylon 1: 321. 1893; Worthington, Ceylon Trees 158. 1959. Type: Kalutara, *C.P. 3338* (K, isotype PDA).

Medium-sized tree. Bark smooth and thin, flaking off. Young parts quite glabrous. Leaves almost sessile, small, thick; blades large, thick, coriaceous, 15–30 cm long, lanceolate, tapering or rounded at base, often shortly acuminate, lateral nerves 10–15 pairs, tertiary nerves reticulate, very prominent on lower face. Inflorescence of terminal panicles 15–30 cm long, minutely puberulous. Flowers 5 mm long. Drupe pointed, striate; receptacle small, narrower than the drupe.

D i s t r. Endemic. A tree of the lowland forests of the wet zone.
E c o l. Flowering September–October.
S p e c i m e n s E x a m i n e d. GALLE DISTRICT: Kottawa Arboretum, *Jayasuriya 1545* (PDA, US).
N o t e. Possibly one of the endemic plants of Ceylon which is nearly extinct now since little or no forest is left at its type locality, or possibly only a form of *S. nigro-viridis.*

6. Semecarpus coriacea Thw., Enum. Pl. Zeyl. 78. 1858; Engler, Mon. Phan. 4: 490. 1883; Hook. f., Fl. Br. Ind. 2: 32. 1876; Trimen, Handb. Fl. Ceylon 1: 321. 1893; Worthington, Ceylon Trees 156. 1959. Type: Maturata, Hakgala, Feb. 1896, 6000 ft, *C.P. 313* (K, isotype PDA).

Medium-sized tree with smooth shining bark. Ultimate branchlets thick, with prominent leaf scars. Leaves with short stalks; blades thick, coriaceous, obovate, oblong, base cuneate, apex rounded or slightly retuse; lateral nerves 6 (8–10) pairs, curved and connected near the margin, tertiary nerves and veins prominent on lower face. Inflorescence of terminal panicles, rather short (8–15 cm), with thick glabrous or slightly pilose branches. Drupe over 2.5 cm wide, 2 cm long, compressed, apiculate; receptacle small, 10 mm, scarcely cupped.

D i s t r. A tree common in montane forests above 1200 m. Endemic.
E c o l. Flowering in April, fruits June–November.
S p e c i m e n s E x a m i n e d. NUWARA ELIYA DISTRICT: Ramboda Pass, *Worthington 2895* (BM), *Worthington 5084, 5766* (K), *Alston 449* (PDA); Hakgala Gardens, *Worthington 5735* (K); Glen Devon Estate, *Worthington 6207* (K). RATNAPURA DISTRICT: along road to Peak, *Worthington 3010* (K), *Wirawan 750* (PDA), *Gunawardena 637* (Forest Dept. Herb.), *Dassanayake, Balasubramaniam & Meijer 607* (PDA, US); Mile 51, culvert 7, 6200 ft, *Meijer 48a* (PDA, US). BADULLA DISTRICT: Roehampton Estate, Haputale, *Worthington 6711* (K).

7. Semecarpus walkeri Hook. f., Fl. Br. Ind. 2: 33. 1876; Engler, Mon. Phan. 4: 491. 1883; Trimen, Handb. Fl. Ceylon 1: 322. 1893; Alston in Trimen, Handb. Fl. Ceylon 6: 62. 1931. Type: *C.P. 2490* (K, PDA isotype, US).

Medium-sized trees, without buttresses. Bole closely shallowly fissured. Twigs glabrous. Leaf stalks about 2.5–8 cm long, base corky, swollen, cracked when dried; blade stiff, coriaceous, undulate along margin when dried, oblong-lanceolate, ovate-elliptic in saplings, up to 38 cm long, cuneate, almost decurrent at base, lower face drying ochre-brown; apex acuminate, often twisted; lateral nerves 8–14 pairs, almost at right angles with the midrib, 4–5 intermediate nerves reaching halfway towards the margin between adjacent laterals dissolved into a marginal network with the laterals. Panicles terminal and axillary, (2) 10–15 cm, slightly branched or almost simple, cauliflorous, slender. Flowers nearly 12 mm long. Drupe over 12 mm, ovoid, not oblique; receptacle cup-shaped, enclosing the drupe halfway or slightly more.

D i s t r. A common tree in the wet zone, in lowlands up to about 2000 ft. Endemic.

E c o l. Flowering February–March; fruits July.

S p e c i m e n s E x a m i n e d. COLOMBO DISTRICT: Labugama Reservoir, *Worthington 3486* (BM). GALLE DISTRICT: Bona Vista Hill, *Meijer & Cramer 235* (PDA, US), *Cramer 3009, 3521* (PDA, US); Kanneliya Forest Reserve, *Worthington 3681* (BM), 13 April, *Meijer 561* (PDA, US); near camp, *Meijer 979* (PDA, US); Nelluwa, hilly slope at base of secondary forest, Kalubowitiya Kande, 170 m alt., *Cramer* 4002 (PDA, US), *Tirvengadum 257* (PDA, US); Udugama, base of Nerugalkande Peak, 300 m alt., *Cramer 3698, 3704* (PDA, US). MATARA DISTRICT: Dediyagala Forest Reserve, *Worthington 2574* (K). KEGALLE DISTRICT: Dambatenna, Kitulgala, *J.M. Silva 212* (PDA). KALUTARA DISTRICT: Matugama—Morapitiya Road, along river, *Kostermans 24963* (PDA, US); Badureliya, Morapitiya—Badureliya Road, Culvert 31/11, 75 m alt., *Cramer 4169* (PDA, US). RATNAPURA DISTRICT: Kudawa side of Sinharaja Forest, 600 m alt., *Mueller-Dombois & Balakrishnan 72042309* (PDA, US); Weddagala entrance, *Jayasuriya & Burtt 1131* (PDA, US); mile 1, Carney Road, Gilimale, *Meijer 398* (PDA, US); Sinharaja Forest Reserve, near old camp-site at end of Jeep track from Weddagala, *Meijer 518* (PDA, US); Morapitiya Forest Reserve, 6.5 m South of main road, *Meijer 462a, 463a* (PDA, US). KANDY DISTRICT: Peradeniya Botanic Gardens, planted tree D 100, *Meijer 379* (PDA, US), older coll. from tree C 191, *Worthington 6498* (K); Kitulgala-Laxapana, 15 May 1971, fr., *Kostermans 24107* (PDA, US). NUWARA ELIYA DISTRICT: Mile marker 3/8, Ginigathena—Adam's Peak Road, *Balakrishnan 1193* (PDA, US). LOCALITY UNKNOWN: *s. coll. C.P. 173* (PDA); *Mrs. Walker s.n.* (K).

8. Semecarpus gardneri Thw., Enum. Pl. Zeyl. 76. 1858; Engler, Mon. Phan. 4: 491. 1883; Hook. f., Fl. Br. Ind. 2: 33. 1876; Trimen, Handb. Fl. Ceylon 1: 322. 1893; Alston in Trimen, Handb. Fl. Ceylon 6: 62. 1931; Worthington, Ceylon Trees 137. 1959. Type: Sinharaja, *C.P. 1257* (K, isotype PDA, US).

Medium-sized to large tree with finely grooved grey bark. Twigs glabrous. Leaves with stalk 2.5–3 cm, stout; blade rather thick, elliptic-oblong, about 18–25 cm long; rather rounded at the very base, apex (shortly) acuminate; midrib relatively broad, flat at upper face; lateral nerves 10–12 under 60° angle with midrib, rather prominent on lower face, diminishing along the margin, one prominent tertiary nerve intermediate between the laterals, flanked by a few shorter; lower face drying dark brown with lateral nerves, tertiary nerves and veins straw-coloured and well visible against the dark background. Inflorescence 20–30 cm long, panicles terminal and axillary, slightly branched; male flowers 5 mm long, bisexual ones over 12 mm. Drupe very oblique, nearly 25 mm wide, apiculate; receptacle large, swollen, much wider than the drupe except when dried, cup-shaped, red.

D i s t r. A tree from the wet lowlands and hills up to 4000 ft. Common. Endemic.

N o t e s. This species is on sterile characters difficult to distinguish from *S. walkeri*. The leaves have more ascending lateral nerves; they dry a more dark colour; the base is very slightly rounded near the stalk, not decurrent as in *S. walkeri*. Fruits of this species are oblique, those of *S. walkeri* not, and the inflorescences are longer: 20–30 cm against 10–15 cm in *S. walkeri*.

Semecarpus ochracea Alston in Trimen, Handb. Fl. Ceylon 6: 63. 1931 is probably best to be considered as a form of this species with lower face of leaves drying ochre. No other differences could be found so far. *C.P. 631* p.p. near Kandy (K, PDA) is the type. Collections of this form were also made at Sinharaja (Gunatillekes). See also Ratnapura District *Alston 1692* (PDA), Laksapana, *Jayasuriya* and *Sumithraarachchi 1554* (PDA, US), Bible Rock, *Fernando* and *Sumithraarachchi 159* (PDA).

S p e c i m e n s E x a m i n e d. KANDY DISTRICT: Peradeniya Botanic Garden, D 404 tree 4 ft girth, *Meijer 385* (PDA, US); above Moray Estate, 1709 m, 16 May 1971, fl., *Kostermans 24181* (PDA, US); Peak Wilderness W. of Laxapana, *Worthington 5514* (K); Ambagamuwa, Dec. 1852, *s. coll. C.P. 1257* p.p. (PDA). RATNAPURA DISTRICT: Balangoda Estate, Denegama, *Worthington 3251* (K), *Worthington 3246* (BM); Sinharaja Forest near Beverley Estate, *Worthington 2594, 2590* (BM); Peak Sanctuary above Gilimale, *Meijer, 502* (PDA, US); Gilimale Forest Reserve, *Jayasuriya 1861* (PDA, US); Botala Kande, near Pelawatta, Agalawatte, *Bernardi 15766* (PDA, US); Demanhandiya, Kuruwita Korale, Jan. 1892, *s. coll. s.n.* (PDA). COLOMBO DISTRICT: Labugama Reservoir, 20 miles from Colombo, *Worthington 3503, 3485* (BM). MATARA DISTRICT: Deniyaya, *Worthington 2184* (BM), *6616, 2219* (For. Dept.). GALLE DISTRICT: Nelluwa, 200 m, *Balakrishnan 230* (PDA, US); Hiniduma, Godekande Hill, *Bernardi 15429* (PDA, US), *Cramer 4008* (PDA, US), *Tirvengadam 4008* (PDA, US), *Kostermans 25672* (PDA, US); Hiniduma, 19 Jan. 1973, fr., alt. 250 m, *Tirvengadum &*

Cramer 261 (PDA, US); Kottawa along road half m East of Forest Arboretum, *Meijer 279* (PDA, US); Kottawa-Galle, Udugama Road, *Peeris 537A* (PDA, US); Udugama, ascent to Nerugalkande Peak, 300 m, *Cramer 3699* (PDA, US); Udugama, sec. jungle, *Worthington 2338* (K); Kanneliya, *Jayasuriya 1529* (PDA, US), *Huber 580* (PDA, US); Kanneliya F.R. *Worthington 5263* (K); Nakiyadeniya, *Worthington 6047* (K); Norton Road, *Worthington 6555* (K). KEGALLE DISTRICT: Pelampitiya, 4 miles W. of Dolosbage, 800 m alt., *Jayasuriya & Dassanayake 1012* (PDA, US). KALUTARA DISTRICT: Morapitiya, *Waas 899* (PDA, US); Hewesse, March 1857, *s. coll. s.n.* (PDA). DISTRICT UNKNOWN: Morowe Korale, March 1881, *s. coll. s.n.* (PDA).

9. Semecarpus acuminata Thw., Enum. Pl. Zeyl. 76. 1858; Engler, Mon. Phan. 4: 495. 1883; Hook. f., Fl. Br. Ind. 2: 33. 1876; Trimen, Handb. Fl. Ceylon 1: 323. 1893. Type: Sinharaja Forest, *C.P. 2676* (K, isotype PDA).

Medium-sized tree. Twigs glabrous. Leaf-stalk 15–20 mm, stout; blades rather thin, (10) 15–20 (25) cm long, lanceolate-oblong to elliptic-oblong; base rounded, apex long-acuminate; lateral nerves 8–10 pairs, oblique (ascending), prominently raised on lower face; tertiary nerves and veins widely reticulate. Panicles axillary or terminal, small, 8–30 cm long. Flowers small, under 5 mm long. Fruits unknown.

Distr. Moist low country. Endemic.

Note. var. *intermedia* Trimen, Handb. Fl. Ceylon 1: 323. 1893, syn. *S. intermedia* (Trimen) Alston in Trimen, Handb. Fl. Ceylon 6: 62. 1931 has been interpreted by me as a form of *S. nigro-viridis* Thw.

Specimens Examined. The type *C.P. 2676* from Sinharaja Forest is in the PDA herbarium, besides more recent collections from KALUTARA DISTRICT: main stream in Sinharaja Forest c. 7 miles south of Atweltota, For. Dept. road, *Theobald & Krahulik 2812* (PDA), *Kostermans 27127* (PDA), *Waas 1472* (PDA); Morapitiya, *Waas 896* (PDA, US). MATARA DISTRICT: North Ensalwatte along Medaella stream, *Sohmer & Waas 10478* (PDA). Further interpretation of this species and its variability will have to wait until more material comes to hand.

10. Semecarpus nigro-viridis Thw., Enum. Pl. Zeyl. 76. 1858; Engler, Mon. Phan. 4: 492. 1883; Hook. f., Fl. Br. Ind. 2: 34. 1876; Trimen, Handb. Fl. Ceylon 1: 323. 1893; Alston in Trimen, Handb. Fl. Ceylon 6: 63. 1931; Worthington, Ceylon Trees 159. 1959.

Semecarpus laevigata Thw. in Hook. f., Fl. Br. Ind. 2: 35. 1876; Engler, Mon. Phan. 4: 493. 1883; Trimen, Handb. Fl. Ceylon 1: 325. 1893.

Semecarpus intermedia (Trimen) Alston in Trimen, Handb. Fl. Ceylon 6: 62. 1931.

Semecarpus cuneata Engler, Mon. Phan. 4: 493. 1883.

Semecarpus obscura Thw., Enum. Pl. Zeyl. 76. 1858; Engler, Mon. Phan. 4: 494. 1883; Hook. f., Fl. Br. Ind. 2: 33. 1876; Trimen, Handb. Fl. Ceylon 1: 324. 1893; Alston in Trimen, Handb. Fl. Ceylon 6: 63. 1931; Worthington, Ceylon Trees 160. 1959. Type: "Suffragam", 2 Aug. 1867, *C.P. 631* (K, PDA isotype, US).

Small to medium sized tree, glabrous throughout. Leaves often crowded at ends of branches. Petiole 5–20 mm; blades 8–15 cm thick, coriaceous, obovate-oblong; base narrowed and tapering into petiole; apex suddenly acuminate or obtusely rounded with a narrow cartilaginous margin; lower face drying dull brown; lateral nerves 5–8 (12) pairs, slightly ascending, archingly connected beyond the margin into a reticulate network of tertiary nerves, some of which stretch towards the midrib. Panicles about (6) 10–20 cm long. Flowers 8–10 mm long. Drupe 12–20 mm, ovoid, slightly compressed or not, short-acuminate; receptacle cup-shaped, covering one-third of the drupe, narrower than the drupe.

D i s t r. Moist low country, extending to the dry zone and montane zone. Endemic.

E c o l. Flowering February–April. Fruiting July–August (some collected in February).

N o t e. As described and interpreted here, a rather variable species from the intermediate to the dry zone and from the lowlands on to the montane zone in moist country, up to 1200 m. Forms with more rounded leaf apex have been found and called *S. obscura*. It is not possible to distinguish two species in this form-complex without a lot of haggling over the correctness of identifications.

By far the most common species on the island. The submontane form with rather small leaf blades common near Corbet's Gap and Rangala at the base of the Knuckles could easily be confused with *S. parvifolia* except for the fine details of nervation. The form collected near Moray Estate above Maskeliya, *Kostermans 24249, 24519* (PDA, US), *Sohmer* and *Waas 8698* (PDA, US) and *Maxwell, Hepper* and *Jayasuriya 917* (PDA, US), might be a local variety or subspecies, described as *S. intermedia* (Trimen) Alston (see also *C.P. 637*, Deltota) based on var. *intermedia* Trimen, Handb. Fl. Ceylon 1 : 323. 1893.

S p e c i m e n s E x a m i n e d. BATTICALOA DISTRICT: Batticaloa Gardens, *s. coll. C.P. 1258* (PDA). RATNAPURA DISTRICT: Gilimale, *Worthington 4831* (PDA), Sinharaja, Balangoda, 3 miles above tea estate, montane forest, *Meijer 442* (PDA, US); Southern escarpment above Pinnawala on Balangoda Road, *Comanor 1100* (PDA, US); Belihul Oya, *Worthington 4757* (K). KANDY DISTRICT: Deltota, *s. coll. C.P. 2556* (isotype of *S.*

obscura Thw., PDA); Galaha Road, Nilambe Estate, *Cooray 68050801* (PDA); Hunnasgiriya-Mahiyangana, 14 Sept. 1971, fr., *Balakrishnan 802* (PDA, US); Corbet's Gap, 3000 ft, *Dassanayake & Meijer 659* (PDA, US), *Kostermans 23480* (PDA, US); Udawattakele Forest Reserve, Kandy, *Meijer 86* (PDA, US); Peradeniya, University circuit bungalow Road, *Balasubramaniam & Meijer 652, 653* (PDA, US); Moray Estate, Maskeliya, E. of Adam's Peak, 16 May 1971, fl., *Kostermans 24162* (PDA, US), *Maxwell & Hepper 917* (PDA, US); Hantane, above University grounds, *Meijer 294* (PDA, US); Rangala, *Balasubramaniam 120* (PDA, US); Peradeniya Botanic Garden, (C 191 ?) labelled *S. moonii*, *Meijer 378* (PDA, US); Between Hunnasgiriya and Mahiyangana, roadside jungle, *Balakrishnan s.n.* (PDA, US); Forest near Gartmore Estate, *J.M. Silva s.n.* (PDA); Madugoda, *Worthington 1567* (K). MATALE DISTRICT: Kandanuwara, *Worthington 2385* (K); Matale Estate, Madulkele, *Worthington 1991* (K); Mile 37 between Laggala and Ilukkumbura, 4 Oct. 1971, fr., *Jayasuriya 279* (PDA, US); Kalupahana, *s. coll. s.n.* (PDA). NUWARA ELIYA DISTRICT: Ramboda, *Thwaites 631* (PDA). KURUNEGALA DISTRICT: Kurunegala-Badegama Forest, *Worthington 6265* (K). MONERAGALA DISTRICT: Wellawaya, *Worthington 4754* (K). MATARA DISTRICT: Enselwatte Estate above Deniyaya, 1000 m, *Kostermans s.n.* (PDA, US). EXACT LOCALITY UNKNOWN: South of the island, *s. coll. C.P. 3948* (type of *S. laevigata* Thw., K, PDA).

11. Semecarpus parvifolia Thw., Enum. Pl. Zeyl. 77. 1858; Engler, Mon. Phan. 4: 492. 1883; Hook. f., Fl. Br. Ind. 2: 34. 1876; Trimen, Handb. Fl. Ceylon 1: 324. 1893. Type: Hiniduma, *C.P. 3444* (K, isotype PDA, US).

Small tree, glabrous throughout. Leaves stiffly coriaceous, crowded at the ends of the annual growth; petiole 12 mm, channelled; blade small, 5–7.5 cm, elliptic-ovate to lanceolate, at base tapering into petiole; apex shortly and obtusely acuminate; margin narrow, cartilaginous; lateral nerves (7) 9–10 pairs, at right angle with the midrib; upper face drying dark brown, lower dull pale-ochre; lateral nerves arching and united near the margin, slightly raised, hardly more so than the tertiary nerves, which stretch towards the midrib besides forming a more marginal network with the veins. Flowers in terminal and axillary panicles or racemes, few per branch, 5–7.5 cm long. Drupe 2 cm or more, ovoid-conical, very sharp-pointed, only slightly oblique; receptacle nearly 12 mm, turbinate.

Distr. A tree of the lower wet zone, re-collected near the type-locality, Haycock Hill, Hiniduma. Endemic.

Specimens Examined. KANDY DISTRICT: Norton Road, *Worthington 6556* (K); Laksapana Power House Road, 2500 ft, *Worthington 5513* (K); Caroline, Norton Bridge, *Worthington 2718* (K); Imboolpitiya, Nawalapitiya, *Worthington 907* (K); Kellie Estate, Dolosbagie, *Worthington*

1865, 1889, 1906 (K). RATNAPURA DISTRICT: Bulutota, *Alston 1692* (PDA); Rakwana, *Worthington 2173, 2633* (K); Peak Sanctuary above Carney, *Meijer 497* (PDA, US). GALLE DISTRICT: Haycock Hill, Hiniduma, *Meijer 579* (PDA, US); Kanneliya Forest Reserve, *Meijer 1044* (PDA, US).

6. NOTHOPEGIA

Blume, Ann. Mus. Bot. Lugduno-Batavum 1: 203. 1850. Type species: *Nothopegia colebrookiana* Blume.

Small to medium-sized tree. Inner bark with black-drying juice. Leaves spirally arranged or more or less in two rows or subopposite, coriaceous. Flowers in small spicate or more or less spicate axillary racemes or panicles, polygamous. Calyx 4–5-lobed, persistent, with imbricate lobes. Petals 4–5, imbricate, spreading. Stamens 4–5, inserted under the margin of a 4–5-lobed disk. Filaments free, hairy. Anthers introrse, longitudinally dehiscing. Ovary abortive in male flowers, sessile in female, ovoid, 1-celled; style short, stigma capitate. Fruit a globose, acute, depressed drupe, tipped with the style. Seed pendulous, without albumen; cotyledons thick, plane-convex.

A genus with 6 species in India (Gamble, Fl. Pres. Madras, 1935). One also in Ceylon. This genus seems to be narrowly related with *Melanochyla* Hook. f., which has at least 12 species in Malaya, but differs by having valvate petals and unisexual flowers. In case they would be lumped the name *Nothopegia* would have to be used, being the earliest published.

Nothopegia beddomei Gamble, Kew Bull. 1918: 227. 1918; Alston in Trimen, Handb. Fl. Ceylon 6: 63. 1931.

Nothopegia colebrookeana Trimen, Handb. Fl. Ceylon 1: 323. 1893, non Blume; Worthington, Ceylon Trees 163, t. 19. 1959.
Glycycarpus racemosa Thw., Enum. Pl. Zeyl. 78. 1858, non Dalz.

Small to medium-sized tree. Bark closely fissured; inner bark red-brown, with white latex which slowly turns darker. Sapwood ochre. Buds pilose. Twigs and leaves glabrous. Leaf stalk about 1 cm long, partly twisted, bringing all the leaves into one plane. Leaf blades oblong-lanceolate, about 10–15 cm long; apex acuminate, base cuneate, slightly decurrent towards the stalk. Midrib sunken on upper surface, keeled and slightly furrowed on lower. Lateral nerves up to 20 pairs, more dense towards the base than in the middle of the blade, joining the midrib under an angle of 60°, disappearing into the thickened recurved leaf margin, raised above the surface but flattened; tertiary nerves mainly more or less wavy, parallel, stretched at right angles with the lateral, partly dichotomously branched near the midrib, and curved towards the midrib, also flat with very low profile. Veins forming a more or

less waffle-like network with blind branched endings in the finest nets. Inflorescences bisexual, spicate, short (2–3 cm) in upper axils; lower longer, male
7–8 cm, paniculate with lowest side branches 1.5 cm long. All branches short
patent-hairy. Flowers in bud up to 1 mm long. Calyx shallowly lobed. Petals
oblong, obtuse. Ovary glabrous. Stamens with hairy (villous) filaments.
Drupe about 15 mm long; about twice as broad as long (high), fig-like, longitudinally striate, purple, pulp copious.

D i s t r. West Peninsular India and Ceylon. In Ceylon a tree of the wet
lowlands, the hill zone and rather common in the intermediate zone; also observed in the rather undisturbed forest on Ritigala Hill (Meijer, Balasubramaniam and Dassanayake).

E c o l. Flowering March–July.

V e r n. Bala (S).

N o t e. "Wood yellowish, rather heavy, smooth-grained, easily splitting"
(Trimen).

S p e c i m e n s E x a m i n e d. KANDY DISTRICT: s.loc., 1550 ft,
Worthington 6225, 484 (BM), *Worthington 6899* (K); Teldeniya, Mile 15,
Worthington 489 (BM); east of Corbet's Gap, *Worthington 3584* (K); Kadugannawa, *Worthington 331* (K); Alagalla Rock, 1000 m, 8 May 1971, *Kos-
termans 24045* (PDA, US); Doublecut Road, Laxapana to Maskeliya,
Kostermans 24097 (PDA, US); new damsite, Maskeliya Road, 1000 m,
Kostermans 24105 (PDA, US). MATALE DISTRICT: Rattota, *Worthington
6225* (BM), 6 miles east of Naula along Elahera Road, 5 Oct. 1974, fr., *Jaya-
suriya 295* (PDA, US). POLONNARUWA DISTRICT: Gunners Quoin,
Worthington 5290 (K). MONARAGALA DISTRICT: 1 mile east of Wel-
lawaya, *Meijer 181* (PDA, US); Bibile, *Worthington 5120* (K). GALLE DIS-
TRICT: Bona Vista Hill, July 1970, fl., *Meijer 251* (PDA, US); Galle Point,
Worthington 2360 (K). RATNAPURA DISTRICT: Embilipitiya Road,
Worthington 3654 (K); Balangoda-Bogawantalawa Road, 3 miles above
Estate, in *Doona gardneri* forest, *Meijer 947* (PDA, US). BADULLA DIS-
TRICT: Horabora Wewa, *Worthington 1545* (K).

7. LANNEA

A. Rich. in Guillemin and Perrottet, Fl. Senegal 1: 153. 1831, nom. cons.
Type species: *Lannea acida* A. Rich.

Odina Roxb., Fl. Ind. 2: 293. 1832.
Calesiam Adans., Fam. 2: 446. 1763.
Haberlia Dennst., Schluess. Hort. Mal. 30. 1818.
Kalesiam Rheede, Hort. Mal. 4: 67 t. 32. 1683.

Tree. Leaves spirally arranged, imparipinnate. Flowers dioecious, in
axillary panicles, 4– (5) merous; stamens 8 (–10), inserted at outer base of the

disk, sterile and very small in female flowers. Disk annular, 8 (–10)-lobed, glabrous. Ovary 1-celled, 1-ovuled, barren and reduced to 4 lobes in male flowers. Styles 4, free, very short; stigmas capitate. Fruit a drupe, bean-shaped with a hard stone.

A genus with one species from N.W. India to Ceylon and Indo-China and Hainan and cultivated in other parts of S.E. Asia, and 70 species in tropical Africa.

Lannea coromandelica (Houtt.) Merr., J. Arnold. Arbor. 19: 353. 1938.

Dialium coromandelicum Houtt., Nat. Hist. 2: 39. t. 5. f. 2. 1774; Christm., Pflanzen. Syst. 1: 208. t. 5. f. 2. 1777, in nota. Type: A Coromandel specimen from Burman illustrated by Houtt. (l.c.).

Odina wodier Roxb., Fl. Ind. 2: 293. 1832; Engler, Mon. Phan. 4: 267. 1883; Thw., Enum. Pl. Zeyl. 78. 1858; Hook. f., Fl. Br. Ind. 2: 29. 1876; Wight, Ic. Pl. Ind. Or. t. 60. 1838; Bedd., Fl. Sylv. t. 123. 1871; Trimen, Handb. Fl. Ceylon 1: 318. 1893; Lecomte, Fl. Gen. Indo-China 2: 34. 1908; Gamble, Fl. Pres. Madras 1: 187. 1915.

Lannea grandis (Dennst.) Engler in Pflanzenfam. Nachtr. I: 213. 1897; Alston in Trimen, Handb. Fl. Ceylon 6: 60. 1931; Worthington, Ceylon Trees 155. 1959.

Haberlia grandis Dennst., Schluess. Hort. Mal. 30. 1818.

Odina pinnata Rottl., Ges. Naturf. Freunde Berlin Neue Schriften 4: 209. 1803; Clarke, Kew Bull. 1894: 202. 1894.

Medium-sized deciduous tree; bole scaly-fissured or smooth, inner bark with sticky gum, fibrous, laminated with alternating layers of red and white. Young parts stellate-hairy pubescent and lenticellate. Leaves 15–30 cm long; stalks 6–12 cm, terete, swollen at base; rachis with (5) 7–11 (17) leaflets. Leaflets not brown at lower surface when dried; more or less opposite except the terminal; the basal on 1–2 mm long stalks, those near the apex sessile, ovate, the basal ones slightly unequal at the rounded base; apex cordate-acuminate; lower face and part of the upper with scattered stellate pubescence; 8 pairs of lateral nerves rather prominent, diminishing towards the margin; tertiary nerves only visible with a lens, the main ones connecting adjacent laterals more or less at right angles in a wide network dissolved in a network with rectangular branched veins with alternate branchlets dead-ending in the maze; margin entire or finely crenate. Panicles branched, 10–25 cm long in male trees; apparently less branched and up to about 15 cm on female trees; stellate-pubescent, appearing on deciduous trees with the young leaves on the shoots. Flowers almost sessile or on 2 mm long stalks. Calyx segments minute, about 0.75 mm, ovate-triangular, obtuse with scattered stellate hairs outside or glabrous. Petals ovate-oblong, with obtuse apex, about twice as long as the sepals, reflexed in female flowers. Stamens about 2 mm long in male flowers, in female 1 mm or shorter. Fruits in bunches of about 20 on 2 cm long common stalk, almost sessile, with persistent calyx; flattened, kidney-shaped, trapezoid or rounded-rectangular; about 1 cm long and 0.5 cm in diameter, with a hard stone.

D i s t r. From N.W. India to Ceylon, Burma, Indo-China, Hainan. Cultivated especially in coastal regions in Sumatra, Borneo and Java, planted in hedges. Apparently easy to grow from cuttings.

E c o l. In Ceylon one of the rather common deciduous trees of the dry zone but also found in the lowlands of the wet zone—in the latter more or less evergreen. Flowering in the dry zone about June–July, but some trees might already be fruiting at that time.

U s e s. On good soil and given time to grow trees grow to a fairly large size (1.5 m girth at least) and timber can be used for planks. Trees are apparently fire-resistant because of the thick bark. The gum has been used in India for cotton printing. The bark is useful for tanning fishing nets and young leaves and twigs are edible for cattle and man (Heyne, Nutt. Pl. Indon. 977. 1950).

V e r n. Hik (S); Odi (T).

S p e c i m e n s E x a m i n e d. POLONNARUWA DISTRICT: near resthouse, Polonnaruwa, *Balakrishnan 348* (PDA, US). TRINCOMALEE DISTRICT: Trincomalee, Welcombe, *Worthington 571* (BM); Deadmans cove, seashore, *Worthington 203* (BM). BATTICALOA DISTRICT: mile 78, Polonnaruwa-Batticaloa Road, *Meijer 127* (PDA, US); Batticaloa, *Mueller-Dombois 67081401* (PDA, US); Katiankudi, *Balakrishnan 3761* (PDA, US). GALLE DISTRICT: near Kanneliya Forest Reserve, *Meijer 562* (PDA, US). HAMBANTOTA DISTRICT: Yala Nat. Park, Block T, Kotabandu Wewa, *Wirawan 780* (PDA, US). MONERAGALA DISTRICT: 4 miles W. of Wellawaya, *Meijer 636* (PDA, US); Monaragala, 480 ft, *Worthington 4746* (K); a few miles N.W. of Kuda Oya, N. of Tanamalwila, *Meijer 193* (PDA, US). RATNAPURA DISTRICT: Kalawana, Riverbank, *Worthington 4606* (K). KANDY DISTRICT: Kadugannawa, *Hancock & Worthington 1381, 1382* (K), also *Worthington 1412* (BM); Patanas, Madugoda, *N.O. Simpson 8476* (BM). MATALE DISTRICT: main road, mile 38, *Meijer 323* (PDA, US); Mile 36, near Naula-Dambulla Road, *Cramer 3028* (PDA, US); Dambulla, on the road, 15 May 1969, *Kostermans 23538* (PDA, US).

8. SPONDIAS

L., Sp. Pl. 371. 1753. Type species: *Spondias mombin* L.

Trees, often deciduous; bole and twigs often lenticellate. Bark exuding a gum (not seen by me—W.M.). Leaves when crushed with turpentine smell, spirally arranged, imparipinnate; petiole much thickened at the base. Leaflets short-stalked, thin, margin entire or crenate-serrate; lateral nerves connected by a marginal nerve running close along the margin; tertiary nerves between the laterals often with 1–3 intermediates running towards the midrib. Panicles in the axils of leaves or of fallen leaves or terminal. Flowers bisexual or male and female flowers on one tree. Calyx 4–5, dentate, deciduous. Petals 4–5, imbricate, valvate. Stamens 8 or 10, inserted below a disk. Disk annular, deeply 10-lobed, yellow. Ovary partly immersed in disk, 4–5-celled with 1 pendulous ovule in each cell; styles 3–5, short, thick; stigmas at last divergent. Drupe oblong, fleshy, ripening orange or purple. Pyrene woody, with longitudinal ridges, between them fibrous, cells 4–5, each containing a single seed—usually only 1-seeded. Cotyledons flat.

A genus of 10–12 species in S.E. Asia and tropical America. One wild and two cultivated in Ceylon.

KEY TO THE SPECIES

1 Bole with sharp spiny corky ridges. Buttresses far spreading. Lateral nerves about 10–15 pairs; prominent on upper and lower face as well as the tertiary nerves and veins. Flowers polygamous..**3. S. mombin**
1 Bole without sharp spiny corky ridges. Buttresses short, rounded. Lateral nerves of leaflets 15–20 pairs. Flowers bisexual
  2 Deciduous tree of the dry zone. Flowers sessile. Fruits 3–5 cm long, bitter, green, ripening yellow-brown to orange-brown. Endocarp without radiating spinose processes....
....**1. S. pinnata**
  2 Tree of the moist low country (deciduous or not?). Flowers on 2–4 mm long pedicels. Fruits 7–10 cm long, sourish, yellow when ripe. Endocarp bearing numerous radiating, straight or curved, spinose processes....................................**2. S. dulcis**

1. Spondias pinnata (L. f.) Kurz, Pegu. Rep. 44. 1875; Alston in Trimen, Handb. Fl. Ceylon 6: 63. 1931. Type: A Koenig specimen collected in India, labelled *Mangifera pinnata.*

Mangifera pinnata L. f., Suppl. Pl. 156. 1781.
Spondias mangifera Willd., Sp. Pl. 2: 751. 1799; Trimen, Handb. Fl. Ceylon 1: 327. 1893, pro parte; Airy Shaw and Forman, Kew Bull. 21: 8. 1967.

As interpreted here this is a dry zone species of *Spondias* not well recognised in Trimen's Handbook and confused with the presumably introduced *S. dulcis.*

D i s t r. India, Ceylon and Malesia.

U s e s. The fruits said to be inferior compared with those of the other species though they are used in Malesia. Leaves are edible. Wood useful for matches (Heyne, Nutt. Pl. Indon. 975. 1950).

S p e c i m e n s E x a m i n e d. MATALE DISTRICT: Dambulla, 45 miles N. of Kandy, *Douglas Simpson 9787* (BM); Nalanda, about 30 miles N. of Kandy, *Worthington 3126, 5057* (K). ANURADHAPURA DISTRICT: Habarana, along Dambulla-Trincomalee Road, *Worthington 687* (K); Ritigala, *Meijer 339* (PDA, US). TRINCOMALEE DISTRICT: Cloppenburg, *Worthington 4877* (K).

2. Spondias dulcis Soland. ex Parkinson, Voy. South Seas 39. 1773; Forst. f., Pl. Esculent. 133. 1786; Merr., Chron. Bot. 14 (5–6): 360. 1954; Airy Shaw and Forman, Kew Bull. 21: 10. 1967; Backer and Bakh., Fl. Java 2: 151. 1965.

Spondias cytherea Sonn., Voy. Ind. 3: 342 t. 123. 1782.
Spondias mangifera Wild. sensu Trimen, Handb. Fl. Ceylon 1: 327. 1893; Worthington, Ceylon Trees 165. 1959.

This is the tree presumably introduced into S.E. Asia from the Society Islands (see Backer and Bakh., l.c.). It occurs as a cultivated fruit tree in Java, the Moluccas, W. Sumatra and Malaya.

V e r n. Ambarella (S).
S p e c i m e n s   E x a m i n e d. KANDY DISTRICT: Kadugannawa, 10 miles W. of Kandy, *Worthington 363* (BM), 603 (K); Peradeniya Bot. Garden, F72, *Meijer 390* (PDA, US). KEGALLE DISTRICT: Colombo-Kandy Road, mile 41, Nelundeniya, village plantation, *Meijer 286* (PDA, US). RATNA-PURA DISTRICT: Pelmadulla, near mile 74, tree in village, *Meijer 438* (PDA, US).

3. Spondias mombin L., Sp. Pl. 371. 1753; Backer and Bakh., Fl. Java 2: 151. 1965; Airy Shaw and Forman, Kew Bull. 21: 11. 1967.

Spondias lutea L., Sp. Pl. ed. 2. 613. 1762.

The tree planted under No. D. 102 in the Peradeniya Bot. Garden most likely belongs to this species. Backer and Bakhuizen van den Brink (l.c.) describe the typical spiny corky ridges of the bark. However, they state that leaflets are obtusely acuminate which fits less with this specimen which has acuminate leaflets with crenate margin. Flowering and fruiting specimens will have to substantiate our tentative identification. This tree is cultivated and naturalized in Java and originates from tropical America.

V e r n. Hog plum tree (E).
N o t e. Corner, Wayside Trees of Malaya 115. 1940, considers this species to be *S. lutea* which he separates from *S. mombin* L. Fruits as described by him—pleasantly fragrant, like plums in turpentine.

The original manuscript of this revision was submitted and accepted for printing in December 1976. Since that time Dr Ding Hou (Leiden) published his excellent revision of the Malesian species in Flora Malesiana I, 8 (3): 395–548. 1978 and in the precursor in Blumea 24: 1–41. 1978. No reference to this could be made while this manuscript was in the press. Students of the flora of Sri Lanka should consult also the Flora Malesia revision, especially for more extensive literature citations.

APOCYNACEAE

(by Herbert Huber*)

Type Genus: *Apocynum* L.

Erect or climbing woody plants or perennial, very rarely annual, herbs with internal phloem and milky** latex, sometimes in small quantities. Leaves opposite or whorled or occasionally alternate; simple, entire, pinnately veined, without definite stipules. Flowers with calyx and corolla, actinomorphic, usually 5-merous (exceptionally some flowers 6-merous), bisexual, indeterminate, terminal or axillary inflorescences or inflorescences arising laterally from between two petioles; sometimes the inflorescences reduced to one or two axillary flowers. Sepals shortly connate or almost free, imbricate. Corolla gamopetalous, frequently salver-shaped, the lobes contorted or rarely imbricate, overlapping in bud to the right or to the left. Stamens as many as corolla-lobes and alternating with them, inserted in the corolla-tube; anthers distinct, rarely connate by their points, free or adnate to the style-apex, longitudinally dehiscent along their inner side. Pollen granular (grains distinct, not united in tetrads except in *Pagiantha*). Corona absent or consisting of one or several series of scales inserted in the mouth of the corolla-tube. Disk annular when present. Carpels two, superior or semi-inferior, 2- to multi-ovulate, free or joined by their common style only, or united into a one- or two-locular ovary; style simple, often much thickened at the apex. Fruit consisting of two connate or more frequently distinct carpels, baccate, drupaceous or capsular, with one to many seeds in each carpel; merocarps paired or solitary by abortion, indehiscent or dehiscent along the ventral suture. Seeds with or without endosperm, with or without a tuft of hairs at one end or at both ends, rarely winged, without an aril but sometimes with a pulpy envelope derived from the pericarp.

A large family of about 300 genera with more than 1400 species, predominantly in the tropics and subtropics, represented in Ceylon by 20 genera and a total of 24 truly native species, nine of which are endemic.

Apocynaceae are related to Loganiaceae (particularly to the tribe Potalieae), Periplocaceae and Asclepiadaceae. From the first family they can readily be distinguished by the occurrence of lactiferous tubes in the vegetative

*Fachbereich Biologie der Universität Kaiserslautern, Germany.
**Latex absent in *Nerium*; sap watery in *Anodendron*.

25

organs, whereas the latter families deviate in their highly specialised pollen-carriers and pollination mechanism. The subdivision of the Apocynaceae is much more problematic than their delimitation. Here the arrangement of M. Pichon is followed, but one should keep in mind that the Plumerioideae are a rather heterogenous assemblage of well-marked tribes, whereas the Apocynoideae form a thoroughly natural subfamily which hardly can be divided into distinct tribes. The genera native or naturalized in Ceylon can be arranged as follows:

Subfamily **Plumerioideae**
  Tribe **Carisseae:** *Willughbeia, Carissa, Hunteria.*
  Tribe **Tabernaemontaneae:** *Pagiantha,* (*Ervatamia*).
  Tribe **Plumerieae:** *Alstonia, Catharanthus, Holarrhena,* (*Plumeria*).
  Tribe **Rauvolfieae:** *Rauvolfia, Petchia, Ochrosia.*
  Tribe **Allamandeae:** (*Allamanda*).
Subfamily **Cerberoideae**
  Tribe **Cerbereae:** *Cerbera,* (*Thevetia*).
Subfamily **Apocynoideae** (Echitoideae)
  Tribe **Parsonsieae:** *Aganosma, Chonemorpha, Parsonsia.*
  Tribe **Nerieae:** *Vallaris, Walidda, Wrightia,* (*Nerium*).
  Tribe **Apocyneae:** (Ecdysanthereae): *Cleghornia, Anodendron.*
  Tribe **Ichnocarpeae:** *Ichnocarpus.*

The economic importance of this family is limited to a few genera. In Ceylon the introduced *Alstonia macrophylla* Wall. ex G. Don is an important source of timber and *Rauvolfia serpentina* (L.) Benth. ex Kurz has been collected for pharmaceutical purposes. A ruthless exploitation made the latter disappear where it used to be frequent a few decades ago.

The family is of considerable phytochemical interest and there is some correlation between morphological and chemical characters insofar as indolic alkaloids are widely distributed among the Plumerioideae but apparently absent from the rest. On the other hand, Cerberoideae and Apocynoideae are distinguished by the frequent presence of Cardiotoxic glycosides, which indicate a strong affinity of these two subfamilies with Periplocaceae and the tribe Asclepiadeae of Asclepiadaceae.

Most Ceylon Apocynaceae are confined to the tropical lowland, particularly of the moist region, but a few species extend into the drier parts of the island or are restricted to those (e.g. *Wrightia angustifolia* Thw.). Apart from *Carissa spinarum* L., commonly forming dense scrub in the dry zone, and *Alstonia macrophylla* Wall. ex G. Don, which became naturalized and well established in secondary forests of the moist region, Apocynaceae in general do not play an important role in the vegetation of the island.

Due to the rapid destruction of the natural vegetation, especially in the moist zone, some species are disappearing now. On the other hand, a few alien species have become naturalized. These are treated like indigenous plants in this paper. Alien species frequently grown as ornamentals but not or rarely escaping from cultivation are included in the keys. A short description of these species is given below.

Allamanda cathartica L., Mant. 214. 1771.

A straggling and climbing, sparsely puberulous or almost glabrous woody plant. Leaves mostly in whorls of four or occasionally of three or leaves opposite, lanceolate, oblong or elliptic, acuminate, herbaceous to slightly coriaceous, with distant lateral veins including with the midrib an angle of 45–60°. Cymes short-peduncled, terminal but frequently overtopped by axillary branches. Calyx-lobes ovate-oblong, acute. Corolla large, yellow; tube 4–8 cm long, cylindrical in the lower half*, campanulate above; lobes much shorter than the tube, orbicular to obovate-truncate, in bud overlapping to the left. Fruit a spiny, almost globose, unilocular capsule 3–7 cm long and 3–5 cm in diameter; spines up to 1 cm long. Seeds numerous, with a circular wing, without a tuft of hairs; very rarely produced in Ceylon.

A native of tropical America, largely grown for ornament and sometimes naturalized in the moist zone. Apart from the typical form with flowers 5–6 cm in diameter, there is a large-flowered plant with flowers 10 cm or more in diameter; this has been named var. *hendersonii* (Bull) Rafill.

V e r n. Wal-ruk-attana (S).

Ervatamia divaricata (L.) Alston in Trimen, Handb. Fl. Ceylon 6: 191. 1931.

Nerium divaricatum L., Sp. Pl. 209. 1753.
Nerium coronarium Jacq., Collect. 1: 138. 1786.
Tabernaemontana coronaria (Jacq.) Willd., Enum. Hort. Berol. 275. 1809.
Tabernaemontana divaricata (L.) R. Br. ex Roem. & Schult., Syst. Veg. 4: 127. 1819.
Ervatamia coronaria (Jacq.) Stapf in Dyer, Fl. Trop. Africa 4 (1): 127. 1902.

A slender, glabrous treelet. Leaves opposite, elliptic, acuminate, herbaceous, with distant lateral veins including with the midrib an angle of 45–60°. Cymes peduncled, dichasially branched, terminal but often overtopped by axillary branches. Calyx-lobes ovate-oblong, obtuse. Corolla white; tube about 2 cm long, narrowly cylindrical; lobes longer than the tube, obliquely ovate, with the covering side convex and the covered side straight, in bud overlapping to the left. Merocarps distinct, divaricate, spindle-shaped, produced into an acute beak, fleshy, dehiscent along the ventral suture when ripe, 3–4 cm long and about 1 cm in diameter, orange inside. Seeds rather numerous, without a tuft of hairs.

*Tube cylindrical in the lower third or quarter: *Allamanda schottii* Pohl.

This is the well-known Grape Jasmine, frequently grown in tropical gardens, both with single and double flowers. The flowers are heterostylous. A native of the southern Himalayas, but cultivated since ancient times.

V e r n. Nada-wata, Thagara, Watu-sudda (S); Nandi-battai (T).

Nerium oleander L., Sp. Pl. 209. 1753.

A rigid shrub without latex. Young branches and inflorescences puberulous. Leaves mostly in whorls of three, lanceolate, coriaceous, glabrous; lateral veins numerous, including with the midrib an almost right angle. Cymes penduncled, with monochasial branches, terminal or lateral from between the petioles. Calyx- lobes lanceolate, acute. Corolla purple, pink or white, rarely yellowish; tube about 2 cm long, cylindrical in the lower, funnel-shaped in the upper half, with five laciniate scales in the throat; corolla-lobes slightly longer than the tube, obliquely obovate, in bud overlapping to the right. Merocarps cylindrical, 12–18 cm long, 0.6–1 cm in diameter, at first coherent by their tips, finally splitting and dehiscent along the ventral suture. Seeds numerous, densely pilose, with a tuft of hairs at one end.

Introduced from the Mediterranean and occasionally grown as an ornamental.

V e r n. Kaneru, Rath-kaneru (the red flowered plant) (S); Arali (S and T); Alari (T); the names Alariya and Araliya (both S) commonly applied to species of *Plumeria* are also given to *Nerium*.

PLUMERIA

L., Sp. Pl. 209. 1753.

Thick-branched, glabrous or puberulous trees with spirally arranged, large, lanceolate, oblong or obovate leaves, crowded at the top of the branches. Lateral veins numerous, including with the midrib an angle of 60°– almost 90°. Cymes long-penduncled, monochasially branched, terminal but sometimes overtopped by axillary branches. Calyx-lobes minute, truncate or very broadly triangular. Corolla large, white, purple or yellow, fleshy; tube 2–3 cm long, cylindrical, gradually and slightly funnel-shaped towards the mouth; lobes longer than the tube, elliptic to oblong, in bud overlapping to the left. Merocarps distinct, divaricate, cylindrical, up to 25 cm long and up to 3 cm in diameter, dehiscent along the ventral suture. Seeds numerous, winged, without a tuft of hairs.

Two species are frequently grown in Ceylon. The flowers are widely used for temple decoration. Fruits are rarely produced in cultivation.

KEY TO THE SPECIES

1 Leaves lanceolate to lanceolate-oblong, acute or acuminate at apex, rather pale green and opaque above, with tertiary venation hardly prominent beneath. Petiole glabrous. Corolla about 5–6 cm in diameter, tinged with pink or purple at least on the outside of the tube; lobes obliquely patent, pink, yellow or white with a yellow base. Merocarps up to 25 cm long and 2–3 cm wide.......................................**1. P. rubra**
1 Leaves obovate to obovate-oblong, rounded at the apex, dark green and shining above, with tertiary venation strongly prominent beneath. Petiole more or less puberulous. Corolla about 10 cm in diameter, white with a yellow throat, not at all tinged with red; lobes spreading and slightly recurved. Merocarps up to 15 cm long and about 1.5 cm wide...**2. P. obtusa**

1. Plumeria rubra L., Sp. Pl. 209. 1753.

Plumeria acuminata Ait., Hort. Kew. 2: 70. 1789.
Plumeria acutifolia Poir., Enc. Suppl. 2: 667. 1812.

A native of Central America from Mexico to Panama. Commonly grown for ornament in Ceylon and throughout the tropics, sometimes found in a semi-wild state as a relict of cultivation.

2. Plumeria obtusa L., Sp. Pl. 210. 1753.

A native of the Bahama Islands, Cuba, Jamaica, Hispaniola and Puerto Rico. In Ceylon frequently grown in gardens but hardly ever found as an escape.

V e r n. (for both species) Alariya, Araliya (S).

Thevetia peruviana (Pers.) Merr., Philipp. J. Sci. 9: 130. 1914.

Cerbera thevetia L., Sp. Pl. 209. 1753.
Cerbera peruviana Pers., Syn. Pl. 1: 267. 1809.
Thevetia neriifolia Juss. ex Steud., Nom. Bot. ed. 2, 2: 680. 1841 as "nereifolia".

A small, glabrous tree with linear or linear-lanceolate, slightly coriaceous leaves; lateral veins rather distant, including with the midrib an angle of 45–60°. Cymes short-peduncled, monochasially branched, terminal but often overtopped by axillary branches. Calyx-lobes triangular-lanceolate, acute. Corolla large, yellow; tube 4–5 cm long, cylindrical in the lower third, funnel-shaped above; lobes obovate-truncate, shorter than the tube, in bud overlapping to the left. Carpels united into a broadly turbinate drupe, slightly compressed laterally, about 3 cm long and wide, with few, strongly flattened seeds.

A native of Central and South America, now frequently grown throughout the tropics.

KEY TO THE GENERA
(Key to flowering specimens)

1 Corolla-lobes (viewed from outside) overlapping to the right. Erect or twining woody plants
  2 With paired spines in the axils of leaves at alternate nodes. Ovary simple, ovoid..... ....**2. Carissa**
  2 Spines absent. Ovary of two distinct carpels
    3 Erect woody plants with leaves whorled or alternate
      4 Flowers large, funnel-shaped, mostly purple or white. Calyx-lobes about 5 mm long, very acute. Anthers adnate to the style-apex. Introduced ornamental......**Nerium**
      4 Flowers rather small, salver-shaped, white or greenish-white. Calyx-lobes not exceeding 1.5 mm, obtuse. Anthers free
        5 Pedicels several times longer than the calyx, minutely puberulous, rarely glabrescent. Leaves pubescent on the under surface at least when young............... ....**5. Alstonia** (*macrophylla*)
        5 Pedicels about as long as the calyx, glabrous. Leaves glabrous even when young.. ....**10. Ochrosia**
    3 Twining or semi-scandent woody plants with opposite leaves. Anthers adnate to the style-apex
      6 Anthers exserted from the corolla-tube
        7 Stamens inserted near the base of the corolla-tube. Filaments long, spirally twisted. Young stems glabrous...**14. Parsonsia**
        7 Stamens inserted near the mouth of the corolla-tube. Filaments short and straight. Young stems pubescent...**15. Vallaris**
      6 Anthers included in the corolla-tube
        8 Young stem and inflorescence glabrous
          9 Corolla-lobes ovate, half as long as the tube....................**18. Cleghornia**
          9 Corolla-lobes linear, almost twice as long as the tube............**19. Anodendron**
        8 Young stem and inflorescence densely pubescent or tomentose
          10 Corolla very large, 7–10 cm in diameter when expanded. Leaves 8–18 cm wide, cordate at the base....................................**13. Chonemorpha**
          10 Corolla not exceeding 2 cm in diameter. Leaves rounded or acute at base
            11 Calyx-lobes linear-lanceolate, 7–10 mm long, longer than the corolla-tube..... ....**12. Aganosma**
            11 Calyx-lobes minute, not exceeding 1 mm, shorter than the corolla-tube........ ....**20. Ichnocarpus**
1 Corolla-lobes (viewed from outside) overlapping to the left. Plants woody or herbaceous, erect or climbing with tendrils
  12 Anthers exserted from the corolla-tube, adnate to the style-apex. Mouth of corolla-tube with one or several series of erect scales. Calyx-lobes obtuse or almost obtuse
    13 Corolla-tube 1.7–2.8 cm long; the lobes little shorter than the tube. Slender treelet.. ....**16. Walidda**
    13 Corolla-tube not exceeding 0.5 cm in length; the lobes much longer. Trees.......... ....**17. Wrightia**
  12 Anthers included in the corolla-tube, not adnate to the style-apex. Scales in the mouth of the corolla-tube absent
    14 Calyx-lobes rounded or obtuse
      15 Leaves whorled or alternate
        16 Flowers large. Stamens inserted near the base of the corolla-tube. Calyx glabrous. Introduced ornamental...**Plumeria**

16 Flowers rather small. Stamens inserted in the upper part of the corolla-tube. Calyx densely puberulous.............................**5. Alstonia** (*scholaris*)
15 Leaves opposite
  17 Flowers small, yellow, in sessile or short-peduncled cymes. Climbing with long, whip-like tendrils..**1. Willughbeia**
  17 Flowers large, white. Trees or treelets, not climbing
    18 Calyx-lobes connate at the very base only. Corolla fleshy. Leaves firmly coriaceous; lateral veins horizontally patent...........................**4. Pagiantha**
    18 Calyx-lobes connate for at least half of their length. Corolla membranous. Leaves herbaceous; lateral veins including with the midrib an angle of 45–60°. Introduced ornamental...**Ervatamia**
14 Calyx-lobes acute
  19 Corolla large, 4 cm in diameter or more; tube funnel-shaped towards the mouth. Calyx-lobes 7–20 mm long
    20 Flowers pure white, turning black when dried. Calyx deciduous. Ovary of two distinct carpels...**11. Cerbera**
    20 Flowers yellow. Ovary ovoid, simple. Introduced ornamentals
      21 Leaves alternate, linear, up to 1 cm wide. Corolla-tube cylindric in the lower third. Ovary bilocular, with two ovules in each loculus. Trees........**Thevetia**
      21 Leaves mostly whorled or opposite, lanceolate, 2–4 cm wide. Corolla-tube most frequently cylindric in the lower half. Ovary unilocular with numerous ovules. Scrambling or erect shrubs......................................**Allamanda**
  19 Corolla medium-sized or small; tube not widened towards the mouth. Calyx-lobes not exceeding 5 mm in length
    22 Flowers solitary or paired in the axils of the leaves. Low subshrubs or herbs....
    ....**6. Catharanthus**
    22 Inflorescence of more than two flowers, peduncled
      23 Corolla puberulous without; lobes longer than the tube. Stamens inserted near the base of the corolla-tube...............................**7. Holarrhena**
      23 Corolla glabrous without; lobes shorter than the tube. Stamens inserted near the mouth of the corolla-tube
        24 Leaves at the branching usually in whorls of three, otherwise opposite. Corolla-lobes narrowly oblong; the tube pubescent in the mouth...........**9. Petchia**
        24 Leaves either opposite or whorled throughout. Corolla-lobes ovate or orbicular; tube glabrous in the mouth
          25 Leaves opposite, coriaceous. Small trees.......................**3. Hunteria**
          25 Leaves in whorls of three, thinly membranous. Treelets or almost herbaceous plants...**8. Rauvolfia**

KEY TO THE GENERA
(Key to fruiting specimens)

1 Seeds with a tuft of hairs at one end or at both ends. Erect or twining woody plants
  2 Leaves whorled. Erect woody plants
    3 Tall trees with slender merocarps of 2.5–3.5 mm in diameter. Seeds with a tuft of hairs at both ends...**5. Alstonia**
    3 Shrubs with rather stout merocarps of 0.6–1 cm in diameter. Seeds with a tuft of hairs at one end only. Introduced ornamental...........................**Nerium**
  2 Leaves opposite
    4 Young stems glabrous
      5 Trees or treelets

    6 Slender treelet. Merocarps acuminate, 9–15 cm long...............**16. Walidda**

    6 Trees. Merocarps obtuse or acute but not acuminate, 17–45 cm long

       7 Seeds dark brown. Branchlets dark purplish-brown; lenticels not conspicuous. Merocarps 30–45 cm long, obtuse..........................**7. Holarrhena**

       7 Seeds yellowish-grey or pale greyish-brown. Branchlets greyish-brown; lenticels whitish, very conspicuous. Merocarps 17–30 cm long, acute...................

        ....**17. Wrightia** (*angustifolia*)

  5 Twining plants

    8 Fruit a bilocular, septicidally dehiscent capsule 11–18 cm long. Seeds linear, 1.2–1.8 cm long..**14. Parsonsia**

    8 Fruit soon splitting into two distinct merocarps dehiscent along the ventral suture. Seeds 2–almost 5 cm long

      9 Merocarps slender, about 25–30 cm long and 0.5 cm in diameter, many-seeded. Seeds narrowly lanceolate..................................**18. Cleghornia**

      9 Merocarps stout, about 10–15 cm long and 1–1.5 cm in diameter, few-seeded. Seeds ovate-oblong..**19. Anodendron**

 4 Young stems pubescent or tomentose

  10 Seeds linear, 1–scarcely 2 mm wide. Trees or twining plants

    11 Seeds yellowish-grey or pale brown. Trees........................**17. Wrightia**

    11 Seeds blackish-brown. Twining plants........................**20. Ichnocarpus**

  10 Seeds lanceolate or ovate, 3 mm wide or wider. Twining plants

    12 Fruit tardily splitting into two rather fleshy merocarps 10–15 cm long. Seeds 1–1.2 cm long, pale yellowish-grey...................................**15. Vallaris**

    12 Merocarps soon distinct, 15–32 cm long. Seeds about 1.5–2 cm long, dark brown or black

      13 Leaves glabrous, tapering to the base. Merocarps 0.5–0.7 cm in diameter........

       ....**12. Aganosma**

      13 Leaves pubescent above, tomentose beneath, cordate at the base. Merocarps 1–2 cm in diameter....................................**13. Chonemorpha**

1 Seeds without a tuft of hairs. Woody or herbaceous plants, erect or climbing with tendrils

14 Fruit simple, globose, ovoid or turbinate, formed by two united carpels, unilocular with two parietal placentas or bilocular

  15 Fruit a spiny, unilocular capsule. Leaves whorled or opposite. Introduced ornamental...**Allamanda**

  15 Fruit not spiny, indehiscent

    16 Leaves alternate, linear, up to 1 cm wide. Fruit a turbinate drupe, slightly compressed laterally. Introduced ornamental.................................**Thevetia**

    16 Leaves opposite. Fruit a globose or ovoid berry, not compressed laterally

      17 Berry large, many-seeded. Climbing plants with long, whip-like tendrils.........

       ....**1. Willughbeia**

      17 Berry rather small, few-seeded. Small rigid trees with paired spines in the axils of the leaves at alternate nodes.....................................**2. Carissa**

14 Fruit consisting of two merocarps (sometimes solitary by abortion), distinct or connate in the lower half only

18 Merocarps many-seeded, dehiscent along the ventral suture

  19 Leaves spirally arranged. Seeds winged. Introduced ornamental.........**Plumeria**

  19 Leaves opposite. Seeds not winged

    20 Merocarps narrowly cylindrical, dry, 1–3 mm in diameter. Low subshrubs or annual or perennial herbs....................................**6. Catharanthus**

    20 Merocarps fleshy, spindle-shaped or ovoid, much thicker than above. Trees or shrubs

21 Merocarps obliquely ovoid, 3–5 cm in diameter, blunt. Leaves coriaceous; lateral veins horizontally patent..**4. Pagiantha**
21 Merocarps spindle-shaped, about 1 cm in diameter, produced into an acute beak. Leaves herbaceous; lateral veins including with the midrib an angle of 45–60°. Introduced ornamental..**Ervatamia**
18 Merocarps one- to about four-seeded, indehiscent
22 Merocarps fleshy, not exceeding 1.5 cm in diameter. Herbs, shrubs or slender-branched trees
23 Leaves in whorls of three throughout. Merocarps sessile, 0.5–1.2 cm long, one-seeded..**8. Rauvolfia**
23 Leaves mostly or entirely opposite. Merocarps 1.2–5 cm long, usually two- to about four-seeded, stipitate
24 Leaves opposite throughout. Merocarps with two collateral seeds, not constricted between the seeds; blunt...**3. Hunteria**
24 Leaves at the branching usually in whorls of three, otherwise opposite. Merocarps normally two- to four-seeded, constricted between the seeds; produced into a slender beak...**9. Petchia**
22 Merocarps woody-fibrous, 3–9 cm in diameter. Trees with rather stout branches
25 Leaves rounded or very short-acuminate at the apex, not turning black when dried. Merocarps obliquely ovoid, distinctly longer than wide, usually both developed....
....**10. Ochrosia**
25 Leaves acuminate, turning black when dried. Merocarps almost globose, mostly solitary..**11. Cerbera**

1. WILLUGHBEIA

Roxb., Pl. Corom. 3: 77, t. 280. 1820 nom. cons. Type Species: *Willughbeia edulis* Roxb.

Large, woody climbers, glabrous, twining when young, climbing when fully developed by long, whip-like tendrils which are leafless or bear one or two pairs of leaves at their base, with short, reflexed branchlets at the apex, ending in two hooks. Leaves opposite, elliptic, with numerous lateral veins including with the midrib an angle of 80–90°. Flowers in small, sessile or short-peduncled panicles, solitary or paired from the axils of the leaves. Calyx eglandular, with broadly rounded lobes. Corolla yellow, glabrous without; the tube very shortly cylindrical, slightly constricted at the mouth: the lobes about as long as the tube, linear-oblong, acute, in bud somewhat overlapping to the left. Stamens inserted near the base of the tube; anthers distinct, ovate-lanceolate. Disk absent. Ovary paracarpous, with two parietal placentas. Fruit a large, globose, many-seeded berry. Seeds ovoid, compressed, without endosperm and without a tuft of hairs, surrounded by a fleshy envelope.

A mainly Malesian genus with one species endemic in Ceylon.

Willughbeia cirrhifera Abeywick., Ceylon J. Sci., Biol. Sci. 2: 84. 1959. Type: *Gardner* in Herb. Wight *550* (K, lectotype).

Chilocarpus ceylanicus Wight, Ic. Pl. Ind. Or. 4 (2): 1. t. 1288. 1848.

Willughbeia ceylanica (Wight) Thw., Enum. Pl. Zeyl. 191. 1860, not *W. ceila-nica* (Thunb.) Spreng., 1825; Hook. f., Fl. Br. Ind. 3: 624. 1882; Trimen, Handb. Fl. Ceylon 3: 123. 1895 as "zeylanica".

Petiole 0.5–1.8 cm long. Leaf-blade 5–13 cm long, 2.5–7 cm wide, widest about in the middle, cuneate at the base, markedly or obsoletely acuminate and obtuse at the apex, coriaceous; dried leaves with the midrib flat or faintly raised on upper side, prominent and broadly rounded beneath; lateral veins and reticulate venation raised on both surfaces but more strongly so on the upper side; meshes elongate, parallel to the lateral veins. Pedicels as long as the calyx or slightly longer. Calyx-lobes 1.5–2 mm long, glabrous. Co-rolla-tube little longer than the calyx. Fruit 8–15 cm in diameter, yellow, ting-ed with red, entirely filled with pulp in which are embedded the seeds, each of them 1.8–2.5 cm long.

D i s t r. Endemic in the rain-forest area of Ceylon. According to Thwait-es not uncommon in the low country and up to an elevation of 1300 m. Nowadays becoming rare by the destruction of the forests.

V e r n. Kiri-gedi, Kiri-wel (S); the latter also used for *Ichnocarpus frutes-cens* (L.) R. Br.

N o t e. The handsome fruit, like a very large, pink-cheeked apple, is a favourite food of monkeys (Trimen).

S p e c i m e n s E x a m i n e d. KANDY DISTRICT: Deltota, *s. coll. C.P. 1829* partly (PDA); Hantane, 2300 ft, *Gardner* in Herb. Wight *550* (BM, K), *Gardner C.P. 1829* partly (PDA). NUWARA ELIYA DISTRICT: Ras-sawa, *s. coll. C.P. 1829* partly (PDA). KALUTARA DISTRICT: Kalutara, *s. coll. s.n.* (PDA). RATNAPURA DISTRICT: Ratnapura, *s. coll. C.P. 1829* partly (PDA); Eratnagoda near Kuruwita, *Huber 17* (PDA, US). GALLE DISTRICT: Kanneliya Forest Reserve, Compartment 19, *Huber 62* (PDA, US); southern slope of Haycock, *Huber 64* (PDA, US); Nerugalkande—Udugama, 800 ft, *Balakrishnan 530* (PDA).

2. CARISSA

L., Mant. 7. 1767 nom. cons. Type Species: *Carissa carandas* L.

Arduina Miller, Fig. 499. 1759.

Small, densely branched trees with rigid, minutely puberulous or glabres-cent axes and paired, divaricate, simple or forked spines in the axils of the leaves at alternate nodes. Leaves opposite, orbicular, ovate, obovate or ob-long, glabrous on both sides, with few lateral veins including with the midrib an angle of 30–60°. Flowers in poor, sessile or peduncled cymes from the

axils of the leaves* at alternate nodes. Calyx eglandular, with ovate-lanceolate, sharply pointed lobes. Corolla white or pink, glabrous or slightly
puberulous without; the tube narrowly cylindrical, slightly widened in or above
the middle; the lobes shorter than the tube, linear to lanceolate, acute, in
bud overlapping to the right. Stamens attached to the tube in or a little above
the middle, not exserted; anthers distinct, linear-oblong, apiculate. Disk absent. Ovary bilocular. Fruit an ovoid, two- to four-seeded berry. Seeds obliquely ovate, strongly compressed, scutellate, with fleshy endosperm, without
a tuft of hairs.

A genus of about 30 species widely distributed through the drier parts of
southern and tropical Africa, tropical Asia and Australia.

KEY TO THE SPECIES

1 Leaves widest in or below the middle, acute at the apex, very rigid. Peduncles obsolete
   or short, not exceeding 1.5 cm in length. Berry up to 1 cm in diameter...............
   ....**1. C. spinarum**
1 Leaves widest in or above the middle, obtuse, rather thin. Peduncle well developed, 1.2–
   2.5 cm long. Berries almost 2 cm in diameter......................**2. C. carandas**

1. Carissa spinarum L., Mant. Alt. 559. 1771 excl. syn. Rumph.; Hook. f., Fl.
Br. Ind. 3: 631. 1882; Trimen, Handb. Fl. Ceylon 3: 125. 1895. Type: *Koenig*
in the Linnaean Herb. *295/2* (LINN).

Carissa diffusa Roxb., [Hort. Beng. 19. 1814 nom. nud.] Fl. Ind. ed Carey 2:
524. 1824; Thw., Enum. Pl. Zeyl. 191. 1860.

An intricately branched, erect or occasionally slightly scandent tree.
Spines simple or forked, 1.2–6 cm long. Leaves short-petioled; the blade 1.5–
5 cm long and 1.2–4 cm wide, broadly ovate or rhomboid, widest in or below
the middle, as long as wide to twice as long as wide, acute or rounded at the
base, acute and apiculate at the apex, coriaceous; dried leaves with the midrib broadly channelled on the upper surface and the margins of the midrib
often slightly raised, midrib not or faintly elevated beneath; lateral veins prominent above, more slightly so beneath, the strongest narrowly sulcate on
upper side; reticulate venation raised or indistinct above, normally raised beneath, at least in mature leaves. Peduncle not developed or up to 1.2 (rarely
up to 1.5) mm long. Pedicels shorter to slightly longer than the calyx. Calyx-
lobes 2–2.5 mm long, glabrous or puberulous without. Flowers scentless.
Corolla-tube 1.2–2 cm long. Fruit 0.7–1.2 cm long, shining, black. Chromosome number: $2n = 28$.

D i s t r. From the Punjab through India to Ceylon and Burma.

*Cymes apparently but not truly terminal when arising from the axils of the upper-
most leaves.

E c o l. In Ceylon common throughout the dry zone, especially in over-grazed and otherwise disturbed vegetation, along roads and at the edge of forests. Absent from the hill country and from the moist region. Flowering all the year.

V e r n. Heen-karamba (S); Chiru-kila, Chiru-kula, Kilatti (T).

N o t e. The flowers but not the berries are eaten by macaques (Dittus).

S p e c i m e n s   E x a m i n e d. JAFFNA DISTRICT: Southeast Point Pedro, sea level, *Bernardi 14264* (US); near Pooneryn, *Bernardi 14286* (PDA). VAVUNIYA DISTRICT: Vavuniya to Parayalankulam, mile 121, *Hepper & Jayasuriya 4640* (PDA, US); Mullaitivu-Mankulam Road, *Sumithraarachchi 800* (PDA). PUTTALAM DISTRICT: milepost 8, 20 miles south of Kalpitiya, *Fosberg 52780* (US); mile 15 of Puttalam-Anuradhapura Road, *Huber 49* (PDA, US); 4 km east of Puttalam, *Fosberg & Jayasuriya 52790* (PDA, US); Wilpattu National Park, *Bernardi 14212* (US). ANURADHAPURA DISTRICT: Anuradhapura, *Alston 1049* (PDA); 5-6 miles northeast of Anuradhapura, *Fosberg & Balakrishnan 53440* (PDA, US); between Anuradhapura and Nochchiyagama, *Huber 7* (PDA, US); circa Rambewa, 50 m, *Bernardi 14301* (PDA, US); Wilpattu National Park, Kokkare Villu, *Koyama 13347* (PDA); Erige Ara, Wilpattu National Park, *Wirawan 1409* and *6809* (both PDA); Mihintale Sanctuary, *Sohmer 8139* (PDA); roadside marker 73/3 of Anuradhapura-Trincomalee Road, *Sohmer 8155* (PDA); Kekirawa, 200 m, *C.F. & R.J. van Beusekom 1590* (US). POLONNARUWA DISTRICT: Polonnaruwa Sacred Area, 60 m, *Dittus 70032601, 71051901 & 71060501* (all PDA & US), *Hladik 652* (PDA, US), *Ripley 137, 159, 273* (all PDA & US), *Ripley 652* (US); Polonnaruwa, near Pabulu Vehera, 61 m, *Ripley 105* (PDA, US). KURUNEGALA DISTRICT: Barigoda Forest Reserve, *Waas & Peeris 310* (PDA, US). MATALE DISTRICT: Road from Naula to Dambulla, 36/4 mile marker, *Novicke et al. 327* (PDA, US), *Sohmer 8070* (PDA, US), *Tirvengadum & Waas 401* (PDA, US); near Illukkumbura, road marker 37/10 east of Lagalla, *Novicke & Jayasuriya 201 & 202* (both PDA & US); Dik Patana near Illukkumbura, mile marker 38/2, 900 m, *Tirvengadum et al. 20* (PDA, US). KANDY DISTRICT: Kandy-Mahiyangana Road, 28th mile marker, *Sohmer 8268* (PDA); c. 9 miles northeast Hunnasgiriya, near mile post 29/21 on the road to Mahiyangana, 810 m, *Davidse & Jayasuriya 8422* (PDA, US). BATTICALOA DISTRICT: West of Kathiraveli towards Manicka-Kulam, 30 m, *Bernardi 15663* (PDA). AMPARAI DISTRICT: Lahugala Sanctuary, Kitulana, 30 m, *Comanor 593* (PDA); Lahugala Tank, *Mueller-Dombois & Comanor 67072520* (PDA). BADULLA DISTRICT: Ekiriyankumbura, *Huber 39* (PDA, US); Mahiyangana, 150 m, *Stone 11151* (PDA, US). MONERAGALA DISTRICT: Bibile, 13 July 1924, *Silva s.n.* (PDA). MATARA DISTRICT: Matara-Tangalla Road, sea level, *Cramer 3435* (PDA, US). HAMBANTOTA DISTRICT: Tissamaharama, *Huber 35* (PDA, US); near western boundary of Ruhuna National Park, *Meijer 207*

(PDA, US); Ruhuna National Park, *Bernardi 14203* (PDA), *Kostermans 25442* (PDA); Ruhuna National Park, near Andonoruwa, 20 m, *Mueller-Dombois & Comanor 67062215* (PDA); Ruhuna National Park, Block I, Rakinawala, *Cooray 68102204* (PDA); Ranna, *Alston 1287* (PDA). DISTRICT UNKNOWN: Maduru Odai, Mannar-Puttalam Road, at the junction to Periya Naga Villu, *Wirawan et al. 921* (PDA, US). LOCALITY UNKNOWN: *Macrae 322* (BM), *s. coll. C.P. 1822* (K, PDA).

2. Carissa carandas L., Mant. 52. 1767; Thw., Enum. Pl. Zeyl. 191. 1860; Hook. f., Fl. Br. Ind. 3: 630. 1882; Trimen, Handb. Fl. Ceylon 3: 124. 1895. Type: Rumph., Herb. Amb. 7, t. 25. 1755.

A small tree. Spines usually simple, 1–3 cm long. Leaves short-petioled, the blade 3–7 cm long and 1.5–4 cm wide, obovate, elliptic or oblong, mostly widest above the middle, slightly longer than wide to three times as long as wide; cuneate at the base, obtuse at the apex, rather thin; dried leaf with the midrib impressed above at least in the proximal half, prominent beneath; lateral veins and reticulate venation raised on both surfaces but reticulate venation faintly so. Peduncle 1.5–2.5 cm long. Pedicels about as long as the calyx or slightly longer. Calyx-lobes 2.5–3 mm long, puberulous without. Flowers as in *C. spinarum*. Fruit almost 2 cm long, reddish-purple.

D i s t r. From the Punjab through India to Ceylon, the Malay Peninsula and Malesia. Widespread by cultivation and doubtfully native outside of the Deccan Peninsula.

In the north of Ceylon grown as a fruit tree, probably not native.

U s e s. *Carissa carandas* is appreciated for its palatable berries.

V e r n. Maha-karamba (S); Kalaka, Perunkila (T).

S p e c i m e n s E x a m i n e d. JAFFNA DISTRICT: Jaffna, *Gardner* in *C.P. 1823* partly (PDA). KURUNEGALA DISTRICT: Kurunegala, *s. coll. C.P. 1823* partly (PDA).

3. HUNTERIA

Roxb., [Hort. Beng. 84. 1814 nom. nud.] Fl. Ind. ed. Carey 1: 695. 1832. Type Species: *Hunteria corymbosa* Roxb.

Small, glabrous trees. Leaves opposite, oblong-elliptic or lanceolate, with rather numerous lateral veins including with the midrib an angle of about 60°. Flowers in short-stalked, terminal cymes, sometimes apparently axillary by overtopping. Calyx eglandular, with triangular-ovate, acute lobes. Corolla yellow to white, glabrous without; the tube cylindrical, inflated in the upper half; the lobes shorter than the tube, narrowly to broadly ovate, obtuse, in bud strongly overlapping to the left. Stamens attached to the corolla-tube within the inflated portion, not exserted; the anthers distinct, ovate-lanceolate, apiculate. Disk absent. Merocarps distinct, ovoid, short-stipitate, slightly apiculate or almost obtuse at the apex, fleshy, indehiscent, mostly two-seeded. Seeds ovoid, with fleshy endosperm, without a tuft of hairs.

A genus of six species, centered in tropical Africa, with one species extending to India, Ceylon and Malesia. Apart from this another species has been described from Ceylon, *Hunteria legocii* Livera in Ann. R. Bot. Gard. Peradeniya 10: 140. 1926. This name is based on an inaccurate drawing at PDA.

Hunteria zeylanica (Retz.) Gardn. ex Thw., Enum. Pl. Zeyl. 191. 1860; Alston in Trimen, Handb. Fl. Ceylon 6: 190. 1931; M. Pichon, Bot. Soc. Brot. 27: 104. 1953. Type: *Koenig s.n.* (LD holotype not seen, BM isotype).

Cameraria zeylanica Retz., Obs. 4: 24. 1786.
Hunteria corymbosa Roxb., [Hort. Beng. 84. 1814 nom. nud.] Fl. Ind. ed. Carey 1: 695. 1832; Hook. f., Fl. Br. Ind. 3: 637. 1882; Trimen, Handb. Fl. Ceylon 3: 128. 1895.
Tabernaemontana salicifolia Wall. ex A. DC. in DC., Prod. 8: 376. 1844.
Hunteria lanceolata Wall. ex A. DC. in DC., Prod. 8: 350. 1844.
Hunteria roxburghiana Wight, Ic. Pl. Ind. Or. 4 (2): 2, t. 1294. 1850.
Hunteria corymbosa Roxb. var. *salicifolia* (Wall. ex A. DC.) Hallier f., Jahrb. Hamburg. Wiss. Anst. Beih. 17, 3: 195. 1900.
Hunteria zeylanica (Retz.) Gardn. ex Thw. var. *lanceolata* (Wall. ex A. DC.) Alston in Trimen, Handb. Fl. Ceylon 6: 190. 1931.
Hunteria zeylanica (Retz.) Gardn. ex Thw. var. *salicifolia* (Wall. ex A. DC.) M. Pichon, Bot. Soc. Brot. 27: 111. 1953.

Petiole 0.6–1.6 cm long. Leaf-blade 5–16 cm long and 1–6 cm wide, broadest in or below the middle, obtuse or rounded at the base in the broad-leaved form, acute or obtuse in the narrow-leaved form; short- to long-acuminate with a narrowly triangular acumen up to 1.5 cm long or not at all acuminate but obtuse at the apex; coriaceous; dried leaf with the midrib faintly raised and longitudinally channelled at least in the proximal half on the upper side, prominent beneath; lateral veins faintly raised above, more strongly so beneath, almost straight up to their fusion with the marginal vein, which runs parallel to the leaf-margin at a distance of 1–2 mm; reticulate venation slightly prominent on both surfaces. Pedicels usually longer than the calyx. Calyx-lobes 1–2 mm long, glabrous. Flowers strongly fragrant. Corolla-tube 0.5–0.9 cm long. Merocarps 1.1–2.7 cm long, yellow when ripe.

D i s t r. Southern part of the Deccan Peninsula, Ceylon, the Andaman Islands, the Malay Peninsula, Hainan and Sumatra. A variety in tropical East Africa.

E c o l. In Ceylon formerly not uncommon in the moist low country, but now disappearing rapidly by the destruction of the rain-forests.

U s e s. According to Trimen the leaves have been used externally for wounds and cuts.

V e r n. Mediya, Wal-mediya (S).

S p e c i m e n s E x a m i n e d. KURUNEGALA DISTRICT: Barigoda Forest Reserve, *Waas & Peeris 308* (US), broad leaved form. KANDY DISTRICT: Kandy, Udawattakele Sanctuary, 500 m, *Jayasuriya 1879* (PDA), broad leaved form; Madugoda, *Alston 262* (PDA), narrow leaved form. NUWARA ELIYA DISTRICT: Rikiligaskada, *s. coll. C.P. 2518* (PDA), narrow leaved form. COLOMBO DISTRICT: Colombo, *Koenig s.n.* (K). KALUTARA DISTRICT: Kalutara, *s. coll., C.P. 1827* partly (PDA), broad leaved form. GALLE DISTRICT: Galle, *Gardner 554* partly (BM) and *Gardner* in *C.P. 1827* partly (PDA), both broad leaved form; Bona Vista near Galle, *Balakrishnan 958* (PDA, US), intermediate form. DISTRICT UNKNOWN: Baddelagoda, *Lewis 818* (PDA), narrow leaved form. LOCALITY UNKNOWN: *Gardner 554* partly (K), *Koenig s.n.* (BM), *Macrae 356* (BM), *s. coll. C.P. 1827* (BM, K), *Walker s.n.* (PDA), all representing the broad leaved form; *s. coll. C.P. 2518* (K), narrow leaved form.

4. PAGIANTHA

Markgraf, Notizbl. Bot. Gart. Berlin-Dahlem 12: 546. 1935. Type Species: *Pagiantha dichotoma* (Roxb.) Markgraf.

Small, glabrous trees. Leaves opposite, oblong elliptic, with rather numerous lateral veins including with the midrib a right angle. Flowers five- or six-merous, in long-peduncled, dichasially branched cymes arising from the axils of the terminal pair of leaves. Calyx glandular within; the lobes broadly ovate, obtuse. Corolla white with the throat and tube yellow within; glabrous without; the tube cylindrical, fleshy; the lobes longer than the tube, oblong, obliquely truncate and almost obtuse at the apex, in bud strongly overlapping to the left. The stamens inserted below the middle of the tube; anthers distinct, sagittate with the auricles appressed to the filament, acute, filled with pollen to the base. Disk absent. Merocarps distinct, obliquely ovoid, strongly convex on the ventral side, slightly so on the back, blunt, fleshy but dehiscent along the ventral suture, many-seeded. Seeds ovoid-oblong, not compressed, with endosperm, without a tuft of hairs, surrounded by a pulpy envelope.

Eleven species ranging from India and Ceylon through Malesia to the Fiji Islands.

Pagiantha dichotoma (Roxb.) Markgraf, Notizbl. Bot. Garten Berlin-Dahlem 12: 546. 1935. Type: Coloured drawing no. 1811 of *Tabernaemontana dichotoma* by Roxburgh at K.

Tabernaemontana dichotoma Roxb., [Hort. Beng. 20. 1814, nom. nud.] Fl.

Ind. ed. Carey 2: 21. 1832; Thw., Enum. Pl. Zeyl. 192. 1860; Hook. f., Fl. Br. Ind. 3: 645. 1882; Trimen, Handb. Fl. Ceylon 3: 132. 1895.
Rejoua dichotoma (Roxb.) Gamble, Fl. Pres. Madras 812. 1923; Alston in Trimen, Handb. Fl. Ceylon 6: 191. 1931.

Young parts covered with a shining, resinous coat. Petiole 2–4 cm long, bearing at the base on the upper side a semicircular rim of rudimentary, coalescent stipules. Leaf-blade 8–21 cm long and 2.5–9 cm wide, broadest in or above the middle, tapering to the base, rounded or very short-acuminate at the apex; coriaceous; dried leaf with the midrib convex on the upper side, bordered by a narrow furrow on each side, prominent beneath; lateral veins faintly impressed above, hardly distinct beneath; reticulate venation scarcely noticeable on either side. Pedicels much longer than the calyx. Calyx-lobes 3–4 mm long, glabrous. Corolla-tube 1.8–2.5 cm long. Merocarps pendulous, paired or solitary by abortion, 3.5–7 cm long and 3–5 cm in diameter, glabrous, orange when ripe. Seeds with a coat of crimson pulp.

D i s t r. Western and southern Deccan Peninsula and Ceylon.
E c o l. A common member of the secondary forest of the moist part of Ceylon, mostly at low altitudes but occasionally ascending to about 1200 m.
U s e s. The wood is employed for carving, in particular for manufacturing the kandyan dancing masks.
V e r n. Divi-kaduru (S); Nanthia-vattai (T).
N o t e. The white latex of the plant can cause a two-week inflammation of the eye (Worthington).
S p e c i m e n s E x a m i n e d. KEGALLE DISTRICT: Ambagama, *Gardner* in *C.P. 2834* at least partly (PDA). KANDY DISTRICT: Hantane, *Huber 3* (PDA, US); Kandy, Udawattakele Sanctuary, 500 m, *Huber 5* (PDA, US), *Kostermans 24010* (US), *Sohmer 8051* (PDA), *Stone 11111* (PDA); Kandy, Hillcrest, *Worthington 7133* (K); Trail to Nitre Cave Area from St. Martin's Estate, *Sohmer & Jayasuriya 10670* (PDA). NUWARA ELIYA DISTRICT: Rikiligaskada, *Huber 57* (PDA, US). COLOMBO DISTRICT: Mattakuliya, banks of Kelani River, *Waas 1170* (PDA). RATNAPURA DISTRICT: Demanhandiya, Kuruwiti Korale, *Trimen s.n.* (PDA); Uda-Parawita, *Waas 2* (PDA); Kalupahana, *Waas 498* (PDA). GALLE DISTRICT: Galle, *Waas & Eliezer 8892* (PDA). LOCALITY UNKNOWN: *Burmann s.n.* (BM), *Gardner s.n.* (K), *Macrae 353* (BM).

5. ALSTONIA

R. Br., Mem. Wern. Nat. Hist. Soc. 1: 75. 1811, prepr. 1810, nom. cons. Type Species: *Echites scholaris* L.

Tall trees with the young branches and leaves glabrous or pubescent. Leaves whorled, obovate, oblong or lanceolate, with rather numerous lateral veins including with the midrib an angle of 60–90°. Flowers in long-peduncled cymes arranged in a sessile, terminal umbel or sometimes in two superposed umbels. Calyx eglandular, with broadly ovate, obtuse or truncate lobes. Corolla white or greenish-white, glabrous or puberulous without; the tube cylindrical, slightly inflated below the mouth; the lobes shorter than or as long as the tube, obovate to oblong, obtuse to almost acute at the apex, overlapping in bud to the left or to the right. Stamens attached at the corolla-tube in the inflated portion near the mouth but not exserted; the anthers distinct, ovate, acute. Disk absent. Merocarps distinct, very long and slender, cylindrical, acute, dry and dehiscent along the ventral suture when ripe, many-seeded. Seeds oblong, flat, with scanty endosperm, with a tuft of hairs at both ends, brown.

A genus of 34 species distributed throughout the Old World Tropics, most numerous in the West Pacific Region. Primarily *Alstonia* was represented in Ceylon by *A. scholaris* (L.) R. Br. only but since the beginning of this century the Malayan *A. macrophylla* Wall. ex G. Don has largely been naturalized.

KEY TO THE SPECIES

1 Leaves in whorls of three or four; the blade membranous, densely pubescent beneath when young, with rather distant lateral veins. Pedicels much longer than the calyx. Corolla-lobes almost as long as the tube, in bud overlapping to the right. Seeds acute at one end, obtuse at the other...**1. A. macrophylla**
1 Leaves in whorls of five to ten; the blade coriaceous, glabrous on both sides, with close and numerous lateral veins. Pedicels as long as or shorter than the calyx. Corolla-lobes one-third or one-quarter as long as the tube, in bud overlapping to the left. Seeds obtuse at both ends...**2. A. scholaris**

1. Alstonia macrophylla Wall. [Num. List no. 1648. 1829 nom. nud.] ex G. Don, Gen. Hist. 4: 87. 1837; Hook. f., Fl. Br. Ind. 3: 643. 1882; Alston in Trimen, Handb. Fl. Ceylon 6: 192. 1931; Monachino, Pacific Sci. 3: 164. 1949. Type: Herb. *Wall.* no. *1648* (K–W).

Leaves in whorls of three or mostly of four. Petiole 1–3 cm long. Leaf-blade 10–50 cm long, 4–14 cm wide, widest in or above the middle, cuneate at the base, abruptly short-acuminate or more rarely obtuse at the apex, membranous, glabrous above, densely pubescent beneath at least when young, with rather distant lateral veins 0.6–2 cm apart from each other, including with the midrib an angle of 60–70°, herbaceous; dried leaf with the midrib faintly impressed on the upper side, prominent beneath; lateral veins scarcely raised above, slightly so beneath; reticulate venation not sculptured or slightly immersed on either side. Cymes rather lax, arranged in a sessile umbel. Pedicels much longer than the calyx. Calyx-lobes up to 1 mm long, semicircular, puberulous to almost glabrous without. Corolla glabrous without except for the ciliolate lobes; the tube 0.5–0.6 cm long, the lobes about as long as the tube, oblong, in bud overlapping to the right. Merocarps pendulous, 30–45 cm long, 0.25–0.35 cm in diameter, glabrous when ripe. Seeds acute but not acuminate at one end, obtuse at the other.

D i s t r. Malay Peninsula, Thailand, Indochina, the Philippines, Celebes and Borneo. Naturalized in Ceylon.

E c o l. Introduced as a forest tree to Ceylon, *Alstonia macrophylla* rapidly became naturalized in the moist region up to an elevation of 1200–1500 m. Now it is one of the most prominent species of the secondary rain forest in the island.

U s e s. The timber of *Alstonia macrophylla* is of superior quality to that of *A. scholaris* and less liable to attack by boring insects. In reforestation the tree is the best pioneer for poor grassland (Worthington).

V e r n. Avarai-nuga, Havari-nuga (S); Velai-maram (T).

S p e c i m e n s E x a m i n e d. COLOMBO DISTRICT: Colombo, 15 ft, *Worthington 2405* (BM). KEGALLE DISTRICT: Koswatte Forest, c. 500 m, *Waas 1674* (PDA). KANDY DISTRICT: Dekkanda, Kadugannawa, 2000 ft, *Worthington 333* (K); Hantane, *Huber 1* (US); Kandy, Hillcrest, 2100 ft, *Worthington 4312 & 4411* (BM); Kandy, Udawattakele Sanctuary, *Huber 4* (PDA, US); Peradeniya, *Mueller-Dombois 67110925* (BISH); c. 4 miles up the Double Cutting Road, 400 m, *Davidse & Sumithraarachchi 8588* (PDA). RATNA-PURA DISTRICT: Bambarabotuwa Rain Forest, 1000 ft, *Worthington s.n.* (K). GALLE DISTRICT: Kanneliya Forest, *Bremer 851* (PDA, S, US).

2. Alstonia scholaris (L.) R. Br., Mem. Wern. Nat. Hist. Soc. 1: 76. 1811, prepr. 1810; Thw., Enum. Pl. Zeyl. 193. 1860; Hook. f., Fl. Br. Ind. 3: 642. 1882; Trimen, Handb. Fl. Ceylon 3: 133. 1895; Monachino, Pacific Sci. 3: 146. 1949. Type: Linnaean Herb. *302/2* (LINN).

Echites scholaris L., Mant. 1: 53. 1767.

Leaves in whorls of five to ten. Petiole 0.5–3 cm long. Leaf-blade 5–28 cm long and 2.5–11 cm wide, widest in or above the middle, cuneate at the base, usually rounded at the apex, coriaceous, glabrous on both sides, with close, numerous lateral veins 0.2–0.4 cm apart from each other, including with the midrib an angle of 80–90°; midrib of dried leaf immersed on the upper and prominent on the lower surface; lateral veins raised on both sides but more clearly so beneath; reticulate venation not or faintly elevated on either side. Cymes dense, almost glomerate, arranged in a sessile umbel or in two super-posed umbels. Pedicel usually as long as or shorter than the calyx. Calyx-lobes 1–3 mm long, ovate, densely puberulous. Corolla puberulous without, at least on the lobes; the tube 0.6–0.8 cm long, the lobes one quarter to one third as long as the tube, broadly obovate, in bud overlapping to the left. Merocarps as in *A. macrophylla*. Seeds obtuse at both ends.

D i s t r. India and Ceylon, Southeast Asia from Burma and South China through Malesia to New Guinea and Queensland.

E c o l. Common throughout Ceylon up to an elevation of 1000 m, both in the moist and the dry zone; in the latter along the banks of streams and other temporarily inundated places.

U s e s. According to Trimen, the bark is a valuable astringent, much used in fevers and the light and soft wood is used for coffins. Mr. Popham inform- ed me that the tree is considered a symbol of immortality and a piece of wood is placed within the coffin for this reason.

V e r n. Eth-mada (S); Ruk-aththana (S & T); Elilaippalai, Mukampelai (T).

S p e c i m e n s E x a m i n e d. ANURADHAPURA DISTRICT: Ritiga- la Strict Natural Reserve, *Bernardi 15276* (PDA), *Jayasuriya 2266* (PDA). POLONNARUWA DISTRICT: Polonnaruwa, *Hladik 1047* (PDA, US); Po- lonnaruwa, Sacred Area, 61 m, *Ripley 166* (PDA, US) & *186* (US); mile 49 of Polonnaruwa-Valaichchenai Road, *Huber 44* (PDA, US). MATALE DIST- RICT: Madipola. 1300 ft, *Worthington 4445* (K); Sigiriya Gala, 654 ft, *Wor- thington 4345* (K). KEGALLE DISTRICT: Ambepussa, *Worthington 2478* (K); near Neludeniya, mile 41 of Colombo-Kandy Road, *Meijer 287* (PDA, US). KANDY DISTRICT: Peradeniya, *Gardner in C.P. 1840* at least partly (PDA). BATTICALOA DISTRICT: Batticaloa, within the town, *Huber 25* (PDA, US). BADULLA DISTRICT: Between mile 14 and 15 of Ella-Wella- waya Road, *Waas 80* (PDA, US). AMPARAI DISTRICT: Lunugala, 500 ft, *Worthington 6317* (K). GALLE DISTRICT: Neluwa, c. 170 m, *Cramer 4005* (PDA). LOCALITY UNKNOWN: *Gardner 558* (BM, K); *s. coll. C.P. 1840* (BM, K).

6. CATHARANTHUS

G. Don, Gen. Hist. 4: 71. 1837. Type Species: *Catharanthus roseus* (L.) G. Don.

Lochnera Reichb., Conspect. Reg. Veg. 134. 1828.

Erect, perennial subshrubs or annual herbs with glabrous or puberulous stems and leaves. Leaves opposite, obovate or narrowly lanceolate, with ra- ther few lateral veins including with the midrib an angle of 30–45°. Flowers solitary or paired from the axils of the leaves. Calyx eglandular, with sharp- pointed, narrowly lanceolate to subulate lobes. Corolla crimson or white, gla- brous or puberulous without; the tube cylindrical, inflated below the mouth; the lobes shorter than the tube, obovate, obtuse or apiculate, in bud much overlapping to the left. Stamens attached to the corolla-tube in the inflated portion near the mouth but not exserted; the anthers distinct, narrowly ovate- lanceolate, acute. Disk absent. Ovary with two oblong glands alternating with the carpels. Merocarps distinct, narrowly cylindrical, obtuse to acuminate, dry, dehiscent along the ventral suture, with about eight seeds. The latter oblong, not compressed, with muricate longitudinal ridges, with fleshy endosperm, without a tuft of hairs.

A small genus of six species, all except one natives of Madagascar.

Stearn, who is followed here, has recently discussed the controversial nomenclature of this genus (Lloydia 29: 196–200. 1966).

KEY TO THE SPECIES

1 Perennial herbs or subshrubs. Leaves obovate or obovate-oblong, usually rounded at the apex. Corolla 3–5 cm in diameter when expanded. Merocarps 0.2–0.3 cm wide, puberulous . . . .**1. C. roseus**
1 Annual herbs. Leaves narrowly lanceolate, very acute. Corolla 0.5–0.6 cm in diameter. Merocarps about 0.1 cm wide, glabrous . . . .**2. C. pusillus**

1. Catharanthus roseus (L.) G. Don, Gen. Hist. 4: 95. 1837; Stearn, Lloydia 29: 196. 1966. Type: Linnaean Herb. *299/4* (LINN).

Vinca rosea L., Syst. ed. 10, 2: 944. 1759; Hook. f., Fl. Br. Ind. 3: 640. 1882; Trimen, Handb. Fl. Ceylon 3: 130. 1895.

Lochnera rosea (L.) Reichb., Conspect. Reg. Veg. 134. 1828; Alston in Trimen, Handb. Fl. Ceylon 6: 191. 1931.

A perennial herb or subshrub with the young stems, leaves and calyx puberulous. Petiole 0.2–about 1 cm long. Leaf-blade 2.5–6 cm long and 1–3 cm wide, widest above the middle, cuneate at the base, rounded but frequently with a minute apiculus at the apex, rarely subacute, herbaceous; dried leaf with the midrib flat or narrowly and shallowly sulcate on the upper side, slightly raised beneath; lateral veins faintly elevated on both sides, reticulate venation not visible on either side. Pedicels shorter than the calyx. Calyx-lobes 3–5 mm long, subulate. Corolla crimson, pink or white; the tube 2–3 cm long, pubescent without; the lobes 1.5–2.5 cm long, obtuse. Merocarps 1.2–2.5 cm long, 0.2–0.3 cm in diameter, obtuse or acute but not acuminate at the apex, puberulous. Chromosome number: 2n = 16.

D i s t r. Endemic in Madagascar. Brought into cultivation in the eighteenth century and soon naturalized in many tropical countries. Recorded from Ceylon since 1804 and now widely distributed in disturbed vegetation, both in the dry and in the moist zone at low elevation, particularly on sandy soil near the coast in the South-West of the island. Also in the Maldive Islands.

U s e. *Catharanthus roseus*, the Madagascar Periwinkle, is rich in various alkaloids and has become an important drug because of its cytostatic properties.

V e r n. Mini-mal (S).

Specimens Examined. JAFFNA DISTRICT: Nagarkovil, *Waas*
241 (PDA). KALUTARA DISTRICT: Molligoda between Panadura and
Kalutara, 5–10 m, *Comanor 1013* (PDA). GALLE DISTRICT: Near Koggala Rail Motor Halt, *Huber 61* (PDA, US). LOCALITY UNKNOWN: *Fraser
175* (BM).

2. Catharanthus pusillus (Murr.) G. Don, Gen. Hist. 4: 95. 1837. Type: Murr.,
Comm. Gotting. 3, t. 1, t. 2. 1773.

Vinca pusilla Murr., Comm. Gotting. 3: 66. 1773; Hook. f., Fl. Br. Ind. 3:
    640. 1882; Trimen, Handb. Fl. Ceylon 3: 130. 1895.
Lochnera pusilla (Murr.) Schum. in Pflanzenfam. 4 (2): 145. 1895; Alston
    in Trimen, Handb. Fl. Ceylon 6: 190. 1931.

A glabrous, annual herb. Petiole 0.15–0.5 cm long. Leaf-blade 2–7 cm long,
0.5–2 cm wide, widest in or below the middle, tapering to both ends, very
sharp-pointed at the apex, herbaceous; dried leaf with the midrib proximally
flat, distally raised on the upper surface, prominent beneath; lateral veins and
reticulate venation hardly sculptured on either side. Pedicels shorter than the
calyx. Calyx-lobes 3–4 mm long, almost filiform. Corolla white, glabrous
without; the tube 0.5–about 1 cm long; the lobes shorter than one-half of the
tube, abruptly apiculate at the apex. Merocarps 2.5–5 cm long and about 0.1
cm wide, acuminate at the apex, glabrous.

Distr. India from the western Himalayas through the Gangetic Plain
and the Deccan Peninsula to Ceylon.

Ecol. In Ceylon, a very local weed of waste and cultivated land in the
dry zone, known from a few places only. Flowering in December.

Specimens Examined. JAFFNA DISTRICT: Jaffna, 25 March
1926, *Cooke s.n.* (PDA); about 4 miles from Jaffna on road to Kankesanturai,
6 Feb. 1890, *Trimen s.n.* (PDA). BATTICALOA DISTRICT: Batticaloa, pre-
mises of Shivananda Vidyalaya, *Balasubramaniam s.n.* (PDA).

7. HOLARRHENA

R. Br., Mem. Wern. Nat. Hist. Soc. 1: 62. 1811, prepr. 1810. Type Species:
Carissa mitis Vahl.

Small trees up to 15 m tall with young branches and leaves glabrous.
Leaves opposite, but on the flowering nodes sometimes slightly displaced,
ovate-lanceolate to lanceolate, with rather few, strongly arched lateral veins
including with the midrib an angle of about 60°. Flowers in short-peduncled,
puberulous cymes which are terminal or terminal and axillary at alternate
nodes. Calyx with glandular scales within; the scales alternating with the
linear, acute lobes. Corolla white, puberulous without; the tube cylindrical,

slightly inflated at the base; the lobes little longer than the tube, linear, obtuse, in bud overlapping to the left. Stamens inserted near the base of the tube; anthers distinct, ovoid-oblong, apiculate. Merocarps distinct, very long, slender, cylindrical, obtuse, dry and dehiscent along the ventral suture when ripe. Seeds numerous, linear, compressed, with scanty endosperm and a tuft of hairs at one end, dark brown.

A few species in tropical Africa and India from the Himalayas to Ceylon and Malacca.

Holarrhena mitis (Vahl) Roem. & Schult., Syst. Veg. 4: 400. 1819; Thw., Enum. Plant. Zeyl. 194. 1860; Hook. f., Fl. Br. Ind. 3: 645. 1882; Trimen, Handb. Fl. Ceylon 3: 131. 1895. Type: *Koenig s.n.* (LD holotype not seen, BM isotype).

Carissa mitis Vahl, Symb. Bot. 3: 44, t. 59. 1794.
. *Echites lanceolata* Moon, Cat. 20. 1824 nom. nud.

Bark of the trunk whitish, smooth. Branchlets slender, drooping, dark purplish-brown; the lenticels inconspicuous. Petiole 0.4–0.6 cm long. Leaf-blade 5–12 cm long and 1–3 cm wide, widest in or below the middle, rather abruptly tapering to almost rounded at the base, acuminate, obtuse at the apex; dried leaf with the midrib flat or proximally elevated and distally impressed on the upper side, prominent beneath; lateral veins slightly raised or inconspicuous on either side; reticulate venation not sculptured. Pedicels much longer than the calyx. Calyx-lobes about 2 mm long, puberulous. Flowers fragrant. Corolla-tube 0.8–1.2 cm long. Merocarps 30–45 cm long, 0.3–0.4 cm in diameter, glabrous.

D i s t r. Endemic in Ceylon.

U s e s. Both wood and bark are used as a remedy in fevers and dysentery; the bark is sold under the name "Kalinda" and is valued as an antiperiodic (Trimen).

V e r n. Kalinda, Kiri-mawara, Kiri-walla (S); Kuluppalai (T), name also applied for *Oxystelma esculentum* (L. f.) R. Br. ex Schult.

S p e c i m e n s   E x a m i n e d. POLONNARUWA DISTRICT: Kosgaha-Ulpata, Gunner's Quoin, Oct. 1893, *Neville 493* (PDA). COLOMBO DISTRICT: Indikade Reserve, *Holmes 393* (Herbarium of Dept. of Forestry, Colombo). MATALE DISTRICT: Sigre (= Sigiriya?), *s. coll. C.P. 756* partly (PDA). KANDY DISTRICT: Kandy, Hillcrest, 2100 ft, *Worthington 4625* (BM) & *5565* (K); Tembiligalla, *2050* ft, *Worthington 4539* (BM). KALUTARA DISTRICT: Kalutara, *Macrae 52* (BM, K). RATNAPURA DISTRICT: Ratnapura, *s. coll. C.P. 756* partly (PDA). GALLE DISTRICT: Godekande near Hiniduma, 100 m, *Jayasuriya et al. 793* (PDA, US). MONERAGALA DISTRICT: Kataragama Peak, 350 m, *Huber 34* (PDA, US); same place, 450 m, *Bernardi 15507* (PDA). LOCALITY UNKNOWN:

Champion s.n. (K), *Koenig s.n.* (BM), *s. coll. C.P. 756* (BM, K), *Walker 1039* (K).

8. RAUVOLFIA

L., Sp. Pl. 208. 1753. Type Species: *Rauvolfia tetraphylla* L.

Erect, glabrous treelets or subshrubs with rather little latex. Leaves in whorls of three, obovate-lanceolate to broadly lanceolate, with few, strongly arched lateral veins including with the midrib an angle of 45–60°. Flowers in mostly long-peduncled cymes, terminal or terminal and lateral from between two petioles. Calyx eglandular; the lobes lanceolate, acute. Corolla pure white or white tinged with violet, glabrous without; the tube cylindrical, slightly inflated above the middle; the lobes shorter than the tube, ovate, obtuse, in bud overlapping to the left. Stamens inserted in the inflated portion of the tube; the anthers distinct, ovate to oblong, apiculate. Disk annular. Merocarps distinct or connate for one-half of their length, ovoid, sessile, short-apiculate to almost obtuse, fleshy, indehiscent, each with one seed. Seeds ovoid, with fleshy endosperm, without a tuft of hairs.

A rather large, pantropical genus, represented in Ceylon by two species only.

KEY TO THE SPECIES

1 Cymes laxly branched. Corolla-tube 0.5–1 cm long and 1–1.5 mm wide when pressed; the lobes longer than one-half of the tube. Merocarps free.............**1. R. densiflora**
1 Cymes dense, almost capitate. Corolla-tube 1–1.8 cm long, less than 1 mm wide when pressed; the lobes shorter than one-half of the tube. Merocarps connate for about half of their length..**2. R. serpentina**

1. Rauvolfia densiflora (Wall.) Benth. ex Hook. f., Fl. Br. Ind. 3: 633. 1882; Trimen, Handb. Fl. Ceylon 3: 126. 1895. Type: Wall., Edward's Bot. Reg. 15, t. 1273. 1829. Described from a living specimen cultivated at Chiswick in 1827.

Tabernaemontana densiflora Wall., Edward's Bot. Reg. 15, t. 1273. 1829.
Ophioxylon ceylanicum Wight, Ic. Pl. Ind. Or. 4 (2): 1, t. 1291. 1848.
Ophioxylon densiflorum (Wall.) Thw., Enum. Pl. Zeyl. 191. 1860.

A treelet 0.5–3 m tall. Petiole 0.7–2.5 cm long. Leaf-blade 6–17 cm long and 2.5–6 cm wide, broadly lanceolate to obovate-lanceolate, widest in or above the middle, tapering to the base, markedly acuminate at the apex, thinly herbaceous; dried leaf with the midrib slightly impressed but frequently provided with a narrow median ridge on the upper surface, prominent beneath; lateral veins faintly immersed above, more or less raised beneath;

reticulate venation not sculptured on either side or shallowly impressed above. Cymes rather laxly branched (in spite of the misleading specific epithet). Pedicels much longer than the calyx. Calyx lobes 2–3 mm long, glabrous. Corolla-tube 0.5–1 cm long, rather stout, 1–1.5 mm wide when pressed, the lobes almost as long as the tube. Merocarps 0.8–1.2 cm long, almost distinct, very slightly pointed, glabrous, bluish-grey pruinose when ripe.

D i s t r. Deccan Peninsula southwards from the Western Ghats, Ceylon, Assam.

E c o l. In Ceylon locally abundant in disturbed and secondary mist forest and along edge of forests of the montane zone between 700 and 2200 m.

S p e c i m e n s E x a m i n e d. MATALE DISTRICT: Hulandoruwa near Illukkumbura, 900 m, Huber obs. KEGALLE DISTRICT: Ambegama, s. coll. C.P. 1834 partly (PDA). KANDY DISTRICT: Hantane, Gardner in C.P. 1834 partly (PDA), Silva 90 (PDA); same place, 2300 ft, Gardner 552 (BM, K) & 555 (BM); same place, 4000 ft, Worthington 261 (K); above University Circuit Bungalow, 950 m, Mueller-Dombois & Cooray 67111319 (PDA); Hunnasgiriya, Silva 51 (PDA); Hunnasgiriya Peak, s. coll. C.P. 1834 partly (PDA); Hunnasgiriya, mountain forest close to the Peak, c. 1500 m, Cramer 4508 (PDA); c. 9 miles northeast of Hunnasgiriya, 810 m, Davidse & Jayasuriya 8424 (PDA); Ferndale near Rangala, Simpson 8732 (BM); Rangala to Corbet's Gap, 1000 m, Kostermans 23487 (PDA, US); near mile marker 23/5 on road from Rangala to Looloowatte, c. 1300 m, Grupe 222 (US); 1 mile west of Herondale, 670 m, Bremer 1018 (PDA, S, US); Madugoda, Cramer 3987 (PDA), Tirvengadum et al. 229 (PDA, US); Deltota, Sumithraarachchi 98 (PDA, US); St. Catherine Estate, c. 1 mile south of Dolosbage, c. 1000 m, Robyns 6905 (PDA, US); base of Sentry Box East Mountain east of Dolosbage, behind Raxawa Tea Estate, c. 1400 m, Grupe 179 (PDA, US). NÚWARA ELIYA DISTRICT: Nuwara Eliya, Gardner in C.P. 1834 (PDA) partly; same place, c. 2000 m, Cramer 4622 (US); Black Pool Lake, 6100 ft, Meijer 31 (PDA); Moon Plains, c. 2000 m, Cramer & Jayasuriya 3759 (US); Nuwara Eliya, surrounding hills, 1850, C.F. & R.J. van Beusekom 1395 (US); Pidurutalagala, 1990–2300 m, Meijer 76 (PDA, US), Sohmer et al. 8366 (PDA, US) & 8417 (PDA), Tirvengadum & Waas 541, 543, 547 (all PDA, US); northern slope of Pidurutalagala, approach from Gonapitiya Tea Estate, Sohmer & Sumithraarachchi 10156 (PDA); between Hakgala and Nuwara Eliya, 26 Feb. 1906, Willis s.n. (PDA); mile 20/2 of Nuwara Eliya-Horton Plains Road, 6000 ft, Meijer 644 (PDA, US), Horton Plains, 6900–7000 ft, Willis s.n. (PDA); Horton Plains, Agrapatana Road, Nowicke & Jayasuriya 256 (PDA, US); about 7 miles northeast of Horton Plains, 2000 m, Gould & Cooray 13755 (PDA, US); Pundaluoya, c. 1300 m, Cramer 3826 (PDA, US); Rikiligaskada, Huber 56 (PDA, US); Pattipola, Silva 91 (PDA).

BADULLA DISTRICT: Jungle back of Hakgala, 1 March 1906, *Willis s.n.* (PDA); near Passara, Jan. 1888, *Trimen s.n.* (PDA). RATNAPURA DISTRICT: Bulutota Pass, Kadamudana, *Waas 513* (PDA, US); same place, Kurulugala Forest, 920 m, *Huber 562* (HBG, PDA, US). MATARA DIST-RICT: Sinharaja Forest north of Deniyaya, entry from Sinharaja Army Camp, 1050 m, *Sohmer & Waas 10380* (PDA). DISTRICT UNKNOWN: Dehigama, *s. coll. s.n.* (PDA); LOCALITY UNKNOWN: *Fraser 125* (BM), *Mackenzie s.n.* (K), *s. coll. C.P. 1834* (BM, K).

2. Rauvolfia serpentina (L.) Benth. ex Kurz, For. Fl. Burma 2: 171. 1877; Hook. f., Fl. Br. Ind. 3: 632. 1882; Trimen, Handb. Fl. Ceylon 3: 126. 1895. Type: Herbarium Hermann (BM).

Ophioxylon serpentinum L., Sp. Pl. 1043. 1753; Thw., Enum. Pl. Zeyl. 191. 1860.
Ophioxylon trifoliatum Gaertn., Fruct. 2: 123. 1791.

Petiole 0.6–1.4 cm long. Leaf-blade 5–16 cm long and 1.5–6 cm wide, broadly lanceolate, widest in the middle, tapering to both ends, acute at the apex but not or only faintly acuminate, thinly herbaceous; dried leaf with the midrib proximally sulcate, distally slightly elevated on the upper side, promi-nent throughout beneath; lateral veins raised above, scarcely so beneath; reti-culate venation hardly sculptured on either side. Cymes dense. Pedicels up to twice as long as the calyx, sometimes shorter than the calyx. Calyx-lobes 1.5–2 mm long, glabrous. Corolla-tube 1–1.8 cm long, very slender, less than 1 mm wide when pressed; the lobes about one fifth to one quarter of the length of the tube. Merocarps 0.5–0.7 cm long, connate with their lower half or a little beyond, minutely apiculate, glabrous, shining blackish-purple when ripe.

D i s t r. Tropical Himalayas, Assam, Burma, Deccan Peninsula, Ceylon.

E c o l. A plant of secondary scrub and grassy places in the moist zone, formerly from the lowland ascending to 700 m. It has not been observed dur-ing the Flora of Ceylon Project and is now possibly extinct in the island due to intense exploitation.

U s e s. Containing reserpine, an alkaloid with hypotensive properties, *Rauvolfia serpentina* has become an important medicinal plant.

V e r n. Ekaweriya, Nakuli, Rath-ekaweriya (S); Chivan-ampelpodi, Co-vannamilpori (T).

S p e c i m e n s E x a m i n e d. KURUNEGALA DISTRICT: Halpan-kande, *s. coll. s.n.* (Herbarium of Dept. of Forestry, Colombo). KEGALLE DISTRICT: Ambepussa Farm (Cultivated?), *Simpson 792*8 (BM). KANDY DISTRICT: Peradeniya, *Gardner* in *C.P. 1836* at least partly (PDA). BADULLA DISTRICT: Batagandawela, Ooma Oya, *Silva 246* (PDA).

LOCALITY UNKNOWN: *Fraser 44* (BM), *Macrae 33* (BM), *s. coll. C.P. 1836* (K), *Walker s.n.* (K).

9. PETCHIA

Livera, Ann. R. Bot. Gard. Peradeniya 10: 140. 1926. Type Species: *Petchia ceylanica* (Wight) Livera.

A slender, glabrous treelet. Leaves usually in whorls of three at the branching, otherwise opposite; ovate to broadly lanceolate, lateral veins rather few, including with the midrib an angle of about 60°. Flowers in poor, short- to long-peduncled cymes, terminal or terminal and lateral from between two petioles. Calyx glandular between the lobes, the latter lanceolate, acute. Corolla dirty white, scentless by daytime, glabrous without; the tube cylindrical, slightly inflated near the mouth and hairy within the swollen portion; the lobes a little shorter than the tube, narrowly oblong, acute, in bud overlapping to the left. Stamens attached to the tube in the inflated portion below the mouth, not or scarcely exserted; anthers distinct, ovate-oblong, acute. Disk absent. Merocarps distinct, stipitate, produced into a slender beak at the apex; mostly moniliform, two- to four-seeded, constricted between the seeds and thus consisting of two to four one-seeded, fleshy, obliquely ovoid joints, rarely the merocarps one-seeded by abortion and ovoid. Seeds ovoid, not compressed nor ruminate, with fleshy endosperm, without a tuft of hairs.

A monotypic genus endemic in Ceylon.

Petchia ceylanica (Wight) Livera, Ann. R. Bot. Gard. Peradeniya 10 : 140. 1926 as "zeylanica"; Alston in Trimen, Handb. Fl. Ceylon 6: 190. 1931 as "zeylanica". Type: *Walker* in Herb. Wight *s.n.* (K).

Alyxia ceylanica Wight, Ic. Pl. Ind. Or. 4 (2): 2, t. 1293. 1848 as "Alexia"; Thw., Enum. Pl. Zeyl. 191. 1860 as "zeylanica"; Hook. f., Fl. Br. Ind. 3: 636. 1882; Trimen, Handb. Fl. Ceylon 3: 127. 1895 as "zeylanica".
Gynopogon zeylanicus (Wight) Schum. in Pflanzenfam. 4 (2) : 151. 1895.

Petiole 0.3–0.5 cm long. Leaf-blade 4–7 cm long and 2–3.5 cm wide, widest in or below the middle, acute at the base, caudate-acuminate, but obtuse at the apex; dried leaf with the midrib not or faintly raised above, moderately prominent beneath; lateral veins more clearly elevated on upper than on under surface; reticulate venation slightly raised above, not or hardly so beneath. Pedicels much longer than the calyx. Calyx-lobes 2 mm long, glabrous. Corolla-tube 0.8–1.3 cm long. Merocarps 1.2–1.8 cm long when one-seeded or each joint about 1–1.2 cm long when moniliform; glabrous, bright red when ripe.

Distr. Endemic in Ceylon.

E c o l. An uncommon treelet of the moist region, growing in disturbed rain forest, not rarely near settlements, where it sometimes is grown as a hedge plant. Mostly at very low elevations but according to Thwaites ascending up to 700 m.

V e r n. Kukul-kaduru, Wal-kaduru, Wasa-kaduru (S).

N o t e. The plant is considered to be poisonous.

S p e c i m e n s E x a m i n e d. KURUNEGALA DISTRICT: Badagama Forest Reserve, c. 140 m, *Faden 76/404* (PDA), *Sumithraarachchi 660* (PDA, US). COLOMBO DISTRICT: Amandoluwa near Seeduwa, sea level, *Cramer 3413* (PDA, US), *Huber 258* (HBG, PDA, US); Kalatuwawa near Colombo, water reservoir, 600 ft, *Worthington 3520* (K); Heneratgoda, 23 Aug. 1923, *Silva s.n.* (PDA). KEGALLE DISTRICT: Dehiowita, 300 m, *Comanor 1136* (PDA, US); Pitakande, 29 Feb. 1928, *Silva s.n.* (PDA); Ambegama, *s. coll. C.P. 1835* at least partly (PDA). RATNAPURA DISTRICT: Kuruwita Kande, *Waas 18* (PDA, US). KALUTARA DISTRICT: Ranwalakelle, *Balakrishnan 1023* (PDA, US); c. 1 mile east of Highway A2, c. 5 miles south of Panadura, c. 10 m, *Theobald & Krahulik 2785* (PDA, US). GALLE DISTRICT: Kottawa Forest Reserve, *Alston 1288* (PDA); Godekande near Hiniduma, 100–120 m, *Huber 324* (PDA, US); Pituwala near Elipitiya, *Huber 319* (US). MATARA DISTRICT: Mahayaya Forest, Masmulla, 100 ft, *Worthington 4163* (K). LOCALITY UNKNOWN: *Champion s.n.* (K), *Mackenzie s.n.* (K), *s. coll. C.P. 1835* (BM, K), *Walker s.n.* (PDA), *Walker* in herb. Wight *s.n.* (K).

10. OCHROSIA

Juss., Gen. Pl. 144. 1789. Type Species: *Ochrosia maculata* Jacq.

Small or medium-sized, glabrous trees with stout branches. Leaves irregularly alternate or in whorls of three or four, oblong to obovate, with rather numerous lateral veins including with the midrib an angle of about 80°. Flowers in monochasial cymes which are arranged in a long-peduncled, terminal or lateral (by overtopping) umbel or in two superposed umbels. Calyx eglandular, with broadly ovate, obtuse lobes. Corolla greenish-white, glabrous without; the tube cylindrical, the lobes longer than the tube, oblong, obtuse, in bud overlapping to the right. Stamens attached to the corolla-tube near the mouth but not exserted; the anthers distinct, oblong-lanceolate, sagittate, acute, filled with pollen to the very base. Disk absent. Merocarps distinct, usually both developed, obliquely ovoid, bluntly pointed, spongy-woody, indehiscent, one-seeded. Seeds ovate, strongly flattened, with scanty endosperm, without a tuft of hairs.

A genus of about 30 species, centered in Malesia and the West Pacific Islands.

Ochrosia oppositifolia (Lam.) Schum. in Pflanzenfam. 4 (2): 156. 1895. Type: Rumphius, Herb. Amb. 2, t. 84. 1741.

Cerbera oppositifolia Lam., Enc. 1: 62. 1783.
Cerbera parviflora Forst., Fl. Austral. Prod. 19. 1786; Moon, Cat. 19. 1824.
Ochrosia borbonica Thw., Enum. Pl. Zeyl. 192. 1860; Hook. f., Fl. Br. Ind. 3: 638. 1882; Trimen, Handb. Fl. Ceylon 3: 129, plate LX. 1895, not *Ochrosia borbonica* J. F. Gmel.

Branches glaucous green with the leaves often crowded at the end of a year's growth. Petiole 2–3.5 cm long. Leaf-blade 14–20 cm long and 4–10 cm wide, widest in or frequently above the middle, tapering to the base, rounded or faintly acuminate and obtuse at the apex, coriaceous, shining; dried leaf not turning black, the midrib impressed on upper surface (the very base partly excepted), prominent beneath; lateral veins faintly sunk above, prominent beneath; reticulate venation loosely meshed, slightly impressed on upper and very faintly raised on under side or not sculptured on either surface. Pedicels as long as or shorter than the calyx. Calyx-lobes 1–1.5 mm long, glabrous. Corolla-tube about 0.5 cm long. Merocarps about 6 cm long and 4 cm in diameter, glabrous, bright yellow when ripe.

D i s t r. Maldive Islands, Ceylon, Andaman Islands, Malay Peninsula, Thailand, Malesia and West Pacific (New Caledonia, Fiji, Ellice Island). Absent from the Deccan Peninsula.

E c o l. In Ceylon, confined to the south west coastal districts; always growing near the seashore and slightly resistant to salt but not a member of the mangrove formation.

V e r n. Gonna, Mudu-kaduru (S).

S p e c i m e n s E x a m i n e d. KALUTARA DISTRICT: Kalutara, *Gardner 551* (BM), *Gardner in C.P. 1833* at least partly (PDA). GALLE DISTRICT: Galle, sea level, *Huber 58* (PDA, US); mile 48 of Colombo-Galle Road, *Worthington 2519* (BM) & *4105* (K); Talpe, *Austin & Jayasuriya 6096* (PDA). LOCALITY UNKNOWN: *Gardner 559* (K), *s. coll. C.P. 1833* (K).

11. CERBERA

L., Sp. Pl. 208. 1753. Type Species: *Cerbera manghas* L.

Small to medium-sized trees 6–17 m tall, glabrous, with stout branches. Leaves alternate, obovate-lanceolate, with 20–30 pairs of lateral veins diverging almost horizontally from the midrib. Flowers in lax, monochasially branched, long-peduncled, terminal inflorescences. Calyx eglandular; the lobes recurved, lanceolate, narrowed to the base, acute, deciduous. Corolla pure white with a yellow throat, glabrous without; the tube cylindrical towards the base, funnel-shaped at the mouth; funnel-shaped portion shorter than to as long as the base; corolla-lobes longer than the tube, obliquely elliptic, obtuse, in bud overlapping to the left. Stamens inserted in the middle of the corolla-tube; anthers oblong-lanceolate, acute, connate with their tips but not adnate to the style-apex, not exserted from the tube. Disk absent. Merocarps distinct, solitary by abortion, globose, woody-fibrous, indehiscent, one- or two-seeded. Seeds ovoid, somewhat compressed, without endosperm and without a tuft of hairs.

A genus of seven to eight species ranging from the Deccan Peninsula and Ceylon through Malesia eastwards to New Caledonia; if *Tanghinia* is included, one species in Madagascar. Represented in Ceylon by one species only.

Cerbera odollam Gaertn., Fruct. 2: 193, t. 124, fig. 1. 1791; Thw., Enum. Pl. Zeyl. 192. 1860; Hook. f., Fl. Br. Ind. 3: 638. 1882; Trimen, Handb. Fl. Ceylon 3: 128. 1895; Furtado, Gard. Bull. Straits Settlem. 10: 274. 1939; Corner, Wayside Trees Malaya 1: 143. 1940. Type: Gaertn., Fruct. 2, t. 124, fig. 1 (in November 1978, no specimen seen by Gaertner has been traced at Tübingen).

Cerbera manghas L., Sp. Pl. 208. 1753 pro parte; Moon, Cat. 19. 1824; Alston in Trimen, Handb. Fl. Ceylon 6: 190. 1931; Pichon, Notul. Syst. (Paris) 13: 223. 1948; Huber in Abeywick., Rev. Handb. Fl. Ceylon 1 (1): 18. 1973; this is not *C. manghas* L. emend. Gaertn.

Branchlets whorled with the leaves crowded at the end of a year's growth. Petiole 2–5 cm long. Leaf-blade 12–30 cm long and 3–7 cm wide, widest above the middle, much tapering to the base, rather suddenly acuminate and almost acute at the apex, slightly coriaceous; dried leaf black, with the midrib shallowly impressed but often provided with a median ridge on the upper side, prominent beneath; lateral veins and reticulate venation faintly raised on both surfaces or not sculptured at all. Peduncle as long as or longer than the calyx. Calyx-lobes 1–2 cm long, glabrous. Corolla-tube swollen just above the middle, 1.5–2 cm long; the lobes 2–3.5 cm long. Merocarps 6–9 cm in diameter, glabrous, green, often tinged with pink when ripe.

D i s t r. Coasts of the Deccan Peninsula, Ceylon, Malay Peninsula and Malesia.

E c o l. Common near the sea, both in the moist and in the dry zone of Ceylon. A plant of tidal river banks and of the back of the mangrove vegetation, less resistant to brackish soil than *Ochrosia oppositifolia* (Lam.) Schum. The tree is frequently planted between paddy fields and along roads, sometimes far from the coast, often together with *Barringtonia racemosa* (L.) Blume ex DC.

V e r n. Gon-kaduru (S); Nangi-ma (T).

Note. The nomenclature of this tree is controversial since *Cerbera manghas* as understood by Linnaeus (1753) comprises elements which belong to three different species, namely (a) the Ceylon *Cerbera* described above, known to Linnaeus by a drawing in Hermann's herbarium; (b) another *Cerbera* species collected by Osbeck in Java, and (c) the plant now known as *Pagiantha dichotoma* (Roxb.) Markgraf. The first to resolve this confusion was Gaertner (1791), who restricted *Cerbera manghas* to the element represented by Osbeck and proposed a new name for the species which occurs in Ceylon.

Specimens Examined. JAFFNA DISTRICT: Jaffna, *Roettler s.n.* (K), *s. coll. C.P. 1832* partly (PDA). PUTTALAM DISTRICT: mile 41 of Colombo-Puttalam Road, between Madampe and Mahawewa, *Huber 52* (PDA, US). COLOMBO DISTRICT: Near Colombo, *Bernardi 15399* (PDA, US); Talahena, *Waas 728* (PDA). KEGALLE DISTRICT: Between Mawanella and Udumulla, planted, *Huber 2* (PDA, US). RATNAPURA DISTRICT: Hills west of Weddagala, *Fosberg 56596* (PDA). TRINCOMALEE DISTRICT: Mutur, *Worthington 1310* (K). BATTICALOA DISTRICT: Batticaloa, *Fosberg et al. 50992* (PDA, US); Batticaloa, by lagoon on Batticaloa-Valaichchenai Road, *Trivengadum et al. 247* (PDA, US); c. 4 miles north of Batticaloa, *Davidse & Sumithraarachchi 8987* (PDA); near Valaichchenai, *Meijer 130* (US); Kalkudah Bay, *Mueller-Dombois 68042009* (BISH). KALUTARA DISTRICT: Kalutara, *s. coll. C.P. 1832* partly (PDA); Alutgama, *Huber 13* (PDA, US); Ihala Hewessa, 200 ft, *Bremer 822* (PDA, S, US); Kurupita, *Sohmer & Waas 10246* (PDA). GALLE DISTRICT: Galle, *Sohmer et al. 8893* (PDA); Aturuwella, *Tirvengadum 629* (PDA, US); Balapitiya, *Worthington 4106* (BM); Kottawa, edge of primary forest, *Waas & Peeris 535* (PDA, US).

12. AGANOSMA

G. Don, Gen. Hist. 4: 77. 1837. Type Species: *Aganosma caryophyllatum* G. Don.

Large, woody twiners with the young branches adpressedly pubescent. Leaves opposite, elliptic, elliptic-lanceolate or obovate-lanceolate, glabrous on both sides, with very few, arched, lateral veins including with the midrib an angle of about 45°. Flowers in dense, rounded, short-peduncled, terminal, tomentose cymes. Calyx with five glandular scales alternating with the lobes; the latter linear-lanceolate, very acute. Corolla yellowish-white, tomentose without; the tube constricted in the lower quarter, broadly cylindrical above; the lobes about twice as long as the tube, oblong, obtuse, in bud slightly overlapping to the right. Stamens inserted in the lower third of the tube; the anthers lanceolate-sagittate, acute, adnate to the style apex, enclosed in the corolla-tube, produced at the base into two tails deprived of pollen. Disk tubular, five-lobed, including the ovary. Merocarps distinct, long, cylindrical, tapering to the apex, dry, dehiscent along the ventral suture, many-seeded. Seeds black, lanceolate, compressed, not or hardly beaked, with scanty endosperm, with a tuft of hairs at one end.

About a dozen species, ranging from the Himalayas to Ceylon and eastwards to the Philippines.

Aganosma cymosum (Roxb.) G. Don, Gen. Hist. 4: 77. 1837; Hook. f., Fl. Br. Ind. 3: 665. 1882; Trimen, Handb. Fl. Ceylon 3: 139. 1895. Type: Coloured drawing no. 2463 of *Echites cymosa* by Roxburgh at K.

Echites cymosa Roxb., [Hort. Beng. 84. 1814 nom. nud.] Fl. Ind. ed. Carey 2: 16. 1832.

Petioles 0.7–1.5 cm long. Leaf-blade 5–13 cm long and 2–6 cm wide, widest in or above the middle, tapering to both ends, very acute and frequently acuminate at the apex; dried leaf with the midrib and lateral veins impressed on the upper surface, prominent on the lower side; reticulate venation faintly impressed above, not or scarcely sculptured beneath. Pedicels much shorter than the calyx. Calyx-lobes 7–10 mm long, tomentose on both sides. Corolla-tube about 0.5 cm long. Merocarps 15–more than 30 cm long, 0.5–0.8 cm wide, tomentose when young, glabrescent when ripe. Seed-body 2–3 cm long and 4–5 mm wide; beak not exceeding 1 mm in length.

D i s t r. Deccan Peninsula, Ceylon and Sylhet.

E c o l. In Ceylon not rare in the dry and intermediate zone at low elevations.

N o t e. The Ceylon plant differs from the typical form, described from Sylhet, by smaller and glabrous leaves with fewer pairs of lateral veins. It can be distinguished as:

var. **elegans** (G. Don) Hook. f., Fl. Br. Ind. 3: 665. 1882. Type: *Heyn* in Herb. Wallich no. *1656* (K-W).

Echites elegans Wall., Num. List no. 1656. 1829 nom. nud.
Aganosma elegans G. Don, Gen. Hist. 4: 77. 1837; Thw., Enum. Pl. Zeyl. 194. 1860.

S p e c i m e n s E x a m i n e d. ANURADHAPURA DISTRICT: Maha-Illuppallama, 16 March 1905, *Silva s.n.* (PDA); between Magoduwewa and Huluwewa, *Balakrishnan 1063* (PDA, US); Ritigala Strict Natural Reserve, 1000 to 1940 ft, *Jayasuriya 882* (PDA, US) & *2150* (US), *Jayasuriya & Burtt 1135* (PDA, US), *Jayasuriya & Pemadasa 1633* (PDA, US). POLONNA-RUWA DISTRICT: Gunner's Quoin, 100 m, *Tirvengadum et al. 234* (PDA, US). KURUNEGALA DISTRICT: Kurunegala, 100 m, *Kostermans 24937*

(PDA). MATALE DISTRICT: Wewala Tank eastnortheast of Dambulla, *Davidse & Sumithraarachchi 8135* (PDA). KANDY DISTRICT: Hunnasgiriya, *Silva 48* (PDA); Haragama, *s. coll. C.P. 1850* at least partly (PDA). KALUTARA DISTRICT: Palewatte, Pasdun Korale, *Trimen s.n.* (PDA). BATTICALOA DISTRICT: West of Kathiraveli towards Kanicka-kulam, 30 m, *Bernardi 15647* (PDA); Vakaneri, sea level, *Cramer et al. 3991* (PDA). AMPARAI DISTRICT: Sastrawela Hill near Arugam Bay, 30–40 m, *Bernardi 15577* (PDA). MONERAGALA DISTRICT: 6 km north of Bibile, *Huber 37* (PDA, US); northern slope of Kataragama Peak, 200 m, *Huber 65* (PDA, US).

13. CHONEMORPHA

G. Don, Gen. Hist. 4: 76. 1837 nom. cons. Type Species: *Chonemorpha macrophylla* (Roxb.) G. Don.

Huge, woody twiners with pubescent to almost tomentose branches, leaves and inflorescences. Leaves opposite, broadly elliptic, short-pubescent above, tomentose beneath, with few lateral veins including with the midrib an angle of 45–60°. Flowers in poor, long-peduncled, terminal cymes. Calyx glandular within; the lobes ovate-deltoid, subacute. Corolla white, tinged with yellow, glabrous without; the tube cylindric, slightly inflated in the lower third, narrowly tubular below, wider above the inflated portion; the lobes up to twice as long as the tube, obliquely obovate, truncate, in bud strongly overlapping to the right. Stamens inserted in the inflated portion of the tube; anthers lanceolate-sagittate, acute, adnate to the style-apex, enclosed in the corolla-tube, produced at the base into two tails deprived of pollen. Disk cupular. Merocarps distinct, long, triquetrous, tapering to the apex, dry and dehiscent along the ventral suture when ripe, many-seeded. Seeds ovate, compressed, with scanty endosperm, with a tuft of hairs at one end, dark brown.

A genus of twelve species ranging from India and Ceylon to South China and the Philippines.

Chonemorpha fragrans (Moon) Alston, Ann. R. Bot. Gard. Peradeniya 11: 203. 1929; Alston in Trimen, Handb. Fl. Ceylon 6: 192. 1931; Chatterjee, Kew Bull. 1947: 52. 1947. Type: Rheede, Hort. Mal. 9, t. 5 et t. 6. 1689.

Echites fragrans Moon, Cat. 20. 1824.
Echites macrophylla Roxb., [Hort. Beng. 20. 1814 nom. nud.] Fl. Ind. ed. Carey 2: 13. 1832.
Chonemorpha macrophylla (Roxb.) G. Don, Gen. Hist. 4: 76. 1837; Thw., Enum. Pl. Zeyl. 194. 1860; Hook. f., Fl. Br. Ind. 3: 661. 1882; Trimen, Handb. Fl. Ceylon 3: 138. 1895.

Chonemorpha rheedei Ridl., Agric. Bull. Straits Fed. Malay States 10: 146. 1911.

A huge climber 10–20 m long. Petiole 0.7– about 2 cm long. Leaf-blade 10–30 cm long and 8–20 cm wide, widest in or slightly below or above the middle, rounded or slightly cordate at the base, obtuse or mostly short-acuminate at the apex; dried leaf with the midrib broadly channelled and filled with yellowish hairs on upper side, prominent beneath; lateral veins narrowly sulcate above, prominent beneath; reticulate venation not or faintly impressed above, slightly raised beneath. Pedicels several times longer than the calyx. Calyx-lobes 3–5 mm long, glabrescent. Corolla-tube 3.5–4.5 cm long, the lobes often undulate-crispate at the margin. Merocarps 20–30 cm long, 1–almost 2 cm in diameter, glabrous when ripe.

D i s t r. Tropical Himalayas, India, Ceylon, Burma and Andaman Islands.

E c o l. In Ceylon rather rare in the moist zone up to an elevation of 800 m. In secondary forests locally abundant (e.g. Udawattakele Sanctuary). Flowering from March to May.

V e r n. Bulu-walanguna, Bu-kiri-wel (S).

S p e c i m e n s E x a m i n e d. KEGALLE DISTRICT: Kitulgala, *s. coll. C.P. 2467* partly (PDA); mile 43/2 of Colombo-Kandy Road, 400 ft, *Worthington 4207* (BM). KANDY DISTRICT: Kandy, Udawattakele Sanctuary, *Huber 6* (PDA, US); Kalugammawa (= Kadugannawa?), 7 May 1890, *Trimen s.n.* (PDA). KALUTARA DISTRICT: Kalutara., *s. coll. C.P. 2467* partly (PDA). RATNAPURA DISTRICT: Delgoda, 24 March 1919, *Lewis & Silva s.n.* (PDA). GALLE DISTRICT: Galle, *Sumithraarachchi et al. 979* (PDA); Bonavista near Galle, *Kundu & Balakrishnan 498* (PDA, US), *Balakrishnan 944* (PDA, US). LOCALITY UNKNOWN: *Mackenzie s.n.* (K), *s. coll. C.P. 2467* (BM), *Walker s.n.* (K).

14. PARSONSIA

R. Br., Mem. Wern. Nat. Hist. Soc. 1: 64. 1811, prepr. 1810 nom. cons. Type Species: *Periploca capsularis* Forster.

Glabrous, moderately woody twiners with scanty, almost colourless latex and opposite, elliptic, ovate or ovate-lanceolate leaves. Lateral veins few, including with the midrib an angle of about 60° (rarely, and in extremely large leaves only, lateral veins diverging almost rectangularly). Flowers in rich, long-peduncled cymes, arising from between the petioles. Calyx eglandular, with triangular, acute lobes. Corolla green or green suffused with purple, glabrous without; the tube short-cylindrical, the lobes one and a half to twice as long as the tube, oblong, obtuse, in bud overlapping to the right. Stamens inserted at the base of the corolla-tube, with long, spirally twisted filaments;

anthers lanceolate-sagittate, acute, adnate to the style-apex, exserted from the corolla-tube, produced at the base into two tails deprived of pollen. Disk consisting of five triangular lobes. Fruit a bilocular, narrowly lanceolate capsule with two longitudinal grooves, tapering to the apex, dry and septicidally dehiscent when ripe, many-seeded. Seeds narrowly linear, compressed, with scanty endosperm, with a tuft of hairs at one end, brown.

A genus of 80 species native in India, Ceylon (one species only), Southeast Asia and Oceania.

Parsonsia laevigata (Moon) Alston, Ann. R. Bot. Gard. Peradeniya 11: 203. 1927; Alston in Trimen, Handb. Fl. Ceylon 6: 192. 1931; M. Pichon, Notul. Syst. (Paris) 14: 16. 1950. Type: Rheede, Hort. Mal. 9, t. 9. 1689.

Echites laevigata Moon, Cat. 20. 1824.
Parsonsia spiralis Wall. [Num. List no. 1631. 1829 nom. nud.] ex G. Don, Gen. Hist. 4: 80. 1837; Hook. f., Fl. Br. Ind. 3: 650. 1882; Trimen, Handb. Fl. Ceylon 3: 134. 1895.
Heligme spiralis (Wall. ex G. Don) Thw., Enum. Pl. Zeyl. 193. 1860.

Petiole 0.7–3.5 cm long. Leaf-blade 6–20 cm long, 2.5–10 cm wide, widest in or below the middle, rounded or very short-cuneate or shallowly cordate at the base, acute and acuminate at the apex, firmly membranous; dried leaf with the midrib flat or faintly raised on upper side, prominent beneath; lateral veins and reticulate venation slightly raised above, less clearly so or not sculptured at all beneath. Pedicels several times longer than the calyx. Calyx-lobes 2 mm long, glabrous. Corolla-tube about 3 mm long. Capsule 10–18 cm long, each loculus 0.5–0.7 cm in diameter, glabrous.

D i s t r. Deccan Peninsula, Ceylon and Southeast Asia from Assam and Burma to South China and Malesia.

E c o l. In Ceylon common in the moist and intermediate zone up to an elevation of 1000 m, less frequent in the dry country. Often in disturbed vegetation, e.g. in forest clearings and near human settlements, twining in fences and hedges. Flowering throughout the year.

V e r n. Kiri-anguna, Val-anguna (S).

S p e c i m e n s E x a m i n e d. ANURADHAPURA DISTRICT: Maha-Illuppallama, *Silva 88* (PDA); Ritigala Strict Natural Reserve, 220–350 m, *Bernardi 16132* (PDA); same locality, 1200 to 1950 ft, *Cramer 4141* (PDA, US), *Huber 42* (PDA, US), *Jayasuriya 920* (PDA, US) & *1087* (PDA, US), *Jayasuriya, Ashton et al. 1342* (PDA, US), *Jayasuriya & Burtt 1144* (PDA, US). PUTTALAM DISTRICT: Puttalam, *Kundu & Balakrishnan 379* (PDA); mile 43 of Colombo-Puttalam Road, near Madampe, *Huber 51* (PDA, US). TRINCOMALEE DISTRICT: Trincomalee, *Roettler s.n.* (K). COLOMBO DISTRICT: Negombo, *Kundu & Balakrishnan 427*

(PDA). MATALE DISTRICT: Kongahawela, along Kalugal-Oya, *Jayasuriya 352* (PDA, US); 5 miles east of Naula, 220 m, *Huber 776* (PDA, US). KANDY DISTRICT: Hantane 2300 ft, *Gardner 559* (BM, K); Madugoda, *Kundu & Balakrishnan 181* (PDA); Talatuoya, *s. coll. s.n.* (PDA). BATTI-CALOA DISTRICT: 50 m east of Lady Manning's Bridge, Kalladai, *Jayasuriya et al. 704* (PDA, US). BADULLA DISTRICT: Haldumulla Road, 26 May 1906, *Smith s.n.* (PDA). GALLE DISTRICT: Bentota, sea level, *Huber 14* (PDA, US). LOCALITY UNKNOWN: *Monroe 225* (BM), *s. coll. C.P. 1862* (BM, K, PDA), *Walker s.n.* (K).

15. VALLARIS

Burm. f., Fl. Ind. 51. 1768. Type Species: *Vallaris pergulana* Burm. f.

Woody twiners with puberulous young branches, petioles and inflorescences. Leaves opposite, oblong-lanceolate, glabrous on both sides, with few, distant, lateral veins including with the midrib an angle of 45–60°. Flowers in rich, peduncled cymes arising from between the petioles. Calyx with glandular scales alternating with the lobes; the lobes ovate-lanceolate, acute. Corolla greenish-white, minutely puberulous without; the tube cylindrical; the lobes twice as long as the tube, broadly obovate to almost orbicular, rounded at the apex, in bud strongly overlapping to the right. Stamens inserted at the mouth of the corolla-tube; filaments short; anthers lanceolate-sagittate, acute, adnate to the style-apex, exserted from the corolla-tube, produced at the base into two tails deprived of pollen. Disk a five-lobed ring. Fruit at first bilocular, tardily splitting from below into two distinct, narrowly oblong, acute, fibrous but rather fleshy merocarps dehiscent along the ventral suture when ripe. Seeds very numerous, ovate-oblong, compressed, tapering at one end and there bearing a tuft of hairs, with scanty endosperm, pale yellowish-grey.

Three or four species in India, Ceylon, Southeast Asia and Malesia.

Vallaris glabra (L.) Kuntze, Syn. *V. pergulana* Burm. f., a native of Bengal, the Malay Peninsula and Malesia, is occasionally grown as an ornamental. It may be distinguished from *V. solanacea* by its broadly elliptic to obovate leaves 7–10 cm wide.

Vallaris solanacea (Roth) Kuntze, Rev. Gen. 147. 1891; Alston in Trimen, Handb. Fl. Ceylon 6: 192. 1931. Type: Heyne, not seen.

Peltanthera solanacea Roth, Nov. Pl. Sp. 132. 1821.
Vallaris heynii Spreng., Syst. Veg. 1: 635. 1825; Hook. f., Fl. Br. Ind. 3: 650. 1882; Trimen, Handb. Fl. Ceylon 3: 135. 1895.
Echites dichotoma Roxb., Fl. Ind. ed. Carey 2: 19. 1832.

Vallaris dichotoma (Roxb.) Wall., Num. List no. 1621. 1829; Thw., Enum. Pl.
Zeyl. 192. 1860.

Petiole 0.6–1.5 cm long. Leaf-blade 5–10 cm long and 2–3.5 cm wide, widest in or slightly above the middle, cuneate, rarely almost rounded at the base,
acute or short-acuminate at the apex, herbaceous; dried leaf with the midrib flat
or impressed towards the base only, with a more or less clearly defined median
ridge on the upper side, prominent beneath; lateral veins flat above, faintly
raised beneath; reticulate venation not sculptured on either side. Pedicels much
longer than the calyx. Calyx-lobes 4 mm long, puberulous. Corolla-tube twice
as long as the calyx. Merocarps 10–15 cm long, about 1 cm in diameter, glabrous. Chromosome number: $2n = 20$.

D i s t r. Tropical Himalayas, Deccan Peninsula, Ceylon, Sylhet and
Burma.

E c o l. A rare plant in Ceylon, known from a few localities in the intermediate region only.

N o t e. According to Trimen, the flowers have the scent of almonds.

S p e c i m e n s E x a m i n e d. NUWARA ELIYA DISTRICT: Hanguranketa, *s. coll. C.P. 2519* at least partly (PDA). BADULLA DISTRICT:
Pallewela, *Balakrishnan & Jayasuriya 805* (PDA, US). DISTRICT UN-
KNOWN: Muppane, *Alston 2462* (K, PDA). LOCALITY UNKNOWN:
s. coll. C.P. 2519 (K), *Walker s.n.* (K, PDA).

16. WALIDDA

(A. DC.) M. Pichon, Notul. Syst. (Paris) 14: 87. 1951. Type Species: *Walidda*
antidysenterica (L.) M. Pichon.

Wrightia sectio *Walidda* A. DC. in DC., Prod. 8: 404. 1844.

A slender, glabrous treelet with opposite, ovate, elliptic or lanceolate
leaves. Leaf-blade with rather few lateral veins including with the midrib an
angle of 45–70°. Flowers in poor, short-peduncled, monochasially branched,
terminal but sometimes overtopped cymes. Calyx with glandular scales alternating with the lobes; the latter ovate, obtuse. Corolla pure white, minutely
papillose-puberulous on the lobes, otherwise glabrous without; the tube narrowly cylindrical, without a fleshy annulus in the mouth; the lobes slightly
shorter than the tube, obovate, obtuse, in bud overlapping to the left. Corona
consisting of three series of segments, the multifid alternipetalous, the multifid but longer epipetalous and the geminate, simple or compound alternating
supplementary segments. Stamens inserted in the mouth of the corolla-tube,
with very short filaments; anthers lanceolate-sagittate, acute at the apex and
produced into a glabrous acumen, adnate to the style-apex, exserted from
the corolla-tube, produced at the base into two tails longer than the filaments
and deprived of pollen. Disk absent. Fruit soon splitting into two distinct,

cylindrical, acuminate merocarps, dry and dehiscent along the ventral suture when ripe. Seeds numerous, linear, compressed, with scanty, salmon-pink endosperm and a tuft of hairs at one end, pale greyish-brown.

A monotypic genus endemic in Ceylon. In his revision of the genus *Wrightia*, Ngan (1965) considered *Walidda* a section of *Wrightia*, as it seems, mostly with respect to the limited distribution of *Walidda*.

Walidda antidysenterica (L.) M. Pichon, Mem. Mus. Natl. Hist. Nat. ser. B, Bot. 1: 74. 1951; M. Pichon, Notul. Syst. (Paris) 14: 88. 1951. Type: Herbarium Hermann. 4: 76 (BM).

Nerium antidysentericum L., Sp. Pl. 209. 1753.
Nerium zeylanicum L., Cent. Pl. 2: 12. 1756.
Wrightia antidysenterica (L.) R. Br., Mem. Wern. Nat. Hist. Soc. 1: 74. 1811, prepr. 1810; Ngan, Ann. Missouri Bot. Gard. 52: 166. 1965.
Wrightia zeylanica (L.) R. Br., Mem. Wern. Nat. Hist. Soc. 1: 74. 1811, prepr. 1810; Thw., Enum. Pl. Zeyl. 193. 1860; Hook. f., Fl. Br. Ind. 3: 654. 1882; Trimen, Handb. Fl. Ceylon 3: 137. 1895.

A treelet 0.7–2 m tall. Petiole 0.1–0.6 cm long. Leaf-blade 4–11 cm long and 1–4 cm wide, widest in or slightly below or above the middle, cuneate or rarely almost rounded at the base, slightly to markedly acuminate at the apex, firmly membranous; dried leaf with the midrib impressed on the upper side, prominent beneath; lateral veins flat or faintly elevated above, more clearly prominent beneath; reticulate venation not sculptured on the upper surface, often slightly raised on the lower. Pedicels much longer than the calyx. Calyx-lobes 1.5–3 mm long, glabrous. Corolla-tube 1.7–2.8 cm long. Corona minutely puberulous throughout. Merocarps 9–15 cm long, about 0.5 cm broad, glabrous.

D i s t r. Endemic in Ceylon.

E c o l. A plant of the moist region at low elevations, up to 600 m, not uncommon in secondary scrub and forest clearings.

U s e s. According to Trimen, bark and wood are used for external application.

V e r n. Idda, Kelidha, Sudu-idda, Wal-idda (S).

S p e c i m e n s E x a m i n e d. PUTTALAM DISTRICT: Mellawa, Lihiriyagama, *Sumithraarachchi 672* (PDA, US); Palavi, sea level, *Cramer 4660* (PDA). KURUNEGALA DISTRICT: "Baddegame Mukelane," *Alston 712* (PDA); Doluwa Kande, June 1886, *Trimen s.n.* (PDA); Kurunegala, *s. coll. C.P. 1825* partly (PDA); Yakdessagala Kanda, 500 ft, *Worthington 4005* (K). KANDY DISTRICT: Kadugannawa, 1800 ft, *Worthington 2872* (K). COLOMBO DISTRICT: Colombo, *s. coll. C.P. 1825* partly (PDA), *s. coll. s.n.* (BM); way to Goluwapottuwa, Negombo, 2 July 1930, *Silva s.n.* (PDA); Talahena, *Waas 729* (PDA). KALUTARA DISTRICT: Kalutara, *Macrae 125* (BM, K); near Kalutara, *Schiffner 3421* (BM); Kalugala Forest south of Badureliya, 210 m, *Huber 282* (HBG, PDA, US); Pelawatte, on top of Rana-waka Rock, sea level, *Cramer 2805* (PDA, US). GALLE DISTRICT: Galle, *Gardner 557* (BM, K); Hiniduma, 350 m, *Cramer 4297* (PDA); Hiniduma, ascent to Haycock, 100 to 270 m, *Bernardi 15468* (PDA, US), *Cramer 2682 & 2763* (both PDA, US), *Davidse 7865* (PDA), *Huber 63* (PDA, US), *Schmid-Hollinger 53* (US); Hulandawa Ganga, 200 ft, *Worthington 2235* (K); Kanne-liya Forest, 300–400 ft, *Balakrishnan 259* (PDA, US), *Bremer 853* (PDA, S, US); Tannahena, Hulandawa Oya, 200 ft, *Worthington 3662* (BM, K); Yakka-tuwa, *Koelmeyer 1391* (Herbarium of Dept. of Forestry, Colombo). LOCA-LITY UNKNOWN: *Moon s.n.* (BM), *Roettler s.n.* (K), *s. coll. C.P. 1825* (BM, K), *Walker s.n.* (K).

17. WRIGHTIA

R. Br., Mem. Wern. Nat. Hist. Soc. 1: 73. 1811, prepr. 1810. Type Species: *Wrightia tinctoria* R. Br.

Small to medium-sized trees with the young branches, leaves and inflores-cences glabrous, pubescent or tomentose. Leaves opposite, narrowly lanceo-late, elliptic, ovate or obovate; lateral veins rather few, including with the midrib an angle of 45–60°. Flowers in poor to fairly rich, dichasially branch-ed, peduncled cymes, terminal but sometimes overtopped by axillary branches. Calyx with glandular scales alternating with the lobes within, the lobes nar-rowly to broadly ovate, obtuse to acute. Corolla creamy white or yellow, sometimes turning orange or purple towards the end of anthesis, puberulous without at least on the lobes; the tube short and stout, with a fleshy ring in the mouth; the lobes much longer than the tube, obovate to narrowly oblong, obtuse, in bud overlapping to the left. Corona consisting of one series of segments, the segments alternipetalous in this case, or of two series, then the segments alternipetalous and epipetalous, very rarely with a third series of segments which alternate with the alterni- and epipetalous ones. Stamens in-serted in the mouth of the corolla-tube; filaments very short; anthers lanceo-late-sagittate, acute, produced into a barbate acumen at the apex, adnate to the style-apex, totally exserted from the corolla-tube, produced at the base into two tails as long as or shorter than the filaments and deprived of pollen. Disk absent. Fruit a bilocular, cylindrical capsule with two longitudinal grooves, blunt, septicidally dehiscent when dry, or soon splitting into two distinct, cylindrical, acute or acuminate merocarps, dry and dehiscent along the ventral suture when ripe. Seeds numerous, linear, compressed, with scanty, pink or mauve endosperm and a tuft of hairs at one end, yellowish-grey or pale greyish-brown without.

Eighteen species ranging from East Africa to the Solomon Islands and from South China to Northern Australia.

KEY TO THE SPECIES

1 Young branches and inflorescence mostly glabrous. Leaves narrowly lanceolate, 1–2 cm wide. Pedicels very slender, 0.2–0.3 mm thick when dried. Corolla 1–1.4 cm in diameter when expanded. Corona consisting of five alternipetalous segments only, exceeding the anther-cone. Merocarps soon distinct, about 0.5 cm thick when ripe. . **1. W. angustifolia**
1 Young branches and inflorescences pubescent or tomentose. Leaf-blade 2–8 cm wide. Pedicels 0.5–almost 1 mm thick when dried. Corolla 2–almost 4 cm in diameter when expanded. Corona consisting at least of five alternipetalous and five epipetalous segments, shorter than the anther-cone. Merocarps thicker or merocarps connate into a stout capsule
  2 Leaves densely pubescent or tomentose beneath. Pedicels stout, about 0.8 mm thick when dried, mostly shorter than the flower. Fruit a blunt, bilocular capsule, warty with prominent lenticels. . . . .**2. W. tomentosa**
  2 Leaves sparsely pubescent beneath. Cymes lax. Pedicels rather slender, about 0.5 mm thick when dried, as long as or slightly longer than the flowers. Fruit (unknown in *W. puberula*) consisting of two smooth and rather slender merocarps distinct except for their points
    3 Corona consisting of five alternipetalous and five epipetalous segments. Carpels glabrous at anthesis. . . . .**3. W. puberula**
    3 Corona consisting of five alternipetalous, five epipetalous and five supplementary segments alternating with the latter. Carpels in flower densely pubescent at the tip. . . . . . .
. . . .**4. W. flavido-rosea**

1. Wrightia angustifolia Thw., Enum. Pl. Zeyl. 193. 1860; Hook. f., Fl. Br. Ind. 3: 653. 1882; Trimen, Handb. Fl. Ceylon 3: 136. 1895; Ngan, Ann. Missouri Bot. Gard. 52: 158. 1965. Type: *s. coll. C.P. 1839* (PDA).

A tree up to 15 m high with branches and inflorescence glabrous even when young. Petiole 0.15–0.6 cm long. Leaf-blade 4–14 cm long, 1–2 cm wide, narrowly lanceolate, widest in or below the middle, very gradually tapering to the base, long-acuminate but obtuse at the apex, glabrous on both sides when fully developed, puberulous along edge of petiole and base of midrib when young, very rarely persistently pubescent along the midrib beneath; firmly membranous; dried leaf with the midrib flat or impressed in the proximal half of the upper side, slightly prominent on the lower side; lateral veins faintly raised on both surfaces or flat on the under side; reticulate venation not sculptured or slightly impressed on both sides. Cymes lax. Pedicels very slender, 0.2–0.3 mm thick when dried, much longer than the flowers. Calyx-lobes 0.7–1.2 mm long, narrowly ovate, ciliolate at the margin, glabrous on the back; the glandular scales alternating with the lobes narrowly lanceolate. Corolla creamy-white, malodorous; the tube 0.2 cm long, the lobes about 0.6 cm long, narrowly oblong. Corona of one series, consisting of five alternipetalous segments, glabrous, bifid or laciniate at the tip, about 0.5 cm long and 1 mm wide, slightly exceeding the anthers. Anthers rather slender, about 4 mm long. Carpels pubescent at the apex. Ripe merocarps distinct, 17–30 cm long and about 0.5 cm wide, acute at the apex, black, smooth and glabrous.

D i s t r. Endemic in Ceylon.

E c o l. A tree of deciduous forest of the dry zone at low elevation. Not uncommon in North Central Province, otherwise rare.

V e r n. Velai-pal-madankai (T).

N o t e. *Wrightia angustifolia* Thw. is easily recognized from a distance by its drooping branchlets which give the tree a willow-like appearance, and the yellowish-green foliage.

S p e c i m e n s E x a m i n e d. VAVUNIYA DISTRICT: Vavuniya, *Jayasuriya 1348* (PDA, US); c. 2 miles southwest of Nedunkeni along road to Puliyankulam, near mile post 21/3, *Davidse & Sumithraarachchi 9062* (PDA). ANURADHAPURA DISTRICT: Anuradhapura, *Trimen 34* (PDA); Borupangala, Hinukkiriyawa, west of Habarana, *Jayasuriya et al. 1389* (PDA, US); Ritigala Strict Natural Reserve, 600 and 650 ft, *Jayasuriya 1250 & 1290* (both PDA, US); summit of Ritigala Kande, 22 & 24 July 1905, *Willis 104* (PDA), *Willis s.n.* (PDA); Ritigala, west of Reserve, *Meijer 335* (PDA); Horowpothana-Kebithigollawa Road, near the 27/2 road marker, *Sumithraarachchi 840* (PDA); mile 71 of Anuradhapura-Trincomalee Road, *Huber 41* (PDA, US), *Worthington 55* (BM, K). POLONNARUWA DISTRICT: Giritale, *Worthington 1243* (K). TRINCOMALEE DISTRICT: Nilaveli Road, 6th mile post, *Worthington 72* (BM, K); mile 99 of Anuradhapura-Trincomalee Road, *Worthington 971* (BM, K); Trincomalee, *Gardner in C.P. 1839* partly (PDA); Trincomalee Town, 10 ft, *Worthington 1005* (BM); Andankulam, Trincomalee, 20 ft, *Worthington 1005* (BM). KURUNEGALA DISTRICT: Badegama, by the Kumbukgala Ridge, 500 ft, *Worthington 4014* (K); Doluwa Kande, 400 m, *Cramer 3048* (PDA, US); Kurunegala Rock, 220 m, *Huber 379* (HBG, PDA, US); same locality, 1100 ft, *Sumithraarachchi 614* (PDA, US); Wewagala, *Waas 752* (PDA). MATALE DISTRICT: Dambulla, *Gardner in C.P. 1839* partly (PDA); Dambulla, on the Rock, *Kostermans 23529* (US), *Sumithraarachchi 505* (PDA, US). AMPARAI DISTRICT: Lahugala Tank, *Mueller-Dombois & Comanor 67072525* (BISH, PDA). MONERAGALA DISTRICT: Kataragama Peak, 470 m, *Bernardi 15508* (PDA).

2. Wrightia tomentosa Roem. & Schult., Syst. Veg. 4: 414. 1819; Thw., Enum. Pl. Zeyl. 193. 1860; Hook. f., Fl. Br. Ind. 3: 653. 1882; Trimen, Handb. Fl. Ceylon 3: 137. 1895; Ngan, Ann. Missouri Bot. Gard. 52: 147. 1965. Type: *Roxburgh* in Herb. BR (according to an unpublished list of Roxburgh's specimens by Merrill, 1952, at K).

Nerium tomentosum Roxb., [Hort. Beng. 84. 1814 nom. nud.] Fl. Ind. ed. Carey 2: 6. 1837.

Wrightia pubescens Roth, Nov. Pl. Sp. 120. 1821, not *W. pubescens* R. Br.,
1810.

A small or medium-sized tree with young branches and inflorescences
pubescent to tomentose. Petiole 0.3–0.8 cm long. Leaf-blade 5–18 cm long,
2–8 cm wide, elliptic-lanceolate, elliptic or obovate, widest in or slightly above
the middle, tapering to the base, obtuse and more or less acuminate at the
apex, pubescent or glabrescent above, tomentose beneath, firmly membranous; bright green alive, turning black when drying; dried leaf with the midrib
impressed in the proximal and raised in the distal half of the upper side, usually hidden by a dense tomentum, prominent beneath; lateral veins faintly impressed above and prominent beneath; reticulate venation impressed on both
surfaces. Cymes few-, mostly three-flowered. Pedicel stout, about 1 mm thick
when dried, mostly somewhat shorter than the flower. Calyx-lobes 2–3 mm
long, broadly ovate, pubescent without; the glandular scales alternating with
the lobes, ovate or orbicular, acute or finely serrate. Corolla salmon pink
within, bright green without, turning inky black when fading, with an acid
smell of decaying fruits; the tube about 0.5 cm long, the lobes 1.2–1.8 cm long,
elliptic. Corona of two series but virtually single by connation, shorter than
the anthers, glabrous; epipetalous segments truncate, almost entire, adnate to
the corolla-lobes; alternipetalous segments deeply bifid, almost entirely fused
with the adjoining epipetalous ones; alternating supplementary segments
absent. Anthers rather stout, about 7 mm long. Carpels glabrous in anthesis,
connate into a cylindrical capsule with two longitudinal grooves, septicidally
dehiscent when ripe, 14–35 cm long and 2–3 cm wide, stoutly apiculate,
blackish, warty with prominent, pale lenticels. Seeds (tuft not included) 13 mm
long, 2 mm wide.

D i s t r. India, Ceylon, Burma and Malay Peninsula.

E c o l. In Ceylon widely distributed but always rare, mostly in deciduous
forest of the dry zone and at low elevation. One locality in the moist region
requires confirmation.

V e r n. Pal-madankai (T).

N o t e. Smell, colour and shape of the flower resemble those of *Uvaria
macropoda* Hook. f. & Thoms. and suggest pollination by saprophilous flies.

According to Ngan, *Wrightia tomentosa* Roem. & Schult. is represented in
Ceylon by an endemic subspecies. This is subsp. *pauciflora* Ngan, Ann. Missouri Bot. Gard. 52: 149. 1965, based on *C.P. 2619* (K, holotype), distinguished from the continental plant by the few-flowered inflorescence and the
connate corona segments.

S p e c i m e n s E x a m i n e d. ANURADHAPURA DISTRICT: Ritigala Strict Natural Reserve, eastern slope, 1650 ft, *Jayasuriya & Premadasa
1634* (PDA, US); same locality, 2000 ft, *Jayasuriya 2282* (PDA) mile 75 of
Anuradhapura-Trincomalee Road, 300 ft, *Worthington 1343* (K); Habarana,

600 ft, *Worthington 683 & 1214* (BM). POLONNARUWA DISTRICT: Alut Oya, 76th mile post and 40 yards, 300 ft, *Worthington 715* (BM) *& 2704* (K); Angamedilla, gallery forest along Amban Ganga, 60 m, *Huber 445* (HBG, PDA, US). TRINCOMALEE DISTRICT: Andankulam, *Worthington 2667* (BM). MATALE DISTRICT: Dambulla, base of the Rock, *Huber 758* (HBG, PDA, US); Erawalagala, 6 miles east of Dambulla, 420 m, *Davidse & Sumithra-arachchi 8084* (PDA). KANDY DISTRICT: Kadugannawa, *s. coll. C.P. 2619* partly (PDA). KEGALLE DISTRICT: Ambagamuwa, *s. coll. C.P. 2619* partly (PDA). BATTICALOA DISTRICT: Batticaloa, *Walker 205* (PDA). AMPARAI DISTRICT: Panama, *Cooray 69073015* (PDA, US). HAMBAN-TOTA DISTRICT: Ruhuna National Park, *Comanor 1044* (PDA, US); Ruhuna National Park, Block 2, Kumbukkan Oya, about 2 miles above mouth, *Fosberg et al. 51098* (PDA, US). COLOMBO DISTRICT: Heneratgoda, Apr. 1883, *Trimen s.n.* (PDA). LOCALITY UNKNOWN: *s. coll. C.P. 2619* (BM, K), *Walker 156* (K), *Walker s.n.* (K).

3. **Wrightia puberula** (Thw.) Ngan, Ann. Missouri Bot. Gard. 52: 145. 1965. Type: *s. coll. C.P. 1837* (K).

Wrightia ? rothii G. Don var. *puberula* Thw., Enum. Pl. Zeyl. 193. 1860.

A small tree with the young branches and inflorescences pubescent. Petiole about 0.7 cm long. Leaf-blade 8–12 cm long and 2.5–3.5 cm wide, narrowly elliptic to ovate, widest in or slightly above the middle, tapering to the base, obtuse and acuminate at the apex, sparsely pubescent on both sides; firmly membranous; dried leaf with the midrib on upper side sulcate in the proximal half, flat or faintly raised in the distal half, prominent beneath; lateral veins slightly raised above, strongly so beneath; reticulate venation not sculptured above, faintly so beneath. Cymes lax and rather few-flowered. Pedicels about 0.5 mm thick when dried, as long as or little longer than the flowers. Calyx-lobes 2–3.5 mm long, ovate to broadly ovate, puberulous without; the glandular scales alternating with the lobes ovate, acute. Colour of the corolla not known; corolla-tube 0.35 cm long, the lobes about 1.3 cm long, narrowly oblong-elliptic. Corona of two series, shorter than the stamens, glabrous; epipetalous segments laciniate, adnate to the corolla-lobes; alternipetalous segments bifid or laciniate, rather broad, about as long as the epipetalous ones; alternating supplementary segments absent. Anthers rather stout, about 6 mm long. Carpels at anthesis glabrous. Fruit not known.

Distr. Endemic in Ceylon. A treelet of the dry zone, known from a single locality only and not collected within the present century.

Note. Trimen in J. Bot. 23: 238. 1885 and in Handb. Fl. Ceylon 3: 136. 1895 incorrectly identified this plant with his *Wrightia flavido-rosea*.

Specimens Examined. MATALE DISTRICT: Dambulla, *Gardner s.n.* (K), *Gardner in C.P. 1834* (BM, K, PDA).

4. Wrightia flavido-rosea Trimen, J. Bot. 23: 238. 1885; Trimen, Handb. Fl. Ceylon 3: 136 partly and plate LXI. 1895; Ngan, Ann. Missouri Bot. Gard. 52: 166. 1965. Type: *Trimen s.n.* (K).

A small tree with young branches and inflorescence pubescent. Petiole about 0.5 cm long. Leaf-blade 10–15 cm long and 2.5–3.5 cm wide, narrowly elliptic, widest in or slightly above the middle, tapering to the base, obtuse and acuminate at the apex, sparsely and minutely pubescent along the veins beneath, almost glabrous otherwise; firmly membranous; dried leaf with the midrib on upper surface impressed in the proximal and indistinct or flat in the distal half, prominent beneath; lateral veins very slightly raised above, strongly so beneath; reticulate venation not sculptured on either side or slightly raised on the lower side only. Cymes lax. Pedicels about 0.5 mm thick when dried, as long as or slightly longer than the flowers. Calyx-lobes about 1.5 mm long, broadly ovate, puberulous without; the glandular scales alternating with the lobes triangular, about half as long as the lobes. Corolla at first pale yellow, afterwards orange-pink, finally purplish-grey; the tube 0.3 cm long, the lobes 1–1.2 cm long, oblong. Corona of three series, shorter than the stamens, glabrous; epipetalous segments rather narrow, adnate to the corolla-lobes, the alternipetalous ones bifid; alternating supplementary segments solitary, simple, as long as the others. Anthers rather stout, about 7 mm long. Carpels densely pubescent at the tips, connate into a cylindrical, longitudinally grooved fruit when young, distinct except for the points and dehiscent along the ventral suture of the merocarps when ripe, 18–22 cm long and 0.7–0.9 cm in diameter, produced at the apex into a slender, acute beak, smooth and finally glabrous.

D i s t r. Endemic in Ceylon. Known from a single station in the intermediate zone only: Doluwa Kande, a hill about 8 miles north of Kurunegala. The treelet has not been collected since 1893.

E c o l. Flowering in May, fruiting in September.

S p e c i m e n s   E x a m i n e d. KURUNEGALA DISTRICT: Doluwa Kande, *Trimen 36 & 37* (both PDA), *Trimen s.n.* Oct. 1892 & 1893 (K, PDA).

18. CLEGHORNIA

Wight, Ic. Pl. Ind. Or. 4 (2): 5, t. 1310. 1848. Type Species: *Cleghornia acuminata* Wight.

Slender, moderately woody twiners with opposite, elliptic, obovate or oblong-lanceolate leaves. Lateral veins fairly numerous, diverging almost horizontally from the midrib. Flowers in rich, peduncled cymes, terminal or lateral from between the petioles. Calyx with five glandular scales within; the lobes oblong, obtuse, with a narrow, scariose margin. Corolla orange-yellow, glabrous without; the tube short-cylindrical, the lobes half as long as the tube, obliquely ovate-oblong, obtuse to almost acute, in bud overlapping to the right. Stamens inserted near the base of the corolla-tube, with very short filaments; anthers lanceolate-sagittate, acute, adnate to the style-apex, included in the corolla-tube, produced at the base into two tails deprived of pollen. Disk large, fleshy, annular. Merocarps distinct, long and slender, tapering to the apex, obtuse, dry and dehiscent along the ventral suture. Seeds numerous, narrowly lanceolate, compressed, short-beaked, with scanty endosperm and with a tuft of hairs at one end, brown.

Two or three species in Ceylon and Malesia.

Cleghornia acuminata Wight, Ic. Pl. Ind. Or. 4 (2): 5, t. 1310. 1848; Thw., Enum. Pl. Zeyl. 194. 1860. Type: Herb. *Wight* propr. *s.n.* (K).

Cleghornia cymosa Wight, Ic. Pl. Ind. Or. 4 (2): 5. 1848.
Baissea acuminata (Wight) Hook. f., Fl. Br. Ind. 3: 663. 1882; Trimen, Handb.
   Fl. Ceylon 3: 140. 1895.

Petiole 0.7–2 cm long. Leaf-blade 5–13 cm long and 2–5 cm wide, widest in or above the middle, cuneate at the base, suddenly contracted at the apex into a narrowly linear acumen; firmly membranous; dried leaf with the midrib narrowly channelled on the upper side, prominent on the lower side; lateral veins faintly impressed above, flat or scarcely elevated beneath; reticulate venation not sculptured on either side, not visible from above. Pedicels up to three times as long as the calyx. Calyx-lobes about 1 mm long. Corolla-tube 0.2–0.3 cm long. Merocarps 20–30 cm long, about 0.5 cm in diameter, glabrous.

D i s t r. Endemic in the hill country of Ceylon. According to Trimen, common at an elevation of 2000 to 5000 ft, but having become rather rare within the last decades.

S p e c i m e n s   E x a m i n e d. MATALE DISTRICT: mile 37 of Rattota-Illukkumbura Road, 950 m, *Huber 711* (HBG, PDA, US), *Jayasuriya 286* (PDA). KANDY DISTRICT: Kadugannawa, *Silva 89* (PDA); Kadugannawa, Poilakande, along rocky embankment of tributary of Hingula Oya, c. 550 m, *Cramer 4212* (PDA, US); Doublecutting Road between Laxapana and Maskeliya, 900 m, *Kostermans 24064* (PDA, US); Kotagala hill, just outside of Hatton (5 miles from Hatton on road to Nuwara Eliya), *Burtt & Townsend 70* (PDA). KALUTARA DISTRICT: "Kalutara Prov." *s. coll. C.P. 1861* at least partly (PDA). BADULLA DISTRICT: Jungle below Hakgala on way to former Fort Macdonald, 25 Apr. 1906, *Smith s.n.* (PDA). RATNAPURA DISTRICT: Kuruwita Kande, 29 March 1919, *Silva s.n.* (PDA); along pilgrims path to Adam's Peak, 350–400 m, *Bernardi 14142* (PDA). LOCALITY UNKNOWN: *Champion s.n.* (K), *Gardner 555* (K), *Macrae 103* (BM), *Macrae 545* (BM), *Moon 113* (BM), *s. coll. C.P. 1861* (BM, K), *Walker s.n.* (K).

19. ANODENDRON

A. DC. in DC., Prod. 8: 443. 1844. Type species: *Anodendron paniculatum* (Roxb.) A. DC.

Woody twiners with watery sap turning green and opposite, elliptic, ovate-oblong or oblong-lanceolate leaves. Lateral veins rather numerous, including with the midrib an angle of about 60°. Flowers in diffuse, peduncled cymes, terminal or lateral from between the petioles. Calyx glandular within, the lobes ovate to triangular-ovate, with a whitish, scarious margin, obtuse to acute. Corolla dull orange, glabrous without; the tube shortly cylindrical, the lobes almost twice as long as the tube, narrowly linear, falcate, in bud overlapping to the right. Stamens inserted near the base of the corolla-tube, with very short filaments; anthers lanceolate-sagittate, acute, adnate to the style-apex, included in the tube, produced at the base into two tails deprived of pollen. Disk cupular. Merocarps distinct, stout, broadest near the base, tapering to the apex, obtuse, dry and dehiscent along the ventral suture when ripe. Seeds few, ovate-oblong, compressed, beaked, with endosperm and with a tuft of hairs at one end, brown to black.

At least 17 species in India, Ceylon, the Malay Peninsula and Malesia.

KEY TO THE SPECIES

1 Leaf-blade rather abruptly contracted into the petiole; lateral veins strongly prominent beneath. Pedicels mostly one to three times as long as the calyx. Beak of the seed not exceeding 1 cm...**1. A. manubriatum**
1 Leaf-blade gradually tapering towards the base; lateral veins scarcely prominent beneath. Pedicels usually three to several times as long as the calyx. Beak of the seed 1.5–2.5 cm long..**2. A. rhinosporum**

1. Anodendron manubriatum Merr., Philipp. J. Sci., 7: 333. 1912. Type: Francis de Silva in Herb. Wall. no. *1663* (K-W).

Echites manubriata Wall., Num. List no. 1663. 1829 nom. nud.

Echites paniculata Roxb., [Hort. Beng. 20. 1814 nom. nud.] Fl. Ind. ed. Carey 2: 17. 1832, not *Echites paniculata* Poir. 1812.

Ichnocarpus paniculatus Moon, Cat. 20. 1824 nom. nud.

Anodendron paniculatum (Roxb.) A. DC. in DC., Prod. 8: 444. 1844; Thw., Enum. Pl. Zeyl. 194. 1860; Hook. f., Fl. Br. Ind. 3: 668. 1882; Trimen, Handb. Fl. Ceylon 3: 141. 1895.

A huge twiner, often more than 20 m tall. Petiole 0.7–2 cm long. Leaf-blade 8–17 cm long and 3.5–8 cm wide, widest in or below the middle, abruptly contracted into the petiole and sometimes almost rounded or truncate at the base, shortly and suddenly acuminate but obtuse at the apex, thinly coriaceous; dried leaf with the midrib flat or slightly raised on upper side, strongly prominent beneath; lateral veins not sculptured above, strongly prominent on under surface; reticulate venation not sculptured on either side. Pedicels one to three times as long as the calyx with a few pedicels somewhat longer. Calyx-lobes 0.6–1 mm long, glabrous. Corolla-tube 0.15–0.2 cm long; the lobes slightly falcate. Merocarps 10–14 cm long, 2–3 cm wide, widest above the base, glabrous. Seeds (including beak but not coma) 2–3 cm long, the beak not exceeding 1 cm.

D i s t r. Deccan Peninsula, Ceylon and from Sylhet southwards through the Malay Peninsula to the Philippines.

E c o l. In Ceylon according to Thwaites common in the moist zone up to an elevation of 700 m, but actually rare except for central and southern Matale District, where the plant is frequent.

V e r n. As-wel, Dul, Girandi-dul (S).

S p e c i m e n s E x a m i n e d. KURUNEGALA DISTRICT: Dunkanda, Arankele, *Jayasuriya & Balasubramaniam 529* (PDA, US). MATALE DISTRICT: Rattota Oya (mile 25 of Rattota-Illukkumbura Road), 410 m, *Huber 700* (HBG, PDA, US), *Jayasuriya et al. 415* (PDA, US); Naula-Elahera Road, Huber obs. RATNAPURA DISTRICT: Sinharaja Forest, Rakwana-Depdene Road, *Tirvengadum & Balasubramaniam 337* (PDA, US). LOCALITY UNKNOWN: *Macrae 687* (BM), *Moon 596* (BM), *s. coll. C.P. 1843* (BM, K, PDA).

2. Anodendron rhinosporum Thw., Enum. Pl. Zeyl. 194. 1860; Hook. f., Fl. Br. Ind. 3: 669. 1882; Trimen, Handb. Fl. Ceylon 3: 141. 1895. Type: *s. coll. C.P. 2579* (K).

Petiole 0.7–1.4 cm long. Leaf-blade 6–12 cm long and 1.8–4 cm wide, widest in or above the middle, cuneate at the base, short-acuminate and obtuse at the apex, thinly coriaceous; dried leaf with the midrib impressed on upper side, prominent on under surface; lateral veins and reticulate venation prominent on upper surface, not sculptured and hardly visible beneath. Pedicels usually three to several times as long as the calyx. Calyx-lobes 0.5–0.8 mm long, glabrous. Corolla-tube 0.12–0.15 cm long; the lobes strongly falcate. Merocarps 7–12 cm long, slightly narrower than in *A. manubriatum*, glabrous. Seeds (including the beak but not the coma) 2.5–4.5 cm long, the beak 1.5–2.5 cm long.

D i s t r. Endemic in Ceylon. A rare plant of the hill country with an outlying station on Ritigala Kande.

S p e c i m e n s E x a m i n e d. ANURADHAPURA DISTRICT: Summit of Ritigala Kande, 24 March 1905, *Willis s.n.* (PDA); Ritigala Strict Natural Reserve, 1950 ft, *Jayasuriya 2149* (PDA, US). KEGALLE DISTRICT: Ambagamuwa, *s. coll. C.P. 2579* partly (PDA). NUWARA ELIYA DISTRICT: Maturata, *s. coll. C.P. 2579* partly (BM, K, PDA).

20. ICHNOCARPUS

R. Br., Mem. Wern. Nat. Hist. Soc. 1: 61. 1811, prepr. 1810. Type Species: *Apocynum frutescens* L.

Slender, moderately woody twiners with brown-tomentose branches, petioles and inflorescences. Leaves opposite, ovate-elliptic or obovate, with very few lateral veins including with the midrib an angle of 45–60°; glabrous above, pubescent beneath, especially on the veins. Flowers in elongate, rusty-pubescent panicles composed of small, dichasially branched, sessile or peduncled cymes. Calyx with five glandular scales within or scales absent; the lobes oblong-ovate. Corolla white, puberulous on outside of tube, at least towards the base; tube short-cylindrical, slightly wider in or little below the middle; the lobes a little longer than the tube, oblong, minutely apiculate, in bud overlapping to the right. Stamens inserted in the widened portion of the tube, with very short filaments; anthers lanceolate-sagittate, acute, adnate to the style-apex, included in the corolla-tube; produced at the base into two tails deprived of pollen. Disk five-lobed. Merocarps distinct, long and very slender, cylindrical, tapering to the apex, dry and dehiscent along the ventral suture when ripe. Seeds numerous, linear, compressed, with endosperm and with a tuft of hairs at one end, blackish-brown.

A genus of 10 species ranging from the western Himalayas to Ceylon, South China, the Philippines and Queensland.

Ichnocarpus frutescens (L.) R. Br. in Ait. f., Hort. Kew. ed. 2, 2: 69. 1811; Thw., Enum. Pl. Zeyl. 194. 1860; Hook. f., Fl. Br. Ind. 3: 669. 1882; Trimen, Handb. Fl. Ceylon 3: 142. 1895. Type: Herbarium *Hermann* 3: 29 (BM).

Apocynum frutescens L., Sp. Pl. 213. 1753.
Echites frutescens (L.) Roxb., Hort. Beng. 20. 1814.

Petiole 0.3–0.8 cm long. Leaf-blade 3–8 cm long, 1.5–4 cm wide, widest in or slightly above the middle, obtuse or rounded at the base, acute or faintly short-acuminate at the apex, firmly membranous; dried leaf with the midrib and lateral veins faintly impressed on the upper side, both prominent beneath; reticulate venation slightly impressed above and faintly raised beneath or not sculptured at all on either side. Pedicels one to three times as long as the calyx. Calyx-lobes about 0.7 mm long, tomentose. Corolla-tube 0.2–0.3 cm long; the lobes undulate at the margin, glabrous on the outer side, hairy within. Merocarps 5–22 cm long, about 0.2 cm wide, rusty pubescent when young, more or less glabrescent when ripe.

D i s t r. From the western Himalayas to Ceylon and through South East Asia to Australia.

E c o l. In Ceylon common throughout the dry region, especially in scrub-like secondary vegetation, up to an elevation of about 1000 m. Rather scattered and probably in secondary vegetation only in the moist region.

V e r n. Gcrandi-wel, Gopi, Priyawarna (S).

N o t e. Macaques feed on the leaves of *Ichnocarpus frutescens* (L.) R. Br. *Hemidesmus indicus* (L.) R. Br. ex Ait. f. and *Toxocarpus kleinii* Wight & Arn. ex Wight are superficially similar but readily distinguished from *Ichnocarpus* even without flowers by their leaves, which are quite glabrous, also on midrib and lateral veins of the under side.

S p e c i m e n s E x a m i n e d. JAFFNA DISTRICT: Nagarkovil, *Waas 240* (PDA, US). VAVUNIYA DISTRICT: 5 miles south of Mullaittivu, sea level, *Meijer 748* (PDA, US). ANURADHAPURA DISTRICT: Borupangoda Rock, *Wass 350* (PDA, US); Kekirawa, Aug. 1885, *Trimen s.n.* (PDA); Mihintale, *Townsend 73/198* (PDA); Maradankadawela, *Simpson 9186* (BM). POLONNARUWA DISTRICT: Polonnaruwa, Sacred Area, 61 m, *Bernardi 14321* (PDA), *Fosberg 51880* (PDA, US), *Hladik 1129* (US), *Ripley 170, 187 & 297* (all US) *& 258 & 285* (both PDA and US); south of Minneriya Tank, 90 m, *Bremer 919* (PDA, S, US). TRINCOMALEE DISTRICT: near Kambakkodai, 30 m, *Bernardi 14224* (PDA); Monkey Bridge, *Waas 1266* (PDA). KURUNEGALA DISTRICT: Baddegama, close to Pitadeniyagala by the Tittawela-Gonagama Road, *Cramer 3589* (PDA, US); eastern slope of Doluwa Kande, 100 m, *Jayasuriya & Balasubramaniam 555* (PDA, US); Kurunegala, 18 Dec. 1883, *Trimen s.n.* (PDA). MATALE DISTRICT: Dambulla, *Huber 766* (US), *Kostermans 23527* (US); east of Dambulla, *Simpson 9808* (BM), Sigiriya, c. 140 m, *Cramer 4903* (PDA). KANDY DISTRICT: Guru Oya, *Kundu & Balakrishnan 172* (US); Hantane, 250 ft, *Gardner 561* (BM, K), *Gardner in C.P. 1863* partly (PDA); Kadugannawa, Belungala Road, c. 600 m, *Cramer 3890* (PDA, US); Mahiyangana, *Stone 11150* (PDA); Moragahamula, *Waas 1012* (PDA); Trinity College Estate, 28 Oct. 1926, *Alston s.n.* (PDA); 2 miles east of Urugala, *Sohmer et al. 8244* (PDA). COLOMBO DISTRICT: Colombo, *s. coll. C.P. 1863* partly (PDA). BATTICALOA DISTRICT: Kathiraveli, *Alston 566* (PDA). BADULLA DISTRICT: Ooma Oya, *s. coll. C.P. 1863* partly (PDA); Bolagandawela village, Ooma Oya, *Silva 272* (PDA). MONERAGALA DISTRICT: Between Timbolketiya and Tanamalwila, 110 m, *Bernardi 15500* (PDA). HAMBANTOTA DISTRICT: Ranna, *Alston 1289* (PDA). Ruhuna National Park, Block 1, *Cooray & Wirawan 69011810* (US). LOCALITY UNKNOWN: *Champion s.n.* (K), *Fraser 199* (BM), *Macrae 102* (BM), *s. coll. C.P. 1863* (BM, K).

ASCLEPIADACEAE

(by Herbert Huber*)

Type Genus: *Asclepias* L.

Erect, creeping, scrambling or most frequently twining, woody or herbaceous perennials, sometimes succulent; with internal phloem and usually a milky latex; rarely latex scanty or sap watery. Leaves opposite, simple, entire, pinnately veined; sometimes reduced to scales or absent in succulent genera. Flowers with calyx and corolla, actinomorphic (except *Ceropegia* with the corolla-tube mostly curved), 5-merous, bisexual, in determinate, usually lateral inflorescences arising from between the petioles (except *Caralluma*), rarely the inflorescence reduced to a single flower. Sepals shortly connate or almost free, imbricate. Corolla gamopetalous, rotate, campanulate or tubular, the lobes valvate or contorted in bud, rarely imbricate or reduplicate, when contorted overlapping to the right (except *Toxocarpus*). Stamens five, alternating with the corolla-lobes and inserted at the very base of the tube; anthers distinct or connate, adnate to the style-apex, longitudinally dehiscent or opening by terminal slits. Pollen united into waxy masses, corresponding with the content of an anther-sac: the pollen-masses of adjacent loculi of different anthers connected by caudicles to five pollen-carriers derived from the angle of the style-apex and concealing the stigmatic tissue. Corona of one or two series, attached to the corolla or to the staminal column or to the corolla-tube or the outer series to the corolla and the inner to the staminal column. Disk absent. Carpels two, superior, multi-ovulate, free but joined by their common style: the latter much thickened at the apex. Fruit consisting of two distinct, many-seeded merocarps; dry, dehiscent along the ventral suture, sometimes solitary by abortion. Seeds with scanty endosperm, with a tuft of hairs at one end, without an aril.

More than 250 genera with about 3000 species, mainly in the tropics and in warm-temperate regions, most abundant in Africa south of the equator. In Ceylon, 22 genera indigenous with 40 species. Five or six species seem to be endemic: *Bidaria celsicola* Huber, *B. cuspidata* (Thunb.) Huber, *Brachystelma lankanum* Dassanayake & Jayasuriya, *Ceropegia parviflora* Trimen, *Ceropegia taprobanica* Huber and *Gymnema rotundatum* Thw.

The genera represented in the flora of Ceylon may be arranged as follows:

*Fachbereich Biologie der Universität Kaiserslautern, Germany.

73

Tribe **Asclepiadeae:** *Calotropis, Cynanchum, Holostemma, Sarcostemma, Oxystelma, Pentatropis, Pergularia, (Asclepias, Gomphocarpus).*

Tribe **Secamoneae:** *Secamone, Toxocarpus.*

Tribe **Marsdenieae:** *Tylophora, Gymnema, Bidaria, Marsdenia, Cosmostigma, Heterostemma, Wattakaka, Hoya, Dischidia.*

Tribe **Ceropegieae:** *Leptadenia, Brachystelma, Ceropegia, Caralluma.*

In the tribe Secamoneae according to Sawfat (1962) all four pollen-sacs are fertile, whereas otherwise in Asclepiadaceae only two pollen-sacs remain fertile, the two other pollen-sacs having become transformed into horny grooves leading the respective organs of visiting insects to the pollen-carrier. Based on this character, the family has been divided into two subfamilies, Secamonoideae and Asclepiadoideae. This division, however, is somewhat arbitrary, neglecting the even more fundamental differences between the tribe Asclepiadeae with their pollen-sacs embedded in the basal part of the anther, and the rest of the family with the pollen-sacs embedded in the apical portion of the anther.

Also phytochemical observations substantiate the distinction of the tribe Asclepiadeae from the other tribes and its primary position in this family. In Asclepiadeae, cardiotoxic glycosides are widely distributed (e.g., in *Asclepias curassavica* L., *Calotropis gigantea* (L.) R. Br. in Aiton f., *Gomphocarpus physocarpus* E. Mey., *Pergularia daemia* (Forsk.) Chiov.), indicating a rather close affinity with Periplocaceae and Apocynaceae, particularly with the subfamily Apocynoideae. In the tribes Marsdenieae and Ceropegieae these cardiotoxic glycosides are gradually replaced by more specialized types of picric substances, related to condurangine.

Most Asclepiadaceae are plants of a rather dry climate or of a climate with a pronounced dry season. In spite of the fact that the family is represented in Ceylon by only two truly geophytic species (i.e. *Brachystelma lankanum* Dassanayake & Jayasuriya and *Ceropegia candelabrum* L.), some Asclepiadaceae are frequently met with in areas where the vegetation is repeatedly destroyed by fire. A few species confine themselves to the moist parts of the island and the hill country and some of them have become very rare or even extinct within this century.

The following two species have become naturalized:

Asclepias curassavica L., Sp. Pl. 215. 1753.

An erect, herbaceous plant 0.5–1 m tall, with young stems and inflorescence minutely puberulous. Leaves lanceolate, tapering at both ends, with a short petiole. Flowers in long-peduncled, umbel-like cymes solitary at the nodes. Peduncle shorter than the leaves. Calyx-lobes lanceolate, acute. Corolla red, rotate, 1–1.5 cm in diameter when expanded, glabrous throughout; the lobes reflexed, ovate, much longer than the radius of the united portion, valvate in bud. Corona in one series, consisting of five erect segments attached to the staminal column, not adnate beyond the point of insertion; segments not compressed laterally, concave on the inner face and there bearing a conspicuous, erect tooth. Anthers with the connective produced into a membranous tip. Pollen-masses solitary in each anther-loculus, pendulous. Merocarps fusiform, 7–10 cm long, 1–1.2 cm in diameter, long-tapering and acute at apex, smooth and glabrous.

A native of the West Indies, commonly cultivated and occasionally found as an escape.

V e r n. Kan-kumbala (S).

Gomphocarpus physocarpus E. Mey., Comm. Pl. Afr. Austr. 202. 1838.

A slender treelet 1–2 m tall with young stems and inflorescence pubescent. Leaves narrowly lanceolate, tapering at both ends, short-petioled. Flowers in peduncled, umbel-like cymes solitary at the nodes. Peduncle shorter than the leaves. Calyx-lobes lanceolate, acute. Corolla white, rotate, 1.4–2 cm in diameter; the lobes reflexed, ovate, much longer than the radius of the united portion, densely bearded on the margin, valvate in the bud. Corona in one series, of five erect segments attached to the staminal column, not adnate beyond the point of insertion; the segments folded lengthwise and strongly compressed laterally, without a projection from the inner side but with two rhomboid teeth on the inner edges. Anthers with the connective produced into a membranous tip. Pollen-masses solitary in each anther-loculus, pendulous. Merocarps obliquely ovoid, strongly inflated, 4–7 cm long, 2.5–5 cm in diameter, blunt, covered with long, soft bristles, tomentellous when young, glabrescent when ripe.

A native of South and tropical Africa, escaped from cultivation and naturalized below Hakgala, Badulla District, on the way to the former Fort Macdonald.

KEY TO THE GENERA

1 Leafless or almost leafless succulent plants
  2 Corolla narrowly tubular, inflated at the base; lobes 1.5–2.5 cm long, connate by their tips..**21. Ceropegia** (*juncea*)
  2 Corolla rotate or shallowly campanulate, not swollen at the base; lobes not exceeding 1 cm in length, not connate by their tips
    3 Stem jointed, cylindrical, scrambling and twining. Flowers pale yellowish-green. Corolla-lobes glabrous...**4. Sarcostemma**
    3 Stem not jointed, more or less quadrangular, decumbent, ascending or erect. Flowers purplish-brown or yellow with purple spots and streaks. Corolla-lobes ciliate on the margin or puberulous within...**22. Caralluma**
1 Leaves well developed

4 Cymes arising strictly from the leaf-axils........................(see Periplocaceae)
4 Cymes arising from the node between the petioles
  5 Stem erect, not rooting from the nodes. Plants not epiphytic
    6 Corolla small, 0.3–0.8 cm in diameter. Pollen-masses minute, about as long as wide
      7 Plants without a tuber, mostly more than 20 cm tall. Cymes with several flowers.
        Corolla rotate...**10. Tylophora**
      7 Plants less than 20 cm tall, with a globose or flattened tuber. Cymes 1- to 3-flow-
        ered. Corolla campanulate...................................**20. Brachystelma**
    6 Corolla 1–4.5 cm in diameter. Pollen-masses elongate, narrowly drop-shaped
      8 Leaves oblong, obovate or panduriform, 3–8 cm wide, glaucous, cordate at the base.
        Corolla 3–4.5 cm wide, pale violet, rarely white....................**1. Calotropis**
      8 Leaves lanceolate, much narrower, not glaucous, tapering at both ends. Corolla 1–
        2 cm in diameter
        9 Corolla red; lobes glabrous. Corona-segments not compressed laterally. Mero-
          carps fusiform, smooth...**Asclepias**
        9 Corolla white: lobes bearded on the margin. Corona-segments strongly compres-
          sed laterally. Merocarps obliquely ovoid, echinate with long, soft bristles.......
          ....**Gomphocarpus**
  5 Stem twining, scrambling, prostrate or creeping, occasionally rooting from nodes and
    internodes
    10 Pollen-masses solitary and pendulous in each anther-loculus; anthers with the con-
      nective ending in a membranous tip. Flowers in sessile or peduncled, umbel- or ra-
      ceme-like cymes solitary at the nodes. Corolla glabrous without; the lobes not
      connate by their tips
      11 Corolla salver-shaped; the lobes densely pilose within. Merocarps echinate with
        long bristles. Pollen-masses with a narrow hyaline margin reaching from the in-
        sertion of the caudicle to the distal end..........................**7. Pergularia**
      11 Corolla rotate or shallowly campanulate. Merocarps smooth. Pollen-masses with-
        out pellucid margin
        12 Corona in one series, cup-shaped, the segments connate at least in their lower
          half, arising from the very base of the corolla-tube, not attached to the staminal-
          column. Petiole 1 to about 7 cm long
          13 Flowers small, not exceeding 1 cm in diameter when expanded. Merocarps slen-
            der, long-tapering to an acute apex. Frequently with a pair of small, roundish
            leaves in the leaf-axils...................................**2. Cynanchum**
          13 Flowers 2–3.5 cm in diameter when expanded. Merocarps stout, tapering to a
            blunt apex. Without roundish leaves in the leaf-axils...........**3. Holostemma**
        12 Corona in two series: outer series a short, entire annulus, inner series consisting
          of five distinct segments attached to the staminal column. Petiole 0.2–1 cm long
          14 Inflorescence long-peduncled, lax, raceme-like. Corolla 2–3 cm in diameter.
            Outer corona pubescent. Merocarps stout. Leaf-blade 3–10 cm long, ovate-lan-
            ceolate to linear-lanceolate..................................**5. Oxystelma**
          14 Inflorescence sessile or short-peduncled, umbel-like. Corolla 0.7–1.2 cm in dia-
            meter. Outer corona glabrous. Merocarps slender. Leaf-blade 1–3.5 cm long,
            ovate or oblong...**6. Pentatropis**
    10 Pollen-masses solitary or paired in each anther-loculus, ascending or rarely the cau-
      dicles ascending and the pollen-masses pendulous; the latter in this case very small
      and roundish
      15 Flowers in dichasially branched, dense or lax cymes; the latter sometimes apparent-
        ly paired at the nodes by suppression of the peduncle. Pollen-masses without a
        pellucid margin

16 Corolla-lobes as long as or shorter than the tube. Pollen-masses solitary in each anther-loculus

17 Corona consisting of five scales adnate to the corolla-tube between the lobes. Petiole 0.4–1.2 cm, very rarely up to 3 cm long.....................**11. Gymnema**

17 Corona consisting of five flat segments adnate to the staminal column. Petiole 3–9 cm long..**13. Marsdenia**

16 Corolla-lobes longer than the tube. Corona consisting of five segments adnate to the staminal column

18 Calyx-segments acute, glabrous or not. Pollen-masses solitary in each anther-loculus. Style-apex short..**10. Tylophora**

18 Calyx-segments obtuse, pubescent. Pollen-masses paired in each anther-loculus

19 Stem glabrous. Corolla small, 0.3–0.5 cm in diameter; corolla-lobes overlapping to the right. Style-apex short....................................**8. Secamone**

19 Stem rusty puberulous when young. Corolla 1–1.5 cm diameter when expanded; corolla-lobes overlapping to the left. Style-apex elongate, fusiform.............. ....**9. Toxocarpus**

15 Cymes umbel- or raceme-like, sessile or peduncled, never bifid, always solitary at the nodes. Pollen-masses solitary in each anther-loculus

20 Corolla densely mealy-puberulous without; the lobes with the margins replicate, keeled on the inside with the keel produced into a tooth projecting inwards. Corona double; outer series attached to the corolla-tube....................**19. Leptadenia**

20 Corolla glabrous or rarely sparsely pubescent without; the lobes without a tooth.

21 Corolla tubular, salver-shaped or urceolate; the lobes usually about as long as or shorter than the tube

22 Corolla tubular, more or less ventricose at the base; lobes connate by their tips. Corona double, not attached to the corolla-tube...................**21. Ceropegia**

22 Corolla-lobes not coherent by their tips. Corona of one series only.

23 Stem not radicant; internodes with two lines of pubescence. Leaves 3–15 cm long, not succulent. Corolla salver-shaped. Corona reduced to five double ridges adnate to the corolla-tube..**12. Bidaria**

23 Stem rooting at nodes and internodes, quite glabrous. Leaves up to 1 cm long. Corolla urceolate. Corona of five segments attached to the staminal column..... ....**18. Dischidia**

21 Corolla rotate or almost rotate; lobes not coherent by their tips. Corona of one series, not adnate to the corolla

24 Stem rooting from nodes and internodes. Leaves fleshy; petiole up to 1 cm long. Corona-segments turgid, entire, stellately spreading, without an appendage....... ....**17. Hoya**

24 Stem not radicant. Leaves not or scarcely fleshy

25 Corona-segments with a fleshy tooth at the apex which projects horizontally inwards. Inflorescence many-flowered, long-peduncled. Corolla green. Merocarps stout, longitudinally ridged....................................**16. Wattakaka**

25 Corona-segments without an apical tooth projecting inwards. Merocarps smooth

26 Calyx-lobes acute. Corona-segments entire, not spreading nor appendaged. Merocarps slender...**10. Tylophora**

26 Calyx-lobes obtuse. Corona-segments not as above, spreading

27 Inflorescence peduncled, at first umbel-like, soon becoming raceme-like. Corolla-lobes much longer than the tube, contorted in bud. Corona segments flat, bifid or truncate, not appendaged. Merocarps stout, blunt.............. ....**14. Cosmostigma**

27 Inflorescence sessile or very short-peduncled, umbel-like. Corolla-lobes as long as or
   slightly longer than the tube, valvate in bud. Corona-segments laterally compressed,
   with a fleshy dorsal appendage. Merocarps slender, acute.........**15. Heterostemma**

1. CALOTROPIS

R. Br., Mem. Wern. Nat. Hist. Soc. 1: 39. 1811, prepr. 1810. Type Species:
Asclepias procera Ait.

Shrubby treelets with young stems and inflorescences cottony pubescent.
Leaves oblong, obovate or panduriform, rather thick, cottony tomentose
when young, frequently glabrescent when fully developed. Flowers in long-
peduncled, umbel-like or furcate cymes solitary at the nodes. Calyx-lobes
ovate, acute. Corolla pale violet or occasionally pure white, rotate, glabrous;
the lobes much longer than the radius of the united portion, ovate, valvate in
bud. Corona in one series, of five segments adnate to the staminal column for
their total length, strongly compressed laterally, keeled on the back, with two
small teeth just below the top and a spur curved upwards at the base.
Anthers with the connective produced into a membranous tip; pollen-masses
solitary in each anther-loculus, pendulous, elongate, drop-shaped, without a
pellucid margin. Merocarps half-ovoid, thick and fleshy, slightly corrugated.
    Three species in northern Africa, Arabia and tropical Asia, mainly in arid
regions.

Calotropis gigantea (L.) R. Br. in Ait. f., Hort. Kew. ed. 2, 2: 78. 1811; Thw.,
Enum. Pl. Zeyl. 196. 1860; Hook. f., Fl. Br. Ind. 4: 17. 1883; Trimen, Handb.
Fl. Ceylon 3: 148. 1895. Type: Herbarium Hermann 2: 74 (BM).

Asclepias gigantea L., Sp. Pl. 214. 1753.

Stems 1–5 m high. Petiole 0.3–2 cm long. Leaf-blade 6–18 cm long and
3–8 cm wide, cordate at the base, acute, rarely rounded at the apex, glaucous
green. Peduncles shorter than to as long as the leaves. Calyx-lobes 3–4 mm
long, puberulous. Corolla 3–4.5 cm in diameter. Merocarps 7–10 cm long
and 2.5–4 cm broad, glabrous.

    D i s t r. From Pakistan and Nepal through India to Ceylon, the Maldive
Islands (Hulula), South China and Malesia.
    E c o l. Common in disturbed vegetation and in waste places throughout
the dry and arid parts of Ceylon, less frequently as a weed in the humid zone.
Confined to the low country. Flowering all the year.
    U s e s. According to Trimen the bark of the root is used in medicine as a
tonic and the milky juice is given as a remedy for leprosy. A fine fibre is
obtained from the stem.

V e r n.   Ela-wara, Hela-wara, Wara (S); Manakkovi, Errukalai, Urkkovi (T).

S p e c i m e n s E x a m i n e d.   MANNAR DISTRICT: Giant's Tank, *Gardner* in *C.P. 1830* partly (PDA); Madhu Road, *Kostermans 25232* (PDA). ANURADHAPURA DISTRICT: Mihintale Sanctuary, *Sohmer 8126* (PDA); between Maragahawewa and the Wilpattu National Park, *Huber 9* (PDA, US); Wilpattu National Park, Kali Villu, *Mueller-Dombois 67051814* (PDA); Wilpattu National Park, Malimaduwa, *Wirawan et al. 1140* (PDA, US). TRINCOMALEE DISTRICT: Trincomalee, *Worthington 1102* (K); Sandy Cove, *Worthington 2664* (K); 5 miles north of Trincomalee, *Theobald & Grupe 2326* (PDA); between Nilaveli and Trincomalee, *Comanor 801* (PDA). PUT-TALAM DISTRICT: Karaitivu Island, 2 m, *Grupe 111* (PDA, US); Mara-wila, *Kundu & Balakrishnan 549* (PDA). MATALE DISTRICT: Dambulla, along road to Wewala Tank, *Sumithraarachchi 449* (PDA); Sigiriya, *Reitz 30022* (PDA). RATNAPURA DISTRICT: Ratnapura, *Singho s.n.* (PDA); Chandrika Wewa near Embilipitiya, *Waas & Eliezer 8834* (PDA); Kolonna Korale, 150 m, *Bernardi 14158* (PDA, US). BADULLA DISTRICT: Kurundu Oya, July 1890, *Trimen s.n.* (PDA). AMPARAI DISTRICT: Padiyatalawa, *Huber 40* (PDA, US). GALLE DISTRICT: Galle, *Champion s.n.* (K); Fort of Galle, *Huber 16* (PDA, US). HAMBANTOTA DISTRICT: Ruhuna National Park, Block 1, *Mueller-Dombois & Cooray 67121008* (BISH); Ruhuna National Park, Katagamuwa, *Cooray 68102301* (PDA); Ruhuna National Park, Pata-nagala Beach, *Mueller-Dombois 67082505* (PDA).

2. CYNANCHUM

L., Sp. Pl. 212. 1753. Type Species: *Cynanchum acutum* L.

Twining, glabrous or puberulous herbs with triangular, ovate or lanceo-late leaves. Flowers in rather short-peduncled, umbel-like cymes solitary at the nodes. Calyx-lobes ovate-lanceolate, acute. Corolla greenish or purple-brown, rotate, glabrous; the lobes much longer than the radius of the united portion, ovate-oblong, contorted in bud. Corona in one series with the segments connate at least in the lower half or the lower two-thirds, cup-shaped, distally lobed, arising from the very base of the corolla. Anthers with the connective produced into a membranous tip; pollen-masses solitary in each anther-loculus, pendulous, without a pellucid margin. Merocarps fusi-form, long-tapering to the apex, smooth.

A large genus widely distributed throughout the warmer regions of the Old World including Australia.

KEY TO THE SPECIES

1 Stem puberulous at the nodes, with two longitudinal lines of pubescence at the inter-

nodes, at least when young. Peduncle with one line of pubescence. Pedicels puberulous. Leaves ovate-lanceolate...1. C. alatum
1 Stem, peduncle and pedicels quite glabrous. Leaves triangular-ovate...2. C. tunicatum

1. Cynanchum alatum Wight & Arn. ex Wight, Contr. Bot. India 57. 1834; Hook. f., Fl. Br. Ind. 4: 23. 1883; Alston in Trimen, Handb. Fl. Ceylon 6: 194. 1931. Type: Herb. Wight propr. *1552* (K).

Cynoctonum alatum (Wight) Decne. in DC., Prod. 8: 529. 1844.

Stem puberulous at the nodes and at the internodes, here the pubescence confined to two longitudinal lines, sometimes glabrescent with age. Leaves frequently with a pair of small, round leaves in their axil. Petiole 1–3 cm long, puberulous along the upper side. Leaf-blade 3–6 cm long, 0.7–2 cm wide, shallowly cordate with a rather narrow sinus or almost truncate at the base, acute and acuminate at the apex, glabrous or almost glabrous when fully developed. Peduncle mostly shorter than the petiole, with a longitudinal line of pubescence. Pedicels puberulous. Calyx-lobes about 1.5 mm long, slightly puberulous. Corolla purplish-brown, 0.5–0.6 cm in diameter. Merocarps as in *Cynanchum tunicatum*.

D i s t r. Mountains of the southern Deccan Peninsula and of Ceylon. In Ceylon known only from two places, both on the eastern slope of the main block in the moist or intermediate region.

E c o l. Flowering from January to May.

N o t e. The species has not been collected in Ceylon since 1906.

S p e c i m e n s   E x a m i n e d. NUWARA ELIYA DISTRICT: Maturata, *Trimen 39* (PDA). BADULLA DISTRICT: Hakgala, *Simpson 9075* (BM, PDA), *Smith s.n.* 3 May 1906 (PDA). LOCALITY UNKNOWN: *Gardner s.n.* (K).

2. Cynanchum tunicatum (Retz.) Alston in Trimen, Handb. Fl. Ceylon 6: 194. 1931. Type: *Koenig s.n.* (LD holotype not seen, BM isotype).

Periploca tunicata Retz., Obs. Bot. 2: 15. 1781.
Cynanchum pauciflorum R. Br., Mem. Wern. Nat. Hist. Soc. 1: 45. 1811, prepr. 1810; Hook. f., Fl. Br. Ind. 4: 23. 1883; Trimen, Handb. Fl. Ceylon 3: 151. 1895.
Cynoctonum pauciflorum (R. Br.) Decne. in DC., Prod. 8: 528. 1844; Thw., Enum. Pl. Zeyl. 195. 1860.

Stem glabrous. Leaves mostly with a pair of roundish leaves of about 1 cm in diameter in their axils. Petiole 2–7 cm long, glabrous. Leaf-blade 5–10 cm long and 3–6 cm wide, cordate at the base with a widely open sinus, acuminate and very acute at the apex, glabrous. Peduncle shorter than the petioles, glabrous. Pedicels glabrous. Calyx-lobes 1.5–3 mm long, glabrous.

Corolla greenish-white, sometimes suffused with purple, 0.6–0.9 cm in diameter. Merocarps 4–7 cm long, about 1 cm in diameter, glabrous.

D i s t r. Deccan Peninsula southwards from the Konkan; Ceylon.

E c o l. A plant of the dry region, twining in hedges and fences. According to Thwaites very common in the Central Province but now rare. Flowering from November to March.

V e r n. Kan-kumbala (S); name also used for *Asclepias curassavica* L., *Pygeum* and *Turpinia.*

S p e c i m e n s E x a m i n e d. ANURADHAPURA DISTRICT: Maha-Illuppallama, *Huber 47* (PDA, US), *Silva 82* (PDA). BATTICALOA DISTRICT: Valaichchenai, *Balasubramaniam 253* (PDA). MATALE DISTRICT: Dambulla, *Fosberg & Balakrishnan 53383* (US). KANDY DISTRICT: Deltota, *s. coll. C.P. 2466* (BM, PDA).

3. HOLOSTEMMA

R. Br., Mem. Wern. Nat. Hist. Soc. 1: 42. 1811, prepr. 1810. Type Species: *Holostemma annulare* (Roxb.) Schum.

Large, herbaceous or slightly woody twiners with glabrous stems and inflorescences. Leaves rather thick, cordate, puberulous on the veins beneath. Flowers in poor, short-racemiform, peduncled cymes solitary at the nodes. Calyx-lobes ovate, obtuse. Corolla purplish-crimson, shallowly cup-shaped, glabrous; the lobes about twice as long as the radius of the united portion, ovate-elliptic, contorted in the bud. Corona in one series, cup-shaped, entire, arising from the very base of the corolla. Anthers very large, with the connective produced into a membranous tip; pollen-masses solitary in each anther-loculus, pendulous, without a pellucid margin. Merocarps stout, oblong-fusiform, slightly tapering to a very blunt apex.

A few species in India and China.

Holostemma annulare (Roxb.) Schum. in Pflanzenfam. 4 (2): 250. 1895. Type: Rheede, Hort. Mal. 9, t. 7. 1689.

Asclepias annularia Roxb., Hort. Beng. 20. 1814, based on Rheede.
Holostemma ada-kodien Schult., Syst. Veg. 6: 95. 1820.
Sarcostemma annulare Roth, Nov. Pl. Sp. 178. 1821.
Holostemma rheedianum Spreng., Syst. Veg. 1: 851. 1825.
Holostemma rheedei Wall., [Num. List 4409. 1828 nom. nud.] Pl. As. Rar. 2: 51. 1831; Hook. f., Fl. Br. Ind. 4: 21. 1883; Trimen, Handb. Fl. Ceylon 3: 150. 1895.

Petiole 2–6 cm long. Leaf-blade 6–12 cm long, 2–8 cm wide, short-acuminate and very acute at the apex. Peduncle shorter than the petioles.

Calyx-lobes about 3 mm long. Corolla 2–3.5 cm wide. Merocarps 8–14 cm long and about 4 cm in diameter, deeply furrowed along each side, glabrous.

D i s t r. Tropical Himalayas, southern Deccan Peninsula, Ceylon and Burma. In Ceylon known from a few places only, probably all in Uva Province.

E c o l. Flowering in January.

S p e c i m e n s E x a m i n e d. BADULLA DISTRICT: Ekiriyankumbura, June 1901, *s. coll. s.n.* (PDA). BADULLA or MONERAGALA DISTRICT: Between Bibile and Ekiriyankumbura, 19 Jan. 1888, *Trimen s.n.* (PDA). MONERAGALA DISTRICT: Nilgala, *s. coll. C.P. 3582* (PDA), *Trimen s.n.* 15 June 1888 (PDA).

4. SARCOSTEMMA

R. Br., Mem. Wern. Nat. Hist. Soc. 1: 50. 1811, prepr. 1810. Type Species: *Cynanchum viminale* L.

Scrambling and twining, succulent plants, woody at the base, with glabrous, cylindrical, fleshy, stems; leafless or the leaves reduced to minute, deciduous scales. Flowers in sessile, umbel-like, puberulous clusters solitary at the nodes. Calyx-lobes ovate, acute. Corolla pale or yellowish green, rotate or shallowly campanulate, glabrous; the lobes much longer than the radius of the united portion, ovate-oblong, slightly contorted in the bud. Corona in two series, the outer a glabrous, lobed annulus arising from the base of the staminal column, the inner of five ovoid segments attached to the staminal column. Anthers with the connective produced into a membranous tip; pollen-masses solitary in each anther-loculus, pendulous, without a pellucid margin. Merocarps narrowly fusiform, smooth.

If construed in a narrow sense, the genus *Sarcostemma* comprises about a dozen species native to Africa, tropical Asia and Australia. They are all succulent, almost leafless xerophytes. *Oxystelma*, included in *Sarcostemma* by Holm (1950), is maintained as a separate genus here.

Sarcostemma brunonianum Wight & Arn. ex Wight, Contr. Bot. India 59. 1834; Thw., Enum. Pl. Zeyl. 196. 1860; Hook. f., Fl. Br. Ind. 4: 27. 1883; Trimen, Handb. Fl. Ceylon 3: 152. 1895. Type: Herb. Wight propr. *1557* (K).

Sarcostemma viminale Moon, Cat. 20. 1824, not *S. viminale* (L.) R. Br. in Ait. f.

Stems jointed, dark green, with abundant latex. Peduncle absent. Calyx-lobes about 1.5 mm long, puberulous. Corolla 0.8–1.2 cm wide. Merocarps 8–9 cm long, up to 0.5 cm in diameter, glabrous.

D i s t r. Deccan Peninsula and Ceylon.

E c o l. In Ceylon rather common in the dry and arid regions.

V e r n. Muwa-kiriya (S).

S p e c i m e n s E x a m i n e d. ANURADHAPURA DISTRICT: Riti-gala Strict Natural Reserve, southern slope, 1820 ft, *Jayasuriya 850* (PDA); eastern slope of Ritigala Hill, *Sohmer & Sumithraarachchi 10769* (PDA); Wilpattu National Park, *Cooray 69100110* (PDA); same locality, about 2 miles south of Maduru Odai, *Fosberg et al. 50861* (PDA); same locality, near Sadpuda Kallu 2 miles east of Kattankandal Kulam, *Fosberg et al. 50813* (US). TRINCOMALEE DISTRICT: Trincomalee, *Gardner in C.P. 1830* partly (PDA). PUTTALAM DISTRICT: Chilaw, *Simpson 8156* (BM). MATALE DISTRICT: Dambulla Rock, *Kostermans 23535* (PDA). KANDY or NUWARA ELIYA DISTRICT: Between Haragama and Hanguranketa, 14 Oct. 1921, *Silva s.n.* (PDA). BADULLA DISTRICT: Mahiyangana-Padi-yatalawa Road, mile post 51, *Jayasuriya 2111* (PDA). BATTICALOA DISTRICT: Batticaloa, *Gardner in C.P. 1830* partly (PDA); Mankeni, *Waas 2105* (PDA). AMPARAI DISTRICT: Tirukkovil, *Jayasuriya 2041* (PDA). MONERAGALA DISTRICT: Nilgala, Galoya National Park, *Jayasuriya 1957* (PDA); about 25 miles west of Pottuvil along road to Wellawaya, 100 m, *Davidse & Sumithraarachchi 8952* (PDA). HAMBANTOTA DISTRICT: Ruhuna National Park, Block 1, *Cooray 69111733* (PDA); same locality, Butawa Bungalow, *Comanor 374* (PDA), *Fosberg & Sachet 52878* (PDA); same locality, Patanagala, *Fosberg & Sachet 52890* (PDA). DISTRICT UN-KNOWN: On road from Yodakandiya to Bambowa, *Cooray 69042203* (PDA).

5. OXYSTELMA

R. Br., Mem. Wern. Nat. Hist. Soc. 1: 40. 1811, prepr. 1810. Type Species: *Periploca esculenta* L.f.

Twining, glabrous herbs with thin, ovate-lanceolate to linear-lanceolate leaves. Flowers in lax, few-flowered, long-peduncled, raceme-like cymes soli-tary at the nodes. Calyx-lobes lanceolate, acute. Corolla cream-coloured, tinged with purple; shallowly campanulate to almost rotate, glabrous with-out; the lobes about as long as the radius of the united portion, triangular, in bud valvate below, imbricate above. Corona in two series, the outer a densely pubescent, entire annulus at the base of the corolla-tube, the inner of five ovate-lanceolate segments attached to the staminal column and exceeding the anthers. Anthers with the connective produced into a membranous tip; pollen-masses solitary in each anther-loculus, pendulous, without a pellucid margin. Merocarps obliquely ovoid, paired or solitary by abortion.

A genus of two species, native in western tropical Africa, Egypt and India including Ceylon. Holm (1950) united *Oxystelma* with *Sarcostemma*, but this is not followed here: the shallowly lobed corolla, the pubescent outer corona attached to the corolla and the lanceolate tips of the inner corona segments clearly distinguish the two genera.

Oxystelma esculentum (L.f.) R. Br. ex Schult., Syst. Veg. 6: 89. 1820; Thw., Enum. Pl. Zeyl. 196. 1860; Hook. f., Fl. Br. Ind. 4: 17. 1883; Trimen, Handb. Fl. Ceylon 3: 147. 1895. Type: *Koenig* in the Linnaean Herb. *307/7* (LINN).

Periploca esculenta L. f., Suppl. Pl. 168. 1781.
Sarcostemma esculentum (L.f.) Holm, Ann. Missouri Bot. Gard. 37: 482. 1950.

Petiole 0.4–1 cm long. Leaf-blade 3–10 cm long, 0.3–1.5 cm wide, rounded at the base, tapering to and very acute at the apex. Peduncle shorter than or almost as long as the leaves. Calyx-lobes 2–3.5 mm long, glabrous. Corolla 2–3 cm wide, the lobes densely ciliate. Merocarps 6–7 cm long and up to 2 cm in diameter, glabrous.

D i s t r. Egypt, Pakistan, India, Ceylon and Burma.
E c o l. In Ceylon rare in the drier parts of the island, usually near tanks. Flowering throughout the year.
U s e s. The plant is said by Trimen to be employed by the native doctors as a remedy in hydrophobia.
V e r n. Usepale (S); Kulappalai (T).
S p e c i m e n s E x a m i n e d. JAFFNA DISTRICT: Jaffna, *Gardner* in *C.P. 2837* (PDA). MANNAR DISTRICT: about 8 miles northeast of Mantai, *Davidse & Sumithraarachchi 9167* (PDA). ANURADHAPURA DISTRICT: Galkulama, *Jayasuriya & Sumithraarachchi 1601* (PDA). TRINCOMALEE DISTRICT: Mahaweli Ganga North Forest Reserve, *Jayasuriya et al. 635* (PDA). PUTTALAM DISTRICT: Puttalam-Palavi Road, *Cooray 69100606* (PDA, US); about 10 miles from Kalpitiya along road to Palavi, *Sumithraarachchi 708* (PDA, US); Nochchiyagama-Puttalam Road, *Wirawan et al. 1154* (US). HAMBANTOTA DISTRICT: Tissamaharama, *Alston 1290* (PDA), *Simpson 9919* (BM, PDA); Tissamaharama Tank, Dec. 1882, *Trimen s.n.* (PDA).

6. PENTATROPIS

Wight, Contr. Bot. India 53. 1834. Type Species: *Pentatropis microphylla* (Heyne ex Roth) Wight.

Glabrous twiners, herbaceous or slightly woody at the base, with small, fleshy, broadly ovate to oblong leaves. Flowers in poor, sessile or almost sessile, umbel-like cymes solitary at the nodes. Calyx-lobes ovate-lanceolate, acute. Corolla green, suffused with purple on the inner side, rotate, glabrous without; the lobes much longer than the radius of the united portion, ovate-oblong, contorted in bud. Corona of two series: outer series a low, entire annulus, inner series consisting of fives egments attached to the staminal column above its base; segments laterally compressed, produced at the base into a short, radially divergent spur and at the apex into a slender tip appressed to the staminal column. Anthers with the connective ending in a membranous tip; pollen-masses solitary in each anther-loculus, pendulous, without a pellucid margin. Merocarps fusiform, produced into a slender beak, smooth.

A genus of about six species ranging from Africa through Arabia, India and Madagascar to Australia.

Pentatropis capensis (L.f.) Bullock, Kew Bull. 1955: 284. 1955. Type: *Koenig* in the Linnaean Herb. *308/8* (LINN).

Cynanchum capense L.f., Suppl. Pl. 168. 1781.
Asclepias microphylla Heyne ex Roth, Nov. Pl. Sp. 177. 1821.
Cynanchum acuminatum Thunb. (Alner), Obs. in Cynanchum 5. 1821.
Asclepias microphylla Roxb., [Hort. Beng. 85. 1814 nom. nud.] Fl. Ind. ed. Carey 2: 35. 1832.
Pentatropis microphylla (Heyne ex Roth) Wight, Contr. Bot. India 52. 1834; Thw., Enum. Pl. Zeyl. 196. 1860; Hook. f., Fl. Br. Ind. 4: 20. 1883; Trimen, Handb. Fl. Ceylon 3: 149. 1895.

Stems twining, up to 3 m. Petioles 0.2–0.7 cm long. Leaf-blade 1–3.5 cm long and 0.5–2.2 cm wide, rounded or subcordate at the base, obtuse or occasionally acute but always mucronate at the apex. Peduncle 0–2 mm long. Calyx-lobes about 1 mm long, glabrous. Corolla 0.7–1.2 cm in diameter, the lobes glabrous on the margin, minutely puberulous within. Merocarps 4–5 cm long, 0.7–1 cm in diameter, glabrous.

D i s t r. Northeastern and peninsular India, Ceylon. This species does not occur in South Africa as unfortunately suggested by the specific epithet.

E c o l. In Ceylon a common twiner in the coastal scrub of the dry and arid region, never found far from the sea and well adapted to soil salinity as shown by the fleshy leaves. Absent from the humid zone. Flowering from September to April.

U s e s. *Pentatropis capensis* (L.f.) Bullock is appreciated in native medicine as a remedy against diseases of the excretive organs.

N o t e. Similar to *Tylophora tenuissima* (Roxb.) Wight & Arn. ex Wight but easily distinguished by its sessile or very short-peduncled, umbel-like cymes.

S p e c i m e n s E x a m i n e d. JAFFNA DISTRICT: Jaffna, *Gardner* in *C.P. 1853* (PDA); Punakari, Feb. 1890, *Trimen s.n.* (PDA). TRINCOMALEE DISTRICT: Nilaveli, *Bernardi 15304* (PDA); Foul Point, *Simpson 9622*

(PDA). PUTTALAM DISTRICT: Near Puttalam, Aug. 1883, *Trimen s.n.*
(PDA); south end of Puttalam Lagoon, *Fosberg & Jayasuriya 52812* (PDA,
US); mile 73 of Colombo-Puttalam Road, near Madurankuli, *Huber 50*
(PDA, US); Anuradhapura-Puttalam Road, *Kundu 296* (PDA, US). KURU-
NEGALA DISTRICT: Kurunegala, *Gardner* in *C.P. 1853* partly (PDA).
BATTICALOA DISTRICT: Kannankudah Ferry, *Huber 22* (PDA, US),
about 4 miles northwest of Batticaloa, *Davidse & Sumithraarachchi 8976*
(PDA); Keeli-Kudah, *Waas 2139* (PDA). AMPARAI DISTRICT: Karativu,
Huber 24 (PDA, US). HAMBANTOTA DISTRICT: Ruhuna National
Park, Block 1, *Cooray & Balakrishnan 69012103* (PDA, US), *Fosberg &
Mueller-Dombois 50147* (US), *Huber 29* and *32* (both PDA, US), *Mueller-
Dombois & Cooray 69030802* (US), *Mueller-Dombois et al. 67093002* (BISH).
DISTRICT UNKNOWN: Mail Villu, *Mueller-Dombois et al. 69043023*
(PDA, US).

7. PERGULARIA

L., Syst. ed. 12, 191. 1767; L., Mant. 8: 53. 1767. Type Species: *Pergularia
tomentosa* L.

Twining herbs with pubescent, hispid or prickly stems. Leaves cordate,
sparsely to densely tomentose on both sides. Flowers in long-peduncled,
umbel-like to almost raceme-like, pubescent or hispid cymes solitary at the
nodes. Calyx-lobes ovate-lanceolate, acute. Corolla yellowish- or greenish-
white, salver-shaped, glabrous without; the lobes one and a half to twice as
long as the tube, ovate, contorted in the bud. Corona in two series, the outer
a glabrous, five-lobed, denticulate annulus at the base of the staminal
column, the inner consisting of five long segments attached to the staminal
column above its base, produced at the base into a short, radially divergent
spur and at the apex into an acute, lanceolate tooth exceeding the staminal
column. Anthers with the connective ending in a membranous tip; pollen-
masses solitary in each anther loculus, pendulous, with a narrow hyaline
margin reaching from the insertion of the caudicles to the distal end. Merocarps half-ovoid, tapering to a long beak, echinate with long, soft bristles.

Four species in the drier parts of Africa and southern Asia.

Pergularia daemia (Forsk.) Chiov., Result. Sci. Miss. Stefani-Paoli Somal.
Ital. 1: 115. 1916. Type: *Forskal*, not seen (C?).

Asclepias daemia Forsk., Fl. Aegypt.-Arab. 51. 1775.
Cynanchum extensum Jacq., Misc. 2: 353. 1781–82.
Daemia extensa (Jacq.) R. Br. in Ait. f., Hort. Kew. ed. 2, 2: 76. 1811, prepr.
    1810; Thw., Enum. Pl. Zeyl. 196. 1860; Hook. f., Fl. Br. Ind. 4: 20. 1883;
    Trimen, Handb. Fl. Ceylon 3: 150. 1895.

Cynanchum echinatum Thunb. (Alner), Obs. in Cynanchum 8. 1821.
Gomphocarpus volubilis Moon, Cat. 20. 1824 nom. nud.
Daemia cordifolia (Retz.) Schum. in Pflanzenfam. 4 (2): 258. 1895.

Petiole 2–9 cm long. Leaf-blade 3–9 cm long and about as wide, acute or short-acuminate at the apex. Peduncle often exceeding the leaves. Calyx-lobes about 2 mm long, glabrous or puberulous. Corolla 1.2–1.8 cm in diameter, the lobes densely hairy within. Merocarps 5–8 cm long, 1.5–2 cm wide, puberulous, also on the bristles. Chromosome number: $2n = 24$.

D i s t r. Ranging from South and tropical Africa through Arabia to Lower Bengal and Ceylon.

E c o l. Common throughout the dry and arid parts of Ceylon in disturbed vegetation, particularly in hedges and fences near or within villages. Absent from the moist zone and from most of the hill country.

V e r n. Langali, Maha-medahangu, Meda-hangu, Wissani (S); Uttama-kam, Veliparatti (T).

N o t e. The plant contains cardiotoxic glycosides and is said to have emetic properties.

S p e c i m e n s E x a m i n e d. JAFFNA DISTRICT: Jaffna, *Gardner* in *C.P. 1841* partly (PDA); Karaitivu, *Bernardi 15328* (PDA). MANNAR DISTRICT: About half mile inland from the landward end of the causeway to Mannar Island, *Townsend 73/108* (PDA, US). ANURADHAPURA DISTRICT: Anuradhapura, *Alston 1291* (PDA), *Townsend 73/195* (PDA, US); 4 miles north of Anuradhapura, *Hepper & Jayasuriya 4658* (PDA, US); Mihintale Hill, *Kundu & Balakrishnan 343* (PDA); between Anuradhapura and Galkulame, *Huber 10* (PDA, US); Anuradhapura-Trincomalee Road, near mile marker 79, *Sohmer 8157* (PDA); Wilpattu National Park, Kurutu Pandi Villu, *Wirawan W5–26* (US). TRINCOMALEE DISTRICT: North end of Kinniyai Ferry, *Gould & Cooray 13661* (PDA, US); Kuchchaveli Ferry, *Comanor 797* (PDA), *Huber 55* (PDA, US). PUTTALAM DISTRICT: South end of Puttalam Lagoon, *Fosberg & Jayasuriya 52813* (PDA, US); Tabbowa, *Cramer 4075* (PDA). POLONNARUWA DISTRICT: Polonnaruwa Sacred Area, *Ripley 302* (PDA, US). BATTICALOA DISTRICT: Kannankudah Ferry, *Huber 20* (PDA, US); Panichchankeni, *Balakrishnan 366* (PDA, US). MATALE DISTRICT: Just north of Dambulla, *Fosberg & Balakrishnan 53399* (PDA, US). KANDY DISTRICT: Haragama, s. coll. *C.P. 1841* partly (PDA). NUWARA ELIYA DISTRICT: Hanguranketa, s. coll. *C.P. 1841* partly (PDA). BADULLA DISTRICT: Ooma Oya, *Gardner* in *C.P. 1841* partly (PDA). AMPARAI DISTRICT: East side of Ulpasse Wewa, 2 miles north of Panama, *Fosberg & Sachet 52965* (PDA, US); Pottuvil, *Bernardi 16017* (PDA). HAMBANTOTA DISTRICT: Ruhuna National Park, Block 1, *Huber 33* (PDA, US), *Wirawan 682* (PDA); same locality, Patanagala, *Cooray 69111630* (PDA, US); same locality, Butawa Modera, *Fosberg 50296* (US), *Comanor 870* (PDA).

8. SECAMONE

R. Br., Mem. Wern. Nat. Hist. Soc. 1: 55. 1811, prepr. 1810.

Glabrous twiners, herbaceous or slightly woody at the base, with wiry stems. Leaves ovate-lanceolate to linear-lanceolate, slightly coriaceous, glabrous. Flowers in short-peduncled, minutely puberulous, dichasially branched cymes. Calyx-lobes broadly ovate, obtuse. Corolla yellow, rotate, glabrous outside; the lobes much longer than the united portion, ovate, contorted in bud. Corona single, of five erect segments which are compressed laterally and produced at the apex into a triangular point, attached to the staminal column. Anthers with the connective produced into a membranous tip; pollen-masses two in each anther-loculus, ascending, minute, almost orbicular, without a pellucid margin. Style apex short, obtuse, not exceeding the staminal column. Merocarps spindle-shaped, flattened on the ventral side, convex on the back, long-tapering to an acute apex, smooth.

A genus of about 40 species ranging from South and tropical Africa through Madagascar and India to the Philippines and Australia. The structure of the flower of *Secamone* has recently been studied by Sawfat in Ann. Missouri Bot. Gard. 49: 95–119. 1962.

Secamone emetica (Retz.) R. Br. ex Schult., Syst. Veg. 6: 124. 1820; Thw., Enum. Pl. Zeyl. 195. 1860; Hook. f., Fl. Br. Ind. 4: 36. 1883; Trimen, Handb. Fl. Ceylon 3: 146. 1895. Type: *Koenig s.n.* (LD holotype not seen, BM isotype).

Periploca emetica Retz., Obs. 2: 14. 1781.

Petiole 0.1–0.5 cm long. Leaf-blade 3–7 cm long, 0.6–1.8 cm wide, acute at the base, tapering to, and very acute at, the apex. Inflorescence shorter than the leaves; the peduncle, so far developed, exceeding the petioles. Calyx-lobes 0.5–0.7 mm long, puberulous. Buds broadly ovoid. Corolla 0.3–0.5 cm in diameter. Merocarps 4–5.5 cm long, about 0.6 cm wide, glabrous.

D i s t r. Southern Deccan Peninsula and Ceylon. According to K. Schumann also in East Africa.

E c o l. Not uncommon in Ceylon in coastal scrub of the dry and arid zone, usually near the sea; rare inland. Flowering throughout the year.

S p e c i m e n s   E x a m i n e d. JAFFNA DISTRICT: Jaffna, *Gardner in C.P. 1851* partly (PDA); about 12 km south of Pooneryn along road to Mannar, *Bernardi 15336* (PDA). PUTTALAM DISTRICT: Puttalam, July 1884, *Trimen s.n.* (PDA). ANURADHAPURA DISTRICT: Ritigala Strict Natural Reserve, ascent along eastern slope of Wannati Kanda, 1400 ft, *Jayasuriya 1034* (PDA). KURUNEGALA DISTRICT: Kurunegala, *Gardner in C.P. 1851* partly (PDA). MATALE DISTRICT: Palbandiyawa, *Sumithraarachchi 734* (PDA). KANDY DISTRICT: Guruoya, 500 m, *Jayasuriya et al.*

479 (US); Haragama, *Alston 861* (PDA). NUWARA ELIYA DISTRICT: Hanguranketa, *s. coll. C.P. 1851* partly (PDA). BADULLA DISTRICT: Path to Dunhinda Falls, 580 m, *Huber 476* (HBG, PDA, US). AMPARAI DISTRICT: Ruhuna National Park, Kumana, *Jayasuriya 2018* (PDA). MONERAGALA DISTRICT: Between Sellakataragama and Pelessa, *Cooray et al. 69102306* (PDA). HAMBANTOTA DISTRICT: Ruhuna National Park, Block 1, *Huber 30* (PDA, US), *Mueller-Dombois 68101812* (PDA) and *68101904* (PDA), *Mueller-Dombois & Cooray 67121029* (BISH, PDA) and *67121051* (BISH, PDA), *Wirawan 711* (PDA); same locality, Block 2, *Mueller-Dombois & Comanor 67083010* (PDA); same locality, about 2 miles above mouth of Kumbukkan Oya, *Fosberg et al. 51100* (US).

9. TOXOCARPUS

Wight & Arn. ex Wight, Contr. Bot. India 61. 1834. Type Species: *Toxocarpus kleinii* Wight & Arn. ex Wight.

Slender, herbaceous or slightly woody twiners with stem and inflorescence puberulous. Leaves elliptic, obovate or lanceolate, glabrescent above except for midrib and veins which are puberulous, glabrous or rusty puberulous beneath. Flowers in sessile or peduncled, dichasially branched cymes, often by suppression of the peduncle apparently paired at the nodes. Calyx lobes ovate, obtuse. Corolla yellowish-green, sometimes brownish without; tube broadly campanulate, glabrous, the lobes about twice as long as the tube, linear-oblong, recurved, contorted in bud and overlapping to the left. Corona single, consisting of five erect, triangular-lanceolate, dorsally flattened segments attached to the staminal column and appressed to the base of the style-apex. Anthers with the connective produced into a membranous tip; pollen-masses two in each anther-loculus, ascending, minute, almost orbicular, without a pellucid margin. Style apex elongate, fusiform, much longer than the staminal column, reaching the mouth of the corolla tube. Merocarps elongate-fusiform, tapering to an acute apex, smooth.

About a dozen species in tropical Africa, India, Ceylon, Malesia and South China. Included in *Secamone* by Schumann, *Toxocarpus* differs markedly by its dorsally flattened corona segments and the long, narrowly conical or clavate style apex.

Toxocarpus kleinii Wight & Arn. ex Wight, Contr. Bot. India 61. 1834; Thw., Enum. Pl. Zeyl. 195. 1860; Hook. f., Fl. Br. Ind. 4:14. 1883; Trimen, Handb. Fl. Ceylon 3:146. 1895. Type: Herb. Wight propr. *1560* (K).

Petiole 0.7–1.2 cm long. Leaf-blade 4–7 cm long and 1.2–4 cm wide, acute or obtuse at the base, short-acuminate or obtuse at the apex. Inflorescence shorter than the leaves; peduncle, so far developed, as long as or slightly longer than the petiole. Calyx-lobes 1.3–2 mm long, rusty puberulous without. Corolla narrowly conical in bud, 1.5 cm in diameter when expanded. Merocarps 12–15 cm long and about 1 cm wide.

D i s t r. Deccan Peninsula southwards from the Konkan; Ceylon.

E c o l. In Ceylon very rare in the lowland and hill country up to an elevation of 1000 m, both in the dry and the intermediate zone.

N o t e. Without flowers, this species is easily mistaken for *Hemidesmus indicus* (L.) R. Br. or *Ichnocarpus frutescens* (L.) R. Br., both of which differ by the firmer texture of their leaves and the midrib strongly impressed on the upper surface when dried.

S p e c i m e n s E x a m i n e d. NUWARA ELIYA DISTRICT: Hanguranketa, *s. coll. C.P. 2578* (BM, K, PDA). BADULLA DISTRICT: Ekiriyankumbura, *Fosberg & Sachet 53134* (US). GALLE DISTRICT: Galle, *Champion s.n.* (K).

10. TYLOPHORA

R. Br., Mem. Wern. Nat. Hist. Soc. 1: 28. 1811, prepr. 1810. Type Species: *Tylophora flexuosa* R. Br.

Twining, prostrate or rarely erect plants, herbaceous or slightly woody, with the stems, leaves and inflorescences glabrous, pubescent or hairy. Leaves thin or rather fleshy, ovate-oblong or ovate-lanceolate. Flowers in sessile or peduncled, umbel-like or laxly dichasially branched cymes, usually solitary at the nodes; occasionally the cyme reduced to a single flower. Calyx-lobes triangular, ovate or lanceolate, acute. Corolla greenish-yellow, often tinged with purple, or uniformly purple-brown, rotate, glabrous; the lobes little to much longer than the united portion of the tube, ovate, slightly contorted in the bud. Corona single, consisting of five erect, fleshy, triangular segments, adnate to but not exceeding the staminal column. Anthers with the connective produced into a membranous tip; pollen-masses solitary in each anther-loculus, ascending or the caudicles ascending and the pollen-masses pendulous; minute, almost orbicular, without a pellucid margin. Merocarps fusiform, tapering to the apex, smooth.

A difficult and little-understood genus centered in tropical Asia, extending to Africa, Japan and Australia. *Tylophora* is related to *Secamone*, from which it differs mainly by the presence of only one pollen-mass in each anther loculus.

KEY TO THE SPECIES

1 Calyx-lobes 0.5–0.8 mm long. Corolla 3–6 mm in diameter
  2 Internodes with two lines of pubescence alternating at the nodes. Cymes reduced to one or two flowers, rarely with up to four flowers. Corolla about 6 mm in diameter..
....5. T. cordifolia

2 Stem quite glabrous. Flowers more numerous; cymes usually laxly dichasially
   branched. Corolla 3–4 mm in diameter
   3 Stem very slender. Petiole not exceeding 1 cm in length. Leaf-blade 0.4–3.2 cm
      wide. Cymes few-flowered. Merocarps 5–6.5 cm long..............**6. T. tenuissima**
   3 Stem stout. Petiole 1.4–2.5 cm long. Leaf-blade 6–10 cm wide. Cymes many-flowered.
      Merocarps about 12 cm long....................................**7. T. zeylanica**
1 Calyx-lobes (1.2–) 1.5–2.5 mm long. Corolla 6–about 15 mm in diameter
   4 Calyx-lobes lanceolate, three times as long as wide or longer. Corolla 1–1.5 cm in
      diameter. Flowers in an umbel-like cyme or in two superposed umbel-like cymes....
      ....**1. T. indica**
      5 Stem, undersurface of the leaves and inflorescence more or less hairy.....var. **indica**
      5 Stem, leaves and inflorescence quite glabrous.........................var. **glabra**
   4 Calyx-lobes triangular-ovate, hardly up to twice as long as wide. Corolla not reaching
      1 cm in diameter
      6 Stem minutely pubescent when young. Petiole up to 0.7 cm long. Leaf-blade up to
         1.5 cm wide. Flowers in an umbel-like cyme or in two superposed umbel-like cymes
         ....**2. T. fasciculata**
      6 Stem quite glabrous. Petiole 0.7–2.5 cm long. Leaf-blade 1.2–4 cm wide
         7 Leaf-blade firmly membranous, not pellucid when dried. Flowers in an umbel-like
            cyme or more commonly in two superposed umbel-like cymes......**3. T. multiflora**
         7 Leaf-blade thinly membranous, pellucid when dried. Flowers arranged in laxly di-
            chasially branched cymes.....................................**4. T. pauciflora**

1. Tylophora indica (Burm. f.) Merr., Philipp. J. Sci. 19: 373. 1921. Type: not seen.

Cynanchum indicum Burm. f., Fl. Ind. 70. 1768.
Asclepias asthmatica L. f., Suppl. Pl. 171. 1781.
Cynanchum bracteatum Thunb. (Alner), Obs. in Cynanchum 7. 1821.
Hoya hirsuta Moon, Cat. 21. 1824 nom. nud.
Tylophora asthmatica (L.f.) Wight & Arn. ex Wight, Contr. Bot. India 51.
   1834; Thw., Enum. Pl. Zeyl. 197. 1860; Hook. f., Fl. Br. Ind. 4: 44. 1883;
   Trimen, Handb. Fl. Ceylon 3: 153. 1895.

Stem elongate, twining or prostrate, hairy, pubescent or glabrous. Petiole
0.5–2 cm long. Leaf-blade 3.5– about 10 cm long, 1.5–7 cm wide, broadly
ovate to ovate-oblong, rounded, truncate or very shallowly cordate at the
base, acute or obtuse but apiculate at the apex, slightly fleshy, puberulous or
glabrescent above, densely puberulous beneath, or quite glabrous. Inflorescence an umbel-like cyme or sometimes two superposed umbel-like cymes,
hairy, puberulous or glabrous, shorter than to as long as the leaves, sessile or
with a peduncle shorter or longer than the petioles. Calyx-lobes 1.5–2.5 mm
long, lanceolate, hairy or glabrous. Corolla greenish-yellow, frequently tinged
with brown on the inside, 1–1.5 cm in diameter; the lobes slightly longer than
the radius of the united portion. Merocarps 5–10 cm long, about 1 cm wide,
produced into an acute, slender beak.

D i s t r. From the Seychelles through India and Ceylon to Southeast Asia including Malesia.

E c o l. Common along the coasts of Ceylon on sandy soil, particularly on stabilised dunes [here often associated with *Spinifex littoreus* (Burm. f.) Merr.] and in sandy coconut-groves, in the dry part of the island as well as in the moist; rare in the hill country.

Tylophora indica is represented in Ceylon by two varieties which can be distinguished in most cases.

1. var. indica

Stem, leaves, the latter especially beneath, and cymes pubescent or hairy. Flowers greenish, tinged with brown on the inside, about 1 cm wide.

D i s t r. That of the species.

E c o l. This is the common plant in Ceylon except in the southwest, where it is rare.

U s e s. According to Trimen the root of this plant is a valuable substitute for *Ipecacuanha*.

V e r n. Bim-nuga, Bin-nuga, Mi-nuga (S); Nancharapanchan, Pey-palai (T).

S p e c i m e n s E x a m i n e d. JAFFNA DISTRICT: Chavakachcheri, 4 Nov. 1890, *Trimen's collector s.n.* (PDA); Kayts Island, *Bernardi 14272* (PDA); Kurikkaduvan, sea level, *Cramer 3356* (US). MANNAR DISTRICT: Mannar, *Kostermans 24905* (PDA). PUTTALAM DISTRICT: Mile 35 of Colombo-Puttalam Road between Katuneriya and Marawila, *Huber 53* (PDA, US). TRINCOMALEE DISTRICT: Mutur Ferry, *Huber 27* (PDA, US), *Jayasuriya et al. 654* (US); Trincomalee, *Alston 526* (PDA), *s. coll. C.P. 1857* partly (PDA). BATTICALOA DISTRICT: Batticaloa, *Huber 23* (PDA, US); 4 miles northwest of Batticaloa, *Davidse & Sumithraarachchi 8981* (PDA). COLOMBO DISTRICT: Negombo, *Simpson 7915* (PDA), intermediate between var. *indica* and var. *glabra*. KALUTARA DISTRICT: Pelawatte, 9 Oct. 1894, *Trimen's collector s.n.* (PDA); about 1/2 mile north of Pahala Hewessa, 200 ft, *Bremer 809* (PDA). GALLE DISTRICT: Galle, *Gardner* in *C.P. 1857* partly (PDA); Hiyare Reservoir, *Alston 1292* (PDA). RATNAPURA DISTRICT: Bulutota, Muduna Kande Jungle, *Sumithraarachchi 314* (PDA). BADULLA DISTRICT: Haputale, *s. coll. C.P. 3694* (PDA). AMPARAI DISTRICT: Ruhuna National Park East, Kumana, *Jayasuriya 2017* (PDA). HAMBANTOTA DISTRICT: Hambantota, near beach, *Alston 1293* (PDA), intermediate between var. *indica* and var. *glabra*; east of Hambantota on coastal sand dunes, *Fosberg et al. 51215* (US), intermediate between var. *indica* and var. *glabra*; Ruhuna National Park, Block 1, *Cooray 68053008* (PDA), *Mueller-Dombois 68101839* (PDA), *Mueller-Dombois & Cooray 67121056* (PDA, BISH); same locality, Butawa, *Wirawan 806*

(PDA); same locality, Patanagala, *Huber 31* (PDA, US); southern periphery of Ruhuna National Park, *Jayasuriya 2252* (PDA). MATARA DISTRICT: Devundera, S. Prov., *Trimen 42* (PDA). KANDY DISTRICT: Le Vallon Estate, Hewaheta, *Trimen s.n.* Sept. 1883 (PDA). LOCALITY UN-KNOWN: *Fraser 3* (BM), *Gardner 575* (K), *s. coll. C.P. 1858* (BM, K), *Walker 1130* (K).

2. var. **glabra** (Decne.) Huber in Abeywick., Rev. Handb. Fl. Ceylon 1 (1): 43. 1973. Type: not seen.

Cynanchum flavens Thunb. (Alner), Obs. in Cynanchum 7. 1821.
Tylophora asthmatica (L. f.) Wight var. *glabra* Decne. in DC., Prod. 8: 611. 1844 pro parte.
Tylophora asthmatica (L. f.) Wight var. *glabra* Decne. emend. Thw., Enum. Pl. Zeyl. 197. 1860.
Tylophora flava Trimen, J. Bot. 23: 239. 1885; Trimen, Handb. Fl. Ceylon 3: 159, plate LXII. 1895.

Stem, leaves (except of the upper side of the petiole) and inflorescence glabrous. Flowers greenish-yellow, not tinged with brown, slightly larger than in var. *indica*.

D i s t r. Seychelles, Ceylon and southern Deccan Peninsula. Given for Mauritius by Decaisne but absent from this island.
This variety partly replaces var. *indica* in the southwest of Ceylon.
V e r n. Mudu-bin-nuga (S).
S p e c i m e n s E x a m i n e d. COLOMBO DISTRICT: Colombo, near sea shore, Aug. 1883, *Trimen s.n.* (PDA). RATNAPURA DISTRICT: Ratnapura, *s. coll. C.P. 1849* partly (PDA). GALLE DISTRICT: Between Bentota and Induruwa, *Huber 15* (PDA, US). HAMBANTOTA DISTRICT: Hambantota, *Balasubramaniam 2140* (PDA), *Davidse & Sumithraarachchi 8821* (PDA); 1 mile east of Hambantota on A2, along beach, *Sohmer et al. 8862* (US).
N o t e. Intermediate forms have been collected at Negombo and Hambantota; they are enumerated under var. *indica*.

2. **Tylophora fasciculata** Buch.-Ham. ex Wight, Contr. Bot. India 50. 1834; Thw., Enum. Pl. Zeyl. 424. 1864; Hook. f., Fl. Br. Ind. 4: 40. 1883; Trimen, Handb. Fl. Ceylon 3: 156. 1895. Type: *Buchanan-Hamilton 758* (K).

Stem erect or very slightly twining, minutely pubescent when young. Petiole 0.5–0.7 cm long. Leaf-blade 2–4 cm long, 0.8–1.5 cm wide, ovate, ovate-oblong, or ovate-lanceolate, acute or rounded at the base, acute or rarely obtuse at the apex, glabrous above, puberulous on the veins beneath. Inflorescence an umbel-like cyme or two superposed umbel-like cymes, pubescent, shorter than or about as long as the leaves, with the peduncle as long as or slightly longer than the petioles. Calyx-lobes 2–2.5 mm long, triangular-ovate, almost glabrous. Corolla about 0.6 cm in diameter, the lobes longer than the radius of the united portion. Merocarps not seen.

D i s t r. Nepal, Deccan Peninsula and Ceylon.

In Ceylon very rare and reported from two stations only.

S p e c i m e n s E x a m i n e d. BADULLA DISTRICT: Pettiyagoda, Uraniya-Ekiriyankumbura Road, *Balasubramaniam 2071* (PDA). RATNA-PURA DISTRICT: Between Muttetuwegama and Balangoda, *s. coll. C.P. 3792* (PDA).

3. Tylophora multiflora (Wight & Arn. ex Wight) Alston in Trimen, Handb. Fl. Ceylon 6: 195. 1931. Type: Herb. Wight propr. *1544* (K).

Iphisia multiflora Wight & Arn. ex Wight, Contr. Bot. India 52. 1834.
Tylophora iphisia Decne. in DC., Prod. 8: 610. 1844; Thw., Enum. Pl. Zeyl.
  197. 1860 as "*T. fasciculata*" and l.c. 424. 1864 as "*T. iphisia*"; Hook. f.,
  Fl. Br. Ind. 4: 40. 1883; Trimen, Handb. Fl. Ceylon 3: 157. 1895.

Stem twining or almost erect, glabrous. Petiole 0.7–1.5 cm long. Leaf-blade 4–6 cm long, 2.5–3.5 cm wide, ovate or ovate-oblong, rounded or very shallowly cordate at the base, very acute and apiculate at the apex, glabrous on both sides. Inflorescence an umbel-like cyme or more commonly compos-ed of two superposed umbel-like cymes, glabrous, shorter than or as long as the leaves, with a peduncle usually longer than the adjoining petioles. Calyx-lobes 1.2–1.7 mm long, triangular-ovate, glabrous. Corolla purple or yellow tinged with purple, 0.7 cm in diameter, the lobes longer than the radius of the united portion. Merocarps 6–8 cm long, about 1 cm in diameter, gradually tapering to the apex.

D i s t r. Mountains of the southern Deccan Peninsula and of Ceylon. According to Thwaites (1860) common in the more elevated parts of the Central Province of Ceylon, but already referred to as rather rare by Trimen (1895).

S p e c i m e n s E x a m i n e d. NUWARA ELIYA DISTRICT: Horton Plains, Agrapatana Road, *Nowicke & Jayasuriya 246* (PDA, US). BADUL-LA DISTRICT: Haputale, *s. coll. C.P. 369* (PDA). LOCALITY UN-KNOWN: *Gardner 568* (K), *Maxwell s.n.* (K), *Walker s.n.* (K).

4. Tylophora pauciflora Wight & Arn. ex Wight, Contr. Bot. India 49. 1834; Hook. f., Fl. Br. Ind. 4: 41. 1883 excl. syn. *Tylophora asthmatica* var. *glabra* Decne. and *Cynanchum flavens* Thunb. Type: Herb. Wight propr. *1539* (K).

Tylophora membranifolia Thw., Enum. Pl. Zeyl. 424. 1864; Trimen, Handb.
  Fl. Ceylon 3 : 157. 1895.

Stem long-twining, glabrous. Petiole 1–2.5 cm long. Leaf-blade 3.5–7 cm long, 2–4 cm wide, ovate, truncate or very shallowly cordate at the base, acute and apiculate at the apex, very thin, glabrous on both sides. Cymes laxly and dichasially branched, rather few-flowered, glabrous, shorter to longer than the leaves, with a peduncle usually exceeding the petioles. Calyx-lobes (1.2–) 1.5–2 mm long, broadly ovate, glabrous. Corolla greenish white with the centre dark purplish-brown; 0.6–0.7 cm in diameter, the lobes longer than the radius of the united portion. Merocarps up to 6 cm long and up to 1 cm broad, produced into a slender beak.

D i s t r. Deccan Peninsula southwards from South Kanara; Ceylon.

E c o l. A rare plant, growing at low elevations, particularly in the dry region but according to Thwaites also at Colombo.

N o t e. The Ceylon plant has been considered a distinct species but the only difference I could discover, the slightly longer calyx-lobes of the Ceylon plant, does not make an important character.

S p e c i m e n s E x a m i n e d. ANURADHAPURA DISTRICT: Anuradhapura, *Trimen 41* (PDA). MATALE DISTRICT: Nalanda, Nov. 1882, *Trimen s.n.* (PDA); mile 26 of Rattota-Illukkumbura Road, 560 m, *Huber 707* (PDA, US). LOCALITY UNKNOWN: *s. coll. C.P. 1860* (PDA), *s. coll. s.n.* (K).

5. Tylophora cordifolia Thw., Enum. Pl. Zeyl. 196. 1860; Hook. f., Fl. Br. Ind. 4: 44. 1883; Trimen, Handb. Fl. Ceylon 3: 158. 1895. Type: *s. coll. C.P. 717* (K).

Tylophora thwaitesii Schum. in Pflanzenfam. 4 (2): 286. 1895.

Stem slender, long-twining, with two lines of minute pubescence alternating at the nodes. Petiole 0.2–0.6 cm long. Leaf-blade 1–3 cm long, 0.4–2 cm wide, triangular-ovate to ovate-oblong or ovate-lanceolate, rounded, truncate or very shallowly cordate at the base, acute or obtuse but apiculate at the apex, glabrous on both sides. Cymes one- or two-flowered, very rarely of up to four flowers, in an almost umbel-like inflorescence, glabrous, shorter than or as long as, rarely longer than, the leaves, with the peduncle exceeding the adjoining petioles. Calyx-lobes 0.6–0.8 mm long, triangular-ovate, glabrous. Corolla normally dark purplish-brown, rarely greenish suffused with purple, about 0.6 cm in diameter, the lobes longer than the radius of the united portion. Merocarps 3.5–4.5 cm long, up to 1.2 cm wide, long-tapering to an acute apex.

D i s t r. Southern Deccan Peninsula and Ceylon.

E c o l. According to Thwaites and Trimen common or rather common in the Central Province respectively in the moist region at an elevation of 600 to 1500 m, but recently collected only on the intermediate to dry northern

and eastern slopes of the Northeast and Main Mountain Blocks and on Ritigala Kande as an outlying station.

Specimens Examined. ANURADHAPURA DISTRICT: Riti-
gala Kande, July 1887, *Trimen s.n.* (PDA); Summit of Ritigala Kande, 730 m,
Huber 43 (PDA, US), *Willis 105* (PDA); Ritigala Strict Natural Reserve,
south western slope below Weweltenna, 1780 ft, *Jayasuriya 1687* (PDA).
MATALE DISTRICT: Mile 38 of Rattota-Illukkumbura Road, 900 m,
Cramer 5009 (US); Bambragalla near Rattota (= mile 29 of same road), 770
m, *Huber*, obs. KANDY DISTRICT: Dolosbage, *Gardner* in *C.P. 717* partly
(PDA); Deltota, *s. coll. C.P. 717* partly (PDA). BADULLA DISTRICT:
Namunakula Kande, 13 March 1907, *Smith s.n.* (PDA), *Sumithraarachchi 280*
(PDA); same locality, 1670 m, *Cramer 4726* (PDA), *Huber 902* (PDA, US);
Yelamalai, Namunakula, 13 March 1907, *Smith s.n.* (PDA).

6. Tylophora tenuissima (Roxb.) Wight & Arn. ex Wight, Contr. Bot. India 49.
1834. Type: Coloured drawing no. 1383 of *Asclepias tenuissima* by Roxburgh
at K.

Asclepias tenuissima Roxb., [Hort. Beng. 20. 1814 nom. nud.] Fl. Ind. ed.
Carey & Wall., 2: 41. 1821.
Tylophora tenuis Blume, Bijdr. 1062. 1826–27; Hook. f., Fl. Br. Ind. 4: 42.
1883; Trimen, Handb. Fl. Ceylon 3: 158. 1895.
Tylophora carnosa Wall. ex Wight, Contr. Bot. India 49. 1834; Thw., Enum.
Pl. Zeyl. 196. 1860.

Stem very slender, long-twining, glabrous. Petiole 0.2–0.9 cm long. Leaf-
blade 1.2–6.5 cm long and 0.4–3.2 cm wide, ovate, ovate-oblong to oblong-
lanceolate, acute or rounded at the base, acute and apiculate at the apex,
fleshy, glabrous on both sides. Cymes laxly and dichasially branched, very
rarely condensed to an umbel-like structure; rather few-flowered, glabrous,
shorter or frequently longer than the leaves, with a peduncle exceeding the
petioles. Calyx-lobes about 0.6 mm long, triangular, glabrous. Corolla purplish-brown, 0.3–0.4 cm in diameter; the lobes longer than the radius of the
united portion. Merocarps 5–6.5 cm long, 0.7–1 cm in diameter, produced
into a slender, acute beak.

Distr. Coasts of the Deccan Peninsula, of Ceylon, Bengal, Burma, the
Malay Peninsula, Java and Borneo.

Ecol. In Ceylon rather common in halophilous scrub near the coast,
both in the moist and in the dry parts of the island, but more frequent in the
latter; rare inland and confined there to the dry zone, where it ascends to an
elevation of more than 600 m.

Specimens Examined. JAFFNA DISTRICT: Jaffna, *Gardner* in
C.P. 1852 partly (PDA). ANURADHAPURA DISTRICT: Anuradhapura,

Trimen 40 (PDA); Ritigala Strict Natural Reserve, northern edge of Wewel-tenna, 1940 ft, *Jayasuriya 877* (PDA, US). COLOMBO DISTRICT: Negombo, *Kundu & Balakrishnan 412* (PDA); southwest edge of Negombo Lagoon, *Huber 12* (PDA, US); Uswetakeiyawa, *Waas 1655* (PDA). BATTICALOA DISTRICT: Between Batticaloa and Chenkaladi, *Huber 21* (PDA, US). GALLE DISTRICT: Galle, *s. coll. C.P. 1852* partly (PDA). MONERAGALA DISTRICT: Above the falling point of Diyaluma Falls, *Sumithraarachchi & Waas 299* (PDA). DISTRICT UNKNOWN: Delatura, *Simpson 8941* (PDA); Maragala, *Alston 1658* (PDA). LOCALITY UNKNOWN: *Gardner 573* (K), *Mackenzie s.n.* (K), *Walker s.n.* (K).

7. Tylophora zeylanica Decne. in DC., Prod. 8: 608. 1844; Hook. f., Fl. Br. Ind. 4: 42. 1883; Trimen, Handb. Fl. Ceylon 3: 157. 1895. Type: *Reynaud* (P not seen).

Cynanchum micranthum Thunb. (Alner), Obs. in Cynanchum 5. 1821.
Tylophora micrantha (Thunb.) Thw., Enum. Pl. Zeyl. 197. 1860. Not *Tylophora micrantha* Decne.

Stem stout, long-twining, glabrous. Petiole 1.4–2.5 cm long. Leaf-blade 6–15 cm long, 6–10 cm wide, broadly ovate, rounded or truncate at the base, shortly acuminate at the apex, slightly fleshy, glabrous on both sides. Cymes laxly and dichasially branched, many-flowered, glabrous, as long as or longer than the leaves, with a peduncle equalling or exceeding the petioles. Calyx-lobes about 0.6 mm long, ovate, glabrous. Corolla purplish, 0.3–0.4 cm in diameter, the lobes longer than the radius of the united portion. Merocarps about 12 cm long and 0.5–0.8 cm wide, tapering to a slender point.

D i s t r. Doubtfully endemic; a similar and perhaps conspecific plant in the southern Deccan Peninsula. In Ceylon rare, if still existing at all, in the Central Province at an elevation of 700 to 1400 m.

S p e c i m e n s E x a m i n e d. KANDY DISTRICT: Hantane, *Gardner* in *C.P. 2517* partly (PDA). District unknown: Wattegodde, *s. coll. C.P. 2517* partly (PDA). LOCALITY UNKNOWN: *Gardner 572* (K).

11. GYMNEMA

R. Br., Mem. Wern. Nat. Hist. Soc. 1: 33. 1811, prepr. 1810. Type Species: *Asclepias lactifera* L.

Twining or straggling woody plants with the young branches and inflorescences puberulous to tomentose. Leaves broadly ovate to ovate-lanceolate, glabrous or more or less pubescent to tomentose, especially beneath. Flowers in sessile or short-peduncled, mostly bifid cymes condensed to an umbel-like structure or with umbel-like branches; cymes often apparently paired at the nodes by suppression of the peduncle; the latter, so far developed, shorter than the adjoining petioles. Calyx-lobes ovate, obtuse, about as long as wide. Corolla pale yellowish or greenish, campanulate, glabrous without, the lobes about as long as the tube, ovate, slightly contorted in bud. Corona single, consisting of five fleshy, elongate scales adnate to the throat of the corolla tube between the lobes, leading downwards as a villous, double ridge. Anthers with the connective produced into a membranous tip; pollen-masses solitary in each anther-loculus, ascending, without a pellucid margin. Merocarps ovoid-oblong to narrowly fusiform, tapering to the apex, acute or blunt, smooth.

A genus of about 20 species centered in India and continental Southeast Asia with one species extending to Africa.

In the herbarium, species of *Gymnema* and *Leptadenia reticulata* are most commonly confounded with each other. Distinction of the two genera does not present any problem nor does it require dissecting, so far as flowers or buds are available: in *Gymnema*, the corolla is invariably quite glabrous without, not mealy puberulous as in *Leptadenia reticulata*; nor has *Gymnema* the replicate corolla-lobes nor the projection on the inner side of the lobes, which characterize the other genus. Identification becomes more difficult in fruiting material, not so far as *Gymnema sylvestre* is concerned, as this stands apart by its rather slender, acutely tapering merocarps not exceeding 1 cm in diameter, but as to *Gymnema lactiferum* and *Leptadenia reticulata*, both of which present similarly ovoid-oblong and rather blunt merocarps. For their distinction, the short petioles of *Gymnema lactiferum*, hardly more than 1 cm long, and the frequently truncate or shallowly cordate leaf-bases of *Leptadenia reticulata* may prove helpful.

KEY TO THE SPECIES

1 Petiole 1.8 to 3 cm long. Leaf-blade 5.5–9 cm wide, puberulous on both sides. Calyx-lobes 1.2–2 mm long..**3. G. rotundatum**
1 Petiole 0.4–about 1.5 cm long. Leaf-blade 1.2–5.5 cm wide
  2 Petiole and pedicel densely pubescent with obliquely erect or ascending, more or less spreading but not tightly appressed hairs. Leaf-blade mostly rounded, truncate or shallowly cordate at the base, mostly pubescent on both sides, rarely glabrous above. Calyx-lobes 0.7–1.2 mm long. Corolla about 0.3 mm in diameter. Merocarps narrowly spindle-shaped, 0.5–0.7 cm in diameter, acute........................**2. G. sylvestre**
  2 Petiole and pedicel rather laxly puberulous with the hairs densely appressed. Leaf-blade mostly obtuse at the base; upper surface quite glabrous, even on the midrib. Calyx-lobes 1.5–2 mm long. Corolla 0.4–0.5 cm in diameter. Merocarps ovoid-oblong, 1.2–2 cm in diameter, blunt......................................**1. G. lactiferum**
    3 Leaves glabrous or puberulous only on the veins beneath............var. **lactiferum**
    3 Leaves densely velvety beneath......................................var. **thwaitesii**

1. Gymnema lactiferum (L.) R. Br. ex Schult., Syst. Veg. 6: 57. 1820; Thw., Enum. Pl. Zeyl. 198. 1860; Hook. f., Fl. Br. Ind. 4: 30. 1883; Trimen, Handb. Fl. Ceylon 3: 154. 1895. Type: Herbarium Hermann 2: 11 (BM).

Asclepias lactifera L., Sp. Pl. 216. 1753.
Gymnema zeylanicum Decne. in DC., Prod. 8: 622. 1844.

Petiole 0.4– about 1 cm long, laxly puberulous with the hairs densely appressed. Leaf-blade 3–8 (–10) cm long, 1.2–4 (–5.5) cm wide, usually two or three times as long as wide, obtuse at the base and acuminate at the apex, quite glabrous on both sides or more or less pubescent beneath. Cymes umbellike, much shorter than the leaves. Calyx-lobes 1.5–2 mm long, appressedly puberulous on the back. Corolla 0.4–0.5 cm in diameter. Merocarps 6–7 cm long, 1.2–about 2 cm in diameter, ovoid-oblong, tapering to a rather blunt apex, glabrous.

D i s t r. Ceylon, Assam, Malay Peninsula and Malesia.

E c o l. According to Trimen, in Ceylon not uncommon in the moister part up to an elevation of 1000 m, supposed to be rare in the dry zone, but recently met with mainly in the dry region. Flowering from July to November. Two varieties can be distinguished:

1. var. lactiferum

Leaf-blade up to 8 cm long and up to 4 cm wide, glabrous on both sides or puberulous only on the veins below.

V e r n. Kurinnan (S, T).
S p e c i m e n s E x a m i n e d. ANURADHAPURA DISTRICT: Maha-Illuppallama, *Huber 46* (PDA, US); Summit of Ritigala, July 1887, *Trimen s.n.* (PDA); Ritigala Strict Natural Reserve, plain below summit, 2300 ft, *Jayasuriya & Pemadasa 1652* (US); Wilpattu National Park, *Bernardi 15388* (PDA). KANDY DISTRICT: Peradeniya, *s. coll. C.P. 2580* partly (PDA). BATTICALOA DISTRICT: Batticaloa-Kalmunai Road, near Kaluthaveli-Tethathivu, *Balasubramaniam 2057* (PDA). GALLE DISTRICT: Bona Vista near Galle, *Balakrishnan 977* (US). HAMBANTOTA DISTRICT: Ruhuna National Park, Block 1, *Wirawan 807* (PDA, US), intermediate between *G. lactiferum* var. *lactiferum* and *G. sylvestre*. LOCALITY UNKNOWN: *Gardner 571* (K), *s. coll. C.P. 2580* partly (BM, K, PDA), *Walker 61* (K).

2. var. thwaitesii Hook. f., Fl. Br. Ind. 4: 31. 1883; Trimen, Handb. Fl. Ceylon 3: 154. 1895. Type: *s. coll. C.P. 1847* (K).

Leaf-blade up to 10 cm long and up to 5.5 cm wide, densely velvety beneath.

D i s t r. Endemic in Ceylon.
S p e c i m e n s E x a m i n e d. NUWARA ELIYA DISTRICT: Maturata, *s. coll. C.P. 1847* (BM, PDA).

2. Gymnema sylvestre (Retz.) R. Br. ex Schult., Syst. Veg. 6: 57. 1820; Thw., Enum. Pl. Zeyl. 197. 1860; Hook. f., Fl. Br. Ind. 4: 29. 1883; Trimen, Handb. Fl. Ceylon 3: 153. 1895. Type: *Koenig s.n.* (LD not seen).

Periploca sylvestris Retz., Obs. 2: 15. 1781.

Petiole 0.4–1.2 cm long, usually densely pubescent with obliquely erect or ascending, more or less spreading hairs. Leaf-blade 2–about 6 cm, rarely up to 8.5 cm long, 1–3 (–5.5) cm wide, one and a half to three times as long as wide, usually rounded, truncate or shallowly cordate at the base, shortly or not at all acuminate at the apex, pubescent to glabrous above (when glabrous, at least midrib persistently puberulous), pubescent to tomentose or glabrous except for the veins beneath, rarely tomentose on both sides. Cymes umbel-like, much shorter than the leaves. Calyx-lobes 0.7–1.2 mm long, pubescent. Corolla about 0.3 cm in diameter. Merocarps 5–7 cm long, 0.5–0.7 cm in diameter, produced into an acute beak, glabrous.

D i s t r. Tropical Africa, Deccan Peninsula and Ceylon.

E c o l. Rather frequent in the drier parts of Ceylon, twining and struggling in deciduous secondary scrub. Flowering from November to February.

V e r n. Masbedde (S).

N o t e s. According to Stevens in Saldanha & Nicolson, Flora of Hassan District, Karnataka, India (1976), chewing the leaves makes one for some time unable to taste sugar.

Gymnema sylvestre varies considerably in the pubescence of its leaves. In the Ceylon specimens the upper surface of the leaves is mostly more or less pubescent, the underside more densely so, or the leaves are glabrescent on both sides. Only in two specimens seen (*Schlechter s.n.* from Hantane near Kandy and *C.P. 1844*, locality not known) the leaves, slightly larger than usual, are velvety tomentose on both sides. This plant is *Gymnema sylvestre* (Retz.) R. Br. ex Schult. var. *decaisneanum* Thw., Enum. Pl. Zeyl. 197. 1860 excl. syn., of which *Gymnema sylvestre* (Retz.) R. Br. ex Schult. var. *ceylanicum* Hook. f., Fl. Br. Ind. 4: 29. 1883 is synonymous. Both these varieties are based on the same nomenclatural type, *C.P. 1844*. This plant strongly resembles *Gymnema hirsutum* Wight & Arn. ex Wight from the Deccan Peninsula, which, however, differs from *Gymnema sylvestre* including var. *decaisneana* by its much larger flowers, 0.5–0.8 cm in diameter.

S p e c i m e n s   E x a m i n e d. ANURADHAPURA DISTRICT: Anuradhapura, 17 Dec. 1881, *Trimen s.n.* (PDA); mile 18 of Eppawala-Talawa Road, near Eppawala, *Huber 45* (US). MATALE DISTRICT: Dambulla, *s. coll. C.P. 2549* partly (PDA); mile 38 of Rattota-Illukkumbura Road, 900 m, *Jayasuriya et al. 437* (US), *Tirvengadum et al. 22* (US). KANDY DISTRICT: Hantane, *Schlechter s.n.* (K). NUWARA ELIYA DISTRICT: Hanguranketa, *s. coll. C.P. 2549* partly (PDA). BADULLA DISTRICT: Bolagandawela, Ooma Oya, *Silva 249* (PDA); Ekiriyankumbura, *Trimen s.n.* June 1888 (PDA). MONERAGALA DISTRICT: Near Wellawaya, *Alston s.n.* (PDA). MATARA DISTRICT: Dondra Head, *Sohmer et al. 8867* (PDA). HAMBANTOTA DISTRICT: Tissamaharama, Dec. 1882, *Trimen s.n.* (PDA); Ruhuna National Park, Block 1, *Cooray 69011205* and *69111717* (both US). LOCALITY UNKNOWN: *s. coll. C.P. 1844* (K, PDA), *Walker 1470* (K).

3. Gymnema rotundatum Thw., Enum. Pl. Zeyl. 197. 1860; Hook. f., Fl. Br. Ind. 4: 30. 1883; Trimen, Handb. Fl. Ceylon 3: 153. 1895. Type: *s. coll. C.P. 3086* (PDA).

Petiole 1.8–3 cm long, densely pubescent with obliquely erect or ascending hairs. Leaf-blade 6–10 cm long, 5.5–9 cm wide, one to one and a half times as long as wide, mostly truncate at the base, shortly or not at all acuminate at the apex, puberulous on both sides. Cymes usually divided dichasially into two short branches, much shorter than the leaves. Calyx-lobes 1.2–2 mm long, pubescent. Corolla 0.3–0.5 cm in diameter. Merocarps not seen, according to Trimen about 7 cm long, narrow, glabrous.

D i s t r. Endemic in Ceylon.

E c o l. A rare plant of the dry and intermediate zone. Flowering from November to February.

S p e c i m e n s E x a m i n e d. ANURADHAPURA DISTRICT: Anuradhapura, Dec. 1881, *Trimen's collector s.n.* (PDA). MATALE DISTRICT: Nalanda, Nov. 1882, *Trimen s.n.* (PDA). NUWARA ELIYA DISTRICT: Hanguranketa, about 3000 ft, *s. coll. C.P. 3086* partly (BM, PDA). KALUTARA DISTRICT: "Calutara Prov.", *s. coll. C.P. 3086* partly (PDA).

N o t e. No recent collection can be referred to this species. As Trimen (1895) pointed out. *Gymnema rotundatum* is doubtfully distinct from *G. sylvestre.*

12. BIDARIA

(Endl.) Decne. in DC., Prod. 8: 623. 1844. Type Species: *Asclepias tingens* Roxb.

Gymnema sect. *Bidaria* Endl., Gen. Pl. 595. 1838.

Twining, slightly woody plants; internodes of young stems with two lines of pubescence. Leaves ovate-lanceolate to elliptic-lanceolate, glabrous or slightly puberulous on both sides. Flowers in short-peduncled, umbel-like cymes arising solitary at the nodes; peduncle frequently as long as or longer than the adjoining petioles. Calyx-lobes ovate to oblong, longer than broad, acute or obtuse. Corolla greenish yellow, pink or purple, campanulate with the tube somewhat narrowed at the mouth, glabrous without; the lobes slightly shorter to longer than the tube, oblong, spreading or recurved, contorted in bud. Corona single, reduced to five narrow double ridges, membranous at their edge, entirely adnate to the corolla-tube. Anthers with the connective produced into a membranous tip; pollen-masses solitary in each anther-loculus, ascending, without a pellucid margin. Merocarps narrowly spindle-shaped, long-tapering to an acute apex, smooth.

This genus, closely related to *Gymnema* and included in it by most authors, is formed by a few species ranging from India to Ceylon and Malesia. Apart from the different shape of the corolla and the corona, *Bidaria* most easily can be recognized by the bifarious pubescence of the internodes and the umbel-like cymes, which are neither bifid nor apparently paired at the nodes.

The representatives of *Bidaria* are rare in Ceylon and insufficiently understood. The specimens available are inadequate to decide if two or three species occur in the island or if Trimen was correct when uniting them all in one very polymorphic species.

KEY TO THE SPECIES

1 Calyx-lobes one-third to scarcely half as long as the corolla tube; the latter (0.2–) 0.3–0.45 cm long; corolla yellow or pale green (colour not known in var. *cuspidata*). Merocarps 12–15 cm long...**1. B. cuspidata**
  2 Cyme 7- to 15-flowered. Pedicel not much longer than the calyx. Corolla-lobes as long as the tube or shorter..var. **cuspidata**
  2 Cyme few-flowered. Pedicel three to five times longer than the calyx. Corolla-lobes as long as the tube or longer than the tube............................var. **stenoloba**
1 Calyx-lobes one half to about as long as the corolla-tube; the latter 0.2–0.3 cm long; corolla purplish. Merocarps 5–7 cm long............................**2. B. celsicola**

1. Bidaria cuspidata (Thunb.) Huber in Abeywick., Rev. Handb. Fl. Ceylon 1 (1): 47. 1973. Type: *Thunberg* (UPS not seen).

Cynanchum cuspidatum Thunb. (Alner), Obs. in Cynanchum 5. 1821.
Bidaria pergularioides Thw., Enum. Pl. Zeyl. 198. 1860.
Gymnema pergularioides (Thw.) Hook. f., Fl. Br. Ind. 4: 32. 1883; Trimen, Handb. Fl. Ceylon 3: 154. 1895.
Gymnema cuspidatum (Thunb.) Kuntze, Rev. Gen. 420. 1891.

Petiole 0.7–2 cm long. Leaf-blade 4–15 cm long, 1.8–5 cm wide, rounded or shortly cuneate at the base, long-acuminate at the apex, thinly membranous. Inflorescence much shorter than the leaves; the peduncle shorter to longer than the petiole. Calyx-lobes ovate, 0.7–1.5 mm long, almost glabrous. Corolla yellow or pale green (colour unknown in var. *cuspidata*), the tube 0.2–0.45 cm long; lobes slightly shorter to longer than the tube, narrowly oblong. Merocarps 12–15 cm long, about 0.5 cm in diameter, puberulous when young.

D i s t r. Endemic in Ceylon.

E c o l. Rare or overlooked in the hill country, apparently not ascending much beyond 1000 m; indicated at low elevations (100 m) in Ratnapura District.

Bidaria cuspidata is a somewhat variable species.

1. var. cuspidata. Cyme 7- to 15-flowered. Pedicel up to twice as long as the calyx. Corolla-lobes as long as the tube or mostly a little shorter.

S p e c i m e n s E x a m i n e d. LOCALITY UNKNOWN: *Gardner 569* (K), *s. coll. C.P. 1848* (K but not the specimen of the same number at PDA), *s. coll. C.P. 2671* (BM, K but not the specimen of the same number at PDA), *s. coll. C.P. 2672* (PDA partly but not the specimen of the same number at K), *Walker 97* (K).

2. var. stenoloba (Hook. f.) Huber in Abeywick., Rev. Handb. Fl. Ceylon 1 (1): 47. 1973. Type: *Walker s.n.* (K).

Gymnema stenolobum Hook. f., Fl. Br. Ind. 4: 32. 1883.
Gymnema pergularioides (Thw.) Hook. f. var. *stenolobum* (Hook. f.) Trimen, Handb. Fl. Ceylon 3: 155. 1895.

Cyme few-flowered. Pedicel three to five times longer than the calyx. Corolla-lobes as long as or slightly longer than the tube.

S p e c i m e n s E x a m i n e d. RATNAPURA DISTRICT: Lankagama-Sinharaja, c. 100 m, *Waas 2035* (PDA); Palabaddala, *Sumithraarachchi 1023* (PDA). LOCALITY UNKNOWN: *s. coll. C.P. 2671* (PDA but not the specimens of the same number at BM & K), *s. coll. C.P. 2672* (K; PDA partly), *Walker 79* (K), the same *1713* (K), the same *s.n.* (K).

2. Bidaria celsicola Huber in Abeywick., Rev. Handb. Fl. Ceylon 1 (1): 48. 1973. Type: *Gardner 567* (K).

Bidaria pergularioides Thw. var. *β* Thw., Enum. Pl. Zeyl. 198. 1860.
Gymnema pergularioides (Thw.) Hook. f. var. *gardneri* Thw. ex Hook. f., Fl. Br. Ind. 4: 32. 1883; Trimen, Handb. Fl. Ceylon 3: 155. 1895.

Petiole 0.5–1 cm long. Leaf-blade 3–6 cm long, 1–2.5 cm wide, acute or rarely almost rounded at the base, mostly acuminate at the apex, rather firm in texture. Inflorescence much shorter than the leaves; the peduncle slightly shorter to longer than the leaves. Pedicels shorter to little longer than the calyx. Calyx-lobes oblong, 1.8–2.4 mm long, glabrous or sparsely puberulous at the base. Corolla yellowish-purple to purplish-pink; tube 0.2–0.3 cm long, lobes about as long as the tube, ovate-oblong. Merocarps 5–7 cm long, 0.6 cm in diameter, glabrous.

D i s t r. Endemic in Ceylon.

N o t e. *Bidaria celsicola* replaces *B. cuspidata*, of which it is perhaps a subspecies, at higher elevations (no record known from below 1500 m).

S p e c i m e n s   E x a m i n e d. KANDY DISTRICT: Hunnasgiriya, 4500 ft, *Waas 980* (PDA). NUWARA ELIYA DISTRICT: Nuwara Eliya, *Gardner 567* (K). BADULLA DISTRICT: Namunakula Peak, 29 Apr. 1907, *Smith s.n.* (PDA), 29 Apr. 1924, *Silva s.n.* (PDA); same locality, ascent from the south, c. 1500 m, *Cramer 4733* (PDA). LOCALITY UNKNOWN: *Gardner 569* (K), *s. coll. C.P. 1848* (PDA but not the specimen of the same number at K), *Walker 228* (K), *Walker s.n.* (K).

13. MARSDENIA

R. Br., Mem. Wern. Nat. Hist. Soc. 1: 28. 1811, prepr. 1810. Type Species: *Marsdenia tinctoria* R. Br.

Woody twiners with the young branches, leaves and inflorescence glabrous to sparsely and minutely puberulous or persistently tomentose. Leaves ovate, usually cordate, rarely some rounded at the base, acute or acuminate at the apex. Flowers in sessile or short-peduncled, dichasially branched cymes solitary at the nodes; cymes shorter than the leaves; peduncle, so far developed, shorter than the adjoining petioles. Calyx-lobes roundish ovate, to ovate-oblong, obtuse. Corolla greenish-white, campanulate, glabrous or puberulous without; the lobes about as long as the tube or slightly shorter, ovate-oblong, contorted in bud. Corona single, consisting of five flat, erect segments attached to the staminal column. Anthers with the connective produced into a membranous tip; pollen masses solitary in each anther-loculus, ascending, without a pellucid margin. Merocarps (seen only of *M. tenacissima*) ovoid-oblong, tapering to a blunt apex, smooth.

A large genus of almost a hundred species distributed throughout the tropics and extending into the warm-temperate zones.

KEY TO THE SPECIES

1 Leaves velvety puberulous above, densely tomentose beneath. Corolla 0.4–0.5 cm in diameter. Corona-segments truncate, emarginate or shortly bifid........**1. M. tenacissima**
1 Leaves sparsely and minutely puberulous on midrib and veins beneath, otherwise almost glabrous. Corolla 0.8–1 cm in diameter. Corona-segments narrowly triangular or broadly lanceolate, acute...**2. M. brunoniana**

1. Marsdenia tenacissima (Roxb.) Moon, Cat. 21. 1824; Thw., Enum. Pl. Zeyl. 197. 1860; Hook. f., Fl. Br. Ind. 4: 35. 1883; Trimen, Handb. Fl. Ceylon 3: 155. 1895. Type: *Roxburgh* in Herb. Wallich *8176/a* (K).

Asclepias tenacissima Roxb., Pl. Corom. 3: 35, t. 24. 1815.

Stem and petiole densely hairy. Petiole 5–9 cm long. Leaf-blade 7–18 cm long, 6–16 cm wide, velvety pubescent above, densely tomentose beneath. Cymes hairy. Calyx-lobes about 2 mm long, densely hairy without. Corolla 0.4–0.5 cm in diameter, densely pubescent without; lobes about as long as the tube. Corona-segments truncate, emarginate or shortly bifid. Merocarps 7–17 cm long, up to 6 cm wide, velvety pubescent.

D i s t r. From the western Himalayas through Nepal and Bengal to Upper Burma; Ceylon.

E c o l. In Ceylon rare in the dry and intermediate zone; not collected during the last decades. Flowering in June and July.

U s e s. According to Trimen the stems afford a strong, silky fibre and the leaves are given as a remedy for flatulence.

V e r n. Muruwa, Muruwa-dul (S).

S p e c i m e n s E x a m i n e d. KURUNEGALA DISTRICT: Kurune-gala, *s. coll. C.P. 2860* partly (PDA). BADULLA DISTRICT: Ekiriyankum-bura, Jan. 1888, *Trimen s.n.* (PDA); Ooma Oya, *s. coll. C.P. 2860* partly (PDA). LOCALITY UNKNOWN: *Silva s.n.* (PDA).

2. Marsdenia brunoniana Wight & Arn. ex Wight, Contr. Bot. India 40. 1834; Hook. f., Fl. Br. Ind. 4: 36. 1883. Type: Herb. Wight propr. *1524* (K).

Stem glabrous. Petiole 3–6 cm long, glabrous or with minute, adpressed pubescence. Leaf-blade 6–12 cm long, 4–10 cm wide, shallowly cordate at the base but in some leaves truncate or rounded at the base; glabrous on both sides except for the midrib and veins beneath, which bear some minute, ad-pressed pubescence; thinly membranous. Peduncle 1–1.5 cm long, glabrous; pedicels minutely puberulous. Calyx-lobes roundish ovate, 2–2.5 mm long, sparsely puberulous on the back. Corolla 0.8–1 cm in diameter, glabrous throughout; the lobes little longer than the tube. Corona-segments narrowly triangular or broadly lanceolate, acute, exceeding the staminal column.

D i s t r. Southern Deccan Peninsula.

E c o l. In Ceylon, recently discovered by Mr. Jayasuriya growing in the dry zone in a luxuriant forest, twining among low trees.

V e r n. Et-anguna (S).

S p e c i m e n s E x a m i n e d. MATALE DISTRICT: Ridielle, 10 miles north of Naula-Elahera Road, off mile post 5, *Jayasuriya 312* (US).

14. COSMOSTIGMA

Wight, Contr. Bot. India 41. 1834. Type Species: *Cosmostigma racemosum* (Roxb.) Wight.

A slightly woody twiner with the stems and leaves glabrous. Leaves ovate, rather thin. Flowers in peduncled cymes; the latter at first umbel-like, soon elongating and raceme-like, slightly pubescent, solitary at the nodes. Calyx-lobes triangular-ovate, obtuse. Corolla greenish-yellow with red dots, rotate, glabrous; the lobes much longer than the radius of the united portion, ovate to ovate-oblong, contorted in bud. Corona single, consisting of five flat, erect segments bifid or truncate at the apex, attached to the base of the staminal column, but not exceeding it. Anthers with the connective produced into a membranous tip; pollen-masses obliquely-ovate, solitary in each anther-loculus, ascending, without a pellucid margin. Merocarps ovoid-oblong, blunt, smooth.

This genus consists of only one species.

Cosmostigma racemosum (Roxb.) Wight, Contr. Bot. India 42. 1834; Thw., Enum. Pl. Zeyl. 197. 1860; Hook. f., Fl. Br. Ind. 4: 46. 1883; Trimen, Handb. Fl. Ceylon 3: 160. 1895. Type: Coloured drawing no. 1813 of *Asclepias racemosa* by Roxburgh at K.

Asclepias racemosa Roxb., [Hort. Beng. 20. 1814 nom. nud.] Fl. Ind. ed. Carey 2: 32. 1832.

Petiole 1-3.5 cm long. Leaf-blade 6-10 cm long, 3.5-7 cm wide, shortly cuneate, rounded, truncate or shallowly cordate at the base, acuminate at the apex. Inflorescence shorter than to about as long as the leaves; the peduncle shorter than or as long as the petioles. Calyx-lobes 1-1.7 mm long, glabrous. Corolla 0.7-1.2 cm in diameter. Merocarps not seen, according to Trimen 6-8 cm long.

D i s t r. Southern Deccan Peninsula, Ceylon, Assam and Burma.

E c o l. A plant of the dry and intermediate regions of Ceylon, according to Thwaites rather common, but actually rare and collected only once within this century.

S p e c i m e n s E x a m i n e d. KURUNEGALA DISTRICT: Kurunegala, *Gardner* in *C.P. 1854* (BM, PDA). BATTICALOA DISTRICT: Mankeni, *Worthington 4897* (K).

15. HETEROSTEMMA

Wight & Arn. ex Wight, Contr. Bot. India 42. 1834. Type Species: *Heterostemma tanjorense* Wight & Arn. ex Wight.

An almost glabrous (except for the ventral side of the petioles, pedicels, outer side of calyx and corolla), herbaceous or scarcely woody twiner with thin, ovate or ovate-oblong leaves. Flowers in sessile or very short-peduncled, umbel-like cymes solitary from the nodes. Calyx-lobes ovate-oblong, obtuse. Corolla purplish-brown, yellow or green, tinged with maroon, rotate, sparsely puberulous without, glabrous within; the lobes as long as or slightly longer than the radius of the united portion, triangular-ovate, valvate in bud. Corona single, consisting of five large segments, laterally compressed, with a fleshy dorsal appendage. Anthers with the connective produced into a membranous tip; pollen-masses almost orbicular, solitary in each anther-loculus, ascending, with a narrow pellucid margin near the insertion of the caudicles half as long as the pollinium. Merocarps slender, cylindrical, long-tapering to an acute apex, smooth.

About a dozen species, ranging from India to China, the Philippines and Samoa.

Heterostemma tanjorense Wight & Arn. ex Wight, Contr. Bot. India 42. 1834; Thw., Enum. Pl. Zeyl. 198. 1860; Hook f., Fl. Br. Ind. 4: 47. 1883; Trimen, Handb. Fl. Ceylon 3: 163. 1895. Type: Herb. Wight propr. *1527* (K).

Heterostemma tanjorense Wight & Arn. ex Wight var. *zeylanicum* Hook. f., Fl. Br. Ind. 4: 48. 1883.

Petiole 1.4–3 cm long. Leaf-blade 6–12 cm long, 2.5–5 cm wide, rounded, truncate or shallowly cordate at the base, acute and sharply acuminate at the apex. Inflorescence shorter than the leaves. Peduncle up to 3 mm long. Calyx-lobes about 1.5 mm long, puberulous on the back. Corolla 1.2–1.5 cm in diameter. Merocarps 8–12 cm long and 0.5 cm in diameter, glabrous.

D i s t r. Western Deccan Peninsula and Ceylon.

E c o l. According to Trimen, a rare plant of the moist zone; not found there during this century but apparently not uncommon in the dry country along the east coast (Trincomalee to Amparai Districts).

S p e c i m e n s E x a m i n e d. KANDY DISTRICT: Hantane, *Gardner* in *C.P. 1856* (PDA). TRINCOMALEE DISTRICT: Mutur, *Jayasuriya et al. 652* (PDA, US). BATTICALOA DISTRICT: Batticaloa-Kalmunai Road, near Kaluthaveli-Tethathivu, *Balasubramaniam 2056, 2115, 2116* (all PDA). AMPARAI DISTRICT: Arugam Bay, *Jayasuriya 2033* (PDA). LOCALITY UNKNOWN: *s. coll. C.P. 1859* (K, holotype of var. *zeylanicum* Hook. f.).

16. WATTAKAKA

Hassk., Flora 40: 99. 1857. Type Species: *Wattakaka viridiflora* (R. Br.) Hassk.

Glabrous, slightly woody twiners with ovate, rather firm but not fleshy leaves. Flowers numerous, long-pedicelled, in peduncled, umbel-like cymes solitary at the nodes. Calyx-lobes triangular-ovate, obtuse to almost acute. Corolla entirely green, rotate, glabrous; the lobes about twice as long as the radius of the united portion, ovate, contorted in bud. Corona single, consisting of five fleshy, top-shaped segments attached to the upper part of the staminal column, truncate above, with an apical tooth projecting horizontally inwards. Anthers with the connective produced into a membranous tip; pollen-masses ovate-oblong, solitary in each anther-loculus, ascending, without a distinct, pellucid margin. Merocarps ovoid-oblong, tapering to a blunt apex, sharply ridged longitudinally.

Two species ranging from India and Ceylon to South China and Malesia.

Wattakaka volubilis (L.f.) Stapf, Bot. Mag. sub t. 8976. 1923. Type: *Koenig* in the Linnaean Herb. *310/6* (LINN).

Asclepias volubilis L.f., Suppl. Pl. 170. 1781.
Hoya viridiflora R. Br., Mem. Wern. Nat. Hist. Soc. 1: 27. 1811, prepr. 1810; Thw., Enum. Pl. Zeyl. 199. 1860.
Wattakaka viridiflora (R. Br.) Hassk., Flora 40: 99. 1857.
Dregea volubilis (L.f.) Benth. ex Hook. f., Fl. Br. Ind. 4: 46. 1883; Trimen, Handb. Fl. Ceylon 3: 161. 1895.

Petiole 1.2–5.5 cm long. Leaf-blade 5–13 cm long, 3–10 cm wide, obtuse, truncate or shallowly cordate at the base, acute and acuminate at the apex. Inflorescence shorter than to as long as the leaves; peduncle as long as or longer than the adjoining petioles. Calyx-lobes 1.2–2.5 mm long, glabrous. Corolla about 1.5 cm in diameter, Merocarps 6–10 cm long, 2–3 cm wide, glabrous when ripe, tomentellous when young.

D i s t r. From Nepal through India to Ceylon and Malesia.

E c o l. In Ceylon not uncommon in the dry zone from the lowland up to an elevation of 1000 m. Flowering in March and April, rarely in autumn.

U s e s. The leaves are eaten in curries and also used in native medicine for fevers in children (Trimen).

V e r n. Anguna, Anúkkola, Kiri-anguna, Thitta-anguna (S); Kodi-palai, Kurincha (T).

S p e c i m e n s E x a m i n e d. JAFFNA DISTRICT: Jaffna, *s. coll. s.n.* (PDA). MANNAR DISTRICT: Giant's Tank, *Simpson 9358* (BM); Kovil-kulam, *Kundu & Balakrishnan 581* (PDA). ANURADHAPURA DISTRICT: Thoru Wewa, 2 miles east of Maradankadawela, *Sumithraarachchi & Jaya-suriya 215* (PDA); Wilpattu National Park, *Bernardi 15375* (PDA); Wilpattu National Park, Marai Villu, *Cooray 69092502* (PDA). POLONNARUWA DISTRICT: Kalahagala near Polonnaruwa, 60 m, *Huber 434* (HBG, PDA, US). MATALE DISTRICT: Dambulla Hill, *Simpson 9776* (BM); Nalan-da Gorge, *Worthington 6384* (K). KANDY DISTRICT: Hantane, 2500 ft, *Gardner 564* (BM, K), *Trimen s.n.*, Apr. 1885 (PDA). BADULLA DIS-TRICT: Namunakula, 29 Apr. 1907, *Smith s.n.* (PDA); Beragala-Wellawaya Road, mile post 120/25, *Sumithraarachchi 285* (PDA). HAMBANTOAT

DISTRICT: Ruhuna National Park, Block 1, *Wirawan 713* (PDA); same locality, Andunoruwa, *Cooray 69121005* (PDA), *Mueller-Dombois 68022701* (mistyped for *68052701*, PDA); same locality, west of Yala Bungalow, *Fosberg et al. 51124* (PDA); same locality, Block 2, *Jayasuriya 2250* (PDA). DISTRICT UNKNOWN: Ambagamuwa and Central Province, *s. coll. C.P. 1855* (PDA). LOCALITY UNKNOWN: *Fraser s.n.* (BM), *Walker s.n.* (K), *s. coll. C.P. 6384* (BM).

17. HOYA

R. Br., Mem. Wern. Nat. Hist. Soc. 1: 26. 1811, prepr. 1810. Type Species: *Hoya carnosa* R. Br.

Climbing and twining, herbaceous or scarcely woody epiphytes with rooting stems and fleshy, elliptic, rhomboid, narrowly lanceolate or lanceolate leaves; glabrous. Flowers two to numerous in sessile clusters or in peduncled, umbel-like cymes solitary at the nodes, becoming racemiform with age by producing flowers for several seasons. Calyx-lobes triangular or ovate-oblong, acute or almost acute. Corolla white, pinkish-white or greenish, rotate, glabrous without; the lobes as long as or longer than the radius of the united portion, triangular to ovate, valvate in bud. Corona single, consisting of five large, fleshy, horizontally spreading segments attached to the staminal column. Anthers with the connective produced into a membranous tip; pollen masses ovate-oblong, solitary in each anther-loculus, ascending, with a narrow pellucid margin almost as long as the pollinium. Merocarps linear, tapering to the apex, smooth.

About 80 species, mostly epiphytic and climbing with rooting stems, throughout the moister parts of the Eastern Tropics from Nepal and Ceylon to South China and northern Australia.

KEY TO THE SPECIES

1 Leaves narrowly ovate-lanceolate, 0.5–1 cm wide. Flowers in sessile or almost sessile cymes...**1. H. pauciflora**
1 Leaves elliptic or rhomboid, 2–4 cm wide. Flowers in long-peduncled cymes.........
....**2. H. ovalifolia**

1. Hoya pauciflora Wight, Ic. Pl. Ind. Or. 4 (2): 16, t. 1269. 1848 (page 16 as "*parviflora*"); Hook. f., Fl. Br. Ind. 4: 56. 1883; Trimen, Handb. Fl. Ceylon 3: 162. 1895. Type: *Wight 511* (K).

Hoya wightiana Thw., Enum. Pl. Zeyl. 199. 1860.

Petiole 0.2–0.6 cm long. Leaf-blade 2–5.5 cm long, 0.5–1 cm wide, lanceolate or narrowly ovate-lanceolate, obtuse or rounded at the base, tapering to a rounded apex, frequently dotted with red beneath. Flowers 2–12 in sessile or almost sessile, umbel-like cymes, shorter than the leaves. Calyx-lobes 1–1.2 mm long, narrowly triangular-ovate, glabrous. Corolla 1–1.8 cm in diameter, pentagonal in outline, quite glabrous or the lobes minutely puberulous within towards the margin. Corona-segments rounded at the apex. Merocarps not seen, according to Trimen about 10 cm long, very slender.

D i s t r. Southern Deccan Peninsula and Ceylon.

E c o l. A rare plant of the moist region of Ceylon, growing in dense forests on tree trunks and rocks in the lower montane zone at elevations between 400 and 1700 m. Flowering in March, September and November.

V e r n. Heen-aramessa (S).

S p e c i m e n s E x a m i n e d. KANDY DISTRICT: Hantane, *Champion s.n.* (K). NUWARA ELIYA DISTRICT: Maturata (?hardly legible), *s. coll. C.P. 2762* partly (PDA); Ramboda, *Gardner* in *C.P. 2762* partly (PDA). RATNAPURA DISTRICT: Sudagala near Kuruwita, 440 m, *Huber 521* (HBG, PDA, US). LOCALITY UNKNOWN: *Gardner 563* (K, holotype of *H. wightiana* Thw.).

2. Hoya ovalifolia Wight & Arn. ex Wight, Contr. Bot. India 37. 1834; Thw., Enum. Pl. Zeyl. 198. 1860; Hook. f., Fl. Br. Ind. 4: 60. 1883; Trimen, Handb. Fl. Ceylon 3: 162. 1895. Type: Herb. Wight propr. *1522* (K).

Petiole 0.4–about 1 cm long. Leaf-blade 4–10 cm long, 2–5 cm wide, elliptic to rhomboid, obtuse or acute at both ends, rarely rounded at the base, frequently short-acuminate at the apex. Flowers numerous in peduncled cymes, at first umbel-like, producing flowers for several seasons and thus becoming racemiform with age; the peduncle as long as or longer than the leaves. Calyx-lobes about 1 mm long, triangular, subacute. Corolla about 1 cm in diameter, the lobes glabrous within and not ciliolate. Corona-segments pointed. Merocarps not seen.

D i s t r. Southern Deccan Peninsula and Ceylon.

E c o l. In Ceylon rather rare in forests of the moist region at low altitudes; an outlying station on Ritigala Kande. Flowering in March.

S p e c i m e n s E x a m i n e d. ANURADHAPURA DISTRICT: Summit of Ritigala, 24 March 1905, *Willis s.n.* (PDA); Ritigala Strict Natural Reserve, ascent along southern slope, *Jayasuriya 1311* (PDA, US); same locality, southern edge of Weweltenna, above "Et Adi", 1920 ft, *Jayasuriya 1752* (PDA). KANDY DISTRICT: Ma Oya, 12 miles east of Kandy, *Worthington 6574* (K). KEGALLE DISTRICT: Kitulgala, *s. coll. C.P. 2670* (BM, PDA). KALUTARA DISTRICT: Hallawakellae Forest, Welipenna, *Balakrishnan 1175* (PDA, US). GALLE DISTRICT: On the summit of a hill 12 miles from Galle, *Walker 1714* (K). DISTRICT UNKNOWN: Ellaboda

Kande, 24 March 1919, *Lewis & Silva s.n.* (PDA). LOCALITY UNKNOWN: *Gardner s.n.* (K), *Walker s.n.* (K).

18. DISCHIDIA

R. Br., Mem. Wern. Nat. Hist. Soc. 1: 32. 1811, prepr. 1810. Type Species: *Dischidia nummularia* R. Br.

Collyris Vahl, Skr. Nat. Selsk. Kiobenh. 110. 1810.

Small, glabrous, epiphytic herbs with rooting stems. Leaves fleshy, orbicular. Flowers one to three in sessile or almost sessile cymes solitary at the nodes. Calyx-lobes ovate, acute. Corolla white or pink, urceolate, glabrous without; the lobes shorter than the tube, triangular, valvate in bud. Corona single, consisting of five segments attached to the staminal column; the segments long and narrowly T-shaped, slightly incurved, the arms terminating in two pendulous, obliquely ovoid or cultriform appendages, thinly membranous. Anthers with the connective produced into a membranous tip; pollenmasses solitary in each anther-loculus, ascending, with a narrow, pellucid margin. Merocarps narrowly fusiform.

About 50 species, centered in South east Asia and Malesia from the East Himalayas to Formosa and New Guinea, with a few extending to Queensland. *Dischidia* is absent from the Deccan Peninsula.

Dischidia nummularia R. Br., Prod. Nov. Holl. 1: 461. 1810; Thw., Enum. Pl. Zeyl. 198. 1860; Hook. f., Fl. Br. Ind. 4: 49. 1883; Trimen, Handb. Fl. Ceylon 3: 161. 1895. Type: Rumphius, Herb. Amb. 5, t. 176, fig. 1. 1747.

Collyris minor Vahl, Skr. Nat. Selsk. Kiobenh. 111. 1810.
Dischidia minor (Vahl) Merr., Lingnan Sci. J. 13: 67. 1934.

Stem filiform. Petiole about 0.2 cm long. Leaf-blade 0.7–1 cm long and wide, sometimes slightly wider than long, rounded at both ends or very short-cuneate at the base, mostly with a minute apiculus at the apex. Calyx-lobes 0.5–0.7 mm long, glabrous. Corolla 2.3 mm long. Merocarps 2.5–3 cm long and about 0.3 cm wide, glabrous.

D i s t r. Ceylon, Malay Peninsula, Malesia to Queensland and the Solomon Islands.

E c o l. In Ceylon very rare in the Matale District on tree-trunks at an elevation of 700 to 1000 m in the moist to intermediate zone. It has not been found again since 1867.

S p e c i m e n s E x a m i n e d. MATALE DISTRICT: Lagalla, 2500 ft, *Beckett 1822 = C.P. 3875* (PDA); Matale District, without exact locality, *Williams s.n.* anno 1865 (PDA).

19. LEPTADENIA

R. Br., Mem. Wern. Nat. Hist. Soc. 1: 34. 1811, prepr. 1810. Type Species: *Leptadenia heterophylla* (Del.) Decne.

Rather large, woody twiners with the young parts mealy puberulous. Leaves broadly ovate to ovate-oblong, soon glabrescent above, puberulous or tardily glabrescent beneath. Flowers mostly in short-peduncled, umbel-like cymes solitary at the nodes, rarely dichasially branched or apparently paired at the nodes. Calyx-lobes ovate, acute or obtuse. Corolla greenish or orange-yellow, almost rotate, densely mealy puberulous without, hairy within; the lobes much longer than the tube, ovate-oblong, with the margins replicate, bearing on the inside a keel which is produced into a tooth projecting inwards, valvate in bud. Corona double but the inner series difficult to observe; the outer series consisting of five short, fleshy segments attached to the base of the corolla alternating with the lobes; the segments notched at the apex; the inner series reduced to an undulate annulus at the base of the staminal column. Anthers not produced into a membranous tip; pollen-masses solitary in each anther-loculus, ascending, with a prominent pellucid margin at the distal end. Merocarps ovoid-oblong to oblong, tapering to a blunt apex, smooth.

About 10 species ranging through tropical Africa, Arabia eastwards to Burma and southwards to the Mascarene Islands.

Leptadenia reticulata (Retz.) Wight & Arn. ex Wight, Contr. Bot. India 47. 1834; Thw., Enum. Pl. Zeyl. 198. 1860; Hook. f., Fl. Br. Ind. 4: 63. 1883; Trimen, Handb. Fl. Ceylon 3: 164. 1895; Bullock, Kew Bull. 1955: 291. 1955. Type: *Koenig s.n.* (LD holotype not seen, BM isotype).

Cynanchum reticulatum Retz., Obs. Bot. 2: 15. 1781.
Cynanchum ovatum Thunb. (Alner), Obs. in Cynanchum 6. 1821.
Daemia reticulata (Retz.) Moon, Cat. 20. 1824.

Petiole 0.8–2.5 cm long. Leaf-blade 3–9 cm long, 1.4–6 cm wide, truncate, rounded or very obtuse, rarely shallowly cordate at the base, acute or short-acuminate at the apex. Cymes shorter than the leaves, the peduncles shorter than to as long as the adjoining petioles rarely exceeding them. Calyx-lobes 1–1.7 mm long, densely puberulous. Corolla 0.6–0.8 cm in diameter when expanded, the lobes villous within. Merocarps 6–8 cm long, 2–2.5 cm in diameter, glabrous when ripe.

D i s t r. India from Nepal and the Punjab southwards to Ceylon and eastwards to Burma; also in the Comoro Islands, Madagascar and Mauritius.

E c o l. A plant of the dry zone. In Ceylon rather common in deciduous scrub and at the edge of forests. Flowering from July to October.

V e r n. Pálai, Pala (T).

N o t e. *Leptadenia reticulata* is frequently mistaken for *Gymnema lactiferum* or *G. sylvestre*, from both of which it can easily be separated by the mealy puberulous outside of the corolla. Sterile specimens can be assigned to either genus in most instances by the length of the petiole: in the commoner species of *Gymnema*, this rarely reaches and never exceeds 1.5 cm, whereas in our species of *Leptadenia* mostly at least a few longer petioles are present.

S p e c i m e n s E x a m i n e d. MANNAR DISTRICT: Pesalai, *Silva s.n.* 16 July 1916 (PDA). ANURADHAPURA DISTRICT: Anuradhapura, *Gardner* in *C.P. 1846* partly (PDA); near Hunuwilagama, *Huber 8* (PDA, US); near Maragahawewa, *Huber 48* (PDA, US); Medawachchiya, *Jayasuriya et al. 575* (PDA, US); Hunuwilagama near Wilpattu National Park gate, *Cooray 69093005* (US). PUTTALAM DISTRICT: Puttalam, Aug. 1881, *Neville s.n.* (PDA); Palavi-Kalpitiya Road, *Cooray 69100506* (PDA, US). KURUNEGALA DISTRICT: Near Kolalagala, Wariyapola-Kurunegala Road, *Simpson 8177* (BM). KANDY DISTRICT: Waniagala, Hantane, *Trimen s.n.* Dec. 1889 (PDA). TRINCOMALEE DISTRICT: Trincomalee, *Glenie* in *C.P. 1846* partly (PDA), *Alston 529* (PDA); beach, south of Elizabeth Point, *Davidse 7526* (PDA); Foul Point, *Jayasuriya et al. 670* (PDA, US), *Sumithraarachchi & Jayasuriya 238* (PDA, US). BATTICALOA DISTRICT: Keeli-Kudah (=Kalkudah?), *Waas 2124* (PDA); Panichchankeni, *Balakrishnan 367* (PDA, US), *Huber 26* (PDA, US).

20. BRACHYSTELMA

R. Br., Bot. Mag. t. 2343. 1822. Type species: *Brachystelma tuberosum* R. Br.

Dwarf, geophytic herbs with an almost globose, slightly depressed hypocotyledonary tuber bearing one or very few, erect, glabrous stems 2–14 cm tall. Leaves sessile or almost sessile, narrowly ovate, narrowly elliptic or linear, glabrous. Flowers one to three in a peduncled or almost sessile, umbel-like cyme; peduncle and pedicels puberulous. Calyx-lobes narrowly triangular. Corolla dark purple, broadly campanulate, glabrous without; the lobes erect or slightly spreading, shorter than the tube, triangular, valvate in bud. Corona double, glabrous, attached to the staminal column, the outer series consisting of five deeply bifid segments exceeding the staminal column, inner series consisting of five simple, oblong segments, rounded at the apex, incumbent over the stigmatic head, not or hardly exceeding the staminal column. Anthers not produced into a membranous tip; pollen masses solitary in each anther-loculus, ascending, with a pellucid margin. Merocarps linear, tapering to the apex, smooth.

A genus of more than 100 species, badly delimited and much in need of a revision, ranging from Africa to New Guinea, centered in the drier parts of

Africa south of the equator, with a dozen species in India, one in Ceylon—
here recently discovered during the Flora Project—, in Burma, Thailand, the
Philippines and New Guinea respectively.

Brachystelma lankana Dassanayake & Jayasuriya, Ceylon J. Sci., Biol. Sci.
11: 39. 1974. Type: *Jayasuriya & Dassanayake 988* (holotype PDA, isotypes
E, HBG, K, L, US).

Tuber 1–about 5 cm in diameter. Stem simple or with a few branches.
Leaves 0.7–6.2 cm long, 0.1–0.7 cm wide, tapering at both ends. Peduncle
0.1–1.8 cm long; pedicels in flower up to 1 cm long, elongating in fruit. Calyx-
lobes 1–2 mm long, glabrous. Corolla about 0.3 cm long and wide, the lobes
pilose within with pale purple hairs. Merocarps up to 10 cm long, 0.3 cm in
diameter, glabrous.

D i s t r. Endemic in Ceylon.

E c o l. Strictly seasonal in grassland on shallow soil, wet during the
Northeast Monsoon, almost completely parched in the dry months. Known
from one locality only. Flowering in December.

S p e c i m e n s   E x a m i n e d. MATALE DISTRICT: Dikpatana between Lagalla and Illukkumbura, c. 860 m, *Jayasuriya & Dassanayake 988* (E,
HBG, K, L, PDA, US), *Balasubramaniam 2031* (PDA).

21. CEROPEGIA

L., Sp. Pl. 211. 1753. Type Species: *Ceropegia candelabrum* L.

Twining, glabrous herbs with or without a globose, hypocotyledonary
tuber. Stem succulent with the leaves fleshy, sessile, lanceolate or reduced to
minute scales or absent; or stem slender with membranous, petiolate, ovate,
elliptic, oblong or lanceolate leaves. Flowers in peduncled, or rarely almost
sessile, umbel-like cymes arising solitary at the nodes. Calyx-lobes linear-
lanceolate to subulate, very acute. Corolla white or greenish, frequently
striped and mottled with purple; narrowly tubular with the base inflated,
mostly a little curved, glabrous without; the lobes shorter than to about as
long as the tube, triangular, semicircular, ovate or oblong, rarely almost obsolete, often produced into a long linear beak, always connate by their tips,
valvate or reduplicate in bud. Corona double, the outer series consisting of
five truncate or bifid and often elongated segments, shorter to longer than the
staminal column, hairy, rarely glabrous; inner series consisting of five linear,
subulate or narrowly spathulate segments, erect, much longer than the staminal column and frequently exceeding the outer corona, glabrous. Anthers not
produced into a membranous tip; pollen-masses solitary in each anther-
loculus, ascending, with a pellucid margin. Merocarps linear, tapering to the
apex, smooth.

A genus of about 160 species, widely distributed throughout the Old World Tropics, extending to South Africa, the Canary Islands, the Himalayas, West China and Queensland.

KEY TO THE SPECIES

1 Stem fleshy, leafless or leaves succulent, sessile, lanceolate or reduced to scales. Corolla-lobes 1.5–2.5 cm long, linear from a triangular base. Segments of inner corona recurved at the apex...**1. C. juncea**
1 Stem slender. Leaves well developed. Segments of the inner corona straight or connivent at the apex
  2 Stem arising from a globose tuber; roots slender. Corolla-tube cylindrical except for the inflated base, not funnel-shaped at the mouth, pubescent within throughout the cylindrical portion. Outer corona shorter than staminal column, consisting of five truncate segments, ciliate with long, delicate hairs................**6. C. candelabrum**
    3 Leaf-blade slightly fleshy, pellucid when dried. Corolla-lobes 1.2–about 2 cm long, at least half as long as the tube, suddenly contracted from an ovate base into a narrowly linear beak..subsp. **tuberosa**
    3 Leaf-blade rather firm, not fleshy, hardly or not pellucid when dried. Corolla-lobes up to 0.6 cm long, much shorter than the tube, ovate-oblong....subsp. **candelabrum**
  2 Tuber absent; roots often fleshy. Corolla-tube frequently funnel-shaped at the mouth, glabrous within except for a narrow transverse band of pubescence separating the inflated base from the distal half of the tube. Outer corona exceeding staminal column, consisting of five deeply bifid segments
    4 Corolla-lobes longer than wide, persistently villous within with purple hairs........
    ....**2. C. taprobanica**
    4 Corolla-lobes ciliate with long, stiff, easily detachable hairs, or perfectly glabrous
      5 Corolla (including the lobes) 1.4–2 cm long; upper half of corolla-tube cylindric, not widened at the mouth...**5. C. parviflora**
      5 Corolla 3 to 5 cm long; corolla-tube broadly funnel-shaped at the mouth
        6 Corolla-lobes ovate-oblong, slightly longer than wide............**3. C. thwaitesii**
        6 Corolla-lobes broadly triangular or broadly ovate, sometimes almost obsolete, as long as wide or wider than long.................................**4. C. elegans**
          7 Mouth of the corolla-tube 1–2 cm in diameter, acutely angled in the sinuses between the lobes...var. **elegans**
          7 Mouth of the corolla-tube 2.5–3.5 cm in diameter, strongly prominent into five rounded pouches in the sinuses between the lobes.................var. **gardneri**

1. Ceropegia juncea Roxb., Pl. Corom. 1: 12, t. 10. 1795; Hook. f., Fl. Br. Ind. 4: 68. 1883. Huber, Mem. Soc. Brot. 12: 85. 1958. Type: Roxb., Pl. Corom. 1: 12. t. 10. 1795.

Underground shoot not tuberous, with fleshy roots. Stem succulent. Leaves sessile, 0.7–about 2 cm long, 0.3–0.6 cm wide, lanceolate, fleshy, frequently absent. Cymes few-flowered; peduncle absent or up to 2.5 cm long. Calyx-lobes 5–6 mm long, glabrous. Corolla pale greenish, veined and mottled with purple; 3–6 cm long; the tube inflated in or below the lower quarter, abruptly narrowed above, funnel-shaped at the mouth; the lobes 1.5–2.5 cm long, linear from a triangular base, slightly spathulate and hairy within at the apex. Outer corona consisting of five broadly triangular, bifid segments, ciliate, about as high as or little taller than the staminal column; segments of the inner corona linear, with hooked tips. Merocarps 15–17 cm long, about 0.6 cm in diameter.

D i s t r. Southern Deccan Peninsula and northernmost part of Ceylon.

In Ceylon, recently discovered as a twiner in fences.

S p e c i m e n E x a m i n e d. JAFFNA DISTRICT: Vaddukoddai, *Balasubramaniam s.n.* (PDA).

2. Ceropegia taprobanica Huber, nom. nov.* Type: *Trimen s.n.* 26 Sept. 1888 (PDA).

Ceropegia decaisneana "Wight" Trimen, Handb. Fl. Ceylon 3: 166. 1895; Huber, Mem. Soc. Brot. 12: 62. 1958 as to the occurrence in Ceylon; Huber in Abeywick., Rev. Handb. Fl. Ceylon 1 (1): 54. 1973. Not *C. decaisneana* Wight.

Underground shoot not tuberous; roots fleshy, fasciculate. Stem slender. Petiole 1–3 cm long. Leaf-blade 3–16 cm long and 1–7 cm wide, variable in shape, ovate, elliptic, obovate or lanceolate, truncate or rounded or obtuse at the base, acute and acuminate at the apex. Cymes few-(1- to 8-) flowered; the peduncle much longer than the petioles. Calyx-lobes (3-) 6–7 mm long, glabrous. Corolla greenish-white, mottled with purple, (3) 5–8 cm long; the tube strongly inflated in the lower third or half, abruptly narrowed in the middle and gradually expanding towards the funnel-shaped mouth in the typical form; the lobes 2–3.5 cm long and nearly as long as the tube, linear from a triangular base in the typical form, villous within with purple hairs towards the apex.

D i s t r. Endemic in Ceylon.

E c o l. A rare plant of the mountain country, known from two collections only.

S p e c i m e n s E x a m i n e d. KANDY DISTRICT: Rangala, by the path to Nitre Cave Distr., 3800 ft, 26 Sept. 1888, *Trimen s.n.* (PDA). RATNAPURA DISTRICT: Gilimale, *Balasubramaniam 277* (PDA).

N o t e. Both Trimen and the author (1973) have incorrectly assigned these specimens to *C. decaisneana* Wight, which is a tuberous plant and always

---

*CEROPEGIA ad sectionem Janthinam pertinens, parte subterranea haud tuberosa caule foliisque tenuibus glabris, foliis longius petiolatis, inflorescentiis perpaucifloris glabris longe pedunculatis, calycis segmentis 6 ad 7 mm longis glabris, corolla 5 cm longa vel plus, per dimidiam vel tertiam partem inferiorem forte inflata, lobis 2 cm longis vel plus, e basi deltoidea linearibus, apicem versus pilis purpureis crispis persistentibus nec clavatis villosulis.

shows some pubescence, particularly on the young shoots and frequently also on the upper side of the leaves and the back of the calyx-segments; besides that, the peduncle of *C. decaisneana* bears a line of hairs and the calyx-lobes attain a length of 1 to 1.5 cm. *Ceropegia taprobanica* differs by glabrous shoots, inflorescence and calyx, and the shorter calyx-segments (6 to 7 mm in the Rangala, about 3 mm in the Gilimale, plant).

Balasubramaniam 277, in spite of its short calyx-lobes, smaller flowers hardly 3 cm long, the corolla-tube cylindrical in the distal portion and not or scarcely funnel-shaped at the mouth and the narrowly triangular corolla-lobes only 6 mm long, almost certainly represents the same species as the plant from Rangala. Unfortunately the paucity of the material does not allow one to dissect flowers and complete the description above.

3. Ceropegia thwaitesii Hook., Bot. Mag. t. 4758. 1854; Thw., Enum. Pl. Zeyl. 199. 1860; Hook. f., Fl. Br. Ind. 4: 71. 1883; Trimen, Handb. Fl. Ceylon 3: 166. 1895; Huber, Mem. Soc. Brot. 12: 71. 1958. Type: A specimen grown at Kew Gardens (K).

Underground shoot not tuberous. Stem slender. Petiole 1–3 cm long. Leaf-blade 5–10 cm long and 2.5–5 cm wide, ovate or ovate-lanceolate, rounded or shallowly cordate at the base, acute and acuminate at the apex. Cymes one- to five-flowered; the peduncle shorter to slightly longer than the petioles, at most twice as long. Calyx-lobes 6–8 mm long, glabrous. Corolla greenish with purple blotches towards the mouth of the tube and a purple band across the lobes, 3.5–5 cm long; the tube strongly inflated in the lower third or half, abruptly narrowed in the middle and gradually expanding towards the funnel-shaped mouth; the lobes 1 to 1.8 cm long, about half as long as the tube, ovate-oblong, slightly longer than wide at the base when expanded, glabrous. Outer corona consisting of five bifid, hairy segments exceeding the staminal column; segments of the inner corona linear, connivent-erect, twice as long as the outer corona, with the tips straight.

D i s t r. Southern Deccan Peninsula and Ceylon.

E c o l. A rare plant of the moist hill country. Not found by any recent collector. Flowering in December.

S p e c i m e n s E x a m i n e d. KANDY DISTRICT: Peradeniya, *Gardner* in *C.P. 1842* (PDA). LOCALITY UNKNOWN: Apr. 1866, *s. coll. s.n.* (GH, K).

4. Ceropegia elegans Wall., Bot. Mag. t. 3015. 1830; Thw., Enum. Pl. Zeyl. 199. 1860; Hook. f., Fl. Br. Ind. 4: 68. 1883; Trimen, Handb. Fl. Ceylon 3: 165. 1895; Huber, Mem. Soc. Brot. 12: 72. 1958. Type: A specimen grown at Kew Gardens (K).

Ceropegia walkeriae Wight, Ic. Pl. Ind. Or. 4 (2): 15, t. 1266. 1848; Hook. f., Fl. Br. Ind. 4: 69. 1883.
Ceropegia elegans Wall. var. *walkerae* (Wight) Trimen, Handb. Fl. Ceylon 3: 165. 1895.

Underground shoot not tuberous, with numerous fibrous roots. Petiole 1–3 cm long. Leaf-blade 4–9 cm long and 1.5–5 cm wide, ovate, elliptic or ovate-lanceolate, rounded or truncate at the base, rounded and short-acuminate or acute and long-acuminate at the apex. Cymes normally few-flowered; the peduncle shorter or at most slightly longer than the petioles. Calyx-lobes 4–6 mm long, glabrous. Corolla greenish-white, white or cream-coloured, mottled and dotted with purple, 3–5 cm long; the tube inflated in the lower third, abruptly narrowed in the middle, gradually expanded into a broadly funnel-shaped mouth; the lobes 0.5–1.2 cm long, about as long as the diameter of the mouth or shorter, semicircular, broadly triangular or occasionally almost obsolete, ciliate with long, purple hairs or glabrous (perhaps not under natural conditions). Outer corona consisting of five deeply bifid, elongate segments, glabrous or ciliate, much longer than the staminal column; the segments of the inner corona linear, connivent-erect, as long as or slightly longer than the outer corona, with the tips straight.

D i s t r. Southern Deccan Peninsula and Ceylon.

E c o l. A plant of the intermediate and moist zone ranging from the lowland (but never far from the hills) up to an elevation of 1200 m. Rather common according to Thwaites and Trimen but rarely collected within the last decades.

Ceropegia elegans Wall. is an extremely variable plant with little correlation between the different characters. Therefore apart from the typical plant only one variety is recognized here.

1. var. elegans

Cymes one- or few-flowered, short-peduncled or the peduncles only little longer than the petioles; rarely the cymes almost sessile. Corolla pale green or greenish-white, spotted and stained with purple; the mouth of the tube 1–2 cm in diameter, acutely angled between the lobes.

S p e c i m e n s E x a m i n e d. KANDY DISTRICT: Bambrella, c. 1330 m, *Meïjer 1237* (US); Hantane, *Gardner in C.P. 738* (K, P, PDA); Nitre Cave Area, Sept. 1888, *Trimen s.n.* (PDA). NUWARA ELIYA (or BADULLA?) DISTRICT: Patana on the way from Horton Plains to Belihul Oya, over half elevation, 23 Jan. 1910, *Rothert s.n.* (PDA). BADULLA DISTRICT: Bolandavela Hill, Ooma Oya, *Silva 231* (PDA); Ekiriyankumbura, 20 Jan. 1888, *Trimen's collector s.n.* (PDA). DISTRICT UNKNOWN: Kirivaneliya, *Reitz 30006* (PDA, US); between Kumbukkan and Muppane, 18 March 1927, *Silva s.n.* (PDA). LOCALITY UNKNOWN: *Walker* in herb Gardner *s.n.* (K).

N o t e. Mrs. Walker's collection includes several most strikingly aberrant specimens which differ by exceptionally long-peduncled and many-flowered cymes and partly by their rather small flowers. None of these features, however, seems to be constant enough to allow a clear distinction from var. *elegans*. These plants have nothing to do with *C. walkeriae* Wight. Unfortunately the place where they have been collected is not given.

2. var. gardneri (Thw.) Huber, Mem. Soc. Brot. 12: 73. 1958. Type: *Gardner 565* (K).

Ceropegia gardneri Thw., Enum. Pl. Zeyl. 199. 1860; Hook. f., Fl. Br. Ind. 4: 69. 1883; Trimen, Handb. Fl. Ceylon 3: 165. 1895.

Cymes one- or few-flowered. Peduncle about as long as the petioles or but slightly longer. Corolla white, dotted with purple; the mouth of the tube 2.5–3.5 cm in diameter, strongly prominent into five rounded pouches in the sinuses between the lobes; the latter long-ciliate.

D i s t r. Endemic in Ceylon. A plant of the moist hill country. Not found since the last century and perhaps extinct in the wild state. In Europe grown in greenhouses.

S p e c i m e n s E x a m i n e d. NUWARA ELIYA DISTRICT: Ramboda, 4000 to 5000 ft, *Gardner 565* (K), *Gardner 566* (K, L), *Gardner in C.P. 2838* (PDA). LOCALITY UNKNOWN: *Walker* in herb. Gardner *s.n.* (FI).

5. Ceropegia parviflora Trimen, J. Bot. 27: 164. 1889; Trimen, Handb. Fl. Ceylon 3: 167, plate LXIII. 1895; Huber, Mem. Soc. Brot. 12: 72. 1958. Type: *Trimen s.n.* (K).

Underground shoot not tuberous, with fasciculate roots. Stem slender. Petiole 1–3.5 cm long. Leaf-blade 5–7 cm long and 3–5.5 cm wide, ovate-oblong to broadly ovate, rounded or very shallowly cordate at the base, acute or short-acuminate at the apex. Cymes rather few-(2- to 5-) flowered; the peduncle shorter than or about as long as the petioles. Calyx-lobes about 4 mm long, glabrous. Corolla pale greenish or yellowish, 1.4–2 cm long; the tube strongly inflated in the lower third or half, abruptly narrowed in the middle and narrowly cylindrical above, not or hardly funnel-shaped at the mouth; the lobes 0.2–0.6 cm long, oblong, glabrous in the herbarium. Outer corona consisting of five deeply bifid segments, hairy at their base and exceeding the staminal column; the segments of the inner corona linear, connivent-erect, slightly longer than the outer corona, with the tips straight.

D i s t r. Endemic in Ceylon.

E c o l. A very local plant of the dry zone, known only from a few places near Anuradhapura. Flowering in February.

Specimens Examined. ANURADHAPURA DISTRICT: Near Anuradhapura, Feb. 1889, *Trimen s.n.* (K, PDA).

6. Ceropegia candelabrum L., Sp. Pl. 211. 1753; Thw., Enum. Pl. Zeyl. 199. 1860; Hook. f., Fl. Br. Ind. 4: 70. 1883; Huber, Mem. Soc. Brot. 12: 58. 1958. Type: Rheede, Hort. Mal. 9, t. 16. 1689.

Ceropegia biflora L., Sp. Pl. 211. 1753; Trimen, Handb. Fl. Ceylon 3: 167. 1895.

Ceropegia intermedia "Wight" Hook. f., Fl. Br. Ind. 4: 71. 1883 pro parte, as to the Ceylon specimens, not *C. intermedia* Wight.

Persisting underground organ a usually globose tuber; roots and stem slender. Petiole 0.5–1 cm long. Leaf-blade 3–7 cm long and 0.3–2 cm wide, very variable in shape, ovate, elliptic, obovate, oblong, lanceolate, or linear, the lower often almost orbicular; acute or rounded at the base, obtuse or tapering to and often apiculate at the apex. Cymes few- to rather many-flowered; peduncle longer than petioles. Calyx-lobes 3 to 5 mm long, glabrous. Corolla greenish-white, striped with purple on the tube, the lobes often suffused with purple or brown, yellowish within; corolla 2.4 to 5 cm long, the tube slightly inflated in the lower third or half, cylindric above and not funnel-shaped at the mouth; inflated portion glabrous inside, cylindrical portion evenly pubescent on inside with colourless hairs; lobes much shorter to almost as long as the tube, pubescent inside with crisp, white hairs. Outer corona consisting of five truncate segments much shorter than the staminal column, ciliate with long, delicate, colourless hairs; segments of inner corona slightly spathulate, obtuse or rounded at the apex, much exceeding the staminal column.

D i s t r. Southern and eastern part of Deccan Peninsula; Ceylon.

Within this species, two subspecies can be tentatively distinguished, more strongly differentiated ecologically than in their structure:

1. subsp. **tuberosa** (Roxb.) Huber, stat. nov. Type: Roxb., Pl. Corom. 1, t. 9. 1795.

Ceropegia tuberosa Roxb., Pl. Corom. 1: 12, t. 9. 1795; Hook. f., Fl. Br. Ind. 4: 70. 1883.

Leaf-blade slightly fleshy, pellucid when dried, variable in shape, very frequently apiculate at the apex. Corolla-lobes (1–) 1.2–about 2 cm long, abruptly contracted from an ovate base into a narrowly linear beak.

D i s t r. That of the species, but probably absent from the more humid regions.

E c o l. In Ceylon widely distributed but strictly seasonal in the dry region, rarely extending into the moist zone and confined there to clear, secondary vegetation. Absent from the higher elevations and the north of the island. Flowering from November to March, exceptionally in June.

V e r n. Wel-mottu (S).

S p e c i m e n s   E x a m i n e d. KURUNEGALA DISTRICT: Kurune-gala, 20 Dec. 1883, *Trimen s.n.* (PDA). MATALE DISTRICT: Naula, Jan. 1972, *Balasubramaniam s.n.* (PDA). BATTICALOA DISTRICT: Batticaloa-Kalmunai Road, near Kalathavelai-Tethathivu, *Balasubramaniam 2055* (PDA). COLOMBO DISTRICT: Colombo, (*Thwaites*) *C.P. 774* (PDA, W). BADULLA DISTRICT: Minivangoda near Passara, *Simpson 8849* (BM). MONERAGALA DISTRICT: Ombuwa Forest Reserve, teak plantation, mile post 157/2 of Moneragala-Wellawaya Road, *Faden 76/579* (PDA); near Nilgala, Jan. 1888, *Trimen s.n.* (PDA); Ruhuna National Park, Block 3, on road from Sellakataragama to Galge, *Cooray 69011906* (PDA, US). HAM-BANTOTA DISTRICT: Tissamaharama, Dec. 1882, *Trimen s.n.* (PDA); Near Angunakolapelessa, *Alston 1294* (PDA). DISTRICT UNKNOWN: Wattawelle, 26 Jan. 1923, *Lewis s.n.* (PDA). LOCALITY UNKNOWN: *Walker s.n.* (P).

2. subsp. candelabrum.

Leaf-blade rather firm, not fleshy, hardly or not pellucid when dried, usually elliptic, rounded or obtuse at base, acute, not or not markedly apicu-late at the apex. Corolla-lobes 0.4–0.6 cm long, ovate-oblong.

D i s t r. That of the species, especially in the moister parts of the area.

E c o l. In Ceylon, at present known from two localities only, both situat-ed at higher elevations than those of subsp. *tuberosa*.

S p e c i m e n s   E x a m i n e d. NUWARA ELIYA DISTRICT: Hak-gala Strict Natural Reserve, at the north side of the northern peak, 1900 m, *Klackenberg 175* (M, S). BADULLA DISTRICT: Near Passara, *Trimen s.n.* June 1888 (PDA).

22. CARALLUMA

R. Br., Mem. Wern. Nat. Hist. Soc. 1: 25. 1811, prepr. 1810. Type species: *Stapelia adscendens* Roxb.

Boucerosia Wight & Arn. ex Wight, Contr. Bot. India 34. 1834.

Strongly succulent, leafless or almost leafless plants. Stems decumbent or ascending, with ascending or erect branches, more or less quadrangular, glabrous, with or without conical tooth-like leaf-bases on the ribs; with very deciduous, minute leaves reduced to sessile, lanceolate or subulate scales. Flowers fetid, solitary or in few-flowered, sessile cymes from the teeth of the stem or in a many-flowered umbel-like inflorescence from the top of the stem.

Calyx-lobes ovate-lanceolate to linear-lanceolate, very acute. Corolla uniformly purple-brown within or yellowish with purple streaks, rotate or very shallowly campanulate, glabrous without; the lobes about as long as to much longer than the radius of the united portion, valvate in bud. Corona double, attached to the staminal column, the outer series consisting of five deeply bifid segments, the inner series of five linear segments incumbent on the anthers. Anthers not produced into a membranous tip; pollen-masses solitary in each anther-loculus, ascending, with a pellucid margin. Merocarps slender, fusiform, smooth.

A markedly xerophytic genus of c. one hundred species, often of a cactus-like appearance, centered in southern and eastern Africa, extending to the north into the Mediterranean and to the east through Arabia and India to Burma.

KEY TO THE SPECIES

1 Stems obtusely angled. Flowers solitary or in very few-flowered clusters from distant leaf-scars. Corolla-lobes lanceolate, much longer than the radius of the united portion ....**1. C. adscendens**

1 Stems sharply angled. Cymes several-flowered, crowded on the top of the stems and forming a globose inflorescence. Corolla-lobes broadly triangular, about as long as the radius of the united portion.......................................**2. C. umbellata**

1. Caralluma adscendens (Roxb.) Haworth, Syn. Pl. Succ. 47. 1812; Gravely and Mayuranathan, Ind. Sp. Gen. Caralluma 12. 1931. Type: Roxb., Pl. Corom. 1, t. 30. 1795.

Stapelia adscendens Roxb., Pl. Corom. 1: 28. 1795.

Caralluma adscendens (Roxb.) Haworth is represented in Ceylon by the following variety only:

var. **fimbriata** (Wall.) Gravely and Mayuranathan, Ind. Sp. Gen. Caralluma 13. 1931. Type: Wall., Pl. As. Rar. 1, t. 8. 1829.

Caralluma fimbriata Wall., Pl. As. Rar. 1: 7. 1829; Trimen, Handb. Fl. Ceylon 3: 168. 1895.
Caralluma attenuata Thw., Enum. Pl. Zeyl. 200. 1860; Hook. f., Fl. Br. Ind. 4: 76. 1883. Not *C. attenuata* Wight.

Stem ascending and rooting at the base, then upraised, sometimes arched at the summit, 7–20 cm tall and 4–8 mm in diameter, obtusely quadrangular with the ribs broadly rounded and the sides very faintly sulcate; without prominent teeth; teeth reduced to small tubercles less than 1 mm high, 5 (–10) mm apart from each other; greyish-green. Leaves, when developed, up to 2.5 mm long, subulate. Cymes sessile and mostly reduced to a single flower, arising obliquely from little above the leaf-scars of the upper half of the stem. Pedicel slender, slightly nodding, 2–3 mm long. Calyx-lobes 1.2–1.8 mm long. Corolla 1–1.2 cm in diameter when expanded, slightly campanulate, uniformly purple-brown; the lobes lanceolate, much longer than the united portion, reduplicate, glabrous without and within but densely ciliate with long, purple bristles in the upper half of the margin.

D i s t r. Deccan Peninsula, Ceylon and Burma. *Caralluma adscendens* var. *fimbriata* is more widely distributed than the other varieties of the species, which are restricted to the Deccan Peninsula.

E c o l. A rare plant of the dry region, growing in arid, stony places. Flowering from November to May.

V e r n. Mankalli (T).

S p e c i m e n s   E x a m i n e d. MATALE DISTRICT: About 8 miles east-southeast of Dambulla, hills above Mahaweli Project anicut, *Davidse 7426* (PDA); hill southeast of Dambulla, 340 m, *Huber 765* (US). BADULLA DISTRICT: Ooma Oya, *s. coll. C.P. 3304* (PDA).

2. Caralluma umbellata Haworth, Syn. Pl. Succ. 47. 1812; Gravely and Mayuranathan, Ind. Sp. Gen. Caralluma 23. 1931. Type: not preserved.

Stapelia umbellata (Haworth) Roxb., Pl. Corom. 3: 36. 1819.
Boucerosia umbellata (Haworth) Wight & Arn. ex Wight, Contr. Bot. India 34. 1834; Thw., Enum. Pl. Zeyl. 200. 1860; Hook. f., Fl. Br. Ind. 4: 77. 1883.
Boucerosia campanulata Wight, Ic. Pl. Ind. Or. 4 (2): 1, t. 1287. 1848.
Caralluma campanulata (Wight) N. E. Br., Gard. Chron. 12: 369. 1892; Trimen, Handb. Fl. Ceylon 3: 168. 1895.

Stem long-decumbent or ascending, rooting at the base, up to 50 cm long, 6–10 (–20) cm tall and 1–2 cm in diameter; sharply quadrangular with the sides concave and with prominent, conical teeth on the ribs; teeth 2–3 mm high, 6–about 10 mm apart from each other; bright green. Cymes crowded at the top of the stems, forming a large, umbel-like inflorescence. Pedicels straight, (5–) 20–30 mm long. Calyx-lobes 2.5–3 mm long. Corolla 2–3 cm in diameter, rotate or very shallowly campanulate, uniformly purple-brown or yellow with concentric purplish streaks*, densely velvety within, not ciliate on the margin, with broadly triangular lobes about as long as the radius of the united portion. Merocarps 10–15 cm long, 0.5–1 cm in diameter, glabrous.

D i s t r. Nepal, central and southeastern Deccan Peninsula and Ceylon.

E c o l. In Ceylon, a rare plant of the dry and intermediate zone, usually on rocky outcrops in partial shade of *Euphorbia antiquorum* L. Flowering in

*In Ceylon only the form with one-coloured, purplish-brown flowers.

January (Kurunegala, Minninirainchan) or August/September (Kurunegala, Wikiliya).

Specimens Examined. MANNAR DISTRICT: Minninirainchan, *Jayasuriya et al. 611* (PDA, US). KURUNEGALA DISTRICT: Kurunegala, *s. coll. C.P. 2861* (BM, PDA), *Trimen s.n.* Aug. 1883 (PDA); Toragasyaya, Jan. 1928, *Silva s.n.* (PDA). RATNAPURA DISTRICT: Wikiliya, Haldola Road, on a stony hill near the temple, 540 m, *Faden 76/656* (PDA), *Huber 846* (HBG, PDA, US).

AVICENNIACEAE

(by Harold N. Moldenke and Alma L. Moldenke*)

Type genus: *Avicennia* L.

Shrubs or trees of maritime or other saline regions, mostly inhabiting the saline or brackish coastal mangrove lagoons, with abundant pencil-like erect pneumatophores, very rarely with knee-, aerial-, or stilt-roots; growth in diameter of trunks and stems brought about by concentric layers of mestome rings; branches, branchlets and twigs commonly terete, prominently nodose, and articulate; leaves decussate-opposite, thick-textured or coriaceous, persistent, petiolate, simple, exstipulate, the blades entire, net-veined; inflorescence axillary or terminal, determinate and centrifugal (cymose), spicate or subspicate, often abbreviated to appear capitate or subcapitate, the axillary inflorescences mostly paired; flowers sessile, perfect, hypogynous, small; calyx composed of 5 nearly separate sepals, the free portions ovate and plainly imbricate, mostly unchanged in fruit, subtended by a pseudo-involucre composed of a scale-like bractlet and 2 alternate scale-like prophylla, which are slightly shorter than the calyx and are imbricate with each other and with the calyx-segments; corolla actinomorphic (or practically so), gamopetalous at the base, campanulate-rotate, 4-parted; stamens 4, inserted in the throat of the corolla-tube, equal or subdidynamous, exserted during full anthesis; gynoecium composed of 2 united carpels; ovary superior, sessile, compound but with a free central and often more or less 4-winged placenta; ovules 4, pendent, orthotropous, hanging from the tip of the central columella; fruit a compressed oblique capsule, with a juicy and somewhat fleshy usually tomentellous exocarp, dehiscent by 2 valves, by abortion regularly only 1-seeded; seeds without a testa; endosperm none; embryo viviparous or semi-viviparous; radicle hairy; cotyledons 2, folded lengthwise.

Comprising only the genus *Avicennia*.

The family is often united with the Verbenaceae, but unlike that family is thought to have evolved from the Dipterocarpaceae or Ancistrocladaceae and is perhaps related to the Salvadoraceae.

*Plainfield, New Jersey, U.S.A.

AVICENNIA

L., Sp. Pl. ed. 1. 110. 1753; L., Gen. Pl. ed. 5. 49. 1754. Type species: *Avicennia officinalis* L.

Bontia L. ex Loefl., Iter Hisp. 193. 1758 [not *Bontia* L., 1735].—*Bontia* P. Br., Civil & Nat. Hist. Jamaic. ed. 2. 263. 1789.

Donatia Loefl., Iter Hisp. 193, in syn. 1758 [not *Donatia* Bert., 1849, nor J.R. & K. Forst., 1776].

Horau Adans., Fam. Pl. 2: 80 & 585. 1763.

Upata Rheede ex Adans., Fam. Pl. 2: 12 & 201. 1763.—*Upata* Adans. ex Schau. in Mart., Fl. Bras. 9: 302, in syn. 1851.

Oepata Rheede ex Adans., Fam. Pl. 2: 201, in syn. 1763.

Sceura Forsk., Fl. Aegypt.-Arab. 37. 1775.

Racua J.F. Gmel. in L., Syst. ed. 13, 2: 1612. 1789.

Corna Noronha, Verh. Batav. Gen. 5, ed. 1, art. 4: 2. 1790.

Racka Bruce ex J.F. Gmel. in L., Syst. ed. 13 rev. 2: 245, in syn. 1791; Wittstein, Etymol.-botan. Handwörterb. 749. 1852—*Racka* J.F. Gmel. ex Jacks. in Hook. f. & Jacks., Ind. Kew. 2: 679. 1895.

Halodendrum Thou., Gen. Nov. Madag. 8. 1806.

Halodendron Roem. & Schult. in L., Syst. ed. 15 nov. 3: 485. 1818 [not *Halodendron* P. DC., 1825].

Avicenia Griff., Notul. Pl. Asiat. 4: 173, sphalm. 1854.

Hilairanthus Van Tiegh., J. Bot. 12: 357–358. 1898.

Saltzmanna Roxb. ex Moldenke, Phytologia 7: 140, in syn. 1960.

Glabrous or canescent shrubs or trees, with wide-creeping shallow roots and usually very numerous pencil-like erect pneumatophores, very rarely with knee-, aerial-, or stilt-roots; leaf-blades often quite variable, more or less coriaceous or subcoriaceous, glabrous on both surfaces and quite shiny or densely furfuraceous-tomentellous beneath, often with salty excrescences, frequently insect-galled; cymes contracted, often capituliform, pedunculate, usually paired in the axils of the upper leaves or arranged in a short terminal thyrse or trichotomous corymb on the branchlets; calyx coriaceous, cupuliform, gamopetalous, short, deeply 5-partite, often sericeous, unchanged and not accrescent in the fruiting stage, the sepals nearly separate, the free portions varying from oblong to ovate or broadly ovate, plainly imbricate, usually rounded or obtuse at the apex; corolla campanulate or campanulate-rotate, varying from white or whitish to yellow or orange, its tube very short, wide, cylindric or infundibular, straight, the limb spreading during anthesis, usually 4- (rarely 5-) parted, the lobes subequal or the posterior one a little broader, usually obovate-oblong and rounded at the apex; filaments usually short, filiform; anthers ovoid, scarcely exserted from the corolla-tube, with 2 parallel thecae; style short, bifid or bilobate, the lobes stigmatiferous at their apex; ovary varying from completely 1-celled to imperfectly 2- or 4-celled, with 2 or 1 ovule in each imperfectly formed cell or 4-ovulate; fruit often mucronate or apiculate at the apex, rarely symmetric, with a dry or somewhat fleshy, usually furfuraceous or tomentellous exocarp, mostly dehiscent by 2 thickened valves; embryo naked because of the arrested development of the ovule integuments; radicle inferior, the plumule often commencing to grow before the fruit falls; cotyledons large.

A genus of about 12 living species and 10 named varieties and forms inhabiting the maritime (and sometimes other inland saline) regions of the tropics and subtropics of both the Eastern and Western Hemispheres; one of the chief constituents of almost all coastal mangrove forests and lagoons; at least five (perhaps six) fossil species known from the Tertiary and Pleistocene of the U.S.A., Trinidad, Colombia and Borneo. They are important in land formation from the seas. Some species have extremely nectariferous flowers and are valuable in the honey-making industry. In India the wood of some species is occasionally used for rough walling or fuel and the foliage as fodder. In Ceylon the genus is represented by two species.

It should be noted that the English name, "mangrove", in Ceylon is applied not only to members of this genus, but also to *Aegiceras corniculatum* (L.) Blanco, *Bruguiera* Lam., *Ceriops* Arn. and *Rhizophora* L.

KEY TO THE SPECIES

1 Leaf-blades ovate or lanceolate to lanceolate-oblong or elliptic, usually abruptly acute at the apex; expanded corolla only 5–8 mm wide.........................**1. A. marina**
1 Leaves obovate or broadly oblong, rounded at the apex; expanded corolla 12–15 mm wide...**2. A. officinalis**

1. Avicennia marina (Forsk.) Vierh., Denkschr. Kaiserl. Akad. Wissensch. Wien Math.-Naturwiss wiss. Kl. 71: 435. 1907; Clarke in Hook. f., Fl. Br. Ind. 4: 604. 1885; Trimen, Handb. Fl. Ceylon 3: 363–364. 1895; Alston in Trimen, Handb. Fl. Ceylon 6: 233. 1931; Abeywick., Ceylon J. Sci., Biol. Sci. 2: 218. 1959; Moldenke, Phytologia 7: 210–225 & 293 (1960), 14: 328–331 (1967), 15: 475–476 (1968) & 34: 76–93. 1976; Gaussen, Viart, Legris & Labroue, Trav. Sect. Sci. Techn. Inst. Franc. Pond. Hors 5: 25. 1965; Arulchelvam, Ceylon Forester ser. 2, 8: 73 & 75. 1968; Gunawardena, Gen. & Sp. Pl. Zeyl. 148. 1968; Fonseka & Vinasithamby, Prov. List Local Names Fl. Pl. Ceylon 96. 1971. Type: *Forskål s.n.* from the edge of the Red Sea, Yemen, Arabia (BM).

Sceura marina Forsk., Fl. Aegypt.-Arab. 2: 37. 1775.
Rack Bruce, Trav. Abyss. & Nub. 2: app. 44. 1790.
Racka torrida J.F. Gmel. in L., Syst., ed. 13, 2: 245. 1791.—*Racka torrida* Bruce ex Bakh., Bull. Jard. Bot. Buitenzorg ser. 3, 3: 205, in syn. 1921.
Halodendron thouarsi Roem. & Schult. in L., Syst. ed. 15 nov., 3: 485. 1818.
Racka ovata Roem. & Schult. in L., Syst. ed. 15 nov., 3: 207. 1818.

Avicennia tomentosa L. ex Blume, Bijdr. 14: 821. 1826 (not *A. tomentosa* Blanco, 1845, nor Blume, 1918, nor Jacq., 1760, nor L. & Jacq., 1783, nor R. Br., 1851, nor G.F.W. Mey., 1818, nor Nutt., 1947, nor Nutt. & Br., 1832, nor Roxb., 1835, nor Schau., 1940, nor Sieber, 1844, nor Sw., 1864, nor Willd., 1800, nor Weigelt, 1851).—*A. tomentosa* Wall. ex Schau. in Mart., Fl. Bras. 9: 306, in syn. 1851; Boiss., Fl. Orient. 4: 536–537, in syn. 1876.—*A. tomentosa* Vahl ex Bakh., Bull. Jard. Bot. Buitenzorg ser. 3, 3: 204, in syn. 1921.

Avicennia tomentosa var. *arabica* Walp., Rep. 4: 133. 1845.

Avicennia intermedia W. Griff., Trans. Linn. Soc. London Bot. 20: 6, pl. 1. 1846.

Avicennia officinalis var. *ovatifolia* Kuntze, Rev. Gen. 2: 502. 1891.

Avicennia officinalis var. *ovatifolia* f. *flaviflora* Kuntze, Rev. Gen. 3 (3): 249. 1898.

Avicennia officinalis var. *ovatifolia* f. *tomentosa* Kuntze, Rev. Gen. 3 (3): 249. 1898.

Avicennia mindanaense Elm., Leafl. Philipp. Bot. 8: 2868. 1915.

Avicennia sphaerocarpa Stapf ex Ridl., J. Fed. Malay States Mus. 10: 51. 1920; Ridl., Fl. Malay Pen. 2: 642. 1923.

Avicennia marina var. *typica* Bakh., Bull. Jard. Bot. Buitenzorg ser. 3, 3: 205. 1921.

Avicennia marina var. *intermedia* (Griff.) Bakh., Bull. Jard. Bot. Buitenzorg ser. 3, 3: 211. 1921.

Avicennia alba Wight ex Bakh., Bull. Jard. Bot. Buitenzorg ser. 3, 3: 211, in syn. 1921 [not *A. alba* Blume, 1826, nor Karst., 1907].

Avicennia officinalis var. *nigra* Cowan, Rec. Bot. Surv. India 11: 203 & 220. 1928.

Avicennia officinalis Maxim. ex P'ei, Mem. Sci. Soc. China 1 (3): 186, in syn. 1932 [not *A. officinalis* L., 1753, nor H.J. Lam, 1940, nor Millsp., 1930, nor Schau., 1856].—*A. officinalis* Auct. ex Cuf., Bull. Jard. Bot. Etat 32: Suppl. 803, in syn. 1962 [not *A. officinalis* Auct. ex Allan, 1961].—*A. officinalis* sensu Matsum. ex Liu, Ill. Nat. & Introd. Lign. Pl. Taiwan 2: 1201, in syn. 1962.

Trichorhiza lechenaultii Miq. ex Moldenke, Prelim. Alph. List Invalid Names 43, in syn. 1940.

Avicennia lanceolata Willd. ex Moldenke, Phytologia 7: 210, in syn. 1960 [not *A. lanceolata* (Engelh.) Moldenke, 1960].

Avicennia mariana Vierh. ex Moldenke, Phytologia 7: 110, in syn. 1960.

Avicennia racemosa Cornwell ex Moldenke, Phytologia 7: 110, in syn. 1960.

Avicennia nitida Thunb. ex Moldenke, Phytologia 7: 111, in syn. 1960 [not *A. nitida* Jacq., 1760, nor Blanco, 1837, nor L., 1960, nor L. & Jacq., 1783, nor Rodsch., 1844, nor Sessé & Moc., 1895].—*A. nitida* sensu Blanco ex Liu, Ill. Nat. & Introd. Lign. Pl. Taiwan 2: 1201, in syn. 1962.

Low-growing or large, erect, willow-like, much-branched tree or shrub, to 10 m tall, sending out soft, radiating, horizontal roots about 15 cm below the surface of the ground often to 6 m, with many, erect, thin, finger-like or pencil-like tapering pneumatophores about 10 cm tall; trunk to 25.5 cm in diameter and 60 cm in circumference 2 m from the ground, sometimes with a few aerial roots along the trunk to a height of 2 m but not reaching the ground, occasionally with a few supporting prop-roots; old bark smooth, varying from white to greyish-white or olivaceous, the living bark green; wood pale or white, heavy, hard, burly, with a turnip-like odour; branchlets and twigs rather slender, decussate, subterete or subquadrangular, densely pulverulent-puberulent with buff, greyish or whitish furf, or sometimes merely obscurely pulverulent and brown in colour or even glabrate (after the thin, outer, whitish or greyish, densely pulverulent-puberulent bark has worn off); nodes swollen, conspicuously annulate, articulate; principal internodes 0.8–7.6 cm long; petioles rather stout, 3–14 mm long, flattened above, mostly longitudinally wrinkled beneath in drying, ampliate at the base, usually densely pulverulent-puberulent or tomentellous with incanous, cinereous, or greenish-yellow furf, rarely only very obscurely so or even glabrate; leaf-blades firmly chartaceous, subcoriaceous, or coriaceous, usually light green on both surfaces or silvery beneath when fresh, very dark green and shiny above when dry, mostly brunnescent or nigrescent in drying, varying from sordid-grey or white to flavidous beneath, varying from ovate or lanceolate to lanceolate-oblong or elliptic, 3.5–12 cm long, 1.3–5 cm wide, usually rather abruptly acute at the apex, more rarely sharply acute, entire and with the margins usually very slightly subrevolute, acute or acuminate at the base and prolonged into the petiole, more or less obscurely pulverulent or glabrous and sometimes more or less resinous- or impressed-punctate above, densely pulverulent-puberulent with cinereous or incanous to flavidous furf beneath; inflorescence axillary and terminal, the axillary ones mostly solitary in each axil (or rarely paired), 1.5–5 cm long, 7–15 mm wide, mostly capitate or subcapitate, occasionally short-spicate with about 2 opposite flowers borne a slight distance below the terminal cluster of 3 or 5; terminal inflorescences arranged in paniculate fashion, subfoliose, the cymes few- or many-flowered; peduncles stout or slender, 0.6–4 cm long, deeply sulcate in drying, similar to the twigs in puberulence, but the furf usually more sordid or flavidous and denser; flowers odorous, with the fragrance of honey, usually without a marked blooming season, the single bractlet and 2 prophylla ovate or broadly ovate, about 2.5 mm long, concave, obtuse or rounded at the apex, glabrous on the inner surface, densely silvery-tomentose or sericeous along the margins and on the back or glabrescent; calyx small, urceolate, about as long as the corolla, green, its tube very short, the lobes imbricate, rounded-ovate or broadly ovate to elliptic, 2–4 mm long, rounded at the apex, glabrous on the inner surface, pubescent on the back, ciliate along the margins; corolla white, soon turning yellow, orange-yellow, or orange to dull orange, dark orange, or red-orange, rigid, nigrescent in drying, its tube campanulate, 1–2 mm long, equalling or shorter than the calyx, the lobes 4, ovate or rounded-ovate to oblong, 3–4 mm long, radiately patent or erecto-patent, glabrous on the inner (upper) surface, densely and minutely tomentellous or sericeous on the outside except at the very apex; stamens very shortly exserted during full anthesis; anthers black, subrotund, compressed, about as long as the filaments; style filiform, narrower than and half as long as the ovary or subobsolete, smooth, yellow; stigmas manifest, as long as or shorter than the style, subsessile, filiform, obtuse; fruiting-calyx hardly changed, the bractlet, prophylla, and sepals densely puberulent on the outer surface, closely appressed to the base of the fruit; fruit yellowish-green or pale green to greyish-green, ovate or conic, 1.2–2.5 cm long, 7–20 mm wide, mostly somewhat asymmetric (at least when young), densely cinereous- or incanous-pulverulent, distinctly beaked when young but usually not beaked when mature, mostly dehiscent while still on the tree; seed single, large, compressed; cotyledons reniform, light green, punctate; radicle cylindric, hirsute at the base.

D i s t r. This very variable and widespread species is found in its typical form from Egypt and Arabia, along both shores of the Red Sea and the western Indian Ocean to the Cape of Good Hope, eastward along the shores of the Arabian Sea, the Bay of Bengal, the northern and eastern Indian Ocean, the South China Sea north to Hong Kong and Taiwan, and the islands of the Philippine Sea, Coral Sea, and South Pacific to New Zealand.

E c o l. It inhabits tidal mudflats, low ground flooded by salt water, seashores, brackish swamps, rocky sea beaches, and shallow salt water lakemargins, as well as certain inland salt lakes, flowering and fruiting practically throughout the year.

U s e s. In parts of its range this plant is used by native inhabitants for tooth-picks, fire-wood, and for making boats, the wood being quite resistant to shipworms. The plant is also said to have medicinal properties and the mucilaginous roots are employed as an aphrodisiac.

V e r n. Kannamaram, Kanna, Venkandal (T).

N o t e s. This species has been confused very widely with *A. officinalis* L. in older literature, and in herbaria, but is usually very distinct from it. Where the ranges of both species overlap, hybrids probably occur.

It is possible that especially small-leaved populations found from Malabar to Malaya and Indochina, north to Hong Kong and the Philippines and east to Indonesia and New Guinea, may be worthy of recognition as var. *intermedia* (Griff.) Bakh. Other somewhat better demarked varieties occur in Tasmania, Australia, New Zealand, the Philippines and Indonesia. Spherical-fruited populations have been designated as *A. sphaerocarpa* Stapf. More intensive field work is necessary before the validity of these possible segre-

Avicennia officinalis

Avicennia marina

(Photographs courtesy of S. Balasubramaniam)

gates can be established.

The pollen of *A. marina* has been described by Nair & Rehman in Bull. Bot. Gard. Lucknow 76: 22. 1962. The leaves are often tunnelled by leaf-miners. The trunks and pneumatophores are often heavily coated with algae.

Specimens Examined. JAFFNA DISTRICT: Jaffna, Feb. 1890, with erect root-processes, *s. coll. s.n.* (PDA); in mangrove swamp north of Karaitivu, 10 July 1932, medium-sized tree about 6 m tall, flowers dull-orange, *N.D. Simpson 9850* (BM, PDA); Jaffna, 1857, mixed with *A. officinalis, s. coll. C.P. 1961* in part (G. Gardner coll.) (B, BM, CAL, G, GH, K, P, PDA, W). MANNAR DISTRICT: south of causeway crossing to Mannar, 10 Nov. 1968, *Macnae s.n.* (US). VAVUNIYA DISTRICT: Alampil, south of Mullaittivu, along lagoon, 7 July 1971, tree bole with 2-foot girth 10 ft high, crown 5 ft, living bark green, pneumatophores thin, flowers orange-yellow, *Meijer 752* (PDA, US). DISTRICT UNDETERMINED: "Northern division", *Cleghorn s.n.* (CAL). PUTTALAM DISTRICT: Mampuri, sea-coast on road to Kalpitiya, 7 Dec. 1961, flowers dull orange, *Amaratunga 110* (PDA); Puttalam lagoon, 24 March 1926, small form, *s. coll. s.n.* (PDA); Kollankanatta Beach, Wilpattu National Park, 28 Sept. 1969, tree 2.5 m tall, flowers orange, honey-scented, *Cooray 69092801R* (PDA, US); Palavi, 5 Oct. 1969, pneumatophores present, flowers orange colour, *Cooray 69100505R* (PDA, US); dominant and exclusive in mangrove swamp 1 mile south of Kalpitiya, 14 Nov. 1970, tree up to 5 m tall, flowers orange, leaves white beneath, *Fosberg & Jayasuriya 52773* (LL); occasional near shrub belt well back from beach on sand flat, Pallugaturai, 30 Dec. 1968, shrub 1.5 m tall, leaves white beneath, *Fosberg, Muller-Dombois, Wirawan, Cooray & Balakrishnan 50914* (LL, PDA); locally abundant in moist shallow depression just back of sandy beach, altitude 2 m, Pallugaturai, 10 July 1969, shrub 4–5 ft tall, *Grupe 106* (PDA, US); commonly scattered on dry sandy flat, alt. 2 m, Pallugaturai, 10 July 1969, stem glaucous, *Grupe 110* (PDA, US); near Kalpitiya, 21 Oct. 1968, *Macnae s.n.* (NY, US); in shallow water, sea level, Puttalam lagoon, 25 Jan. 1974, pneumatophores very numerous, closely packed, some as much as 20 ft from the trunk, *H.N. & A.L. Moldenke & Jayasuriya 28246* (AAU, ARIZ, CAI, KARACHI, LL, MO, PDA, US); open beach of Portugal Bay, Wilpattu National Park, 16 June 1969, *Read 2172* (US); Puttalam lagoon, 24 March 1926, *J.M. de Silva s.n.* (PDA); maritime shrub along road to Perukkuwattan, 7°62′ N., 79°48′ E., 16 Feb. 1975, flowers yellow, fruit green, *Sumithraarachchi DBS. 696* (NY, US). COLOMBO DISTRICT: in mangrove swamp, Negombo, 18 Sept. 1969, a small tree, flowers yellow, *Amaratunga 1830* (PDA); shrub in mangrove swamp on moist lagoon bund, Negombo, 19 April 1970, *Amaratunga 2073* (PDA); Panadura, *s. coll. s.n.* (PDA); Negombo, July 1930, *J.M. de Silva s.n.* (PDA); in mangrove vegetation, Negombo Lagoon, low altitude, 19 June 1976, treelet 3 m tall, flowers yellow, fruits silver green and pubescent, *Waas 1648* (NY, US). AMPARAI DISTRICT: among mangroves,

Kumana lagoon, 7 Sept. 1970, treelet 2.5 m tall, with young flowers, *Balakrishnan NBK. 362* (PDA, US); between Panama and Pottuvil, locally common, 30 July 1969, tree 3 m tall, flowers yellow, honey-scented, *Cooray 69073011R* (NY, PDA, US). BATTICALOA DISTRICT: in mangrove, low altitude, 28 Jan. 1977, small tree, *Faden s.n. [Jayasuriya 2413]* (LL); in mangrove near lagoon 15 miles south of Batticaloa, 25 June 1970, tree 10 ft tall, girth 1 ft, pneumatophores thin, flowers orange-yellow, 4-merous, *Meijer & Balakrishnan 131* (PDA, US); in brackish water at high-water line, sea level, east coast, Panichchankerni ferry, small white leaf, "kanna", *Worthington 4891* (PDA); in mangrove by lagoon on Batticaloa to Valaichchenai road, Batticaloa, low altitude, 4 Feb. 1973, small tree, outer bark smooth, *Tirvengadum, Cramer & Balasubramaniam 244* (US); border of mangrove swamp on Batticaloa to Polonnaruwa road close to Ottamvadi railroad bridge, low altitude, 10 Sept. 1974, shrub 3 m tall, bark scaly, flowers yellow, stamens exserted, *Tirvengadum & Waas 465* (NY). TRINCOMALEE DISTRICT: near Nilaveli on the shore road north of Trincomalee, 11 Oct. 1975, inundated tree, branches dark, opaque, leaves greatly bicoloured, canescent beneath, roots exserted, numerous, *Bernardi 15299* (M, NY); at milepost 79 on Trincomalee to Batticaloa road, directly across the bay from Trincomalee, in sandy mangrove sedge area along the bay, 1 m alt., 14 Oct. 1974, *Davidse, 756* (LL); south of causeway at road marker 1 on saline flats along brackish pools, altitude 1–10 m, 2 May 1970, *Gould & Cooray 13670* (PDA, US); Oopar, sealevel, 10 June 1939, "kanna", *Worthington 478* (PDA); Cod Bay, Trincomalee, 24 Nov. 1949, "kanna", *Worthington 4386* (PDA). Erumativu Island, 22 Oct. 1968, *Macnae s.n.* (US). LOCALITY UNKNOWN: *G. Gardner 236* (P); *Herb. Forest Research Inst. Dehra Dun 35684* (DD), *35685* (DD); *s. coll. 488*, 1.8.1934 (AAH, GH, NY, NY, NY, US, Y), *s. coll. s.n.* Aug. 1883 (B); *Herb. Lenormand s.n.* (S); *Holtermann 13* (B), *21* (B), *s.n.* 5 Feb. 1890 (B), *s.n.* Feb. 1890 (B); *N.D. Simpson 8189* (BM), *9944* (BM); *Thunberg s.n.* (UPS); *Thwaites s.n.* (WU); *G.W. Walker 45* (E); *Mrs. Walker s.n.* (B); *Worthington 1014* (BM).

2. Avicennia officinalis L., Sp. Pl. ed. 1, 1: 110. 1753 [not *A. officinalis* H.J. Lam, 1940, nor Maxim., 1932, nor Millsp., 1930, nor Schau., 1856]. Thw., Enum. Pl. Zeyl. 244. 1861; Trimen, Cat. 69. 1885; Trimen, Handb. Fl. Ceylon 3: 363–364. 1895; Willis, Cat. 70. 1911; Alston in Trimen, Handb. Fl. Ceylon 6: 233. 1931; Abeywick., Ceylon J. Sci., Biol. Sci. 2: 218. 1959; Moldenke, Phytologia 7: 267–280 & 293 (1960), 14: 333–335 (1967), and 15: 477–478. 1968; Arulchelvam, Ceylon Forester ser. 2, 8: 74, 75, & 81. 1978; Gunawardena, Gen. & Sp. Pl. Zeyl. 148. 1968; Fonseka & Vinasithamby, Prov. List Local Names Fl. Pl. Ceylon 38 & 93. 1971; Moldenke, Phytologia 34: 179–203. 1976. Type: "the Indian plant which is represented as 'Oepata' in Rheede's Hortus Indicus Malabaricus 5: t. 45. 1683, the restricted type-locality for this being the coast of Cochin, southern India" (Stearn, Kew Bull. 1958: 35. 1958).

Anacardium orientale Houst., Dendr. 156. 1662.

Oepata Rheede, Hort. Mal. 4: 95, pl. 45. 1683.

Arbor indica, fructu conoide, cortice pulvinato nucleum unicum, nullo ossiculo tectum claudente Ray, Hist. 1566–1567. 1693.—*Arbor indica, fructu conoide, cortice pulvinato, nucleum unicum nullo ossiculo tecto claudente* Ray ex Burm. f., Fl. Ind. 138, in syn. 1768.

Avicennia tomentosa Willd. in L., Sp. Pl. ed. 4, 3 (1): 395. 1800 [not *A. tomentosa* Blanco, 1845, nor Blume, 1918, nor R. Br., 1851, nor Jacq., 1760, nor L., 1821, nor L. & Jacq., 1783, nor G.F.W. Mey., 1818, nor Nutt., 1947, nor Nutt. & Br., 1832, nor Schau., 1940, nor Sieber, 1844, nor Sw., 1864, nor Vahl, 1921, nor Wall., 1851, nor Weigelt, 1851].—*A. tomentosa* Roxb. ex Hamilt., Trans. Linn. Soc. London Bot. 17: 221, in syn. 1835; Watt, Dict. Econ. Prod. India 1: 361. 1839.

Avicennia oepata Hamilt., Trans. Linn. Soc. London Bot. 17: 221. 1835.

Avicennia tomentosa var. *asiatica* Walp., Rep. 4: 133. 1845.

Avicennia obovata Griff., Not. Pl. As. 4: 189. 1854.

Avicennia officinalis var. *tomentosa* Cowan, Rec. Bot. Surv. India 11: 199 & 220. 1928.

Avicennia obtusifolia Wall. ex Moldenke, Prelim. Alph. List Invalid Names 5, in syn. 1941.

Shrub or tree, often much branched from near the base, to 25 m tall, mostly of poor form, sending down adventitious roots from low branches overhanging water; trunk to 1 m in diameter, often crooked, the bole to 7 m tall, sometimes with prop roots on the under-side of leaning trunks; crown scraggly; wood grey, with a darker heartwood, hard, heavy, with interlocked grain and prominent ring-pores, consisting of numerous narrow, well-marked, concentric layers, weighing 58 pounds per cubic foot, very brittle, the sapwood often undefined, pale straw-coloured, distinctly ring-pored, the true wood straw-coloured or paler, the rings about 3.5–7 mm apart; bark brownish-grey, thin, with no exudation, becoming rough, blackening progressively in age and loosening, or the outer bark yellowish-green and the inner bark white, about 7 mm thick; branchlets spreading, nutant, terete, the youngest parts closely appressed-tomentellous, glabrescent in age, sparsely resinous-punctate and lenticellate; petioles medium-stout, 0.5–2 cm long, glabrescent; leaf-blades coriaceous, obovate or broadly oblong, dark green above, 4–12 cm long, 2–6 cm wide, rounded at the apex, slightly revolute along the margins, subcuneate or often rounded at the base and shortly attenuate into the petiole, glabrous and eventually shiny above and very minutely glandulose, appressed-tomentellous beneath, often fulvous in drying, resinous-punctate beneath the pubescence, bitter and somewhat salty to the taste; inflorescence paniculate, bracteate, rarely subfoliose, 3–15 cm long, 10–15 cm wide, the panicles terminal and in the axils of the uppermost leaves, solitary or paired, pedunculate, 1–3-branched, the cymes dense, subcapitate or rarely elongate and dissitiflorous, 1–1.5 cm long, 1–2 cm wide, consisting of 2–12 decussate flowers; peduncles green or subfuscous, obsoletely tetragonal, densely appressed-furfuraceous, subglabrescent in age, densely resinous-punctate and densely verruculose with elevated glands; bracts small, sessile, rounded-ovate, densely tomentose from the base to the middle, glabrate toward the apex, green, soon blackening, scarious, caducous; bractlets 2, 3–5 mm long, rounded ovate or subreniform, obtuse at the apex, resinous-punctate on both surfaces, ciliate-margined, rugose beneath and densely tomentellous from the base to the middle, glabrate toward the apex, rather shiny, glabrous on the upper surface or white-pilose toward the base; flowers sessile, comparatively large, unpleasantly scented, said to be narcotic, 7–10 mm long, 12–15 mm wide when fully expanded; calyx persistent, large, the lobes rather unequal, rounded-ovate, 5–6 mm long, 3–5 mm wide, subtrinerved, densely ciliate-margined, sparsely resinous-punctate on both surfaces, soon scarious, glabrous and shiny above, rugulose and green beneath, densely white-tomentellous toward the base beneath but glabrous toward the apex; corolla comparatively large, yellow or yellow-brown, soon becoming almost orange coloured, rather thick-textured, dropping off after anthesis, the tube campanulate, equalling or slightly surpassing the calyx, glabrous on the outside, its throat 5–6 mm wide, the lobes rather unequal, rather obtusely oblong or lingulate, spreading in radial fashion, 3–5 mm long and wide, retuse, the posterior one patent and broader, the 3 anterior ones more patent or reflexed, glabrous on the inner surface, very densely whitish-villosulous on the outer surface but glabrous on the margins; stamens short-exserted, shorter than the corolla-lobes, 2–4 mm long; filaments much longer than the anthers; anthers broadly oblong, fulvous, soon becoming pitch-black, 1–1.2 mm long, the pollen white; ovary conic, completely covered with long, whitish, appressed hairs, densely resinous-punctate; style filiform, elongate, almost completely short-tomentellous with white hairs, resinous-punctate, scarcely exserted, excrescent after anthesis and long-exserted from the calyx; stigma subtabescent, unequally and acutely bifid, incurved; fruit greenish-purple, broadly ovate or amygdaloid, rounded or subcordate at the base, compressed laterally; cotyledons large and thick, almost always very densely long-setose, developing into narrowly lanceolate seed-leaves that are attenuate-acute at both ends, green or (mostly) greenish-purple; hypocotyl at most only half as long as the inner cotyledon, pubescent only for a short distance, the side-rootlets and plumule conspicuous even in the attached fruit.

D i s t r. This is the type species of the genus (and family) and is found in salt marshes and tidal forests at river mouths, and along seashores from

India, Bangladesh, Tenasserim, the Andaman Islands, and Sri Lanka through the coasts of Indo-China, Thailand, and Malaya to the Philippines, Sumatra, Madura, Java, Borneo, Celebes, the Lesser Sunda Islands, Molucca Islands and New Guinea, south to New South Wales. Alston refers to it as "rather rare in Ceylon".

E c o l. It is said to ascend to 50 m above sea-level in Papua and occasionally to grow in fresh water.

U s e s. The bark of *A. officinalis* is astringent and is used as a tanning agent in India and Pakistan. The wood is employed in India as firewood, but there as well as in Java and the Andaman Islands it is also employed for making rice-blocks for husking paddy, rice-pounders, and oil-mills. In the Celebes it is used for the interiors (only) of houses. Being virtually indestructible in salt-water, it is used for making small boats and the piling of wharves. The black heartwood of old trees is powdered in the Celebes and used in ointments to treat headaches. The ashes of the burned wood are used in India in washing, cleaning, and bleaching cotton cloth, by painters "in the mixing of their colours", and also in the treatment of small-pox. The roots are reputed to possess aphrodisiac properties. In Malabar the unripe seeds are cooked with the leaves of *Ipomoea campanulata* L. and with butter to make an ointment or poultice to hasten the suppuration of pimples, boils, abscesses and tumors. The seeds are bitter, but edible after a preliminary preparation, generally by cooking or soaking in water for a long period of time and then often drying in the sunshine to eliminate the bitterness.

V e r n. Kanna and Upatha (T); also about 86 others in other parts of the species' range.

N o t e. In contrast to other species in the genus, e.g., *A. marina* (Forsk.) Vierh. and *A. germinans* (L.) L., this species is remarkably uniform in its characters throughout its range. Unfortunately, however, the name, *A. officinalis*, has been misapplied widely to other species, especially to *A. marina* by workers on the African and Arabian floras and to forms of *A. germinans* by earlier American botanists. Similarly, the name *A. tomentosa* has been applied to *A. alba* Blume, *A. germinans* (L.) L., *A. marina* (Forsk.) Vierh., *A. marina* var. *resinifera* (Forst. f.) Bakh., *A. marina* var. *rumphiana* (H. Hallier) Bakh., and *A. schaueriana* Stapf & Leechman. The *Arbor indica* etc. name of Ray is often regarded as applying to *A. alba* Blume, but clearly cannot belong there because Ray plainly states of it that its leaves are "oblong-rotund".

S p e c i m e n s   E x a m i n e d. JAFFNA DISTRICT: Jaffna, mixed with *A. marina*, 1857, *s. coll. C.P. 1961* in part [G. Gardner coll.] (B, BM, CAL, G, K, P, PDA, W). PUTTALAM DISTRICT: at edge of canal, low altitude, Mundel, 25 Jan. 1974, *H.N. & A.L. Moldenke & Jayasuriya 28249* (AAH, ARIZ, CAI, KARACHI, LL, MO, PDA, US). COLOMBO DISTRICT: Panadura, mixed with *A. marina*, 27 Oct. 1881, *s. coll. s.n.* (PDA). BATTICALOA DISTRICT: in water at margin of mangrove swamp about

4 miles northwest of Batticaloa near milepost 4/6 on the Trincomalee road, alt. 3 m, tree 4 m tall, fruit green, *Davidse & Sumithraarachchi 8978* (LL); in mangrove, Eravur to Batticaloa road, low altitude, 25 Oct. 1973, small tree, 7 m tall, petals 4, orange, stamens 4, *Jayasuriya 1356* (LL, NY, US); at rear of *Avicennia* fringe along lagoon, Batticaloa, 7 Oct. 1968, *Macnae s.n.* (US); in mangrove by lagoon on Batticaloa to Valaichchenai road, Batticaloa, 4 Feb. 1973, *Tirvengadum, Cramer & Balasubramaniam 266* (US); on border of mangrove swamps close to Ottamavadi railway bridge on the Batticaloa to Polonnaruwa road, low altitude, 10 Sept. 1974, shrub 3 metres tall, bark scaly, flowers yellow, stamens exserted, *Tirvengadum & Waas 465* (US). TRINCOMALEE DISTRICT: lagoon margin close to the sea at the Black Sands Camp (ilmenite), Illankaiturai, south of Foul Point, sea-level, 3 Aug. 1939, *Worthington 529* (BM, PDA). LOCALITY UNKNOWN: *s. coll. s.n.* (US); *s. coll. s.n.* (NY); *s. coll. s.n.* (WU).

BEGONIACEAE

(by A.H.M. Jayasuriya*)

Klotzsch, Abh. Akad. Wiss. Berlin 1–135. 1854; A. DC., Prod. 15. 1: 266–408. 1864; Warburg in Pflanzenfam. 3. 6a: 121–150. 1895; Irmscher in Pflanzenfam. 2. 21: 548–588. 1925.

Mostly erect or acaulescent, monoecious herbs or low shrubs. Stems somewhat jointed, succulent or woody at base. Leaves alternate in caulescent species, simple or lobulate, usually asymmetric at base, petioled, often palmately nerved, commonly pubescent with multicellular, non-capitate trichomes. Stipules caducous or early deciduous. Peduncles axillary, bracteate, scapose in acaulescent species; inflorescence usually cymose (dichasial), rarely racemose (umbellate), very often appearing unisexual due to early development of staminate flowers. Flowers unisexual, zygomorphic or actinomorphic; tepals free (connate in *Begoniella*), staminate tepals usually 2+2, valvate in each row, inner tepals smaller; pistillate tepals 2–5, imbricate, outer pair usually larger; stamens numerous in many whorls, free or briefly connate basally; anthers 2-celled, basifixed, dehiscing longitudinally; ovary inferior (half-superior in *Hillebrandia*), 3-celled, roughly 3-angled in cross section, 3-winged; placentation axile or rarely parietal, placentae intrusive, simple or lobed or bilamellate; ovules numerous, anatropous; styles 3, free or basally connate; stigma bifid, strongly papillose on all sides and often twisted. Fruit a loculicidal, 3-winged, often bony capsule. Seeds minute, reticulate, non-endospermous with straight, oily embryo.

Widely distributed in the tropics, with greatest development in northern South America; of the five genera, *Begonia* with over 1,200 species dominates the family while the other four genera, which do not occur in Ceylon, accommodate only eight species. Of the ten taxa of *Begonia* represented in Ceylon, two are endemic, four are also found in India, four are neotropical and, introduced via England, are at present naturalized to a greater or lesser extent in the island. Species of *Begonia* mostly occur in the hilly wet zone at altitudes of 100–1500 m, although *B. cucullata* has been found up to 1900 m; *B. cordifolia* and *B. dipetala* are restricted to the south-eastern intermediate zone at

*National Herbarium, Botanic Gardens, Peradeniya.

lower altitudes while *B. malabarica,* a comparatively hardy species, apart from its wide distribution in the wet zone, occurs in moist shady spots on Ritigala, an isolated hill in the dry zone (altitude 765 m). *B. tenera, B. tenera* var. *thwaitesii* and *B. subpeltata* are in danger of extinction due to the rapid destruction of their natural habitats by man.

Since their introduction to horticulture about 500 years ago, members of this family have attracted much attention as garden plants. Although they have been used as an astringent in haemorrhages and in the treatment of scurvy and low fever, their principal importance is as ornamental plants due to their flowers and especially the attractive and colourful leaves. Apart from hundreds of species of *Begonia* which are cultivated, there are many man-made hybrids and varieties; the compact nature of most of these plants makes them ideal for terrariums, dish gardens or window-sill cultures. Although they are said to be shade-loving, strong filtered light is necessary for their healthy growth and to bring out the true colour of the leaves. As their roots are very sensitive and die in prolonged inundated conditions, they prefer light friable soil with good drainage and moisture in the form of atmospheric humidity. Propagation is by seeds, stem-cuttings and leaf-cuttings.

BEGONIA

L., Sp. Pl. 1056. 1753; L., Gen. Pl. ed. 5. n. 1156. 1754. Type Species: *Begonia acutifolia* Jacq.

Stemless or caulescent herbs, sometimes low shrubs. Leaves alternate, unequal-sided, entire to lobed or partite, irregularly dentate. Flowers often handsome, readily doubling under cultivation; staminate tepals usually 2+2; pistillate tepals 2 to 6; stamens numerous, filaments free or monadelphous; ovary inferior, often 3-locular; styles mostly as many as the ovary loculi, free or connate at base, 2-lobed, lobes entire or split; ovules inserted on placentae adnate to the axis of the ovary, rarely parietal. Fruit mostly a capsule, 3-angled and unequally 3-winged, septicidally or mostly loculicidally dehiscent below the apex or the full length. Seeds very numerous, minute.

The genus was established by Plumier and published in 1700 by Tournefort in the appendix to his Institutiones Rei Herbariae, three years before the Nova Plantarum Americanarum Genera of Plumier appeared. The species have been grouped into 82 sections (Baranov and Barkley, 1972).

The descriptions of all taxa were drawn up from living plants.

KEY TO THE SPECIES AND VARIETIES

1 Acaulescent, scapose herbs with subterranean rhizomes
  2 Inflorescence racemose (umbellate) with non-dichotomous scape. Scape, ovary and outer surface of outer tepals pilose. Placenta entire

3 Leaves uniformly pale green; margin dentate (in typical specimens). Scape villous
with white hairs. Stamens less than 55; connective rounded at apex. Placenta not
lobulate (Section REICHENHEIMIA).............................**1. B. tenera**
3 Leaves variegated with green and purplish blotches; margin crenate. Scape densely
hispid with pink hairs. Stamens more than 55; connective truncate at apex. Placenta
laterally and proximally lobulate...................,..........**B. tenera var. thwaitesii**
2 Inflorescence cymose (dichasial) with a dichotomous scape. Scape, ovary and outer
surface of outer tepals nearly glabrous. Placenta bifid at least in top half of ovary
4 Leaf margin hairy at least on crenae. Tepals peripherally pale pinkish. Stamens
connate at base. Capsule longer than broad, dehiscing more or less irregularly near
base of wings (Section DIPLOCLINIUM)........................**2. B. cordifolia**
4 Leaf margin more or less glabrous. Tepals pure white. Stamens free at base. Capsule broader than long, dehiscing along inner margin of wings (Section REICHEN-
HEIMIA)...**3. B. subpeltata**
1 Herbs with aerial stems, or semi-shrubs
5 Annuals with succulent bases
6 Stem villous. Leaves usually not lobulate, acute; petiole densely villous. Pistillate
bracteoles 2–3 mm long (Section DORATOMETRA)................**4. B. hirtella**
6 Stem glabrous. Leaves usually lobulate, acuminate; petiole glabrous except near
apex. Pistillate bracteoles 1–1.5 mm long (Section DORATOMETRA)............
....**5. B. humilis**
5 Perennials with firm or woody bases
7 Pistillate bracteoles absent or alternately and laxly placed on upper part of pedicel.
Placenta entire. Capsular wings more or less equal
8 Leaves crenate or dentate. Ovary truncate or round at top. Wings of capsule
truncate at top, distally acuteangular or obtuseangular, broader than 5 mm at broadest (Section HAGGIA)......................................**6. B. malabarica**
8 Leaves double-serrate. Ovary acute or attenuate at top. Wings of capsule completely rounded or narrowed at summit, never distally angular, narrower than 5 mm at
broadest (Section HAGGIA)...................................**7. B. dipetala**
7 Pistillate bracteoles appressed to base of ovary. Placenta usually bifid. Capsular
wings distinctly unequal
9 Leaves equally long as broad, glabrous, palmiveined. Cymes lax (Section BEGO-
NIA)..**8. B. cucullata var. hookeri**
9 Leaves 2–3 times longer than broad, hirsute on both sides, penninerved. Cymes
crowded (Section DONALDIA)...............................**9. B. ulmifolia**

1. Begonia tenera Dry., Trans. Linn. Soc. London 1: 169, t. 16. 1791; A. DC.,
Prod. 15. 1: 386. 1864; Clarke in Hook. f., Fl. Br. Ind. 2: 652. 1879; Trimen,
Handb. Fl. Ceylon 2: 263. 1894; Karegeannes, Begonian 38: 232. 1971. Type:
Ceylon: *Koenig* (n.v).

Falkea tenera Koenig in Dry., Trans. Linn. Soc. London 1: 169. 1791.
Begonia thwaitesii Hook., Bot. Mag. 79, t. 4692. 1853.
Reichenheimia thwaitesii Klotzsch, Abh. Akad. Wiss. Berlin 55. 1854.
Begonia zeylanica van Houtte ex Klotzsch, Otto & Dietrich, Allg. Garten-
zeitung 24: 205. 1856.
Reichenheimia zeylanica Klotzsch, Otto & Dietrich, Allg. Gartenzeitung 24:
205. 1856.

Perennial acaulescent herb with subterranean stout rhizome up to 2 cm long. Petioles arising from top of rhizome, 3–20 cm long, succulent, cylindrical, bright pink, white-villous; stipules 1–1.4 cm long, ovate, acuminate to cuspidate, sparsely hairy, brown when old; leaves ovate to rotundate; base cordate to strongly cordate, equal or oblique, apex rounded or acute-acuminate, usually symmetric, 5–11 × 5–12 cm, palmately 7–8-veined; margin crenate-dentate, hairy; pale yellowish-green, more or less uniformly hirsute above; usually sparsely pilose along veins beneath. Inflorescence racemose (umbellate), up to 5-flowered, scapose; scapes arising from axils, 2–23 cm long, erect, rarely exceeding leaves, white-villous; bracts ovate, acute, ciliate, pubescent or lower ones glabrous; staminate pedicels 1–3 cm long, slender, erect, glabrous; tepals white but peripherally pink; staminate tepals 2+2; outer pair rotundate to ovate, 8–10 mm wide, pubescent on outer surface; inner pair ovate-oblong to elliptic, c. 10 × 4 mm; stamens 20–50; filaments connate at base, 1–2 mm long; anther 1 mm long, clavate; connective rounded at apex; pistillate pedicels 4–7 mm long, stout, reflexed, pubescent at base, subtended by a lanceolate, glabrous bract, toothed at base of margin; tepals 5, outer pair as in staminate flower, light pink, inner distinctly smaller; ovary pilose, with a medial, longitudinal septal line on each face, 6 × 7 mm inclusive of wings; wings equal; placentae simple; styles 3, free almost to base, each with two inrolled, distally capitate, spiral arms. Capsule 8–10 × 8–15 mm including wings, rather thick, glabrous or sparsely hairy, dehiscing full length along inner margin of wings; wings roughly equal, 1–4 mm broad, distally obtuse or acute. Seeds brown, ovoid.

1. var. tenera. The typical form as described above.

D i s t r. Endemic; rare; humid lowlands up to 250 m on red-yellow podzol (laterite).

E c o l. Flowering in February–March and June–September.

V e r n. Bim-hakambala (S).

S p e c i m e n s E x a m i n e d. KANDY DISTRICT: Kalugala, *Alston 894* (PDA, K), *Jayasuriya 844* (PDA, US, K); Kalugala Kanda, *Silva s.n.* (PDA); Yatibariya, *Jayasuriya 845* (PDA, US, K, L), *Jayasuriya & Sumithraarachchi 1589* (PDA, US), *Hepper 4508* (PDA, US); Rondura Group, Ginigathena, *Senaratna s.n.* (PDA). KEGALLE DISTRICT: Bulathkohupitiya, *Amaratunga 866* (PDA). KALUTARA DISTRICT: Bodinagala Temple Forest, off Ingiriya, *Sohmer & Waas 10529* (PDA, US, WIS); Bulatsinhala, *s. coll. C.P. 3952* (PDA), *s. coll. C.P. 2808* in part (PDA, K); Pasdun-Korale, *s. coll. C.P. 3952* (PDA), *s. coll. C.P. 2808* in part (PDA). DISTRICT UNKNOWN: Kalugammana, *Silva s.n.* (PDA); Etbedde, Wellawaya river, *Lewis s.n.* (PDA). LOCALITY UNKNOWN: *Walker s.n.* (K); *Trimen s.n.* (K).

2. var. thwaitesii (Hook.) Jayasuriya, comb. et stat. nov. Type: *C.P. 2808* in part (PDA).

Begonia thwaitesii Hook., Bot. Mag. 79: t. 4692. 1853; Thw., Enum. Pl. Zeyl. 2: 128. 1859; A. DC., Prod. 15. 1: 386. 1864; Trimen, Handb. Fl. Ceylon 2: 264. 1894. Type: *C.P. 2808* in part (PDA).
Reichenheimia thwaitesii Klotzsch, Abh. Akad. Wiss. Berlin 55. 1855.
Begonia tenera Dry., Trans. Linn. Soc. London 1: 169, t. 16. 1791; Clarke in Hook. f., Fl. Br. Ind. 2: 652. 1879; Karegeannes, Begonian 38: 232. 1971.

Differs from the typical variety by leaves being variegated with green and purple blotches above, uniformly dull purple beneath; margin broadly crenate, never dentate; apex usually asymmetrical; pubescence pink or purplish. Scape, pedicels, ovary and outer surfaces of outer tepals densely hispid. Stamens about 65; connective truncate-depressed at top; placentae proximally and laterally lobed.

D i s t r. Endemic; rare; lower montane zone at elevations 600–1200 m, especially in the valleys of the Knuckles mountain range.

E c o l. A beautiful plant with characteristic variegated leaves, very marked under proper light conditions. Flowering in November–February and June–September.

N o t e. Hooker's plate in Curtis' Bot. Mag. has been greatly exaggerated with many contrasting colours and is therefore very unnatural. The differences stated in the above description do not warrant it species level.

S p e c i m e n s E x a m i n e d. MATALE DISTRICT: Matale, *s. coll. C.P. 2808* in part (PDA), *C.P. 3953* (PDA); Madakumbura, S.E. of Rattota, *Jayasuriya 1882* (PDA, US, K); *Jayasuriya & Dassanayake 989* (PDA, US, K), *994* (PDA, US, K); *Jayasuriya & Bandaranayake 1758* (PDA, US). KANDY DISTRICT: Hunnasgiriya, *s. coll. C.P. 2808* in part (PDA), *C.P. 3953* (PDA); Rangala, *Waas 1006* (US). NUWARA ELIYA DISTRICT: Kotmale, *Gardner C.P. 2808* in part (PDA), *3953* (PDA).

2. Begonia cordifolia (Wight) Thw., Enum. Pl. Zeyl. 2: 129. 1859; DC., Prod. 15. 1: 328. 1864; Clarke in Hook. f., Fl. Br. Ind. 2: 641. 1879; Trimen, Handb. Fl. Ceylon 2: 262. 1894; Gamble, Fl. Pres. Madras 546. 1915, repr. 1: 385. 1957. Type: Malabar, *s. coll.* (n. v.)

Diploclinium cordifolium Wight, Ic. Pl. Ind. Or. 5. 2: t. 1816. 1852.
Begonia cordifolia var. *insularis* A. DC., Prod. 15. 1: 329. 1864.
Begonia arnottiana A. DC., Prod. 15. 1: 322. 1864.

Perennial acaulescent herb with horizontal, subterranean rhizome up to 3 × 1.5 cm, connected to the preceding rhizome by a short, cylindrical, fragile stolon sometimes growing up to c. 1 cm, forming a short series of rhizomes each corresponding to one growing season after perennation, and bearing up to c. 6 aerial leaves and 7 inflorescences when fully grown. Petioles erect to ascending, 5–40 cm long, rather stout, succulent, cylindrical, pinkish, pilose, with evanescent pubescence; stipules ovate to lanceolate, acuminate, glabrous; leaves ovate to rotundate, 3.5–20 × 4–23 cm, sometimes slightly lobed, deeply and more or less equally cordate at base; apex acute to obtuse, usually symmetrical in mature leaves; margin crenate to dentate; palmately 7–9 veined; upper surface yellowish-green to shiny green to dull blackish-green, sometimes white-speckled at bases of hairs, in young leaves hirsute, when mature pilose; lower surface dull green to dull purple, sparsely pilose in mature leaves. Scapes 1—few per leaf axil, arising from top of rhizome, more or less erect, slender, succulent, cylindrical, rather transparent, reddish-pink, glabrous, or with few scattered white hairs, 5–20 cm long, each subtended by about 2 bracts; dichasium lax, up to 10-flowered; bracts linear-oblong, keeled, c. 10 × 3 mm, entire, glabrous; staminate pedicels 1.5–3 cm long, slender, deflexed when young, more or less erect in mature flower, pale pink, glabrous; tepals white but outer tepals peripherally pink, staminate tepals 2+2; the outer pair rotundate, c. 1.5 × 1.5 cm, truncate to cordate at base, glabrous, the inner oblanceolate, rounded at apex; stamens c. 45, connate at base; staminal column c. 1 mm long; free ends of filaments 2 mm long; anther 1 mm long, clavate, rather cuneate at base; connective truncate at apex; pistillate pedicel 2–8 mm long, stout, almost glabrous, pinkish; bracteoles 1 or 2, alternate, linear to filiform, sometimes forked with unequal branches or with filiform processes; pistillate tepals 3–5, semi-persistent in capsule; outer pair rotundate, up to 17 mm wide, truncate to cordate at base, glabrous; the inner unequal, obovate-oblong, up to 12 × 5 mm; ovary 5–20 × 5–15 mm inclusive of wings, with a longitudinal medial dark purple septal line on each face; wings subequal, c. 4 mm broad at broadest, round to angular, glabrous; placentae simple at the base of ovary, lobed in centre, deeply bifid in top half of ovary, green; styles 3, connate at base, bilobed; stigmatic zone papillose, twisted. Capsule thick, whitish, turning green with maturity, 7–16 × 5–12 mm, dehiscing irregularly on faces; wings somewhat absorbed. Seeds ovoid, dark brown.

D i s t r. India: South Deccan Peninsula, W. Ghats and in forests from Malabar to Tinnevelly. In Ceylon, confined to south-eastern intermediate zone at altitudes of 100–500 m.

E c o l. Principally in pockets of humus on rock surfaces; mostly in shade, but occasionally on exposed moist surfaces. The moisture regime of the environment influences variation in size of plants. Plants perennate during the dry season subsequent to the death of aerial parts. Daughter rhizomes are vigorously produced with the onset of the northeast monsoon in November-December. Flowering in December–March.

Vern. Gal-ambala (S).

Specimens Examined. KANDY DISTRICT: Hasalaka, *Jayasuriya & Tirvengadum 1008* (PDA, US, K); Ududaha below Bintenna Pass, *Jayasuriya, Moldenke & Sumithraarachchi 1420* (PDA, US, K, L, WIS, MO, NY). MONERAGALA DISTRICT: Bibile, *s. coll. C.P. 3584* (PDA, K); *Silva s.n.* (PDA); Arawakumbura, South of Bibile, *Jayasuriya & Tirvengadum 1006* (PDA, US, K, L, WIS, MO, NY); Nilgala, *s. coll. C.P. 3584* (PDA, K); between Baduluwela and Dambagalla, *Koyama & Balakrishnan 13999* (PDA, US); Padda-hela Kanda near Buttala, *Bernardi 15539* (PDA, US); Wellawaya, *Alston 1645* (PDA, K). BADULLA DISTRICT: Kota-talawa, *Jayasuriya & Tirvengadum 1007* (PDA, US, K, L); between Lunugala and Yalakumbura, Jan. 1888, *Trimen s.n.* (PDA); Kuruminiya Kandura, Uma Oya, *Silva 265* (PDA). LOCALITY UNKNOWN: *Wight 1857* (K).

3. **Begonia subpeltata** Wight, Ic. Pl. Ind. Or. 5. 2: t. 1812. 1852; Thw., Enum. Pl. Zeyl. 2: 128. 1859; A. DC., Prod. 15. 1: 386. 1864; Clarke in Hook. f., Fl. Br. Ind. 2: 653. 1879; Trimen, Handb. Fl. Ceylon 2: 264. 1894; Gamble, Fl. Pres. Madras 546. 1915, repr. 1: 386. 1957. Type: Wight, Ic. Pl. Ind. Or. t. 1812. 1852 (lectotype).

Reichenheimia subpeltata Klotzsch, Abh. Akad. Wiss. Berlin 55. 1855.

Perennial acaulescent herb. Rhizome horizontal, up to 5 × 1.3 cm, covered with brownish scale-leaves and large leaf-scars (when old); tissue with red vascular strands and bitter taste; each bearing up to c. 5 aerial leaves and 4 inflorescences when fully grown, connected to daughter rhizome by a short, stout, cylindrical, fleshy stolon up to 3 cm long. Leaves symmetrical, broadly ovate, cordate to strongly cordate at base, acute to acuminate at apex, 8–14.5 × 10–15 cm, sometimes slightly lobed or angular, crenate, palmately 5–6 veined; median vein more prominent; upper surface rather shiny, white-hirsute, white-speckled at bases of hairs in young leaves; lower surface pale, glabrous, pilose along veins; petiole erect, 7–33 cm long, stout, succulent, pale greenish to brown, covered with brown scales in young leaves, glabrescent, cylindrical in lower two-thirds, adaxially 2-alate in upper third; alae narrow. Scapes erect, cylindrical, succulent, rather transparent, almost glabrous, pale pink, 10–55 cm long, axillary or arising near axils from top of rhizome, usually one per axil, each subtended or covered when young by 2 bracts; dichasium lax, up to 25-flowered; bracts ovate, acuminate, almost glabrous, whitish, entire, c. 10 × 5 mm; staminate pedicel up to 0.7–2.5 cm long, erect, glabrous; tepals white, staminate tepals 2 + 2; the outer pair ovate, 10–20 × 8–13 mm, subcordate at base, glabrous; the inner ovate-lanceolate, up to 13 × 7 mm, acute; stamens 35–40, free; filaments c. 1.5 mm long; anther 1–1.5 mm long, oblong; connective truncate or rounded at apex; pistillate pedicels 5–15 mm long, reflexed, glabrous, pale pink, elongating up to 2 cm in capsule; bracteoles 1–2, lanceolate, 5–10 × 2 mm, glabrous, entire, pale pink; pistillate tepals 2 + 3; outer pair larger, rotundate, up to 8 × 10 mm, glabrous; the inner ones up to 9 × 7 mm; ovary glabrous, pale green with pinkish reticulation with a purple septal line on each face, 8–11 × 10 mm inclusive of wings; wings more or less equal, c. 5 mm broad, distally acute to round; margin thickened, rough, slightly undulate; placentae lobulate in lower half of ovary, completely bilamellate in top half, chlorophyllous, ovuliferous throughout; styles 3, connate up to halfway, bilobed above; stigmatic zone papillate, undulate. Capsule 10–15 × 15–24 mm inclusive of 5–9 mm broad wings, dehiscing along inner margin of wings. Seeds oblong-oval, 3 mm long, brown.

D i s t r. India: South Deccan Peninsula, W. Ghats and probably in Malabar. In Ceylon extremely rare, confined to certain parts in lower montane region at elevations c. 1000 m. An endangered species in Ceylon.

E c o l. Flowering January–March.

S p e c i m e n s E x a m i n e d. KANDY DISTRICT: Ambagamuwa, *s. coll. C.P. 2597* (PDA, K). KEGALLE DISTRICT: Windsor Forest, *Jayasuriya & Dassanayake 1018* (PDA).

4. Begonia hirtella Link, Enum. Pl. Hort. Berol. 2: 396. 1822; Klotzsch, Abh. Akad. Wiss. Berlin 29. 1855; A. DC. in Mart., Fl. Bras. 4: 344. 1861; A. DC., Prod. 15, 1: 299. 1864; Schult., Urb. Symb. Ant. 7: 28. 1911; Irmsch. in Pflanzenfam. ed. 2. 21: 586. 1925; Smith & Schubert, Publ. Field Mus. Nat. Hist. Bot. Ser. 13. 4. 1: 192. 1941; Smith & Schubert, Caldasia 4: 82, t. 8. 1946; Smith & Smith, Fl. Ilustr. Catarinense 46. 1971; Smith, Phytologia 27. 4: 215. 1973. Type: Material from Brazil, cultivated in Berlin (B, holotype, n.v.).

Begonia ciliata HBK., Nov. Gen. & Sp. 7: 178. 1825.
Begonia villosa Lindl., Bot. Reg. 15: t. 1252. 1829.
Begonia brasila A. DC., Mem. Soc. Phys. Geneve 7: 295. 1836; A. DC., Prod., 15. 1: 299. 1864.
Begonia diversifolia var. *nana* Walp., Nova Acta Phys. Med. Acad. Caes. Leop.-Carol. Nat. Cur. 19 suppl. 1: 403. 1843.
Begonia brasiliana Schrank ex Steudel, Nom. ed. 2, 1: 193. 1841.
Begonia hirtella var. *nana* A. DC. in Mart., Fl. Bras. 4. 1: 345. t. 8. 1861.

Herb, 5–90 cm high. Stem erect, often branched, succulent, cylindrical, semihyaline, villous with slender multicellular brownish hairs up to 2.5 mm long. Leaves strongly asymmetric, ovate (when young) to transversely ovate, very shallowly cordate to almost truncate at base, acute at apex, 2–11 × 3–8 cm, transparent when dry, palmately 4–5-veined, shallowly lobed, crenate-serrate, pilose above and less so beneath; petioles pale pink, densely villous in the upper part, 1.4–7 cm long; stipules persistent, narrowly ovate, acuminate, up to 1.4 cm long, lacerate-ciliate. Peduncles axillary, glabrous to sparsely pilose, pale pink, 1.5–5 cm long; cymes usually few-flowered; bracts persistent, linear to oblong or ovate, laciniate, smaller than the stipules; pedicels glabrous, 4–12 mm long; tepals white, staminate tepals 2 + 2; the outer suborbicular, up to 4 mm long; the inner smaller, linear-oblong; stamens free, 5–22; pistillate bracteoles elliptic to subspatulate, ciliate-laciniate, 3.5–4 mm long, not persistent in fruit; pistillate tepals 5, roughly unequal, oblong to obovate, acute, c. 3 mm long; styles 3, bifid with the stigmatic tissue forming continuous linear spiral bands; placentae variable, usually deeply bifid, ovuliferous throughout. Capsule glandular-punctate, 6–15 × 10–20 mm, dehiscing along lower margins of faces; wings subdeltoid, obtusely angled, unequal, the largest 5–12 mm wide. Seeds oblong, obtuse, truncate and stalked at base; surface alveolate; the basal alveolae longer than broad; the apical subrectangular.

D i s t r. Native of Tropical America; introduced and naturalized rather widely in the wet mid-country of Ceylon, in humid shady places at altitudes of 50–1300 m; the commonest species in the island.

E c o l. Flowering all the year.

U s e s. Used for treatment of certain skin inflammations such as boils.

V e r n. Fringed Begonia (E); Hakambala (S).

S p e c i m e n s   E x a m i n e d. KANDY DISTRICT: Kandy, *Jayasuriya, Moldenke & Sumithraarachchi 1495* (PDA, US, K); Udawattakele Sanctuary, Kandy, *Jayasuriya, Dassanayake & Pemadasa 1630* (PDA, US, K, L), *Jayasuriya 1841* (PDA, US, K, L, WIS); Doluwa, *Jayasuriya 1506* (PDA, US, K), *Jayasuriya & Bandaranayake 1851* (PDA, US, K, L); Galaha Road, *Jayasuriya 1503* (PDA, US, K), *Jayasuriya 1504* (PDA, US, K); Deltota, *Jayasuriya 1505* (PDA, US); Nawalapitiya, *Jayasuriya 965* (PDA, US, K, L, WIS); East of Dolosbage, *Jayasuriya & Dassanayake 1011* (PDA, US, K, L); Rampadeniya, *Jayasuriya 838* (PDA, US, K, L, WIS); Raxawa Estate, *Wheeler 12262* (PDA, US); Laksapana Falls, *Jayasuriya, Burtt & Townsend 1125* (PDA); Bogawantalawa, *Jayasuriya 1338* (PDA, US, K); Rangala, *Waas 1009* (US); Maousekele, *Waas 940* (PDA, US). NUWARA ELIYA DISTRICT: Sangilipalama, Pussellawa, *Cramer 3862* (PDA, US). KEGALLE DISTRICT: Kitulgala, *Jayasuriya & Sumithraarachchi 1590* (PDA, US); Dewalagama, *Amaratunga 1227* (PDA). RATNAPURA DISTRICT: Illukwatte, South of Gilimale, *Jayasuriya & Burtt 1877* (PDA, US, K, L, WIS), *Jayasuriya 846* (PDA, US, K, L, WIS, MO), *Maxwell, Hepper & Fernando 942* (PDA, US).

5. Begonia humilis Dry. in Aiton, Hort. Kew ed. 1, 3: 353. 1789; Dry., Trans. Linn. Soc. London 1: 166. t. 15. 1791; Willd., Sp. Pl. 4: 417. 1805; A. DC. in Mart., Fl. Bras. 4. 1: 343. 1861; A. DC., Prod. 15. 1: 297. 1864; Smith and Schubert, Publ. Field Mus. Nat. His. Bot. Ser. 13.4. 1: 193. 1941. Type: Trini-

146 BEGONIACEAE

dad, *Alexander Anderson* (BM?).

Begonia lucida Haworth, Saxifr. Enum. 197. 1821.
Begonia meyeniana Walp., Nova Acta Phys. Med. Acad. Caes. Leop.-Carol.
   Nat. Cur. 19. Suppl. 1: 409. 1843; A. DC., Prod. 15. 1: 395. 1864.
Begonia pavoniana A. DC., Ann. Sci. Nat. Bot. 4. 11: 142. 1859; A. DC.,
   Prod. 15. 1: 381. 1864.
Begonia haematotricha Boissier ex A. DC., Prod. 15. 1: 298. 1864.
Begonia hirsuta Pavon ex A. DC., Prod. 15. 1: 381. 1864.

Slender herb 7–60 cm high, branching at base. Stem green, glabrous,
tumid at nodes. Leaves strongly asymmetric, ovate to oblong-ovate, somewhat cordate at base, acuminate, 3–11 × 1–4.5 cm, subpinnately nerved,
shallowly lobed, crenate, ciliate, rather densely pilose above; petioles 1–4 cm,
densely pilose towards upper part; stipules persistent, narrowly ovate, mucronate, serrulate, ciliate, 5–7 mm long. Inflorescence axillary; peduncle 2–4.5
cm long; cymes laxly c. 5-flowered; bracts minute, ovate, lacerate, 1–1.5 mm
long, persistent; staminate pedicels 5–10 mm long; staminate tepals 2+2; the
outer suborbicular, 3–4 mm wide, greenish-white; the inner lanceolate, 3 mm
long, white; stamens free, 8–20; filament 0.5 mm long; anther elliptic, 1–1.3
mm long; connective produced; pistillate pedicels 3–5 mm long; bracteoles
usually present at base of ovary; pistillate tepals 5, oblong-ovate, 2–4 mm
long; styles 3, bifid; stigmatic tissue linear, spiral, continuous; ovary 4–5 mm
long, unequally 3-winged; placentae very variable, usually deeply bifid. Capsule 6–8 × 4–13 cm (inclusive of wings) emarginate at base; pedicel elongating
up to 11 mm; wings subdeltoid, obtuse, unequal; the largest 4–9 mm wide.
Seed 0.25 mm long, ellipsoidal, reddish-purple.

D i s t r. Native of Tropical America (Mexico to Brazil and West Indies);
discovered by Alexander Anderson in the West Indies and first introduced to
England in 1788 by Lee and Kennedy; planted in the Royal Botanic Gardens,
Peradeniya about 1887; naturalized in and around Kandy; Udawattekele
Sanctuary at c. 500 m alt.
   E c o l. Flowering all the year.
   V e r n. Rough-leaved Begonia, Dwarf Begonia (E).
   S p e c i m e n s E x a m i n e d. KANDY DISTRICT: Kandy, Udawatte-
kele, *Jayasuriya 1629* (PDA, US, K, L), *Jayasuriya 1842* (PDA, US, K, L);
Kandy, *Alston s.n.* (PDA); Royal Botanic Gardens, Peradeniya, *Trimen s.n.*
(PDA). LOCALITY UNKNOWN: *Alston 128* (K).

6. Begonia malabarica Lam., Enc. 1: 393. 1783; Jacq., Collect. 129. 1786; Dry.,
Trans. Linn. Soc. London 1: 171. 1791; Moon, Cat. 64. 1824; Roxb., Fl.
Ind. ed. Carey 3: 648. 1832; Thw., Enum. Pl. Zeyl. 2: 128. 1859; A. DC., Prod.
15. 1: 392. 1864; Clarke in Hook. f., Fl. Br. Ind. 2: 655. 1879; Trimen, Handb.

Fl. Ceylon 2: 264. 1894; Gamble, Fl. Pres. Madras 546. 1915, repr. 1: 386. 1957; Saldanha & Nicolson, Fl. Hassan Distr. 173. 1976. Type: Malabar, *s. coll.* (n.v.).

Begonia tuberosa Wall., Cat. 3675. 1831 (nomen invalidum).
Begonia hydrophila Miq., Anal. Bot. Ind. 3: 18. 1853.
Begonia malabarica var. *rheedii* A. DC., Prod. 15. 1: 392. 1864.
Begonia malabarica var. *malabarica* Clarke in Hook. f., Fl. Br. Ind. 2: 656. 1879.
Begonia malabarica var. *hydrophylla* Clarke in Hook. f., Fl. Br. Ind. 2: 656. 1879.
[*Tsjeria-narinampuli* Rheede, Hort. Mal. 9: 167 t. 86. 1689].

Suffrutescent herb 0.2–1 m high. Stem erect, roughly zigzag, cylindrical, glabrous, branched, tumid at nodes. Leaves strongly asymmetric, the larger side cordate at base, the other rounded, acute at apex; chartaceous or membranous. 5–7 veined, 7–20 × 3–9 cm; margin dentate-crenate, sometimes ciliate; reddish-green when young, sometimes white-spotted especially in juvenile leaves; upper surface glabrous when mature, sometimes scabrous or sparsely pilose or hirsute, shiny to dull green; under surface glabrous or pilose along veins, shiny, pale green or purplish; petioles 2–7 cm long, succulent, cylindrical; stipules 10–15 mm long, lanceolate-ovate, acute, membranous, caducous. Peduncle axillary, succulent, pinkish with few shabby hairs, 2–3 cm long; cymes lax, few-15-flowered; bracts ovate, 2–4 × 2 mm; staminate pedicel 8–10 mm long; tepals rosy pink; staminate tepals 2+2, glabrous, outer pair suborbicular, up to 12 × 15 mm, somewhat cordate at base; inner pair (rarely 1 or 3) sometimes absent, oblong-ovate, c. 10 × 5 mm; stamens 25–50; filaments 2–2.5 mm long, shortly monadelphous; anther 1–1.5 mm long, clavate, cuneate at base; connective truncate or rounded on top; pistillate pedicel c. 1 cm long, longer in fruit; bracteoles 2, alternate, on upper part of pedicel, sometimes absent; pistillate tepals 2, similar to outer pair in staminate flower; ovary glabrous, up to 2 × 2 cm including wings; wings equal, distally rounded to angular; placentae simple, ovate in cross section; styles 3, free, 3–5 mm long; stigmatic zone undulate-spiral. Capsule very light, papery, pale brown when dry, pyriform in outline, acutely or bluntly angular, as long as broad or broader than long, 1.5–2.5 × 1.3–3.5 cm (including wings); wings more or less equal, 5–15 mm broad, truncate at top, distally acuteangular or obtuseangular. Seeds ellipsoidal.

D i s t r. India: south-western mountains and Western Ghats up to c. 2000 m alt. in moist woods. In Ceylon, fairly widely distributed in the wet zone at 100–1500 m alt. and in wet and shady places on Ritigala, an isolated hill of 765 m alt. in the dry zone.

E c o l. In humid and shady spots on rocky hill slopes and by streams; the commonest and one of the largest of indigenous species of *Begonia.* Flowering all the year.

V e r n. Hakambala, Maha-Hakambala (S).

N o t e. Tsjeria-narinampuli of Rheede in Hort. Mal. 9: 167. t. 86. 1689 represents *B. malabarica,* although no stipules are depicted and the flowers are not completely illustrated in the plate.

S p e c i m e n s E x a m i n e d. ANURADHAPURA DISTRICT: Ritigala Strict Natural Reserve, *Jayasuriya 1076* (PDA, US, K), *Jayasuriya & Burtt 1147* (PDA, US, K), *Jayasuriya & Pemadasa 1635* (PDA, US, K, L), *Jayasuriya, Wheeler & Cramer 827* (PDA, US, K, L), *Cramer 3833* (PDA, US), *Bernardi 16117* (PDA, US), *Willis s.n.* (PDA). MATALE DISTRICT: Between Rattota and Midlands, *Jayasuriya & Dassanayake 982* (PDA, US, K, L), *983* (PDA), *992* (PDA, US); Midlands, *Jayasuriya & Dassanayake 986* (PDA, US, K, L); Laggala, *Balakrishnan & Dassanayake 1150* (PDA, US). KANDY DISTRICT: Ensalwatte, *Jayasuriya 953* (PDA, US, K, L, WIS); Corbet's Gap, *Grupe 236* (PDA, US); East of Hunnasgiriya, *Jayasuriya, Moldenke & Sumithraarachchi 1415* (PDA, US, K, L); Rangala, *Waas 1008* (PDA, US); Madulkele, *Waas 944* (PDA, US); Hantana Hill, *Jayasuriya, Burtt & Townsend 1105* (PDA, US), *Burtt & Townsend 34* (PDA, US), *Robyns 7181* (PDA, US); Murutalawa, *Amaratunge 184* (PDA); Rampadeniya, *Jayasuriya 839* (PDA, US, K); Laksapana Falls, *Jayasuriya, Burtt & Townsend 1123* (PDA, US, K); Moray Estate, Maskeliya, *Kostermans 24146* (PDA, US). NUWARA ELIYA DISTRICT: Pussellawa, *Jayasuriya & Maxwell 815* (PDA, US, K, L, WIS); Ramboda, *Gardner C.P. 2807* (PDA). KEGALLE DISTRICT: South of Bulathkohupitiya, *Jayasuriya & Burtt 1126* (PDA, US); Bible rock, *Sumithraarachchi 153* (PDA, US). RATNAPURA DISTRICT: Between Rakwana and Deniyaya, *Jayasuriya 1876* (PDA, US); Kukulawa, Vihara kanda, *Waas 376* (PDA, US); Sri Palabaddala, *Waas 426* (PDA, US); Sinharaja Forest, *Tirvengadum & Balasubramaniam 325* (PDA, US), *Jayasuriya 2459* (PDA, US). BADULLA DISTRICT: Ettampitiya, *Jayasuriya & Townsend 1172* (PDA, US, K, L, WIS); Haputale, *Stone 11216* (PDA, US), May 1906, *Willis s.n.* (PDA); between Beragala and Weliweriya, *Sumithraarachchi & Waas 287* (PDA, US); Fort Macdonald, *Willis s.n.* (PDA). GALLE DISTRICT: Hinidun-kanda (Haycock), *Jayasuriya, Cramer & Balasubramaniam 791* (PDA, US, K). LOCALITY UNKNOWN: *Walker 47* (PDA); *s. coll. C.P. 2807* (PDA); *s. coll. 40/3675* (K); *s. coll. s.n.* (PDA).

7. Begonia dipetala R. Grah., Bot. Mag. 55: t. 2849. 1828; Lodd., Bot. Cab. t. 1730. 1831; Wight, Ic. Pl. Ind. Or. 5. 2: t. 1813. 1852; Thw., Enum. Pl. Zeyl. 2: 128. 1859; A. DC., Prod. 15. 1: 391. 1864. Type: t. 2849, Bot. Mag. 55. 1828.

Begonia bipetala Lodd. in Otto and Dietrich, Allg. Gartenzeitung 9. 58. 1841.
Haagia dipetala Klotzsch, Abh. Akad. Wiss. Berlin 104. 1855.

Begonia malabarica var. *dipetala* Clarke in Hook. f., Fl. Br. Ind. 2. 655. 1879.

Closely allied to *B. malabarica* but differs in its more robust and woody habit, forming bushes and reaching up to 1.5 m in height. Leaves 7–22 × 3–12 cm, membranous, transparent when dry, palmately 7–9 veined, irregularly and coarsely doubly serrate; petiole 3–8 cm long. Tepals white or very pale rosy pink; staminate tepals 2; ovary acute or attenuate at top. Capsule ovate-elliptic, acute, round at top, longer than broad, 1.8–3 × 1.3–2 cm (inclusive of wings); wings more or less equal, completely rounded or narrowed at summit, never distally angular, not broader than 5 mm at broadest.

D i s t r. India; Nilgiris at altitudes of 1200–1825 m. In Ceylon rare and confined to hill slopes of the intermediate zone, chiefly in south-eastern regions at low altitudes.

E c o l. Found on very shady rocky slopes. Flowering probably all the year.

N o t e. "This species flowered at the Royal Botanic Garden, Edinburgh, in April 1828, having been raised two years before from seeds sent by Dr. Johnston, from Bombay"—Graham. The plant tastes sour with very bitter aftertaste.

S p e c i m e n s E x a m i n e d. MATALE DISTRICT: Matale, *s. coll. C.P. 3949* in part (PDA); Galagama, *s. coll. C.P. 3949* in part (PDA). MONERA-GALA DISTRICT: Base of Govinda-hela (Westminster Abbey), *Jayasuriya 2058* (PDA, US, K, L, WIS); Sellaka-oya Sanctuary, Gal-oya National Park, *Jayasuriya 2065* (PDA, US, K, L, WIS).

8. Begonia cucullata var. **hookeri** Smith and Schubert, Darwiniana 5: 104. 1941; Schubert, Natl. Hort. Mag. 33: 244. 1954; Smith and Smith, Fl. Illustr. Catarinense 25. 1971. Type: Brazil (B, holotype n.v.). Willdenow in his original description of *Begonia cucullata* states "I have seen only a single exceedingly imperfect specimen".

Begonia semperflorens Link and Otto, Ic. Pl. Rar. 9, t. 5. 1828; Lodd., Bot. Cab. 15. t. 1439. 1829; R. Grah., Edinburgh New Philos. J. 6: 180. 1829; Hook., Bot. Mag. 56: t. 2920. 1829; Klotzsch, Abh. Akad. Wiss. Berlin 28. 1855; A. DC., Prod. 15. 1: 293. 1864.

Begonia setaria Hort. Angl. ex R. Grah., Edinburgh New Philos. J. 6: 180. 1829 (nom. nud.).

Begonia hookeri Sweet, Hort. Brit. ed. 2. 437. 1830.

Begonia sellowii Klotzsch, Abh. Königl. Akad. Wiss. Berlin 40: 28. 1855.

Begonia cucullifolia Hassk., Hort. Bogor. Desc. 311. 1858.

Begonia semperflorens var. *hookeri* A. DC. in Mart., Fl. Bras. 4. 1: 342. 1861; A. DC., Prod. 15. 1: 293. 1864.

Begonia semperflorens var. *sellowii* A. DC. in Mart., Fl. Bras. 4. 1: 342. 1861; A. DC., Prod. 15. 1: 293. 1864.

Perennial, succulent, caulescent, stoloniferous, glabrous herb 0.1–1 m high. Stems erect or ascending, woody at base, more or less branched, reddish. Leaves slightly asymmetric, straight, broadly ovate, truncate and usually inrolled at base, obtuse at apex, palmately 4–6 veined, 4–10 × 4–9 cm, crenateserrate, ciliate, glabrous on both surfaces; petiole 2.5–5 cm long; stipules persistent, oblong or elliptic, obtuse, entire, 1.4–3 cm long, green. Inflorescence axillary; peduncle 3–6 cm long; cymes few-flowered; bracts persistent, ovate, serrulate, glabrous, 5 mm long, pedicels slender; tepals white or rosy pink, staminate tepals 2+2; the outer ones suborbicular, 8–15 mm long; the inner smaller and narrowly obovate; stamens 25–40, free; filaments c. 2.5 mm long; anthers elliptic, c. 2.5 mm long; connective produced; pistillate bracteoles 3, appressed to the faces of ovary; pistillate tepals 4–5, obovate; styles 3, bifid; stigmatic tissue linear, spiral, continuous; placentae bilamellate, ovuliferous throughout. Capsule 2–3 cm long, unequally 3-winged; the largest wing triangular, subacute. Seeds narrowly ovate, obtuse at apex, subtruncate at base.

D i s t r. Native of Tropical America (Brazil to Uruguay); introduced world-wide in tropics and subtropics; very popular in cultivation; in Ceylon, naturalized in central highlands; common on roadsides at elevations of 1300–1900 m.

E c o l. Flowering all the year.

V e r n. Free-flowering Begonia (E); Kaloopulichy (T).

N o t e. Although most specimens enumerated here could be accommodated in *B. cucullata* var. *hookeri* Smith & Schubert, it is possible that they are cultivars with many variations. The above description is not typical of the taxon because the specimens examined are all cultivar escapes: they are almost certainly all hybrids.

S p e c i m e n s E x a m i n e d. KANDY DISTRICT: Talawakele, *Jayasuriya, Hepper & Maxwell 820* (PDA); Hatton, *Jayasuriya, Burtt & Townsend 1121* (PDA, US); Maskeliya, *Stedman s.n.* (PDA), *Beusekom & Beusekom 1521* (PDA, US); between Maskeliya and Norwood, *Jayasuriya & Sumithraarachchi 1560* (PDA, US, K); Moray Estate below Adam's Peak, *Jayasuriya, Hepper & Maxwell 825* (PDA, US), *Jayasuriya & Sumithraarachchi 1564* (PDA, US, MO, K, L, WIS); Adam's Peak, *Alston 937* (PDA). NUWARA ELIYA DISTRICT: Westward Ho, *Jayasuriya & Cramer 768* (PDA); Labukele, *Jayasuriya & Nowicke 1238* (PDA, US), *1239* (PDA, US), *Jayasuriya, Moldenke & Sumithraarachchi 1478* (PDA, US); Ramboda, *Hepper 4421* (PDA, US); Hakgala Botanical Garden, *Silva s.n.* (PDA); Maturata, *Waas 1141* (PDA, US). BADULLA DISTRICT: between Hakgala and Ambawela, *Jayasuriya, Moldenke & Sumithraarachchi 1477* (PDA, US); North of Haputale, *Jayasuriya & Maxwell 811* (PDA, US). RATNAPURA DISTRICT: Maratenna, *Jayasuriya 1200* (PDA, US, K, L).

9. Begonia ulmifolia Willd., Sp. Pl. 4: 418. 1805; Haworth, Saxifr. Enum. 197. 1821; Link, Enum. Hort. Berol. 2. 396. 1822; Lodd., Bot. Cab. 7: t. 638. 1822; Willd. ex Hook., Exot. Fl. 1: 57. 1823; HBK, Nov. Gen. & Sp. 7: 179. 1825; A. DC., Prod. 15. 1: 290. 1864; Schulz in Urban, Symbol. Antill. 7: 3. 1911. Type: Venezuela: Caracas, Federal District, *Humboldt & Bonpland* (B, holotype, n.v.).

Donaldia ulmifolia Klotzsch, Abh. Akad. Wiss. Berlin 78. 1855.

Suffrutescent herb up to 2.8 m high. Stem erect, pilose especially in young parts; internodes 2.5–11 cm long, shallowly grooved longitudinally, bluntly angular in cross section, lenticellate, lenticels whitish, elongated, up to 3 mm; pith large, chlorophyllous; leaf and stipular scars prominent. Leaves petioled, oblong-elliptic or subovate, 5–20 × 2–7 cm; base unequal, rounded; apex acute-subacuminate; margin irregularly and finely serrulate, ciliate; densely strigose-pilose above, disperse flaccid pilose below, pinnately veined; lateral veins up to 9 in larger half, 7 in smaller half, prominent below, grooved above; stipules oblong-lanceolate, acute, entire, brown, chartaceous, transparent, glabrous or sparsely pilose along veins, gland-dotted, 1.5–2 cm long. Inflorescence axillary; peduncle 5–12 cm long, pink, pilose, usually jointed above midway; cymes crowded, 15–60-flowered; lower bracts narrowly lanceolate; the upper linear, mucronate, 4–14 mm long; staminate pedicels c. 1 cm long, densely pubescent; tepals white; staminate tepals 2, broadly ovate, slightly cordate at base, 8–10 mm long, equally broad, sparsely pilose on outer surface; stamens 30–50, free; filaments 2–3 mm long, filiform; anthers oblong, 1–2 mm long; connective produced into a conical protuberance beyond anther lobes; pistillate pedicels 5–10 mm long, densely pilose; bracteoles 2, appressed to base of ovary, linear to subulate, entire, brown, transparent chartaceous, glabrous, up to 10 × 2 mm; pistillate tepals 2 + 3; outer pair up to 4 × 3 mm, ovate, acute, glabrous; the inner rather unequal, upto 8 × 5 mm, ovary up to 12 × 7 mm, hirsute, unequally 3-winged; styles 3, bifid; branches ascending, spiral, papillose; placentae deeply bilamellate. Capsule 7–11 × 12–18 mm; obtuse at base, sparsely pilose; capsular pedicel 12–20 mm long; wings unequal; larger one subobtuse-angular, 7–18 mm broad; others narrow, parallel to obtuse-angular. Seeds 0.3 mm long, oblong, subtruncate.

D i s t r. Native of Venezuela; first cultivated in England by Loddiges before 1820; introduced to Ceylon in 1884.

E c o l. Naturalized especially along roadsides and disturbed jungles in some parts of the central highlands above c. 1000 m. Flowering all the year; largest of all species of *Begonia* found wild or naturalized in the Island.

V e r n. Elm-leaved Begonia (E).

S p e c i m e n s   E x a m i n e d. KANDY DISTRICT: Between Hatton and Watawala, *Jayasuriya 1878* (PDA, US, K, L, WIS). NUWARA ELIYA

DISTRICT: Between Pussellawa and Ramboda, *Jayasuriya & Tirvengadum 998* (PDA, US, K, L), *Jayasuriya, Moldenke & Sumithraarachchi 1455* (PDA, US, K, L), *Comanor 920* (PDA, US); Ramboda, *Jayasuriya, Moldenke & Sumithraarachchi 1479* (PDA, US, K); Between Talawakele and Hatton, *Jayasuriya, Burtt & Townsend 1120* (PDA, US, K); Kotmale, *Amaratunga 1533* (PDA).

BURMANNIACEAE

(by L.H. Cramer*)

Blume, Enum. Pl. Javae 27. 1827. Type genus: *Burmannia* L.

Annual or perennial, saprophytic or autotrophic herbs, the saprophytes often colourless; stem often dwarfed, simple, occasionally branched. Leaves exstipulate, alternate, simple, in autotrophic species the radical leaves rosulate, in autotrophic and saprophytic species the cauline ones scalelike. Bracts usually present. Perianth in 2 ternate whorls, the outer usually of larger conspicuous tepals, the inner of inconspicuous ones; tube campanulate or urceolate, sometimes 3-winged, persistent after anthesis. Anthers 3, sessile or subsessile, included in perianth tube, the thecae dehiscing laterally, or 6, hanging in perianth tube from an annulus, the thecae dehiscing longitudinally; connective large, often appendiculate. Ovary inferior, 1-celled with parietal placentation, or 3-celled with axile placentation; ovules numerous, anatropous; style included in perianth tube. Fruit capsular, crowned by persistent perianth, dehiscing irregularly, or circumscissile; seeds white, endospermous, sometimes with loose, reticulate testa.

About 125 species, pantropic and subtropical; also in Southern Australia, Tasmania and New Zealand. In Ceylon only five species occur, represented among two genera, *Burmannia* and *Thismia,* the latter with only one endemic species.

KEY TO THE GENERA

1 Perianth tube cylindrical or trigonous, prominently 3-winged, the throat smooth; anthers 3, thecae dehiscing laterally. Ovary 3-locular, with axile placentation. Capsule usually dehiscing laterally . . . . **1. Burmannia**
1 Perianth tube campanulate, plain, the throat with an annulus; anthers 6, thecae dehiscing longitudinally; ovary 1-locular, with parietal placentation. Capsule circumscissile
. . . . **2. Thismia**

1. BURMANNIA

L., Sp. Pl. 287. 1753; L., Gen. Pl. ed. 5, 139. 1754; Endl., Gen. Pl. 1: 164. 1837; Jonker, Mon. Burmann. 57. 1938. Type species: *B. disticha* L.

*Flora of Ceylon Project, Peradeniya. Present address: Batticaloa University College, Chenkaladi.

Annual or perennial, erect, saprophytic and colourless or green, autotrophic herbs; stem simple or sparingly branched. Leaves in saprophytic species reduced to small, usually lanceolate scales, in autotrophic ones sometimes large, grass-like, linear in lower part of stem or rosulate at base of stem, the cauline leaves small, scale-like. Flowers solitary or in groups at the top of the stem, or in dense, terminal cymose or head-like inflorescences. Perianth persistent after anthesis; limb usually in 2 whorls, each of 3 lobes, the outer much larger, the inner often minute, sometimes lacking; tube cylindrical-trigonous. Anthers 3, sessile, in perianth throat below inner perianth lobes; connective with 2 apical crests, basally spurred or not. Ovary trigonous, 3-locular; placentation axile; style filiform, with 3 stigmatic branches. Capsule many-seeded, enclosed by persistent, dried perianth, dehiscing irregularly.

According to Jonker 57 species, pantropic and in the Southern U.S.A. and Southern Australia.

KEY TO THE SPECIES

1 Autotrophic, chlorophyllous herbs; stem with a fibrous rootstock: basal leaves rosetted; flowers solitary or in cymes; perianth prominently winged; stigmatic branches sessile
  2 Basal rosette of leaves distinct, the leaves 0.5–12.0 cm long; stem more or less 9.2–65 cm high; flowers 10–17 mm long; lobes of outer tepals with a double margin
    3 Robust herbs 30–65 cm high; radical leaves 0.5–12.0 cm long; flowers many, in 2-flowered cincinni...**1. B. disticha**
    3 Slender herbs 0.2–20.0 cm high; radical leaves 0.5–1.0 cm long; flowers solitary or in lax clusters of 2–3...**2. B. coelestis**
  2 Basal rosette of leaves reduced, the radical leaves 0.4–0.5 cm long; stem 2.5–9.0 cm high; flowers 6–11 mm long; lobes of outer tepals with a single margin....**3. B. pusilla**
1 Saprophytic, whitish herbs; stem with a slender rhizome; basal leaves alternate; flowers usually capitate; perianth plain, 3–6-costate; stigmatic branches subsessile............
....**4. B. championii**

1. Burmannia disticha L., Sp. Pl. 287. 1753; Hook. f., Fl. Br. Ind. 5: 664. 1888; Trimen, Handb. Fl. Ceylon 4: 130. 1898; Jonker, Mon. Burmann. 115. 1938; Abeywick., Ceylon J. Sci., Biol. Sci. 2 (2): 146. 1959. Type: *Hermann s.n.* Ceylon, Mus. Zeyl. 5: 34 (holotype, BM).

Burmannia distachya R. Br., Prod. Fl. Nov. Holl. 1: 265. 1810; Thw., Enum. Pl. Zeyl. 325. 1864. Type: same as for *Burmannia disticha.*
Burmannia sumatrana Miq., Fl. Ind. Bat. Suppl. 1: 616. 1860. Type: *Miquel,* prope Alahan-panjang (n.v.)
Burmannia disticha L. var. *sumatrana* Hook. f., Fl. Br. Ind. 5: 664. 1888.

Robust, autotrophic annual with a fibrous root-stock; stem 14–65 cm high, slender. Basal leaves rosetted, ensiform, 5.0–12.0 × 0.6–1.2 cm, sheathing at base, acuminate, the nerves 5, parallel, with transverse nervules; cauline ones lanceolate, 1.5–0.5 × 0.4–0.6 cm, appressed to stem. Cyme forked;

branches 3.5–7.6 cm long; flowers subsessile, secund. Bracts linear lanceolate, 4–5 × 1.5 mm, acute, concave. Perianth tube to 9 mm long, tapering to base, 3-winged; wings continued as dorsal crests of tepals; outer tepals broadly ovate, to 2 × 1.5 mm, acute, bluish-purple, with a double margin; inner ones linear-spathulate, 1.25 × 0.75 mm, bright yellow. Anthers dehiscing laterally; connective spurred; crests flabellate. Style 3.0–3.5 mm long; branches expanded above. Capsule obovoid, 4–5 mm long; seeds fusiform, 0.7 mm long, obliquely striate.

D i s t r. India through China to tropical Australia.

E c o l. In wet or boggy ground among grass, commonly in the lowlands; occasionally in the uplands. Altitude c. 75–1800 m. Grows in association with *Xyris* sp. and *Eriocaulon* sp. Flowering throughout the year.

S p e c i m e n s   E x a m i n e d. KANDY DISTRICT: Adam's Peak, *Gardner C.P. 2313* (PDA). NUWARA ELIYA DISTRICT: Nuwara Eliya, patanas, Oct. 1952, *Silva 10* (PDA). RATNAPURA DISTRICT: near Karawita, Dec. 1893, *s. coll. s.n.* (PDA); between Karawita and Delgoda, *Lewis & Silva s.n.* (PDA); Weddagala, in damp flush, *Hepper et al. 4547* (K, PDA, US); Rajjuruwatte, boggy grassland, *Faden 76/440* (PDA, US). KALUTARA DISTRICT: Pelwatte, Ranawaka Rock, in damp ground, *Cramer 3176* (PDA, US), *s. coll. C.P. 2313* (PDA). GALLE DISTRICT: Hiyare, in swamp, *Alston 597* (PDA); Hiniduma, in damp ground among short grass at foot of Heycock, *Cramer 3770* (PDA, US); ibid., *Bremer 871* (PDA, S, USA); ibid., *Hoogland 11464* (CANB, L, PDA, US). LOCALITY UNKNOWN: *s. coll.* in Hb. Wt. *s.n.* (PDA), *Col. Joville s.n.* (BM), *Gardner s.n.* in Hb. Miers (BM).

2. **Burmannia coelestis** D. Don, Prod. Fl. Nepal 44. 1825; Royle, Ill. Bot. Himal. 373, t. 91, f. 1. 1839; Hook. f., Fl. Br. Ind. 5: 665. 1888; Trimen, Handb. Fl. Ceylon 4: 131. 1898; Jonker, Mon. Burmann. 120. 1938. Type: *Wallich s.n.*, Nepal (holotype, K).

Burmannia triflora Roxb., Fl. Ind. 2: 117. 1832. Type: Burm. Ic. In Burm., Thes. Zeyl. 50, t. 20, f. 1. 1737.
Burmannia azurea Griff., Not. Pl. As. 3: 236. 1851; Griff., Ic. Pl. As. 3: t. 272, f. 1. 1851. Type: Griff. Ic. in l.c.
Burmannia pusilla Thw., Enum. Pl. Zeyl. 325. 1864. Type: *Gardner C.P. 2312* Ceylon, "Kokool Corle: Cultura" (holotype, PDA).

Slender, autotrophic annual with a shallow root stock; stem erect, 9.2–20 cm high, simple, occasionally sparingly branched above. Basal leaves rosetted, linear-lanceolate to subulate, 5–10 × 1–2 mm, acute to acuminate; cauline ones few, distant, subulate, 4.5–10.0 × 0.5–2 mm, sheathing at base, long acuminate, 1- or 3-nerved. Flowers terminal, solitary or in lax clusters of

2–3. Pedicels to 2 mm long. Bracts linear-lanceolate, 4–8 mm long, long-acuminate. Perianth tube to 6 mm long; wings semi-elliptical or slightly semi-obovate, to 2 mm broad, continued below to stalk; outer tepals broadly ovate, 1.5 × 1.5 mm, subacute, apiculate, with a double margin; inner tepals oblong-lanceolate, 1 mm broad, apiculate. Crests of connective hairy; basal spur infundibular, 0.7 mm long. Style 4–5 mm long, fairly thick. Capsule obovoid, 4.5–5 mm long, truncate at top; seeds cuneiform or linear, 0.5 mm long.

D i s t r. From South India through Ceylon and Burma to Malesia, inclusive of New Guinea.

E c o l. In swampy places in the wet low country, especially in the Kalutara District, occasionally in the uplands. Altitude sea level to c. 1200 m. Flowering December–March; August.

S p e c i m e n s   E x a m i n e d. KALUTARA DISTRICT: Kalutara, *s. coll. C.P. 2312* (PDA); ibid., in fields, *Macrae s.n.* in Hb. Soc. Hort. Lond. (K). GALLE DISTRICT: Baddegama, in swamp, *Alston 1368* (PDA). BADULLA DISTRICT: near Nilgala, *s. coll. s.n.* (PDA). RATNAPURA DISTRICT: Gartmore, Feb. 1981, *Balasubramaniam s.n.* (PDA).

3. Burmannia pusilla (Wall. ex Miers) Thw., Enum. Pl. Zeyl. 325. 1864, excl. var. *β*; Hook. f., Fl. Br. Ind. 5: 665. 1888; Jonker, Mon. Burmann. 130. 1938; Abeywick., Ceylon J. Sci., Biol. Sci. 2 (2): 146. 1959.

Gonyanthes pusilla (Wall. ex Miers) Miers in Trans. Linn. Soc. London 18: 537, t. 38, f. 3. 1841. Type: *Wallich 9008*, Burma, Tavoy (holotype, K).
Burmannia coelestis Don var. *pusilla* Trimen ex Hook. f., in Trimen, Handb. Fl. Br. Ind. 4: 131. 1898.

Slender, autotrophic annual with a shallow root stock; stem 2.5–10 cm high, filiform. Basal rosette of leaves reduced; radical leaves 4.0–5.5 × 1.25 mm, acute, 3-nerved; cauline ones scale-like, 1.0–3.5 × 1.25 mm. Flowers terminal, solitary or in lax clusters of 3, the central one sessile, the lateral ones with peduncles to 1.2 cm long. Bracts subulate, 2–3.5 × 0.75–1 mm, appressed. Perianth tube 4–5 × 1 mm; wings sublunar to broadly semi-obovate, 1.5–2 mm broad, continued below to stalk; outer tepals oval-oblong to triangular-ovate, 1.5 × 1.0 mm, obtuse, with a single margin, purplish-blue; inner ones linear-subulate, 0.5–1.0 mm long, pale blue. Crests of connective hairy; basal spur obtuse. Style 1.5–2.25 mm long; stigmas expanded above. Capsule obovoid, 2 mm long; seeds fusiform, 0.24 mm long, scopiform, pale yellow.

D i s t r. Ceylon. India to Indo-China (Vietnam).

E c o l. Among short grass in damp places in the wet and dry lowlands, common; more abundant in the eastern sectors of the dry lowlands. Altitude sea level to c. 150 m. This species is usually found in association with *Dopat-*

rium nudicaule, **Lindernia ciliata**, **Lindernia srilankana**, *Drosera indica* and *Geniosporum tenuiflorum*. Flowering throughout the year.

Note. This is a smaller plant than *Burmannia coelestis*, and their rosettes of leaves are often hardly distinguishable.

Specimens Examined. COLOMBO DISTRICT: Colombo, *Gardner C.P. 3023* (PDA); Mutturajawela, Nugape, *Faden 76/418* (PDA, US). PUTTALAM DISTRICT: Wilpattu National Park, Kumutu Villu, *Cooray 41 R* (K, PDA, US). KALUTARA DISTRICT. Katukurunda, in water-logged soil, *Waas 1434* (PDA, US); Pelawatte, Ranawaka Rock, in damp ground, *Cramer 2810* (PDA, US). GALLE DISTRICT: Bentota, in grassy ground, *Cramer 3216* (PDA, US); Koggala, in grassy ground beside ditch, *Cramer 4991* (PDA, US). AMPARAI DISTRICT: Lahugala, rocky ground among grass, *Cramer 5046* (K, PDA, US). BATTICALOA DISTRICT: Gunner's Quoin, among short grass, *Cramer 5081* (PDA, US); Tiruperumdurai, on grassy bund of paddy field, *Cramer 5071* (PDA, US). TRINCOMALEE DISTRICT: Trincomalee, *Gardner C.P. 3023* (PDA, US); Somapura, among grass in sandy loam soil, *Cramer 5114* (PDA, US). MATALE DISTRICT: along grassy border of rocky outcrop, *Cramer 5086* (K, PDA, US). LOCALITY UNKNOWN: *s. coll. C.P. 2312* (PDA).

4. Burmannia championii Thw., Enum. Pl. Zeyl. 325. 1864; Hook. f., Fl. Br. Ind. 5: 666. 1888; Trimen, Handb. Fl. Ceylon 4: 131. 1898; Jonker, Mon. Burmann. 138. 1938; Abeywick., Ceylon J. Sci., Biol. Sci. 2 (2): 146. 1959. Type: *s. coll. C.P. 2735*, Ceylon, "Saffragam district and Hinidoon Corle" (holotype, PDA).

White saprophytic annual; stem erect, 5.5–15.5 cm high, simple, 4-angular; rhizomatic part slender, curved tortuous-wise, sometimes covered with hair-like roots. Radical leaves 0; cauline ones few, scale-like, narrowly lanceolate, 2.5–4.0 mm long, appressed. Flowers usually 3–13 in a capitulum; occasionally in a 2-fid cyme. Pedicels 1 mm long. Bracts lanceolate, 3–4 mm long. Perianth 5–10 mm long; tube 5–6 mm long, narrow, plain, 3–6-costate; outer tepals ovate-lanceolate, 2 mm long. Connective broadly oblong, pointed at apex; apical crests hardly distinct; basal spur broad, hanging, transparent. Stigmas subsessile. Capsule elliptic to obovoid.

Distr. Ceylon, Malesia to South China and Japan.

Ecol. Among moss, fallen leaves and on rocks in dense shade of wet, evergreen forests in the lowlands; rather rare. I have not been able to encounter this plant. Altitude c. 150–200 m. Flowering March–May.

Specimens Examined. GALLE DISTRICT: Hiniduma, *s. coll. C.P. 2735* (PDA). RATNAPURA DISTRICT: Palabaddala, *s. coll. C.P. 2735* (PDA); Ellaboda Kande, *Lewis & Silva s.n.* (PDA); Gilimale, *s. coll. s.n.*

(PDA). LOCALITY UNKNOWN: *s. coll. C.P. 2735* (BM), *Maj. Champion s.n.* n Hb. Miers (BM).

2. THISMIA

Griff., Proc. Linn. Soc. London 1: 221. 1844; Jonker, Mon. Burmann. 227. 1938. Type species: *T. brunonis* Griff.

Saprophytic, fleshy herbs; underground part tuberous or vermiform, creeping; stem usually short, unbranched, sparsely beset with small, reduced scale-like leaves. Bracts 1 or more, scale-like, often forming an involucre. Flowers terminal, solitary or few, actinomorphic, occasionally zygomorphic. Perianth urceolate to campanulate; mouth contracted into an annulus; lobes 6, of equal length, or inner ones larger, these sometimes connivent at apex into an erect mitre with 3 holes. Anthers 6, hanging at annulus, free or adherent into an anther-tube; filaments short, filiform or ribbon-shaped. Ovary obconical or obovoid, with 3 stalked placentae; style short, thick, cylindrical or filiform, persistent, with 3 bilobate stigmas. Fruit with basal part of perianth tube turbinate; perianth circumscissile.

According to Jonker 24 species distributed in tropical America, Asia, New Zealand and Tasmania.

According to Jonker's classification (1938) which I follow, *Thismia* belongs to the tribe Thismieae of the Burmanniaceae, the tribe having the following characters: perianth circumscissile; ovary 1-locular, with 3 placentae; style short and thick; anthers 3 or 6, hanging in perianth tube.

Thismia gardneriana Hook. f. ex Thw., Enum. Pl. Zeyl. 325. 1864; Hook. f., Fl. Br. Ind. 5: 666. 1888; Trimen, Handb. Fl. Ceylon 4: 132. 1898; Jonker, Mon. Burmann. 244. 1938; Abeywick., Ceylon J. Sci., Biol. Sci. 2 (2): 146. 1959. Type: *Champion s.n.* Ceylon, in Hb. Hook. (holotype, K).

White or pale yellow saprophytic annual with a vermiform root; stem erect, 2.5–7.5 cm high, or flexuous, 1–5-flowered, fleshy. Leaves ovate-lanceolate, 1.5–3 mm long, appressed. Bracts subulate, to 5.5 mm long. Perianth tube campanulate, 7–12 mm long; outer tepals oblong-orbicular, 1.5–2 mm long; inner ones subulate, 1.4–2.2 cm long, filiform, clavately swollen at tip. Annulus prominent. Anthers connivent into a staminal tube; connective with a 4-angular, wing-like appendage along its median plane, the basal margin 2-dentate; filaments broad. Style thick; stigmas 3, each 2-fid.

D i s t r. Endemic.

E c o l. Among dead leaves in dense shade of wet, evergreen forests of the lowlands; very rare. Altitude c. 100–200 m. I have not been able to find this plant. Flowering September–October.

Specimens Examined. RATNAPURA DISTRICT: Kuruwita Korale, between Eratne and Palabaddala, *s. coll. s.n.* (PDA). LOCALITY UNKNOWN: *s. coll. C.P. 4009* (PDA); *Champion s.n.* (K).

CAMPANULACEAE

(by L.H. Cramer*)

Type genus: *Campanula* L.

Perennial or annual herbs, rarely shrubs, often laticiferous. Leaves exstipulate, alternate, rarely opposite, entire, serrulate or lobed. Flowers solitary or in racemes or panicles, actinomorphic. Bracts small. Bracteoles 0. Calyx persistent; tube adnate to ovary; lobes 5, valvate. Corolla campanulate or campanulate-infundibular; lobes 4–5, valvate. Stamens epigynous, alternating with corolla lobes, free; anthers 2-celled, the cells distinct, linear. Ovary inferior, 3–5-locular; placentation axile; ovules numerous; stigmatic branches equal in number to the ovary loculi. Fruit a capsule or berry; capsule papery, dehiscing by pores or by valves; seeds numerous, small, endospermous.

A cosmopolitan family of over 1500 species, more concentrated in the Northern Hemisphere. In Ceylon the family is represented by only 2 genera, viz., *Campanula* and *Wahlenbergia*, whose species are restricted to the montane zone above about 1300 m. The family is of little economic importance save for its horticultural value. Many species, especially of the genus *Campanula*, are cultivated as ornamentals. In Ceylon *Campanula rapunculoides* L. is the commonest cultivated ornamental of the genus.

KEY TO THE GENERA

1 Capsular dehiscence below calyx lobes, usually poricidal; leaves cauline, often basal, or radical and rosulate; pedicels not longer than 10 mm . . . .**1. Campanula**
1 Capsular dehiscence above calyx lobes, valvular; leaves all cauline and above base of stem; pedicels much longer than 10 mm . . . .**2. Wahlenbergia**

1. CAMPANULA

L., Sp. Pl. 163. 1753; L., Gen. Pl. ed. 5, 77. 1754; DC., Mon. Camp. 213. 1830; Endl., Gen. Pl. 517. 1838; Benth. & Hook., Gen. Pl. 2: 549. 1876. Type species: *C. latifolia* L.

*Flora of Ceylon Project, Peradeniya. Present address: Batticaloa University College, Chenkaladi.

Annual or perennial, erect or ascending herbs. Leaves cauline, spirally arranged, or radical and rosulate, the latter with longer petioles than the former. Flowers solitary, axillary, or in terminal racemes or panicles, 5-merous. Calyx adnate to ovary; tube turbinate or campanulate; lobes short or prolonged into reflexed appendages. Corolla campanulate or rotate; tube variously cleft. Stamens free, alternate with lobes of corolla; filaments overarching ovary with dilated bases. Disk epigynous, not prominent. Ovary 3–5-locular; stigmatic branches 3–5. Capsule obovoid or narrowly oblong, truncate, crowned by persistent calyx lobes, ribbed, dehiscing by valves or pores; seeds numerous, very small, endospermous.

About 300 species in north temperate regions, especially Mediterranean, and in tropical mountains; many species cultivated as ornamentals.

KEY TO THE SPECIES

1 Racemes paniculate or spicate; flowers alternate, some incomplete; corolla tube much shorter than 1.2 cm long; capsule longer than 5 mm
  2 Leaves all cauline; racemes paniculate; corolla lobed to less than half way down tube; capsular dehiscence by basal valves................................**1. C. canescens**
  2 Leaves mostly basal; racemes spicate; corolla lobed to near base; capsular dehiscence by apical pores...**2. C. fulgens**
1 Racemes simple; flowers secund, all complete; corolla tube longer than 1.2 cm long; capsule at least 5 mm long....................................**3. C. rapunculoides**

1. Campanula canescens Wall. ex DC., Mon. Camp. 292. 1830; DC., Prod. 7: 473. 1839; Hook. f., Fl. Br. Ind. 3: 439. 1885; Trimen, Handb. Fl. Ceylon 3: 60. 1895; Abeywick., Ceylon J. Sci., Biol. Sci. 2 (2): 234. 1959. Type: Wall., Num. List. 1289 (holotype, K-WALL.).

Cephalostigma spathulatum Thw., Enum. Pl. Zeyl. 422. 1864. Type: *Thwaites C.P. 3794*, between Boralande and Haputale, Badulla District ("Oova District"). (holotype, PDA).

Annual; stem erect, 21–45 cm high, slender, subangular, thinly hirtellous. Leaves cauline, sessile, the lower spathulate, 2.2–3.0 × 0.7 cm, the upper linear-lanceolate, 1–1.5 × 0.2–0.3 cm, tapering to base, subacute, distantly crenate-serrulate, finely scabrid beneath, hirsute above. Panicles terminal, lax, racemose; flowers small. Bracts linear-spathulate, to 10 × 2 mm. Pedicels to 10 mm long, filiform, bristly. Calyx tube globose, 1–2 mm long, minutely bristly without; lobes ovate-lanceolate, to 1.25 mm long, acute. Corolla broadly campanulate, pale purple (sometimes absent, inclusive of stamens). Capsule globose, 1.5–2 mm broad, dehiscing by basal valves; seeds ovoid-elliptic, 0.33 mm long, smooth, pale brown.

D i s t r. Northern and central India, Ceylon and Burma. "On rocks between Boralande and Haputale."—Thwaites, l.c. Rare. In spite of several attempts in the field I have not located this plant. (The description is based on herbarium material).

E c o l. Flowering April.

S p e c i m e n s E x a m i n e d. Same as type.

2. Campanula fulgens Wall. in Roxb., Fl. Ind. 2: 99. 1824; DC., Mon. Camp. 315. 1830; DC., Prod. 7: 477. 1839; Thw., Enum. Pl. Zeyl. 169. 1864; Hook. f., Fl. Br. Ind. 3: 442. 1885; Trimen, Handb. Fl. Ceylon 3: 60. 1895; Abeywick., Ceylon J. Sci., Biol. Sci. 2 (2): 234. 1959. Type: Wallich, Num. List. 1283 (holotype, K-WALL).

Perennial herb with a short rootstock and large, fusiform roots; stem erect, 15.0–45.0 cm long, terete, grooved on opposite sides, glabrous, not branched above. Leaves few, mostly basal, oval-oblong to ovate-lanceolate, 2.3–3.8 × 0.8–1 cm, acute at base, subacute at apex, crenate-serrate, scabrid above, glabrous beneath, upper ones sessile and narrower; petioles to 1.8 cm long. Flowers few, rather large, 1–3 together. Racemes terminal, spicate, to 12 cm long. Bracts linear to linear-lanceolate, to 8 mm long. Calyx tube campanulate, to 4 mm long; lobes linear-lanceolate, to 5 mm long. Corolla lobed to near base, purple to violet-purple; tube 1 mm long; lobes lanceolate, to 5 mm long, acute. Stigmatic branches linear. Capsule ovoid, to 6.5 mm long, crowned with calyx lobes, dehiscing by apical pores; seeds ovoid.

D i s t r. From the Himalayas along the Western Ghats and Pulney Hills to Ceylon.

E c o l. On patanas of the highlands from c. 1100 to 2100 m. Rare. I have failed to encounter this plant in the field. (The description is based on herbarium material). Flowering February–April; November.

S p e c i m e n s E x a m i n e d. LOCALITY UNKNOWN: *Gardner 428* (K). NUWARA ELIYA DISTRICT: Maturata, patana, 6 April 1906, *Silva* (PDA); Hakgala, 23 April 1915, *Petch* (PDA); Nuwara Eliya, *Gardner C.P. 1775* (PDA).

3. Campanula rapunculoides L., Sp. Pl. 165. 1753.

Perennial herb with a fibrous rootstock; stem erect, to 70 cm high, striate, glabrous. Leaves dimorphic; radical leaves ovate-cordate, 6.5–11.2 × 3.6–6.5 cm, cauline ones ovate-lanceolate, to 7.5 × 3 cm; all acute at apex, serrate, glabrous above, scaberulous on nerves beneath, petioles of former 8–15 cm long, of latter 1.5–4.5 cm long. Racemes simple, axillary and terminal, 5-many-flowered; flowers secund, nodding. Bracts linear-lanceolate, 10–16 × 1.3 mm, acute at apex, strigose-ciliate. Pedicels 4–10 mm, sparsely hirtellous. Bracteoles subulate. Calyx tube 4 mm long, thinly pubescent; lobes linear-lanceolate, 8 × 2 mm, reflexed. Corolla campanulate-infundibular, lilac or violet-blue; tube to 1.5 cm long, glabrous; limb to 3 cm across; lobes lanceolate, to 1.5 cm long, erect, sparsely filamentous-ciliate. Filaments short; anthers introrse. Disk faintly 5-lobed. Stigmatic branches linear-oblong. Capsule ovoid-campanulate, 5 mm long, nodding, dehiscing by basal pores; seeds ovoid-oblong, 1.75 × 1 mm, subcompressed, smooth.

D i s t r. Native of Europe and Western Asia; cultivated in southern and Southeast Asia. A popular garden plant in the highlands on account of its conspicuous racemes.

E c o l. Flowering May–September.

S p e c i m e n s   E x a m i n e d. NUWARA ELIYA DISTRICT: Hakgala, in flower bed of Botanic Gardens, 8 Aug. 1929, *Silva* (PDA), *Cramer 4976* (PDA, US); Boragas, in compound of Tredorne, *Cramer 4968* (PDA, US).

2. WAHLENBERGIA

Schrad. ex Roth, Nov. Pl. Sp. 399. 1821, nom. cons.; DC., Mon. Camp. 129. 1830; Benth. & Hook., Gen. Pl. 555. 1876. Type species: *W. globularis* Schumach., nom. illeg.

Lightfootia L'Hérit., Sert. Angl. 4, t. 4. 1789, non Sw., 1788 nec Schreb., 1789. Type species: *L. serrata* Sw.
Cephalostigma DC., Mon. Camp. 117. 1830. Type species: not recorded.

Annual or perennial herbs; stems erect or ascending, simple or branched, sometimes woody at base. Leaves cauline, mostly sessile, alternate, rarely opposite, linear, elliptic or spathulate. Flowers solitary or in sparsely flowered terminal or axillary peduncles, actinomorphic, distinctly protandrous, nodding. Calyx inferior to semi-superior, persistent, shorter than corolla; tube turbinate or obconico-oblong; limb 5-partite, rarely 3–4-partite. Corolla campanulate-infundibular or turbinate; limb generally 5-lobed to about middle of tube, rarely 3–4-fid. Stamens 5, free from corolla, included; filaments broadened at base, ciliate; anther-cells linear. Ovary inferior or semi-superior, subglobose, 2–5-locular, with numerous ovules in each loculus; stigma 2–5-fid, the branches recurved. Capsule loculicidal by 2–5-valves, dehiscing above calyx lobes.

About 200 species, cosmopolitan, spread chiefly in the southern hemisphere; only two species in Ceylon.

Moeliono & Tuyn (Fl. Mal. I, 6: 112. 1960) hold that the former differential expressions of corolla and style characters between *Wahlenbergia* and *Lightfootia* have broken down with the vast increase in described species. These characters are now seen to fit either genus, hence no sharp separation could any longer be made between the two genera. They confirm their position by reference to the previous opinions of Von Brehmer (1915), R.S. Adamson and R.D. Meikle.

As for *Cephalostigma*, Moelione & Tuyn state that De Candolle's (1830) character of "stigma en tete" is erroneous, as the stigma of this genus is really 3-lobed as in the other two genera. As a distinct genus, therefore, *Cephalostigma* cannot be upheld.

Wahlenbergia marginata (Thunb.) DC., Mon. Camp. 143. 1830; DC., Prod. 7: 433. 1839; Alston in Trimen, Handb. Fl. Ceylon 6 : 176. 1931; Abeywick., Ceylon J. Sci., Biol. Sci. 2 (2) : 234. 1959; Moel. & Tuyn, Fl. Mal. I, 6 : 115. 1960.

Campanula marginata Thunb., Fl. Jap. 89. 1784.
Campanula dehiscens Roxb. ex Wall., Asiat Res. 12 : 571. 1816.
Wahlenbergia gracilis DC., Mon. Camp. 142. 1830, incl. var.; DC., Prod. 7 : 433. 1839, non *Campanula gracilis* Forst., 1786; Thw., Enum. Pl. Zeyl. 169. 1860; Clarke in Hook. f., Fl. Br. Ind. 3: 429. 1882; Trimen, Handb. Fl. Ceylon 3 : 60. 1895.
Wahlenbergia agrestis sensu Wight, Ic. Pl. Ind. Or. t. 473. 1848, non DC., 1830; Hook. f. & Thoms., Proc. Linn. Soc. Lond. 21. 1858.

Perennial herb with a vermiform rootstock; stems solitary or many, to c. 35 cm high, sometimes diffuse, 5–6-angular, rather slender, flexuose, glabrous, often sparsely pilose below, sometimes scabrid. Leaves linear-oblong to linear-elliptic, $7–20 \times 1–4$ mm, the upper ones narrower, subacute at base, acute at apex, serrulate to entire, glabrous above, scabrid to scabrid-pilose beneath, the lower ones sometimes spathulate. Flowers solitary or in binate cymes; pedicels to 10.5 cm long. Bracts linear to linear-lanceolate, $4.5–7 \times 1$ mm. Calyx tube 1.5–4 mm long; ribbed or smooth; lobes erect, linear-lanceolate, $2–2.5 \times 1.5$ mm, acute. Corolla widely campanulate, ashy-blue to lilac; limb 0.6–2 cm in diam.; lobes oval-elliptic, $2.5–10 \times 1.5–3$ mm. Filaments filiform above. Style thickened at top below stigma; stigmatic branches glandular-hispidulous above. Capsule obconical, $3.5–12 \times 2–4$ mm; seeds ellipsoid, 1×0.5 mm, subcompressed, glabrous, dark brown and shining.

D i s t r. Widely distributed from East Africa through Bombay and the Deccan to Ceylon, continental Southeast Asia, China, Japan and through Malesia to Australia and New Zealand.

E c o l. Among grass of the black patanas and rocky crevices of the highlands from c. 1400 to 2400 m; very common. The rootstock often perennates under the bases of the grass tussocks. The flexuose nature of the stems often enables them to bend easily without breaking under the force of the constant wind across the patanas.

The flowers are protandrous. With early shedding of the sticky pollen the anthers wither and are thus often absent in opened flowers. Flowering almost throughout the year; chiefly from December–May.

N o t e. An unusual dwarf of this species, with leaves to 3 mm broad and corollae to 8 mm in diam., grows at lower altitudes in the submontane region and somewhat removed from the black patanas. I do not consider this a variety of *Wahlenbergia marginata*, but Dr. Geesink, commenting on one such specimen of the form (*Cramer 4570*), states (lett. comm.) that this is only one of the many varieties of the species. Towards a re-evaluation of its status, this form is under further investigation, and I am indebted to Dr. Geesink for his valuable comments.

S p e c i m e n s E x a m i n e d. NUWARA ELIYA DISTRICT: Maturata, *Gardner C.P. 1774* (PDA); Hakgala, eastern slopes, *Hoogland 11521* (CANB, L, PDA, US); Ambawela, *Koyama* (PDA, US), near Railway Station, *Mueller-Dombois & Comanor 67070819* (PDA, US); Horton Plains, near Farr Inn, *Fosberg & Sachet 53330* (K, PDA, US), *van Beusekom s.n.* (L, PDA, US), in patana, *Cramer 2952* (PDA, US), *Clayton 5475* (K, PDA, US), *Comanor 976* (K, PDA, US), 20 May, 1911, *Silva* (PDA); Ohiya, railway embankment close to station, *Cramer 4616* (E, PDA, US); Bogawantalawa Road, 26 Jan. 1906, *s. coll.* (PDA); on way to Baker's Falls, *Cramer 4459* (PDA, BO, M). BADULLA DISTRICT: Haputale, rocky road embankment along Haputale-Welimada Rd., *Cramer 4570* (L, PDA, US). LOCALITY UNKNOWN: *Gardner 499* (K), *Walker s.n.* (K), *Walker* in Herb. Wight *167* (PDA).

LOBELIACEAE

(by L.H. Cramer*)

Type genus: *Lobelia* L.

Annual or perennial herbs or undershrubs, often laticiferous; stem prostrate, ascending or erect, sometimes woody below. Leaves alternate or spirally arranged, exstipulate, entire or pinnatifid. Flowers axillary and solitary or in racemes or panicles, subactinomorphic to zygomorphic, bisexual, rarely unisexual by abortion, protandrous. Bracts present or absent. Bracteoles often present. Calyx adnate to ovary, 5-lobed. Corolla subactinomorphic or bilabiate, often posteriorly cleft to base or near base; lobes valvate. Stamens 5, alternate with corolla lobes, free or adherent to base of corolla tube; filaments slender, coherent at various levels, anthers coherent into staminal tube around style, at least one pair penicillate, 2-celled; disk 0. Ovary more or less inferior, 2–3-locular; style simple or 2-lobed, ringed at top with collecting hairs. Fruit baccate or capsular and variously dehiscent; seeds numerous, endospermous.

About 20 genera. Several hundred species; fairly cosmopolitan.

KEY TO THE GENERA

1 Leaves crenate or serrate; corolla tube cleft posteriorly to base; bracts present; stamens free from corolla or only basally epipetalous...........................**1. Lobelia**
1 Leaves coarsely dentate or pinnatifid; corolla tube entire, infundibular; bracts 0; stamens often adnate to corolla......................................**2. Laurentia**

1. LOBELIA

L., Sp. Pl. 929. 1753; L., Gen. Pl. ed. 5, 401. 1754; DC., Prod. 357. 1839; Benth. & Hook. f., Gen. Pl. 2: 551. 1876; Wimmer in Pflanzenr. 107: 408. 1953. Type species: *L. dortmanna* L.

Rapuntium [Tourn.] Miller, Gard. Dict. ed. 8, n. 7. 1768; Presl, Mon. Lobel. 11. 1836. Type species: *R. herbaceum* Lour.

---

*Flora of Ceylon Project, Peradeniya. Present address: Batticaloa University College, Chenkaladi.

Pratia Gaud., Ann. Sci. Nat. 5: 103. 1825; Presl, Mon. Lobel. 46. 1836. Type species: (*P. repens* Gaud., is the only sp. originally described under the genus; lectotype not selected).

Speirema Hook. f. & Thoms., J. Proc. Linn. Soc. Bot. 2: 27. 1858. Type species: (*S. montanum* Hook. f. & Thoms., the only species recorded; lectotype not selected).

Annual or perennial herbs or undershrubs. Flowers axillary and solitary, or in leafy spikes or racemes. Bracts and bracteoles present. Calyx much shorter than corolla-tube, 5-lobed; lobes erect, subequal, often ciliate, sometimes scabrid. Corolla dorsally cleft to base; limb generally 2-lipped, rarely 1-lipped, upper lip erect, generally 2-lobed; lower lip spreading, 3-lobed. Stamens free or basally epipetalous; filaments glabrous or pubescent; staminal tube slightly exserted; often at least one pair of anthers penicillate at apex. Ovary inferior to semi-superior, 2-locular; stigmatic branches 2, pubescent. Capsule or berry often crowned with persistent calyx; seeds numerous, endospermous.

About 300 species, mainly in tropics and subtropics, especially in America. The Ceylon species are mostly restricted to the uplands and highlands, except *L. alsinoides* and *L. zeylanica* which extend from the moist lowlands to c. 2000 m in the highlands.

KEY TO THE SPECIES

1 Stem 3-gonous or subtrigonous; leaves generally ovate
  2 Stem prostrate, erect, or ascending, not rooting at nodes, trigonous, winged; leaves glabrous beneath; calyx glabrous or sparsely puberulous
    3 Calyx lobes entire; all anthers penicillate at apex; seeds 3-gonous....**1. L. alsinoides**
    3 Calyx lobes sparsely denticulate; only 2 anthers (anterior pair) penicillate at apex; seeds ellipsoid, obtuse at both ends..............................**2. L. heyneana**
  2 Stem ascending, rooting at nodes, uniformly subtrigonous; leaves scaberulous to scabrid beneath; calyx usually villous-pilulose........................**3. L. zeylanica**
1 Stem subquadrangular or terete; leaves lanceolate or elliptic-lanceolate
  4 Stem slender, subquadrangular, shorter than 18 cm, with a spongy pith; leaves distichous, sessile; flowers solitary; bracts 0; corolla to 15 mm long; filaments free below to about half way up...**4. L. chinensis**
  4 Stem thickened, terete, much taller than 18 cm, with a hollowed pith; leaves spirally arranged, petiolate; flowers in racemes; bracts present; corolla longer than 15 mm; filaments coherent almost to base
    5 Leaves glabrous or puberulous beneath; flowers spirally arranged; bracteoles 0; corolla white; both pairs of anthers sparsely pubescent at back
      6 Posterior anthers occasionally bristly-pilose at back, occasionally penicillate at apex, anterior ones always bristly-penicillate at apex; leaves sparsely villous or puberulous beneath; calyx finely or densely puberulous..**5. L. nicotianifolia var. nicotianifolia**
      6 Posterior anthers sparsely pilose or villulose at back, they and anterior ones never penicillate at apex; leaves glabrate beneath; calyx glabrous or finely puberulous....
      ....**L. nicotianifolia var. trichandra**
    5 Leaves hirtellous or pilose-hirtellous beneath; flowers in somewhat annular whorls;

bracteoles present; corolla rose or pink; anthers all glabrous at back and at apex....
.... **6. L. leschenaultiana**

1. Lobelia alsinoides Lam., Enc. 3: 588. 1791; DC., Prod. 7: 378. 1839; Wimmer in Pflanzenr. 107: 571. f. 93. g. 1953; Abeywick., Ceylon J. Sci., Biol. Sci. 2 (2): 234. 1959; Moel. & Tuyn, Fl. Mal. I, 6: 126. 1960.

Lobelia trigona Roxb., Fl. Ind. 2: 111. 1824; G. Don, Gard. Dict. 3: 709. 1834; DC., l.c. 359; Thw., Enum. Pl. Zeyl. 169. 1860, p.p.; Clarke in Hook. f., Fl. Br. Ind. 3: 423. 1881; Trimen, Handb Fl. Ceylon 3: 56. 1895; Alston in Trimen, Handb. Fl. Ceylon 6: 174. 1931, in clave.

Annual, stem prostrate, erect, or ascending, to 17 cm high, not rooting at nodes, trigonous, winged, glabrous. Leaves broadly ovate, 0.9–2.0 × 1–1.8 cm, truncate to subcordate at base, subacute to obtuse at apex, serrate-crenate, glabrous on both surfaces; petioles 0.1–0.9 cm long. Flowers axillary and solitary, often in higher axils, and then in a lax, terminal raceme. Bracts subulate, to 3 mm long. Pedicels 1.3–2.5 cm long, slender, glabrous. Bracteoles linear-subulate, to 2 mm long, often caducous. Calyx-tube turbinate, to 3 mm long, 10-nerved, usually glabrous, occasionally minutely bristly; lobes linear-lanceolate, 4–6 × 1 mm, acute, entire, occasionally ciliate, glabrous. Corolla-tube 4–4.5 mm long, glabrous, bluish-white; limb pale blue; upper lip erect, the lobes ovate-elliptic; lower lip spreading, 6–7 mm across, bright blue with 2 white streaks at base of midlobe. Filaments free below to about halfway up, lorate, the anterior ones broader than the posterior; anthers all penicillate. Capsule obovoid to obconical, 2–3 × 1.5–3 mm; seeds ovoid, 0.6–0.75 mm long, 3-gonous, with thickened margins, brown.

D i s t r. From the Deccan through Ceylon to South East Asia and Malesia.

E c o l. Widespread in paddy fields, roadside ditches and wet places in the dry and wet zones, from sea level to about 2400 m. The commonest species of *Lobelia* in the country. Flowering almost throughout the year.

N o t e. A variable species difficult to distinguish from *L. heyneana* in the field as the two are very similar in habitat, glabrousness and shapes of stem and leaves. Only careful examination in the laboratory establishes its identity.

S p e c i m e n s   E x a m i n e d. PUTTALAM DISTRICT: Roadside ditch beside Madampe-Madegama Road, *Cramer 4943* (PDA, US). KALUTARA DISTRICT: Bandaragama, grassy bund of paddy field, *Cramer 2797* (PDA, US). GALLE DISTRICT: Talgaswela, Talgaswela Estate, in boggy bank of artificial lake, *Cramer 2849* (PDA, US). HAMBANTOTA DISTRICT: Tissamaharama, bund of paddy field, *Simpson 9904* (PDA), *s. coll. C.P. 1776* (PDA, K). MATALE DISTRICT: near mile post 35, Rattota-Dikpatana Road, moist roadside banks, *Faden 77/179* (F, PDA, US). KANDY DISTRICT: Hunnasgiriya, in boggy clearing beside road to Hunas Falls, *Cramer*

4497 (PDA, US); Peradeniya, Upper Hantana Road, *Comanor 311* (PDA); Maha Oya, Uda Peradeniya Road, *Cramer 4973* (G, K, PDA, US). NUWARA ELIYA DISTRICT: Pussellawa, Hellbode Tea Estate, *Mueller-Dombois 67052813* (PDA, US); Ambagahakotuwa, border of paddy field, *Cramer 4053* (PDA, US); among short grass along edges of watercourse beside main road to Nuwara Eliya town, *Cramer 4797* (PDA, US), *Faden 77/30* (F, PDA, US); Kellow's Tea Estate, *Willis* 14 March 1906 (PDA); Sita Eliya, Oct. 1920, *A.D.A.* (PDA); Hakgala, Fort MacDonald, in wet patana, 31 May 1906, *s. coll.* (PDA); Ambawela, roadside, 26 March 1906, *s. coll.* (PDA), *Gardner C.P. 1776* (K, PDA, US). ANURADHAPURA DISTRICT: Mihintale, Mahasena Hill, marshy area near stream, *Faden 77/188* (F, PDA, US). POLONNARUWA DISTRICT: Habarana, beside rocky pond, *Cramer 5123* (PDA, US); Sigiriya, under shade on damp walls of ruins, *Cramer 5128* (PDA, US). BADULLA DISTRICT: beside Ella-Wellawaya Road, among *Cymbopogon nardus* in dry patana, *Cramer 4832* (PDA, US); Bokkela, close to watercourse, *Cramer 4481* (F, PDA, US). TRINCOMALEE DISTRICT: Somapura, among short grass in damp sandy ground, *Cramer 5117* (PDA, US).

2. Lobelia heyneana Roem. & Schult., Syst. Veg. 5: 50. 1819, non Spreng. 1825; G. Don, Gard. Dict. 3: 709. 1834; Wimmer in Pflanzenr. 107: 474. 1953; Moel. & Tuyn, Fl. Mal. I, 6: 129. 1960.

Lobelia zeylanica sensibus Moon, Cat. 14. 1824, nom. nud.; Clarke in Hook. f., Fl. Br. Ind. 3: 425. 1881, incl. var. *walkeri* Clarke; Trimen, Handb. Fl. Ceylon 3: 56. 1895; Alston in Trimen, Handb. Fl. Ceylon 6: 174. 1931, in clave, non L., 1753.
Lobelia trigona sensibus Hook. f. & Thoms., J. Proc. Linn. Soc. Bot. 2: 27. 1858, p.p.; Thw., Enum. Pl. Zeyl. 169. 1860, p.p., non Roxb. 1824.
Lobelia dichotoma Miq., Fl. Ind. Bat. 2: 576. 1856; Wimmer, l.c. 476; Abeywick., Ceylon J. Sci., Biol. Sci. 2 (2): 234. 1959.

Annual herb; stem ascending, to 23 cm high, sometimes suberect, trigonous to subtrigonous, winged, glabrous. Leaves broadly ovate to suborbicular, 0.9–1.6 × 1.0–1.8 cm, upper ones occasionally oblong-lanceolate, to 1.6 × 0.8 cm; all truncate at base and decurrent on petiole, obtuse to subacute at apex, crenate-serrate to serrulate, glabrous; petioles 3–5 mm long. Flowers solitary in the upper axils. Bracts linear, 0.75 mm long. Pedicels 7–12 mm long, glabrous. Bracteoles minutely subulate. Calyx tube broadly campanulate, 2 mm long, nerved, glabrous to sparsely puberulous; lobes linear-lanceolate, 4–5 mm long, sparsely denticulate, often sparsely ciliolate towards base. Corolla tube narrow, 3 mm long, glabrous, pale blue; limb dark blue; lower lip to 6–7 mm across, the lobes oval-oblong, with a purplish streak down base of each. Filaments glabrous or puberulous. Anterior anthers penicillate at apex. Capsule obconical to campanulate, 4–6 × 3 mm long, glabrous; seeds ellipsoid, 0.75 × 0.5 mm, rather obtuse at both ends, smooth, orange-brown and shining.

Distr. From Bombay through Malabar to Ceylon; Malesia.

Ecol. Usually under shade among short grass in moist and boggy places of the uplands from c. 2000 to 3400 m. Common. Owing to lack of sufficient material, Trimen has mistakenly attributed the distribution of this species to the "South of the island". Flowering January–October.

Specimens Examined. NUWARA ELIYA DISTRICT: Nuwara Eliya, *Gardner C.P. 1776* (K, PDA); Sita Eliya, Oct. 1920, *A.D.A.* (PDA); Ambawela, roadside, 26 March 1906, *s. coll.* (PDA); Horton Plains, 22 May 1911, *Silva* (PDA); Haldumulla Road, 26 June, 1906, *s. coll.* (PDA); near Farr Inn, *van Beusekom* (NVB, PDA, US), *Cooray 68051718* (PDA, US); under shade in wet embankments beside road to World's End, *Cramer 4601* (CAL, SING, K, BO). BADULLA DISTRICT: Namunukula, 29 April 1907, *s. coll.* (PDA). LOCALITY UNKNOWN: *Walker s.n.*, in Herb. Wight (K); *Walker s.n.*, 6000 ft (K).

3. **Lobelia zeylanica** L., Sp. Pl. 932. 1753; Roxb., Fl. Ind. 2: 113. 1824; Roxb. in Wall., Pl. As. Rar. 2: 43. 1831; G. Don, Gard. Dict. 3: 709. 1834; Abeywick., Ceylon J. Sci., Biol. Sci. 2 (2): 234. 1959; Moel. & Tuyn, Fl. Mal. I, 6: 128. 1960.

Lobelia succulenta Blume, Bijdr. 728. 1826; DC., Prod. 7: 373. 1839; Wimmer in Pflanzenr. 107: 576. 1953, incl. var. *lobbiana* and f. *glabra*.

Lobelia affinis Wall. ex G. Don, Gard. Dict. 3: 709. 1834, non Mirbach, 1805; DC., Prod. 7: 360. 1839; Hook. f. & Thoms., J. Proc. Linn. Soc. Bot. 2: 28. 1858; Clarke in Hook. f., Fl. Br. Ind. 3: 424. 1881, incl. var. *lobbiana*; Trimen, Handb. Fl. Ceylon 3: 57. 1895; Alston in Trimen, Handb. Fl. Ceylon 6: 174. 1931, in clave.

Annual; stem rooting at lower nodes, ascending to 20 cm, diffusely branched, subtrigonous, succulent, glabrous. Leaves broadly ovate, 1.1–3.8 × 1.1–3.2 cm, truncate to cordate at base, obtuse or subacute, crenate-denticulate, penninerved, sparsely scaberulous or scabrid above, more densely so beneath especially on nerves; petioles 0.4–1.2 cm long. Bracts linear-subulate, 1 mm long. Pedicels 2.4–3.6 cm long, glabrous to puberulous. Bracteoles 0. Calyx tube 2–4 mm long, 8-nerved, glabrous or villous-pilulose; lobes linear-lanceolate, subequal, 3–5 × 0.75–1 mm, entire. Corolla tube 4 mm long, pale blue; limb pale blue or lilac; lobes of upper lip lanceolate, 2 mm long, subfalcate, each bristly pubescent beneath; lower lip 6–8 mm across, lobes elliptic-orbicular, to 2 mm broad, bristly pubescent beneath, the midlobe with 2 white streaks towards base. All anthers penicillate at apex. Style glabrous. Capsule obconical to broadly cupular, 4 to 6 × 2 mm, glabrous or villous; seeds ovoid, 0.5 to 0.6 mm long, trigonous, thickened at angles, pale brown.

D i s t r. From the Deccan and Ceylon to S.E. Asia, Hainan and Taiwan.

E c o l. A weed among grass in soggy, clayey soil beside watercourses and in paddy fields, in the wet lowlands and uplands. Altitude: sea level— c. 1500 m. Common. Flowering almost throughout the year.

N o t e. This species closely resembles *L. alsinoides* but is readily distinguished from it by the pubescence of the under surface of its leaves and that of the calyx.

S p e c i m e n s   E x a m i n e d. GALLE DISTRICT: Galle, *s. coll. C.P. 2981* p.p. (PDA); Hapugala, in roadside ditch, *Cramer 4989* (G, K, PDA, US); Kottawa, in rice field, *Meijer 277* (PDA, US). RATNAPURA DISTRICT: Warnagala, under shade beside stream, *Cramer 5015* (PDA, US). KEGALLE DISTRICT: Ruanwella, Nov. 1883, *Ferguson* (PDA). KANDY DISTRICT: Peradeniya, Royal Botanic Gardens, 20 Nov. 1928, *Silva* (PDA), Nov. 1883, *s. coll.* (PDA); Hatton, *s. coll. C.P. 2981* p.p. (PDA); Watawala, *s. coll. C.P. 2981* p.p. (PDA); Norton Bridge, Double-Cut, on roadside embankment, *Balasubramaniam & Cramer 4992* (PDA, US). NUWARA ELIYA DISTRICT: Pussellawa, along watercourse among short grass beside Ramboda Road, *Cramer 4975* (BANG, PDA, US). BADULLA DISTRICT: Erabedde, in soggy ground beside watercourse, *Cramer 4481* (L, PDA, US); Haputale, roadside ditch, 23 May 1906, *s. coll.* (PDA). LOCALITY UNKNOWN: *s. coll.* 22 Feb. 1892 (PDA), *s. coll. C.P. 2981 & C.P. 1776* (K), *Walker s.n.* in Hb. Wt. (K).

4. Lobelia chinensis Lour., Fl. Cochinch. 2: 574. 1790; Roem. & Schult., Syst. Veg. 5: 41. 1819; G. Don. Gard. Dict. 3: 709. 1834; DC., Prod. 7: 360. 1839; Clarke in Hook. f., Fl. Br. Ind. 3: 423. 1881, in adnot.; Wimmer in Pflanzenr. 107: 609. 1953; Abeywick., Ceylon J. Sci., Biol. Sci. 2 (2): 234. 1959; Moel. & Tuyn, Fl. Mal. I, 6: 130. 1960.

Lobelia radicans Thunb., Trans. Linn. Soc. 2: 330. 1794; Roem. & Schult., Syst. Veg. 5: 60. 1819; Roxb., Fl. Ind. 2: 111. 1824; Clarke in Hook. f., Fl. Br. Ind. 3: 425. 1581; Alston in Trimen, Handb. Fl. Ceylon 6: 175. 1931.

Perennial, caespitose herb; stem tufted, with vermiform roots, erect or ascending to 18 cm high, subquadrangular, glabrous, with a spongy pith. Leaves distichous, sessile, lanceolate to elliptic-lanceolate, 1.1–2.5 × 0.3–0.6 cm, truncate at base, acute, subentire to shallowly toothed towards apex, glabrous. Bracts 0. Bracteoles minute, subulate. Pedicels erect, 1.3–2.6 cm long, slightly deflexed at c. 45 degrees, stiff, glabrous. Calyx tube 5 mm long, glabrous, smooth; lobes narrowly lanceolate, 4 × 1 mm, acute, entire, glabrous. Corolla tube 6 mm long, whitish; limb pinkish-white to pinkish-purple; lobes of upper lip linear-subfalcate, to 9 mm long; lower lip spreading, to 1.8 cm across, with green gibbosities at base, the lobes linear-elliptic, 7–8 mm long, midlobe the shorter. Filaments almost flattened, densely hispidulous below; anther tips all penicillate. Stylar branches globose. Capsule not seen.

D i s t r. Native of China and Japan spread into S.E. Asia, Ceylon and the Deccan.

E c o l. A weedy herb in moist ground among short grass bordering streams and rivers in the uplands and highlands. Altitude c. 500–1000 m. Uncommon. Alston in a herbarium label says that this is probably an escape. My collections and observations convince me that this is a wild species. Flowering February–October.

N o t e. Among the Ceylon specimens I have examined in the field I have so far not seen capsules with ripe seeds. Matured ovaries of withered flowers were carefully brought to the laboratory and allowed to dry; but none of these turned into capsules.

S p e c i m e n s E x a m i n e d. KANDY DISTRICT: Pussellawa, Peacock Estate, moist ground beside stream, *Cramer 4958* (G, PDA, US); Peradeniya, on river bank, *de Silva*, 21 April 1926 (PDA); Getambe, along banks of Mahaweli Ganga, *Cramer 4980* (G, PDA, US); Royal Botanic Gardens, *s. coll.* May 1887 (PDA); Haragama, wet place in river, *Alston 862* (PDA).

5. Lobelia nicotianifolia Roth ex Roem. & Schult., Syst. Veg. 5: 47. 1819 ('nicotianaefolia'); Roth, Nov. Pl. Sp. 143. 1831; Wall. in Roxb., Fl. Ind. 2: 110. 1824; Wall., Pl. As. Rar. 2: 42. 1831; G. Don, Gard. Dict. 3: 709. 1834; DC., Prod. 7: 381. 1839; Wight, Ill. 2: 111, t. 135, f. 1–10. 1850; Hook. f. & Thoms., J. Proc. Linn. Soc. Bot. 2: 29. 1858; Clarke in Hook. f., Fl. Br. Ind. 3: 427. 1881; Trimen, Handb. Fl. Ceylon 3: 57. 1895 p.p. quoad descr.; Alston in Trimen, Handb. Fl. Ceylon 6: 175. 1931; Wimmer in Pflanzenr. 107: 643. 1953, incl. var. *bibarbata*; Abeywick., Ceylon J. Sci., Biol. Sci. 2 (2): 234. 1959; Moel. & Tuyn, Fl. Mal. I, 6: 123. 1960, excl. var. *trichandra* & synn. *L. excelsa* Lesch., *L. aromatica* Moon & Wight & *L. leschenaultiana* (Presl) Skottsb.

Rapuntium nicotianifolium Presl, Mon. Lobel. 24. 1836.

Biennial or perennial herb; stem erect, to 3.5 m high, stout, branched and angular above, hollowed and terete below, glabrous. Leaves numerous, spirally arranged, sessile, oblong-lanceolate to elliptic-lanceolate, 9.5–35 × 2–6.5 cm, becoming bracteate above, acute at base and faintly decurrent on petiole, acute, crenate-serrulate, glabrous above, glabrate or puberulous beneath; petioles 0.8–1.2 cm long. Racemes terminal, leafy, to 1.12 m long, usually lax, tapering to apex; peduncles puberulous. Bracts linear-lanceolate, 2–2.4 × 0.4–0.5 cm, acuminate, the upper ones adherent at base to pedicels. Pedicels 2.2–3 cm long, densely puberulous. Bracteoles 0. Calyx broadly campanulate, 0.5–0.7 cm long, strongly 10-nerved, finely or densely puberulous; lobes lanceolate, unequal, 8–15 × 1–1.5 mm, acute, distantly serrulate. Corolla white; tube to 2.2 cm long, curved, thinly hirtellous without; upper lip indistinct; lower lip 5-lobed, to 3.5 cm long, puberulous without, pilose within along central lobes, the outer 2 lobes linear, united at base and apex with central 3-fid lobe. Flaments dilated at base, sparsely puberulous; posterior anthers occasionally bristly-pilose at back, occasionally bristly penicillate at apex, anterior ones sparsely pilose or glabrous at back, always bristly penicillate at apex. Style glabrous; stylar branches ringed with villous collecting hairs. Capsule broadly cupular-campanulate, or depressed-globose, 8–9 × 7–10 mm; seeds ovoid to ovoid-rhomboid, 0.7–0.8 mm long, sub-trigonous; thickened at margins, pale brown.

1. var. nicotianifolia

Description as above.

D i s t r. From Bombay through the Western Ghats and down the Southern Deccan to Ceylon and S.E. Asia (inclusive of Malesia).

E c o l. In open, grassy slopes in the uplands; alt. c. 650–1400 m. Common. The flowers of this variety in Ceylon are always pure white, the buds being a pale mauve especially towards the apices. I have never seen flowers tinged with any colour. Flowering December–April.

N o t e s. The typical variety shows intermediate forms, particularly in the glabrousness or pubescence of the anthers. Wimmer's variety *bibarbata* represents some of these forms all of which are, therefore, only variations of the typical variety.

Alston (l.c.) has unwittingly interchanged the characters of the anthers of this species and of *L. leschenaultiana*. Accordingly, his description should correctly read: "anthers, at least the anterior ones, penicillate, usually hairy at back."

S p e c i m e n s E x a m i n e d. MATALE DISTRICT: Madulkelle, roadside, *Senaratna 10019* (PDA); Laggala, hilly roadside embankment, *Cramer 4878* (PDA, US). KANDY DISTRICT: Hantane, *Gardner C.P. 2592* (K, PDA); Nawalapitiya, sandy slopes by road, *Burtt & Townsend 54* (E, K, PDA, US); Galbage, *Cramer 4628* (PDA, US); Pussellawa, hilly roadside embankment, Pussellawa-Ramboda Road, *Cramer 4620* (PDA, US); Norton, on patana slope beside Diyagala-Watawala Road, *Cramer 5024* (K, PDA, US). NUWARA ELIYA DISTRICT: Maturata, *s. coll.* March 1885 (PDA). BADULLA DISTRICT: Bandarawela, patana, *Silva s.n.* (PDA); Boralande, roadside embankment, *Cramer 4495* (PDA, US); Badulla-Hakgala road, *Read 2265* (PDA, US); Ettampitiya, roadside embankment on Badulla Road, *Cramer 5176* (PDA, US).

2. var. trichandra (Wight) Clarke in Hook. f., Fl. Br. Ind. 3: 427. 1881; Gamble, Fl. Pres. Madras 4: 737. 1921.

Lobelia trichandra Wight, Ic. Pl. Ind. Or. 4: t. 1171. 1850; Skottsb., Acta Horti Gothob. 4: 16, f. 18 et 12 d. 1928.

Stem to c. 2 m high, rather slender. Leaves lanceolate, 6–40 × 1.2–6.2 cm, gradually attenuate at base, subacuminate, glabrous above, glabrate beneath, upper ones sessile, lower petiolate, petioles to 1.2 cm long. Racemes to 53 cm long; peduncles villous-puberulous to hirtellous. Pedicels to 2.5 cm long. Bracteoles sometimes present, subulate, to 5 mm long. Calyx glabrous or finely puberulous. Corolla 20–25 mm long, glabrous or puberulous without, white, lobes occasionally pale pink at tips. Posterior and anterior anthers sparsely villous-pilose or villulose at back, neither penicillate at apex.

D i s t r. From the Southern Deccan peninsula to Ceylon.

E c o l. In open, grassy slopes in the uplands alt. c. 700–1400 m. This is generally a more slender form than the typical variety. Flowering December–April.

N o t e. Despite the opinion of Moeliono and Tuyn (Fl. Mal. I, 6: 123. 1960), disregarding the existence of the var. *trichandra* in this species the objective evidence which many Ceylon specimens provide against this position is noteworthy. Careful examination of the following characters in the two taxa, as tabulated below, reveals the distinctness between them:

| Variety | Anthers | | Leaves | Calyx |
	Posterior	Anterior		
nicotianifolia	sparsely shaggy-pilose at back; occasionally bristly-penicllate at apex	sparsely pilose or glabrous at back; always bristly-penicillate at apex	sparsely villous or puberulous beneath	finely or densely puberulous
trichandra	sparsely villous-pilose or villulose at back; never penicillate at apex	puberulous or villulose at back; never penicillate at apex	glabrate beneath	glabrous or finely puberulous

I am satisfied that these differences are constant, and I uphold the validity of Wight's taxon, correctly reduced to varietal rank.

S p e c i m e n s E x a m i n e d. MATALE DISTRICT: Nitre Cave, *s. coll.* (PDA). KANDY DISTRICT: Hantane, Wariagale, Dec. 1889, *s. coll.* (PDA); Maskeliya, *s. coll.* 1881 (PDA). NUWARA ELIYA DISTRICT: Maturata, *s. coll.* March 1881 (PDA); Ramboda, *s. coll. C.P. 2529* (PDA); Kandapola, hilly embankment, *Cramer 4114* (PDA, US).

6. Lobelia leschenaultiana (Presl) Skottsb., Acta Horti Gothob. 4: 4, f. 3–7. 1928; Wimmer in Pflanzenr. 107: 659. 1953; Abeywick., Ceylon J. Sci., Biol. Sci. 2 (2): 234. 1959.

Lobelia excelsa Lesch. ex Roxb., Fl. Ind. 2: 114. 1824, non Bonpl., 1813;

Wall., Pl. As. Rar. 2: 42. 1831; G. Don, Gard. Dict. 3: 709. 1834.
Rapuntium leschenaultianum Presl, Prod. Mon. Lobel. 24. 1836; DC., Prod. 7:
381. 1839; Thw., Enum. Pl. Zeyl. 170. 1860, excl. syn. *L. nicotianifolia*
Roth ex Roem. & Schult.; Clarke in Hook. f., Fl. Br. Ind. 3: 427. 1881.
Lobelia aromatica Moon ex Wight, Ic. Pl. Ind. Or. 4 (2): t. 1172. 1850; Hook.
f. & Thoms., J. Proc. Linn. Soc. Bot. 2: 29. 1858; Alston in Trimen, Handb.
Fl. Ceylon 6: 175. 1931.
Lobelia nicotianifolia Trimen, Handb. Fl. Ceylon 3: 57. 1895 p.p. quoad
descr.

Biennial or perennial herb; stem to 2.4 m high, stout, naked below, leafy
above, striate and fistular, glabrate. Leaves lanceolate to oblong-lanceolate,
12–38.5 × 2.3–4.5 cm, narrowed at base, subacuminate, callous-denticulate,
ciliolate, rugose and glabrous above, densely hirtellous or pilose-hirtellous
beneath; petioles to 3 cm long. Racemes terminal, 86–103 cm long; flowers
densely whorled. Bracts foliaceous below, linear-lanceolate above, to 3.4 × 0.25
cm. Pedicels 1.2–2 cm long, densely hirtellous with white hairs. Bracteoles
subulate, to 3 mm long, acuminate, densely hirtellous. Calyx broadly cupular-campanulate; tube 2–3 mm long, finely tomentose; lobes subequal, linear-
lanceolate, 12–17 × 2 mm, callous-serrate. Corolla to 3 cm long, rose or pink;
tube to 1.5 cm long, puberulous without; lobes of upper lip linear, to 1.5 cm
long, those of lower lip linear-lanceolate, to 1.3 cm long, reflexed with age.
Filaments sparsely puberulous; anthers all completely glabrous at back and at
apex. Style glabrous; stylar branches ringed with collecting hairs. Capsule
depressed-globose, 7–8 × 6–7 mm; seeds ovoid, 1 × 0.5 mm, biconvex, smooth,
pale brown.

D i s t r. Native of the Nilgiri hills, spread from the Deccan through
Ceylon to S.E. Asia.
E c o l. In open, hilly slopes in the highlands; alt. 2000–2400 m. Fairly
common. The inflorescence is very conspicuous on account of its size and the
mauve or pinkish corollae which are distinctive. The densely whorled flowers
are remarkable. Flowering is seasonal, being restricted to the drier months
on the hills, when the days are brighter. This species and the allied *L. nicotianifolia* form a distinctive feature of the herbaceous vegetation of the montane
region. As in the former, the milk of the plant becomes discoloured and glu-
tinous on drying. Flowering January–March.
N o t e. Merging this species under *L. nicotianifolia*, as has been done by
Moelione and Tuyn, is unsatisfactory. My field observations and examina-
tions of herbarium material have borne out that this species is quite distinct
from the latter according to the differences tabulated below.
Accordingly, I fully endorse Skattsberg's and Wimmer's recognition of
this taxon (11. cc.) as a distinct species. Prof. F. Fagerlind (Sweden) after
examination of specimens in the Peradeniya herbarium confirms this position.

Character	L. nicotianifolia	L. leschenaultiana
Under surface of leaf	glabrous or scaberulous, especially on nerves	densely hirtellous or scabrid
Disposition of flowers	spiral, lax	whorled, dense
Bracteoles	usually 0	always present
Calyx lobes	serrate to serrulate	callous-serrate
Corolla	white	pink or mauve
Anthers	all or posterior ones shaggy pilose on back; anterior ones penicillate at apex	all glabrous on back and at apex
Range of altitude	c. 325–700 m	c. 700–800 m

Alston (l.c.) has erroneously misapplied the penicillate nature of the anthers as belonging to this species. Even under a field lens the complete glabrousness of the back of the anthers and their apices is quite unmistakable. Accordingly, Alston's description (l.c.) should read ".... anthers glabrous at back and at apices."

S p e c i m e n s E x a m i n e d. NUWARA ELIYA DISTRICT: Nuwara Eliya Pass, *Mueller-Dombois 6801154* (PDA, US); hilly slope at top of road, *Cramer 4627* (PDA, US); Ohiya, hilly slope beside Horton Plains—Ohiya Road, *Cramer 4824* (PDA, US), *Alwis* March 1922 (PDA), *Gardner C.P. 2592* (K, PDA), *s. coll.* March 1884 (PDA).

2. LAURENTIA

Mich. ex Adans., Fam. Pl. 2: 134, 568. 1763; Endl., Gen. Pl. 1: 511. 1838; DC., Prod. 7: 409. 1839; Petermann, Pflanzenr. 444. 1845; Wimmer in Pflanzenr. 107: 386. 1953. Type species: not recorded.

Isotoma Lindl., Bot. Reg. 10, t. 964. 1824; Presl, Mon. Lobel. 42. 1836; DC., Prod. 7: 412. 1839. Type species: *Lobelia hypocrateriformis* R. Br.
Hippobroma G. Don, Gard. Dict. 3: 717. 1834. Type species: only one species recorded, *H. longiflora* G. Don.
Enchysia Presl, Prod. Mon. Lobel. 40. 1836. Type species: not recorded.

Annual or perennial laticiferous herbs; stem erect. Leaves spirally arranged, sometimes rosulate. Racemes terminal or flowers solitary, axillary. Calyx shorter than corolla tube, cylindrical or narrowly infundibular; lobes 5, sometimes unequal. Corolla tube cylindric or infundibular, entire; limb 5-lobed, subactinomorphic. Stamens 5, included; anthers connate, rarely hairy on back, often densely penicillate at apex; filaments free at base, sometimes below anthers, free from corolla, or all inserted above the middle of the corolla tube. Ovary inferior, 2-celled; stigma 2-lobed. Capsule loculicidal, crowned with persistent calyx; seeds many, endospermous.

About 25 species distributed in the Mediterranean, South Africa, Australia and the Americas down to Bolivia; one species in tropical Asia.

Wimmer (l.c. 387, 398) includes *Isotoma* as a section under the genus.

Laurentia longiflora (L.) Endl., Gen. Pl. 512. 1838; Petermann, Pflanzenr. 444, t. 118, f. 665. 1845 & ed. 2, 1847; Wimmer in Pflanzenr. 107: 405. 1953.

Lobelia longiflora L., Sp. Pl. 930. 1753.

Rapuntium longiflora Mill., Dict. ed. 8, n. 7. 1768.

Hipppobroma longiflora G. Don, Gard. Dict. 3: 717. 1834; Abeywick., Ceylon J. Sci., Biol. Sci. 2 (2): 234. 1959.

Isotoma longiflora Presl, Prod. Mon. Lobel. 42. 1836; DC., Prod. 7: 413.1839; Alston in Trimen, Handb. Fl. Ceylon 6: 175. 1931.

Perennial herb; stem to 65 cm high, terete, unbranched, hirtellous or glabrate. Leaves alternate, sessile, oblong-lanceolate to oblong-oblanceolate, 10.0–17.0 × 3.0–38 cm, attenuated at base, acute, coarsely sinuate-dentate, sparsely and thinly puberulous on both surfaces. Flowers solitary in the upper leaf axils. Bracts 0. Pedicels 1.0–1.8 cm long, curved outwards. Bracteoles at base of pedicels, subulate, 3–4 mm long. Calyx tube broadly campanulate, 8.5–10 mm long, slightly gibbous anteriorly, usually 10-nerved, hispidulous on ribs; lobes spreading, unequal, linear-lanceolate, 4–13 × 1–4 mm, serrulate, ciliate. Corolla erect, white; tube 7–10 mm long, thinly hirtellous without; limb 4–5.6 cm across; lobes spreading, unequal, oval-lanceolate, 19–25 × 5–7 mm, 2 upper ones slightly erect. Stamens inserted towards top of corolla tube; filaments flattened, thinly hirtellous; anthers curved, the tips all densely penicillate. Style glabrous; stylar branches suborbicular. Capsule nodding, obovoid-turbinate, to 18 × 8 mm, beaked by remnant of style; seeds ellipsoid, 1 mm long, foveolate-reticulate, pale brown.

D i s t r. Native of the West Indies, spread into the lowlands of South America down to Peru; adventive in the Old World tropics.

E c o l. In damp places of the wet, low country and uplands, particularly along roadside ditches, paddy fields, dilapidated walls and bases of coconut palms. Very common. Altitude sea-level to c. 550 m. Flowering almost throughout the year.

S p e c i m e n s E x a m i n e d. KANDY DISTRICT: Kandy town, along embankment of Maligawa, *Cramer 4962* (G, PDA, US); Peradeniya, Royal Botanic Gardens, May 1887, *s. coll.* (PDA); Kadugannawa, Poilakande, along dilapidated wall, *Cramer 4215* (K, E, L, PDA, US); Norton, road embankment, close to habitations, *Cramer 5026* (BM, G, PDA, US). GALLE DISTRICT: Hadiwatte, Habaraduwa, close to coast, around base of coconut palms, *Cramer 3432* (PDA, US).

NYCTANTHACEAE

(by Harold N. Moldenke and Alma L. Moldenke*)

Type genus: *Nyctanthes* L.

Small trees; wood without crystals or spiral thickenings in the xylem fibres; rays 1- or 2-seriate; wood fibres non-septate, the wall-pits conspicuously bordered, not simple; leaves decussate-opposite, mostly ovate, often lobate-dentate, scabrid or hispid on the upper surface, sclerenchymatous idioblasts not present in the mesophyll, no true cystoliths present, but cystolith-like bodies in cells adjacent to white dots on upper surface in some species; inflorescence terminal, composed of trichotomous cymes; flowers sessile, bracteate; no extra-floral nectaries present; calyx ovoid-cylindric, subtruncate; corolla salverform, its tube cylindric, mostly yellow, the lobes 4–8, contorted in bud, usually white, deciduous; stamens 2; anthers subsessile near the top of the corolla-tube; ovary bilocular; style cylindric; stigma very shortly bifid; ovules 1 per cell, basal, erect; fruit an orbicular capsule, compressed parallel to the septum, separating when ripe into 2 one-seeded subdiscoidal cells; seeds erect, orbicular, flattened, the testa thin, albumen absent; cotyledons flat; radicle inferior.

A small puzzling family formerly included in the Oleaceae and by some placed in the Verbenaceae; perhaps belonging in the Loganiales between Strychnaceae and Oleaceae in the Hutchinson system. The family comprises the following genus and *Dimetra* Kerr of Thailand.

NYCTANTHES

L., Gen. Pl. ed. 1. 333. 1737; L., Sp., Pl. ed. 1, 1: 6. 1753; L., Gen. Pl. ed. 5, 7. 1754. Type species: *Nyctanthes arbor-tristis* L.

Nictanthes All., Melanges Philos. Math. Soc. Roy. Turin. 2: 50. 1761.—*Nyctanthos* St.-Lag., Ann. Soc. Bot. Lyon. 7: 56. 1880.—*Nyctanthes* Juss. ex Airy Shaw in Willis, Dict. ed. 7. 834. 1966.

Pariaticu Adans., Fam. Pl. 2: 223 & 588. 1763.—*Pariatica* Adans. ex Post & Kuntze, Lexicon 285 & 417. 1904.

Mogori Adans., Fam. Pl. 2: 223 & 578. 1763.

*Plainfield, New Jersey, U.S.A.

Scabrita L., Mant. 1: 3–4. 1767.
Parilium Gaertn., Fruct. 1: 234–235, pl. 51, fig. 1. 1788.
Omolocarpos Neck., Elem. 2: 40. 1790.—*Homalocarpus* Neck. apud Post &
Kuntze, Lexicon 417. 1904 [not *Homalocarpus* Hook. & Arn., 1833, nor
Schur, 1866],—*Homalocarpus* Post & Kuntze apud Airy Shaw in Willis,
Dict. ed. 7, 1177, in syn. 1966.
Sép'halicá W. Jones, Asiat. Res. 4: 244. 1801.—*Sephalica* W. Jones ex Clarke
in Hook. f., Fl. Br. Ind. 3: 603, in syn. 1882.
Bruschia Bertol., Mem. Reale Acad. Sci. Ist. Bologna 8: 238. 1857.

Shrubs or trees; branches tetragonal; leaves opposite, petiolate, ovate,
entire or unequally dentate, papillose-scabrous with white bulbous-based
hairs above, pubescent beneath; inflorescence in small, sessile, bracteate heads
disposed in terminal trichotomous cymes; calyx gamosepalous, ovoid-cylindric
or tubular, its rim obsoletely denticulate or subtruncate; corolla actinomorphic or subactinomorphic, hypocrateriform, its tube cylindric, yellow, the
lobes 4–8, white, contorted-imbricate in bud, patent or oblique in anthesis;
stamens 2, inserted in the corolla-tube, included; anthers 2, subsessile near
the apex of the corolla-tube; style simple, cylindric, short, very shortly bifid
at the apex; stigma capitate; ovary 2-celled; ovules 1 in each cell, erect, basal,
ascending from the base of the dissepiment, anatropous; fruiting-calyx split
or finally deciduous; fruit capsular, chartaceous, orbicular or obcordate, compressed parallel to the partition, when ripe separating septicidally into 2 sub-
discoid carpels; seed erect, orbicular, flattened; testa thin; albumen none;
cotyledons foliaceous, flat; radicle short, inferior; embryo orthotropous.

A small genus of two known species of tropical Asia, only the following
known from Sri Lanka.

Nyctanthes arbor-tristis L., Sp. Pl. ed. 1, 1: 6. 1753; Burm., Thes. Zeyl. 32.
1737; L., Fl. Zeyl. ed. 1, 4–5. 1747, ed. 2, 4–5. 1748; Moon, Cat. 1: 2. 1824;
Agardh, Theor. Syst. Pl. 285-286. 1858; Hook. f., Fl. Br. Ind. 3: 603. 1882;
Majumdar, Proc. Indian Sci. Congr. Assoc. 23: 298. 1936; Fotidar, J. Indian
Bot. Soc. 18: 43–45. 1939; Majumdar, J. Indian Bot. Soc. 20: 119–122. 1941;
Airy Shaw, Kew Bull. 1952: 272. 1952; Stant, Kew Bull. 1952: 273–276. 1952;
Kundu & De, Bull. Bot. Surv. India 10: 397–408. 1968; Hutchins., Evol.
& Phylog. Fl. Pl. 465. 1969; Hutchins., Fam. Fl. Pl. ed. 3, 487 & 947. 1973;
Moldenke, Phytologia 30: 510 & 31: 374. 1975. Type: *Grimm 116* (LINN).

Arbor tristis Clus., Exot. 225–226 & 279–280. 1605.—*Arbor tristis myrto simi-
lis* C. Bauhin, Pinax ed. 1, 469. 1623.
Manja-pumeram Rheede, Hort. Mal. 1: 35, pl. 21. 1678.
Scabrita triflora L., Mant. 1: 37. 1767.
Scabrita scabra L., Syst. ed. 12, 2: 115. 1767.
Parilium arbor-tristis Gaertn., Fruct. 1: 234–235, pl. 51, fig. 1. 1788.

Nyctanthes tristis Salisb., Prod. 11. 1796.
Sép'halicá W. Jones, Asiat. Res. 4: 244. 1801.—*Sephalica* W. Jones ex Clarke
   in Hook. f., Fl. Br. Ind. 3: 603, in syn. 1882.
Nyctanthes dentata Blume, Ann. Mus. Bot. Lugduno-Batavum 1: 282. 1849.
Bruschia macrocarpa Bertol., Mem. Reale Acad. Sci. Ist. Bologna 8: 238.
   1857.
Nyctanthes arbor-tristis var. *dentata* Hort. ex Moldenke, Résumé 322, in syn.
   1959.

Large straggling but not climbing shrub or small tree to 9 m tall, often
forming a coppice, scabrid-pilose throughout; trunk erect, the bark scabrous;
branches numerous, spreading in every direction, tetragonal, short-pubescent;
young shoots acutely tetragonal, almost alate, with 4 ligneous cord-like
strands under the bark forming the often red angles, short-pubescent, scabrous;
leaves decussate-opposite; petioles 5–20 mm long, not articulate, short-pubescent; leaf-blades ovate or those near the flowers sometimes oblong, 3.5–13
cm long, 2–9 cm wide, apically acute or acuminate, basally rounded or cordate to cuneate, marginally varying from entire to very coarsely and unequally
glandular-dentate or serrate on the lower portions, angular-lobed, very scabrous above with whitish bulbous-based hairs, only the bases persisting, densely short-pubescent beneath; inflorescence axillary or forming a large,
terminal, leafy, decussate-branched panicle, composed of small terminal involucrate corymbs or head-like umbellets, each 2–7-flowered; peduncles and
inflorescence-branches rather slender, acutely tetragonal, short-pubescent,
scabrous, with a pair of ovate-acuminate pubescent bractlets beneath each
furcation; involucre 4-leaved, the bracts sessile, opposite, broadly obovate,
often obcordate, rounded at the apex, densely short-pubescent; flowers sessile,
pleasantly fragrant, medium-sized, opening at sunset, each subtended by 2
broadly ovate or elliptic bracts which almost conceal the calyx and are 7–12
mm long; calyx campanulate, cylindric, subturbinate, about 5 mm long, its
mouth somewhat contracted, downy, withering in age, villous with appressed
hairs, its rim truncate, with 5 very minute teeth; corolla hypocrateriform, deciduous at sunrise, its tube Chinese-red to orange-red or orange, cylindric, 1–3
times as long as the calyx, 5–15 mm long, uniformly coloured outside and within, hairy at the base within, the mouth orange, the limb white, spreading, 5–8
[usually 6- or 7]-parted, more or less contorted, 5–6 mm wide, the segments
imbricate in bud, obliquely triangular or elliptic, the exterior margin erose;
stamens 2, inserted just below the mouth of the corolla-tube, included; filaments subobsolete; anthers ovate-cordate, 2-lobed, included, with a small spur
on the back near the apex; style as long as or shorter than the corolla-tube,
included; stigma capitate or peltate, glandular, with a central depression; ovary
superior, ovate-globose, compressed; capsule cordate or suborbicular, about
2 cm long and wide, 3–4 mm wide, compressed, usually shortly mucronate at

the apex, 2-celled, 2-valved, opening transversely from the apex; seeds 1 per cell, compressed. Chromosomes: $2n = 44$.

D i s t r. A well-known species native to India, Thailand and Indonesia, widely cultivated in the warmer parts of both Eastern and Western Hemispheres.

E c o l. It flowers from August to November, fruiting in the cold season. Methyl salicylate and diterpenes are found in the leaves.

U s e s. In India the fallen flowers are gathered from the ground, strung into garlands, and used in religious worship rites, the wood is used as fuel, the roots are eaten, an orange or yellow impermanent dye is made from the corolla-tubes by dyers, and whole leaves are used as an abrasive substitute for sandpaper. The flowers are also used by perfumers and the leaves, coated with "gram flour" and spices, are made into "pakodies". The dye is used for dyeing cotton cloth and as a cheap substitute for saffron in the manufacture of the robes of Buddhist priests. It is commonly planted in hedges around gardens and temple compounds.

V e r n. Coral jasmine, Sorrowful nyctanthes, Tree of sadness, Tree of sorrow, and about 2 dozen Indian names, including Harsinghar, Khirsaru, Kurri, Morisi, Nibári, Ni'lica, Nirgudí, Navárica, Parajatagom, Parijataka, Saparom, Siharu, Singahár, Suvahá and Sepalika (S).

S p e c i m e n s E x a m i n e d. KANDY DISTRICT: in outdoor cultivation, Medicinal Garden, Royal Botanic Garden, Peradeniya, 1550 ft altitude, 18 Jan. 1974, shrub 5 ft tall from severely pruned-back stump, *H. N. & A. L. Moldenke & Jayasuriya 28162* (PDA, US).

PERIPLOCACEAE

(by Herbert Huber*)

Type Genus: *Periploca* L.

Twining or prostrate woody plants or herbaceous perennials with a woody rootstock; with internal phloem and a white latex. Leaves opposite, simple, entire, pinnately veined, without stipules. Flowers with calyx and corolla, actinomorphic, 5-merous, bisexual, in determinate, axillary** or occasionally terminal (*Cryptostegia*) cymes. Sepals almost free, imbricate. Corolla gamopetalous, deeply lobed in the indigenous genera (funnel-shaped in *Cryptostegia*), the lobes valvate or contorted, overlapping in bud to the right. Stamens five, alternating with the corolla-lobes and inserted near the base of the tube; anthers distinct, connivent above but not adnate to the style-apex, longitudinally dehiscent along their inner side. Pollen granular, the grains united in tetrads, discharged on five funnel- or spoon-shaped pollen-carriers alternating with the stamens, derived from and attached to the style-apex. Corona of five fleshy scales alternating with the corolla-lobes, inserted in the mouth or near the base (*Cryptostegia*) of the corolla-tube. Disk absent. Carpels two, superior (semi-inferior in *Cryptostegia*), multi-ovulate, free and joined by their common style only. Fruit consisting of two distinct, many-seeded carpels, tapering towards the apex, dehiscent along the ventral suture. Seeds with endosperm, with a tuft of hairs at one end, without an aril.

A family of about 40 genera and almost 200 species in the tropics and the warm temperate regions of the Old World, poorly represented in Ceylon.

Periplocaceae are incorporated in Asclepiadaceae by most authors. This, however, is not justified, as the pollination mechanism of the two families, although highly specialised in both, fundamentally differs in structure. Both Periplocaceae and Asclepiadaceae are derived from Apocynaceae. They are not more closely related to each other than to Apocynaceae-Apocynoideae.

The two Ceylon species of Periplocaceae, most commonly *Hemidesmus indicus* (L.) R. Br. in Ait. f., are used as medicinal plants.

This plant is much grown as an ornamental and may be found in a semi-wild state:

---

*Fachbereich Biologie der Universität Kaiserslautern, Germany.
**Cymes never arising laterally from between the petioles.

182

Cryptostegia grandiflora R. Br., Edward's Bot. Reg. 5, t. 435. 1820.

A tall, glabrous twiner. Leaves opposite, broadly ovate, obtuse, sometimes short-acuminate, acute at the base, with rather distant lateral veins including with the midrib almost a right angle. Cymes short-peduncled, dichasially branched, terminal, few-flowered. Calyx-lobes ovate-lanceolate, acute. Corolla large, purple; tube 2.5–4 cm long, funnel-shaped, attenuate in the lower half; lobes broadly obovate, shorter than the tube. Ovary semi-inferior. Merocarps ovoid-oblong, tapering to the apex, 8–12 cm long and 2–2.5 cm wide, sharply angled.

A native of Madagascar, now largely planted in tropical gardens. According to Trimen often naturalized in Ceylon near the shore.

KEY TO THE GENERA

1 Inflorescence terminal. Corolla very large, the tube much longer than the calyx. Corona inserted near the base of the corolla-tube. Merocarps very stout, ovoid-oblong. Introduced ornamental...**Cryptostegia**
1 Inflorescence axillary. Corolla rather small, the tube about as long as the calyx-lobes. Corona inserted in the mouth of the corolla-tube.
  2 Leaves with numerous, close, lateral veins, shining, not variegated. Buds produced into a slender beak. Corolla yellowish-white, the lobes contorted in bud. Corona-scales almost as long as the anthers. Merocarps rather stout..........**1. Cryptolepis**
  2 Leaves with rather few, distant, lateral veins, not shining, often variegated with white along the veins on upper side. Buds ovoid, not beaked. Corolla dull purplish-brown, the lobes valvate in bud. Corona scales much shorter than the anthers. Merocarps slender..**2. Hemidesmus**

1. CRYPTOLEPIS

R. Br., Mem. Wern. Nat. Hist. Soc. 1: 69. 1811, prepr. 1810. Type Species: *Cryptolepis buchananii* Roem. & Schult.

A glabrous, woody twiner. Leaves ovate to obovate, with numerous, straight lateral veins diverging almost horizontally from the midrib. Flowers in rather lax, peduncled, axillary cymes. Calyx-lobes ovate-oblong, obtuse. Corolla yellowish-white, glabrous without; tube about as long as calyx; the lobes much longer than the tube, oblong-linear, contorted in bud and produced into a narrowly conical beak. Corona of five fleshy oblong-spathulate scales notched at the apex, inserted in the mouth of the corolla-tube. Merocarps ovate-lanceolate, rather stout, slightly flattened dorsally.

A palaeotropical genus ranging with several species from tropical Africa through India to South China and Malesia. In Ceylon represented by one species only.

Cryptolepis buchananii Roem. & Schult., Syst. Veg. 4: 409. 1819; Thw., Enum.

Pl. Zeyl. 195. 1860; Hook. f., Fl. Br. Ind. 4: 5. 1883; Trimen, Handb. Fl. Ceylon 3: 145. 1895. Type: *Buchanan-Hamilton s.n.* (BM).

Nerium reticulatum Roxb., [Fl. Ind. 19. 1814 nom. nud.] Fl. Ind. ed. Carey & Wall. 2: 8. 1821.

Cryptolepis reticulata (Roxb.) Schum. in Pflanzenfam. 4 (2): 219. 1895.

Petiole 0.5–1.2 cm long. Leaf-blade 5–18 cm long and 2.5–8 cm wide, rounded or short-cuneate at the base, suddenly narrowed into a short mucronate apex, shining above, not variegated, not coriaceous; dried leaf with the midrib proximally impressed, distally almost flat on the upper side, faintly raised above; lateral veins slightly raised on both surfaces or plain beneath; reticulate venation not sculptured on either side. Inflorescence shorter than the leaves, the peduncle equalling or exceeding the petiole. Pedicels mostly longer than the calyx. Calyx-lobes 1.5–2 mm long, glabrous. Corolla 1.2–2 cm in diameter when expanded. Merocarps 6–10 cm long, 1.2–1.8 cm wide, tapering to the apex, glabrous.

D i s t r. From north of Pakistan, Nepal and Bhutan through India to Ceylon and Burma.

E c o l. In Ceylon rather common in deciduous scrub and forests of the dry and intermediate zone, especially in the eastern part of North Central Province, northern and eastern part of Central Province and in Uva Province, up to an elevation of 1000 m. Flowering from October to March.

U s e s. According to Trimen, the wood is much used in native medicine.

V e r n. Wal-ruk-attana (S).

S p e c i m e n s E x a m i n e d. POLONNARUWA DISTRICT: between Alut Oya and Gal Oya, *Huber 28* (PDA, US). KANDY DISTRICT: between Madugoda and Weragantota, *Huber 38* (PDA, US); east of Madugoda, 600 m, *Jayasuriya et al. 1419* (PDA); c. 10 miles west of Mahiyangana, 450 m, *Davidse & Jayasuriya 8427* (PDA). RATNAPURA DISTRICT: Halpe, *Waas 504* (PDA). BADULLA DISTRICT: Ella Pass, Sept. 1890, *Trimen s.n.* (PDA); Koslanda, 7 March 1927, *Silva s.n.* (PDA); Talabottawa near Passara, *Huber 19* (PDA, US). LOCALITY UNKNOWN: *s. coll. C.P. 2548* (BM, K, PDA).

2. HEMIDESMUS

R. Br., Mem. Wern. Nat. Hist. Soc. 1: 56. 1811, prepr. 1810. Type Species: *Periploca indica* L.

An almost herbaceous perennial with a woody rootstock and prostrate or twining stems, puberulous or glabrescent. Leaves obovate, elliptic, oblong or linear, with distant pinnate veins strongly arched towards the margin and including with the midrib an angle of 45 to 60°; glabrous on both surfaces.

Flowers in small, dense, sessile, axillary cymes. Calyx-lobes broadly ovate, acute. Corolla purplish-brown within, glabrous and greenish without; the tube about as long as the calyx; the lobes two or three times as long as the tube, ovate, valvate in bud. Bud ovoid. Corona of five short, fleshy, broadly truncate scales inserted in the mouth of the corolla-tube. Merocarps slender, cylindrical.
Monotypic.

Hemidesmus indicus (L.) R. Br. in Aiton f., Hort. Kew. ed. 2, 2: 75. 1811; Thw., Enum. Pl. Zeyl. 195. 1860; Hook. f., Fl. Br. Ind. 4: 5. 1883; Trimen, Handb. Fl. Ceylon 3: 144. 1895. Type: Herbarium Hermann 3: 51 (BM).

Periploca indica L., Sp. Pl. 211. 1753.

Petiole 0.1–0.6 cm long. Leaf-blade extremely variable in shape, 3–7 cm long, 0.3–3 cm wide, acute, rounded or truncate at the base, acute, rounded or emarginate and apiculate at the apex, not shining, frequently variegated with white along the veins; leaves when dried with the midrib impressed on the upper side, faintly raised beneath; lateral veins impressed above, not or hardly sculptured beneath; reticulate venation not sculptured on either side or faintly impressed above. Inflorescence shorter than the leaves. Pedicels about as long as or slightly longer than the calyx. Calyx-lobes 1–1.5 mm long, puberulous or glabrescent. Corolla 0.6–0.8 cm in diameter when expanded. Merocarps 10–12 cm long, 0.5–0.6 cm wide, slightly falcate, glabrous.

D i s t r. From North India and Sikkim through the Deccan Peninsula to Ceylon.

E c o l. In Ceylon abundant throughout, up to an elevation of 1000 m, particularly in deciduous scrub and forests of the dry and arid regions, less common in secondary forests and tea gardens of the moist zone. Flowering in February.

U s e s. The roots are much used in native medicine as a tonic (Trimen).

V e r n. Heen-iramusu (S); Nannari (T).

S p e c i m e n s E x a m i n e d. JAFFNA DISTRICT: Jaffna, *Gardner* in *C.P. 1864* (PDA); 3 miles south of Jaffna, *Simpson 7984* (BM); Pallavarayan-kaddu, Feb. 1890, *Trimen s.n.* (K). VAVUNIYA DISTRICT: near 113th mile between Medawachchiya and Mannar, *Jayasuriya et al. 578* (PDA, US). ANURADHAPURA DISTRICT: Ritigala, *Bernardi 14312* (PDA). MATALE DISTRICT: Dambulla, *Huber 767* (US); Sigiriya, *Townsend 73/213* (PDA). KANDY DISTRICT: Kandy, *Champion s.n.* (K); Hakkinda, *Alston 2374* (PDA). RATNAPURA DISTRICT: Balangoda, *Gardner in C.P. 183* partly (PDA). BADULLA DISTRICT: Ooma Oya, *Gardner in C.P. 183* partly (PDA). GALLE DISTRICT: Hiniduma, Huber obs. HAMBANTOTA DISTRICT: Ruhuna National Park, Block 1, sea level, *Mueller-Dombois & Cooray 67121008* (BISH), *Wirawan 690* (PDA); Patanagala Rock, *Cooray 69121609* (US). LOCALITY UNKNOWN: *Walker s.n.* (K).

SPHENOCLEACEAE

(by L.H. Cramer*)

Type genus: *Sphenoclea* Gaertn.

Annual, halophilous, glabrous herbs; stem erect, branched. Leaves exstipulate, alternate, simple, entire. Spikes terminal or leaf-opposed. Pedicels long; flowers small, white, each subtended by a bract and 2 bracteoles. Calyx cupular-semiglobose, persistent; tube adnate to ovary; lobes 5, imbricate at anthesis, subinflexed in fruit, connivent above, ovate, persistent. Corolla broadly campanulate; lobes 5, imbricate in bud, inflexed at anthesis. Stamens as many as and alternate with corolla lobes, included; filaments very short; anther cells rounded, dehiscing longitudinally. Ovary half-inferior, 2-locular; placentae adnate to septa; ovules numerous in each loculus; stigma subsessile. Capsule subglobose, depressed, circumscissile, operculate; seeds minute, endospermous.

A monogeneric family; almost pantropical; two species of which one is represented in Ceylon.

SPHENOCLEA

Gaertn. Fruct. I: 113, t. 24, f. 5. 1788 nom. cons.; Benth. & Hook., Gen. Pl. 560. 1876. Type species: *Sphenoclea zeylanica* Gaertn.

Pongatium [Rheede] Tussac, Gen. 423. 1789. Type species: not recorded.
Rapinia Lour., Fl. Cochinch. 1: 127. 1790. Type species: not recorded.

Characters same as for family.

Sphenoclea zeylanica Gaertn., Fruct. l.c.; Roxb., Fl. Ind. 2: 116. 1824; Hook. f., Fl. Br. Ind. 3: 438. 1881; Trimen, Handb. Fl. Ceylon 3: 59. 1895; Airy-Shaw, Fl. Mal. I, 4: 27. 1948; Abeywick., Ceylon J. Sci., Biol. Sci. (2) 2: 234. 1959.

Sphenoclea pongatium DC., Prod. 7: 548. 1839; Thw., Enum. Pl. Zeyl. 170. 1860.

Erect herb; stem to 125 cm high, divaricately branched, thickened towards

*Flora of Ceylon Project, Peradeniya. Present address: Batticaloa University College, Chenkaladi.

base to 3.5 cm in breadth, with long fibrous roots, fistulous, the cortex replaced by spongy, aerenchymatous tissue. Leaves oval to oblong-elliptic, 8.6–11.5 × 2.2–4.7 cm, cuneate or abruptly acute at base, subacute to obtuse at apex, entire, membranous, glaucous; petioles 1–3 cm long. Spikes ovoid, to 3 cm long, bluntly tapering to apex; peduncles to 6 cm long; flowers many. Bracts spathulate, to 3 × 2 mm, clawed, cuspidate-acute, inflexed over calyx. Bracteoles lateral to bracts, linear, 2–3 mm long. Calyx tube cupular, 1 mm long; lobes obovate-deltoid, 1 × 2 mm, concave, pale green. Corolla white; tube 1–1.5 mm long; lobes ovate-triangular. Filaments glabrous. Top of ovary truncate; stigma flattened, obscurely 2-lobed. Capsule depressed-globose, 3–3.5 mm in diameter, chartaceous; seeds oblong-cuneate, 0.5–0.8 × 0.2 mm, minutely ridged longitudinally, yellowish-brown.

D i s t r. Indigenous to the Old World Tropics, introduced into tropical America and the Southern part of North America; widespread from tropical Africa to tropical Asia.

E c o l. A weedy herb occurring close to the coast in ditches, inundated rice-fields, swamps and streams of the dry and wet low country at sea level. It tends to be gregarious in marshes. On a spike there are never more than a very few flowers open at the same time, and almost every flower matures into fruit. Flowering January–June.

N o t e. The plant is reported to be laticiferous, but I have not been able to confirm this.

S p e c i m e n s E x a m i n e d. JAFFNA DISTRICT: Pallavarayankulam, Feb. 1890, *s. coll.* (PDA). PUTTALAM DISTRICT: Ditch, Chilaw-Puttalam road, *Simpson 8196* (PDA); Mattakotuwa, in marshy ditch beside Mattakotuwa-Todduwawa road, *Cramer 2609* (PDA, US); Madampe, Eratekulama, in marshy ditch by road, *Cramer 4947* (G, PDA, US). GALLE DISTRICT: Gintota, near mangroves, *Alston 1282* (PDA). HAMBANTOTA DISTRICT: Ruhunu National Park, Block 1, in dry mud wallow, *Cooray 68060109* (PDA, US). MONERAGALA DISTRICT: Okkampitiya, in paddy fields, 22 June 1953, *Pinidiyaaramy* (PDA). BATTICALOA DISTRICT: Panama, in marsh beside Pottuvil-Panama Road, *Cramer 5063* (BM, G, PDA, US); s. loc., *Gardner C.P. 1773* (PDA, K). TRINCOMALEE DISTRICT: on way to Foul Point, *Jayasuriya 663* (PDA, US).

SYMPHOREMACEAE

(by Harold N. Moldenke and Alma L. Moldenke*)

Type genus: *Symphorema* Roxb.

A small family of large scandent shrubs; stem-growth normal; branches and branchlets commonly more or less tetragonal, not articulate; nodes not swollen; leaves decussate-opposite, simple, exstipulate, net-veined, entire or toothed, sometimes stellate-tomentose or otherwise pubescent; flowers perfect, zygomorphic, usually sessile, in 3–9-flowered capitate cymes, often aggregated into large terminal panicles, each cyme with an involucre of 3–8 bracts and bracteoles which are mostly equal or subequal, highly coloured, more or less membranous, accrescent, and persistent, serving as floats for the fruit; calyx gamosepalous, mostly tubular or narrow-campanulate, 4–8-lobed, more or less accrescent or inflated in fruit, the teeth scarcely valvate at first, later open; corolla gamopetalous, mostly tubular-campanulate, 5–16-lobed, the lobes imbricate, equal or the corolla somewhat bilabiate; stamens 4–16, epipetalous, included or exserted; ovary 2-carpellary, mostly 2-celled to the middle, with 4 orthotropous ovules pendent from the free central placenta; style filiform, shortly bifid; fruit a small, dry, 1–4-seeded drupe, more or less included by the fruiting-calyx; endosperm none; cotyledons not folded; seeds not viviparous.

Three genera and 43 known species and named varieties of tropical Asia, many widely cultivated in warm climates and naturalized in parts of tropical and subtropical Africa and America. The family is often included in the Verbenaceae, but differs inter alia in its free-central placentation.

KEY TO THE GENERA

1 Involucre 6- or 8-merous
  2 Corolla actinomorphic, 6–16-merous; stamens 6–16..................**1. Symphorema**
  2 Corolla actinomorphic or slightly zygomorphic, 5-merous; stamens 5..............
....**2. Sphenodesme**
1 Involucre 3– or 4-merous...**3. Congea**

1. SYMPHOREMA

Roxb., Pl. Corom. 2: 46, pl. 186. 1798. Type species: *Symphorema involu-*

*Plainfield, New Jersey, U.S.A.

cratum Roxb.

Analectis Juss. in Jaume St.-Hil., Expos. Fam. Nat. 2: 362. 1805.
Sczegleewia Turcz., Bull. Soc. Imp. Naturalistes Moscou 36 (2): 212–213. 1863.
Szeglewia C. Müll. in Walp., Ann. Bot. Syst. 7: 419. 1868.
Symphyromea Wangerin, Bot. Jahresber. (Just) 50 (1): 237, sphalm. 1930.

Scandent shrubs or vines, glabrous, stellate-tomentose, or simply pilose; leaves decussate-opposite, entire or sinuate-toothed; cymes pedunculate, capitate, 7-flowered, involucrate, paniculate at the ends of the branches, often with a small bract at the base of the peduncle; involucre composed of six oblong "bracts" which are foliaceous, patent, often coloured, accrescent in fruit; the flower-head a dichotomous cyme with 3 central and 4 lateral flowers, one pair of opposite larger (true bracts) bracts supporting the primary while 2 smaller pairs (bracteoles) support the 2 secondary bifurcations; flowers sessile, small, centrifugal; calyx obovoid or turbinate, at first closed, later shortly 4–8-toothed, somewhat accrescent; corolla small, white, actinomorphic, normally 6–16-merous, its tube cylindric, widened above, the lobes 6–16, imbricate in bud, equal or subequal, narrowly oblong; stamens 6–16, as many as the corolla-lobes, inserted at the apex of the corolla-tube and alternate with its lobes; anthers exserted, ovate, the connective rather thick, the 2 thecae parallel; ovary basally 2-celled or imperfectly 4-celled, apically 1-celled, 4-ovulate, the ovules pendent from the apex of the free central placenta; style filiform, elongate; stigma shortly bifid, the branches acute; fruit nearly dry, included in the mature calyx, obovoid or subglobose, by abortion 1-seeded, shallowly 2-sulcate, indehiscent; seeds erect, the pericarp and testa thin-membranous, appressed to the embryo, the embryo thick-fleshy, conforming in size and shape to the fruit, the base entire, the radicle not prominent, the 2 cotyledons fleshy, often concave within.

A small genus of three known species native to tropical parts of India and Sri Lanka to Burma, Thailand, and the Philippines. Several species are cultivated in India and the Philippines. Only the following species is known from Sri Lanka.

Symphorema involucratum Roxb., Pl. Corom. 2: 46, pl. 186. 1798 [not *S. involucratum* Llanos, 1858]; Thw., Enum. Pl. Zeyl. 242. 1861; Clarke in Hook. f., Fl. Br. Ind. 4: 599. 1885; Trimen, Cat. 69. 1885; Trimen, Handb. Fl. Ceylon 3: 362–363. 1895; Willis, Cat. 69. 1911; Abeywick., Ceylon J. Sci., Biol. Sci. 2: 218. 1959; Gunawardena, Gen. & Sp. Pl. Zeyl. 148. 1968. Type: *Roxburgh s.n.* from the Coromandel coast, Madras, India.

Analectis speciosa Vahl, Kongel. Danske Vidensk. Selsk. Skriv. 6: 94. 1810.
Lerchea rotundifolia Hamilt. ex Moldenke, Fifth Summ. 2: 548. in syn. 1971.

A large shrubby climber; stems slender, the younger parts stellate-tomentose; bark thick, grey, corky, vertically deeply furrowed; wood white, soft, porous, the pores large, often subdivided by wedges between the few moderately broad medullary rays; leaves decussate-opposite, on the main branches often large, but on the flowering branches often only 0.8–1.6 cm long; petioles normally about 5 mm long; leaf-blades ovate or elliptic, 2–6.5 cm long on non-flowering branches and 4 cm wide, subacute at the apex, usually coarsely crenate-serrate, rounded at the base, pubescent or villous when young, ultimately nearly glabrous above, remaining pubescent beneath with close white stellate pubescence; peduncles about 2.5 cm long; bracts lanceolate-oblong, semi-membranous, during anthesis about 6 mm long, venose, pubescent or villous, in fruit to 3.2 cm long and 1.5 cm wide, spatulate-elliptic, thinly pubescent; calyx green, persistent, about 4 mm long, ribbed, stellate-tomentose, its rim very shortly 6–8-toothed with oval subacute teeth, in fruit 6 mm long or longer, narrowed upwards; corolla white, about 6 mm long, the tube short, cylindric, the 6–8 lobes about as long as the tube, linear, acute, reflexed; pollen 3-colpate (occasionally 6-rugate or more or less polyrugate), prolate, 49×34 μm; involucre in fruit thin-membranous, prominently reticulate, slightly pubescent; fruit about 4 mm long, glabrous.

D i s t r. This plant inhabits monsoon forests in India, dry deciduous forests, the edges of semi-evergreen forests and open evergreen jungles in Burma and Thailand, and has been encountered at altitudes of 100–1330 metres.

E c o l. Flowering in March and April, and fruiting in May and June. In Sri Lanka it is apparently very rare, having been collected only once.

V e r n. In India and Burma it is known as Gubba-dára, Konda-tekkali, Nway-sat, Nwèzat, Sigyi, Surúdú, Suroodo, and Thamaka.

S p e c i m e n s E x a m i n e d. TRINCOMALEE DISTRICT: near Trincomalee, *s. coll. C.P. 3645* [Rev. S.O. Glenie coll.] (PDA).

2. SPHENODESME

Jack, Mal. Misc., ser. 1, 1: 19. 1820; Jack, Calcutta J. Nat. Hist. ser. 4, 13: 43. 1843. Type species: *Sphenodesme pentandra* Jack.

Roscoea Roxb., Fl. Ind. ed. 2 [Carey] 3: 54–55. 1832 [not *Roscoea* J.E. Sm. 1804].

Sphaenodesma Jack apud Schau. in A. DC., Prod. 11: 622. 1847.—*Sphaenodesma* Jacq. ex Schnitzl., Ic. Fam. Nat. Reg. Veg. 2: 137 Verbenac. [3]. 1856.—*Sphaenodesma* Schau. apud Jacks. in Hook. f. & Jacks., Ind. Kew. 2: 959 & 961, in syn. 1895.

Viticastrum Presl, Bot. Bemerk. 147–148. 1844.

Decadontia Griff., Not. Pl. As. 4: 175–176. 1854.

Brachynema Griff., Not. Pl. As. 4: 176–177. 1854 [not *Brachynema* Benth. 1859, nor F. Muell. 1862].
Sphenodesma Jack apud Benth. & Hook. f., Gen. Pl. 2 (2): 1136 & 1159. 1876.—*Sphenodesma* Jacq. apud Junell, Symb. Bot. Upsal. 4: 138. 1934. —*Sphenodesma* Griff., Not. Pl. As. 4: 175, in textu. 1854; Airy-Shaw in Willis, Dict. ed. 7, 1059, in syn. 1966.

Large scandent shrubs, glabrous or tomentose, short-canescent or rufescent; leaves decussate-opposite; petioles short; leaf-blades usually entire; flowers borne in capitate cymes or cymules, the inflorescence terminal or lateral, pedunculate; involucral bracts 6, foliaceous, oblong or obovate, often coloured, in 2 groups of 3 each; cymes more or less paniculate, decussate, generally once or twice dichotomous, with a single terminal flower at each fork, forming either (typically) 3-flowered cymules (if only once dichotomous) or 6-flowered cymes (if twice dichotomous), the flowers terminating the primary forks not bracteate, but the others each subtended by bracts, the bracts therefore in 2 groups of 3 each; leaves at the base of the peduncles greatly reduced and bract-like, mostly deciduous; calyx gamosepalous, shortly infundibular or hypocrateriform, 5- or 10-ribbed, usually 5- or 10-toothed (very rarely and abnormally 4- or 6-toothed), the 5 additional teeth (when present) representing a congenitally fused 5-parted epicalyx, the accessory teeth usually alternate with (rarely opposite to) the true calyx-lobes which may be entire or bifid; corolla gamopetalous, actinomorphic or slightly zygomorphic, normally 5-merous, its tube short, cylindric or slightly widened above, the lobes 5 (rarely 6), ovate-oblong or narrow-lanceolate, patent, equal or unequal, imbricate in bud; stamens 5, inserted just below the mouth of the corolla-tube, included or rarely subexserted; anthers short and ovate or rarely oblong, the thecae 2, parallel or divergent; style filiform, elongate; stigma shortly bifid or obscurely 2-lobed, the lobes acute; ovary 2-celled to above the middle, imperfectly 2-locellate, 1-celled at the apex; ovules 4, pendulous from the apex of a free central placenta; fruit a small, globose or obovoid drupe, more or less completely included by the usually inflated winged calyx; seeds 1 or rarely 2; cotyledons thick.

A small genus of 23 known species and varieties, native to tropical Asia from northeastern and southern India, Bangladesh, Burma, and Thailand to Indochina, Hainan Island, and Borneo. Only a variety of a single species is known from Sri Lanka and that only in cultivation, but members of this group tend to escape from cultivation and become naturalized in tropical areas.

Sphenodesme pentandra Jack var. **wallichiana** (Schau.) Munir, Gard. Bull. Singapore 21: 360. 1966; Clarke in Hook. f., Fl. Br. Ind. 4: 602. 1885; Munir, Gard. Bull. Singapore 21: 360–364, pl. 13. 1966. Type: *Wallich 1735/2* from a cultivated plant in the Calcutta Botanical Garden, originally from Sylhet, Bangladesh, DeCandolle Herbarium (G).

Congea jackiana var. *attenuata* Wall., Num. List [47] no. 1735/2, hyponym. 1829.

Roscoea pentandra Roxb., Cat. Hort. Bot. 46, nom. nud. 1814; Roxb., Fl. Ind. ed. 1, 3: 54. 1832.

Congea pentandra (Roxb.) Wall., Num. List [47] no. 1734. 1829; Walp., Rep. 4: 117. 1848.

Sphenodesme wallichiana Schau. in A. DC., Prod. 11: 622. 1847.

Sphenodesme pentandra (Roxb.) Griff., Not. Pl. As. 4: 176. 1854 [not *S. pentandra* Jack, 1820].—*S. pentandra* Jack sensu Clark apud Munir, Gard. Bull. Singapore 21: 360, in syn. 1966.

A scandent shrub; branches dark brown, obscurely tetragonal, puberulous when young, finally glabrous, lenticellate; petioles 5–15 mm long, pubescent when young, longitudinally canaliculate above, curved; leaf-blades chartaceous or subcoriaceous, elliptic-oblong to lanceolate-oblong, 5–18 cm long, 3–7 cm wide, acuminate-acute and often mucronulate at the apex, cuneate or subrotund at the base, glabrous and shiny above, dull beneath and glabrous except for the somewhat hairy midrib and the axils of the 4–6 pairs of secondary veins; inflorescence axillary and terminal, puberulous, the panicles 16–37.5 cm long, the rachis pubescent when young, later glabrous except for the ciliate nodes; cymes 7-flowered; peduncles 1.5–3 cm long; involucral bracts oblong-spatulate, 1.5–2.8 cm long, 5–10 mm wide, obtuse, glabrous; calyx very shortly and obscurely 5-lobed or subtruncate, glabrous outside and within, the 5 accessory teeth minute even after anthesis; corolla 5-lobed, tubular or infundibular, the tube 5 mm long, glabrous outside, densely villous on the upper third within, glabrous below, the lobes somewhat rounded, patent, glabrous; stamens 5, exserted; filaments slender; style about 5 mm long, slender, exserted; stigma shortly bifid; fruit globular, about 4 mm long and wide, setose.

D i s t r. Native from Assam to Bangladesh, Burma, the Nicobar Islands, Malaya, and Indo-China, north to Hainan Island and southern China; cultivated in India, Pakistan, and Sri Lanka.

S p e c i m e n s E x a m i n e d. KANDY DISTRICT: in cultivation, Royal Botanic Garden, Peradeniya, December 1859, *s. coll. s.n.* (PDA).

3. CONGEA

Roxb., Pl. Corom. 3: 90, pl. 293. 1819. Type species: *Congea tomentosa* Roxb.

Calochlamys Presl, Bot. Bemerk. 148. 1844.—*Calochlamis* Presl ex Lam & Bakh., Bull. Jard. Bot. Buitenzorg ser. 3, 3: 100, in syn. 1921.

Large scandent shrubs; branches subcylindric, usually tomentose with mixed simple and stellate hairs; leaves simple, decussate-opposite, entire, reticulate, unicostate; inflorescence in axillary and terminal panicles; cymes capitate, pedunculate, 3–9-flowered; involucral bracts 3 or 4, free or united at the base, violet or white, tomentose, elliptic to oblong or spatulate; flowers often sessile, sometimes long-pedicellate; calyx tubular or infundibular, 5-toothed, slightly accrescent; corolla bilabiate, oblique, the tube cylindric, glabrous except for a villous band in the throat, the upper lip erect and 2-lobed, the lower lip 3-lobed; stamens 4, exserted, didynamous, epipetalous, inserted in the throat of the corolla; anthers suborbicular; ovary obovoid, glabrous, glandular at the apex, imperfectly 2-celled, each cell 2-ovulate; style as long as the stamens or longer, filiform; stigma shortly bifid; fruit drupaceous, obovoid, nearly dry, 1-seeded.

A genus of 17 species, varieties, and named hybrids, native from Assam and Bangladesh, through Burma, Thailand, Malaya, and Indo-China, to Sumatra, and north to south-western China. *Roscoea* Roxb. is often included "in part" in the synonymy of *Congea*, but is actually based on *R. pentandra* Roxb., Hort. Beng. 46. 1814 and therefore nomenclaturally is a synonym only of *Sphenodesme* Jack. Two species of *Congea* are known from cultivation in Sri Lanka and may be expected as escapes or persistent after cultivation.

KEY TO THE SPECIES

1 Involucral bracts usually 3, rarely with one more or less split, not narrowed at the base; calyx densely long-hirsute, 5–7 mm long, the lobes 1–2.5 mm long, often long-mucronate at the apex; leaves to 18.5 cm long and 9.5 cm wide..............**1. C. tomentosa**
1 Involucral bracts regularly 4, narrowed to the base; calyx canescent-pilose, 4–5 mm long, the lobes almost 1 mm long, not apiculate; leaves to 12 cm long and 6 cm wide...
....**2. C. griffithiana**

1. Congea tomentosa Roxb., Pl. Corom. 3: 90, pl. 293. 1819; Clarke in Hook. f., Fl. Br. Ind. 4: 603–604. 1885; Brandis, Indian Trees 513. 1906; Munir, Gard. Bull. Singapore 21: 305–312, fig. 10 & 10a. 1966. Type: *Roxburgh s.n.*, from Chittagong, Bangladesh (K).

Congea azurea Wall., Num. List [47], no. 1733/1, hyponym. 1829; Walp., Rep. 4: 116. 1845.
Congea azurea var. *latifolia* Wall., Num. List [47], no. 1733/2, hyponym. 1829.
Roscoea tomentosa Roxb., Fl. Ind. ed. 2 [Carey] 3: 56–57. 1832.
Roscoea villosa Roxb., Fl. Ind. ed. 2 [Carey] 3: 55–56. 1832.
Calochlamys capitata Presl, Bot. Bemerk. 149. 1844.
Congea tomentosa var. *oblongifolia* Schau. in A. DC., Prod. 11: 624. 1847.
Congea tomentosa var. *azurea* (Wall.) Clarke in Hook. f., Fl. Br. Ind. 4: 604. 1885.

Congea villosa (Roxb.) Wight ex Clarke in Hook. f., Fl. Br. Ind. 4: 603. 1885 [not *C. villosa* (Roxb.) Wight apud Munir, 1966].
Congea tomentosa var. *coerulea* (Griff.) Clarke apud Briq. in Pflanzenfam. ed. 1, 4 (3a): 181, nom. nud. 1895.—*C. tomentosa* var. *caerulea* (Griff.) Clarke ex Moldenke, Résumé 275, in syn. 1959.—*C. tomentosa* var. *caerulea* (Wall.) Clarke apud Munir, Gard. Bull. Singapore 21: 305, in syn. 1966.

Branches almost cylindric, fulvescent-tomentose when young, later canescent; petioles 5–13 mm long, deeply striate dorsally, pubescent; leaf-blades elliptic-ovate, to 18.5 cm long and 9.5 cm wide, usually acuminate at the apex (rarely obtuse), subcordate at the base, entire, puberulent above when young, later glabrous, thickly pubescent beneath, the main lateral veins (secondaries) 5 or 6 pairs, the intramarginal vein prominent; inflorescence in axillary and terminal panicles 12–30 cm long, the rachis fulvous-tomentose; peduncles 1–1.8 cm long, densely pubescent; cymes usually 7-flowered (rarely 5- or 9-flowered); involucral bracts 3, one occasionally bifid, violet, free to the base, 2–3 cm long, 8–12 mm wide, elliptic-oblong, tomentose, bearded at the base above with long canescent hairs; flowers sessile; calyx infundibular, 5–7 mm long, 5-lobed, densely sericeous-hirsute on the outside, appressed-pilose within, its tube 4–5 mm long, the accrescent lobes well developed, 1–2.5 mm long, almost half the length of the calyx-tube, acute, often bearing a linear-setaceous mucro or accessory tooth at the tip; corolla white, the tube longer than the calyx, cylindric, glabrous except for a narrow (almost fugaceous) villous band in the throat; stamens 4, the filaments much exserted, the anthers suborbicular; ovary obovoid, about 2 mm long, glabrous, glandular at the apex; style long, exserted; stigma faintly bilobed. Chromosomes: 2n=34.

D i s t r. Native from Bangladesh to Assam, east through Manipur, Burma, and Thailand to Indochina, and north to Yunnan, China. Widely cultivated for ornament in almost all warm parts of the world (and in greenhouses elsewhere) and often persisting or escaping.

V e r n. Japonesa, Lavender-wreath, Shower-of-orchids, Woolly congea, and about a dozen other names in various parts of its range.

S p e c i m e n s E x a m i n e d. KANDY DISTRICT: in cultivation, Royal Botanic Garden, Peradeniya, 22 March 1926, *F.W. de Silva 4* (PDA).

2. **Congea griffithiana** Munir, Gard. Bull. Singapore 21: 285–289, fig. 3. 1966; Clarke in Hook. f., Fl. Br. Ind. 4: 603. 1885; Munir, Gard. Bull. Singapore 21: 285–290, fig. 3 & 3a. 1966. Type: *Curtis 2962* from near Poongah, Thailand (SING).

Congea villosa Roxb. ex Wight, Ic. Pl. Ind. Or. 4 (3): pl. 1479/B, hyponym. 1849.—*C. villosa* Wight apud Munir, Gard. Bull. Singapore 21: 285, in syn. 1966.—*C. villosa* (Roxb.) Wight apud Munir, Gard. Bull. Singapore 21: 285, in syn. 1966 [not *C. villosa* (Roxb.) Wight ex Clarke, 1885].

Congea tomentosa var. *velutina* (Wight) Bakh. ex Moldenke, Résumé 275, in syn. 1959.

Congea tomentosa Roxb. sensu King & Gamble apud Munir, Gard. Bull. Singapore 21: 285, in syn. 1966 [not *C. tomentosa* Roxb., 1819].

Congea griffithiana var. *griffithiana* Munir, Gard. Bull. Singapore 21: 285. 1966.

A scandent shrub; branchlets cylindric, tawny-tomentose; petioles 5–10 mm long, pubescent; leaf-blades subcoriaceous to chartaceous, elliptic, to 12 cm long and 6 cm wide, acuminate at the apex, cuneate at the base, entire, glabrous above, ferruginous-pubescent beneath, the main lateral veins (secondaries) 4 pairs; inflorescence in axillary and terminal panicles to 45 cm long; rachis tawny-tomentose; cymes 5-flowered; involucral bracts 4, free to the base, spatulate to oblanceolate, violet, much narrowed to the base, thickly tomentose above, pubescent beneath, to 3 cm long and 1.3 cm wide; peduncles almost 1 cm long, pubescent; calyx campanulate, 4–5 mm long, 5-lobed, densely canescent-pilose outside, appressed-pilose within, the lobes almost 1 mm long, acute, crisped on the margins; corolla exserted, white, the tube slightly longer than the calyx, glabrous except for a villous band in the throat, the lobes almost rounded; stamens 4, exserted, the filaments elongate, to 1 cm or more long, the anthers almost orbicular; ovary more or less obovoid, glabrous, glandular at the apex; style longer than the filaments; stigma indistinctly bilobed.

D i s t r. Native to southern Burma, Thailand, and Malaya; rather widely cultivated in the Indo-Malayan region and Africa.

S p e c i m e n s E x a m i n e d. KANDY DISTRICT: in cultivation, Royal Botanic Garden, Peradeniya, 22 Feb. 1917, *s. coll. 125/58* (PDA); in cultivation, Royal Botanic Garden, Peradeniya, 29 March 1926, *F.W. de Silva 3* (PDA); in outdoor cultivation on arbour, Pergola garden, Royal Botanic Garden, Peradeniya, 18 January, 1974, *H. N. & A. L. Moldenke & Jayasuriya 28135* (AAU, LL, PDA, US). RATNAPURA DISTRICT: in outdoor cultivation on arbour, Ratnapura, 12 Feb. 1974, *H. N. & A. L. Moldenke, Jayasuriya & Dassanayake 28339* (LL, PDA, US).

VERBENACEAE

(by Harold N. Moldenke and Alma L. Moldenke*)

Type genus: *Verbena* (Dorst.) L.

Herbs, shrubs, woody vines, or trees; no pneumatophores, aerial-, knee-, prop-, or stilt-roots present, but sometimes extensive buttresses; branches, branchlets, and twigs mostly tetragonal, not prominently nodose nor articulate, often annulate; leaves mostly decussate-opposite, sometimes whorled, alternate, or scattered, thick- or thin-textured, deciduous, exstipulate, sessile or petiolate, simple or sometimes palmately (rarely pinnately) compound or 1-foliolate, the blades entire or variously dentate, incised, or cleft. Inflorescence axillary or terminal, rarely cauliflorous or epigeous, determinate and centrifugal (cymose) or indeterminate and centripetal (racemose), in the form of cymes, racemes, spikes, panicles, thyrsi, heads, or false-umbels, sometimes involucrate, the axillary inflorescences mostly solitary; flowers sessile or pedicellate, perfect or imperfect, hypogynous, sometimes heterostylous or polygamous, large or small, mostly irregular, not individually involucrate; calyx gamosepalous, campanulate to tubular or salverform, persistent, usually accrescent, mostly 4- (rarely 2-, 5-, or 7-) lobed or toothed or sometimes subentire; corolla regular or irregular, gamopetalous, funnel- or salverform, usually with a well-developed tube, the limb 4- or 5 (rarely 7–many-) parted, often somewhat 2-lipped; stamens mostly 4 and didynamous or reduced by abortion to 2, sometimes 4 or 5 and equal, inserted on the corolla-tube; staminodes often present; gynoecium mostly 2- (sometimes 4- or 5-) carpellate, syncarpous, 1 carpel sometimes aborted, the ovary mostly compound, sessile, or sometimes subtended by a disk, mostly somewhat 4-lobed, at first 2–5-loculate, usually becoming 4–10-loculate through formation of false partitions, never with a free central placenta or columella, the axile placenta-lobes each bearing 1 anatropous and basal or hemianatropous and lateral ovule, so that locules not subsequently divided by partitions each contain 1 ovule; style terminal or ± gynobasic (in *Faradaya* and *Oxera*); fruit usually a dry schizocarp, or drupaceous with a thick and dry or fleshy exocarp and more or less hard endocarp, 2–4-loculate and indehiscent when mature or dehiscent into 2 (sometimes 4–10) 1- or 2-loculate pyrenes; seeds plainly testate, the embryo never vivi-

*Plainfield, New Jersey, U.S.A.

196

parous, the radicle short and inferior, glabrous, the cotyledons 2, flat, more or less thickened, parallel.

A widely distributed and complex family of about 76 genera and 3,450 specific and subspecific taxa, found in all portions of the world except the driest hottest parts of the Sahara Desert and in the Arctic and Antarctic regions, most abundant in the tropics. The family is closely related to the Lamiaceae (Menthaceae, Labiatae) from which it is distinguished with difficulty. Numerous ornamentals, as well as medicinal and otherwise economic forms, are included in the family. The three families Avicenniaceae, Symphoremaceae and Nyctanthaceae are often included as subfamilies or tribes.

KEY TO THE GENERA

1 Inflorescence spicate or racemiform, indeterminate or centripetal
  2 Inflorescence spicate, often subcapitate during anthesis and elongating in fruit; flowers sessile or subsessile
    3 Fruit composed of four 1-seeded schizocarps..........................**1. Verbena**
    3 Fruit composed of two pyrenes
     4 Pyrenes normally 1-loculate and 1-seeded
      5 Perfect stamens 4
       6 Calyx very small, inconspicuous, thin-membranous, usually hidden by the subtending bractlets
        7 Calyx-rim truncate or shallowly toothed; corolla 4- or 5-lobed; fruit drupaceous, usually with a fleshy and juicy exocarp and hard endocarp, either 2-loculate or separating into two 1-loculate pyrenes...........................**2. Lantana**
        7 Calyx 2–4-cleft or conspicuously toothed; corolla 4-lobed; fruit small, dry, with a hard and thin papery exocarp, separating into two 1-loculate pyrenes
         8 Spikes elongate during anthesis, with scattered, often distant flowers..**3. Aloysia**
         8 Spikes dense and congested during anthesis, often subcapitate, with closely imbricate flowers..**4. Phyla**
       6 Calyx large, elongate-tubular, conspicuous, not hidden by subtending bracts.....
         ....**5. Svensonia**
      5 Perfect stamens 2, with a posterior pair of staminodes..........**6. Stachytarpheta**
     4 Pyrenes normally 2-loculate and 2-seeded (or by abortion only 1-loculate and 1-seeded)..**7. Priva**
  2 Inflorescence racemiform and elongate, or reduced and axillary; flowers pedicellate
    9 Fruit composed of two 1-loculate and 1-seeded pyrenes; woody vines; mature fruit conspicuously 5-winged, with very greatly enlarged, rather stiff, dry, net-veined, often coloured lobes (wings); an epicalyx present..............................**8. Petrea**
    9 Fruit composed of two or four 2-loculate and 2-seeded pyrenes (or less by abortion); mostly not vines; mature fruit not winged; no epicalyx present
     10 Drupes composed of four pyrenes, each 2-loculate and 2-seeded; calyx mostly obvolute and rostrate after anthesis....................................**9. Duranta**
     10 Drupes composed of two pyrenes, each 2-loculate and 2-seeded (or only 1-seeded by abortion); calyx not obvolute nor rostrate after anthesis......**10. Citharexylum**
1 Inflorescence cymose, determinate and centrifugal, the cymes often congested into panicles, false-umbels, umbelloid panicles, thyrsi, or heads, when axillary sometimes reduced to one flower
  11 Fruit usually drupaceous, never capsular

12 Flowers essentially actinomorphic; stamens 4–6, equal
  13 Drupes normally composed of four or five 1-loculate and 1-seeded pyrenes (sometimes less numerous by abortion); fruiting-calyx not inflated
    14 Stigma deeply bifid with long awl-shaped branches; flowers diclinous; fruiting-calyx enlarged and indurated; stamens inserted at or above the middle of the corolla-tube; ovary mostly glabrous..............................**11. Aegiphila**
    14 Stigma depressed-capitate or peltate; flowers mostly polygamous; fruiting-calyx usually unchanged and patelliform; stamens inserted at or very near the base of the corolla-tube; ovary usually more or less pubescent............**12. Callicarpa**
  13 Drupes composed of one 4-loculate pyrene; fruiting-calyx conspicuously inflated..
  ....**13. Tectona**
12 Flowers (especially the corollas) more or less zygomorphic; stamens 4
  15 Drupes composed of one 4-loculate and two 2-loculate pyrenes
    16 Corolla-tube mostly cylindric, usually short
      17 Corolla usually 4-lobed, mostly straight; calyx truncate or obsoletely denticulate or more or less bilabiate, one lip entire or 2-toothed, the other entire or 3-toothed; leaves simple
        18 Mostly trees, shrubs, or woody vines, rarely epiphytic, over 0.5 metre tall; stems erect..**14. Premna**
        18 Mostly dwarf and herbaceous or undershrubs, to 25 cm tall; stems subterranean
        ....**15. Pygmaeopremna**
      17 Corolla usually 5-lobed, more or less 2-lipped, often markedly curvate; calyx usually regularly 5-toothed or 5-cleft, very rarely 3-cleft or 6-lobed; leaves mostly palmately compound or 1-foliolate..............................**16. Vitex**
    16 Corolla-tube large, mostly infundibular and greatly ampliate above...**17. Gmelina**
  15 Drupes composed of four (or through abortion less numerous) 1-loculate pyrenes
    19 Calyx 2- or 3-lobed when mature..............................**18. Faradaya**
    19 Calyx always 4- or 5-toothed or 4- or 5-parted
      20 Fertile stamens 2..**19. Oxera**
      20 Fertile stamens 4
        21 Fruiting-calyx ampliate from the base up or closely appressed to the fruit or more or less inflated....................................**20. Clerodendrum**
        21 Fruiting-calyx with a short tube which encloses the fruit, the edges enlarged and spreading, saucer- or cymbal-shaped, often gayly coloured, subentire..........
        ....**21. Holmskioldia**
11 Fruit capsular, not drupaceous, 4-valved, the valves separating the pyrenes from the placental axis or tearing them apart
  22 Fruiting-calyx not at all or but slightly changed, not accrescent.....**22. Glossocarya**
  22 Fruiting-calyx accrescent
    23 Fruiting-calyx merely ampliate, campanulate, not winged..........**23. Caryopteris**
    23 Fruiting-calyx greatly changed in form and appearance, enlarged, 4-winged, closed at the apex...**24. Hymenopyramis**

1. VERBENA

[Dorst.] L., Mat. Med. 6. 1749; L., Sp. Pl. ed. 1, 1: 18. 1753; L., Gen. Pl., ed. 5, 12. 1754. Type species: *Verbena officinalis* L.

Berbena Macer Floridus, De Virib. Herm., imp. 1, ff. XXIII–XXV. 1477.

Verbena Tourn. ex L., Gen. Pl. ed. 1, 334, [387], [400], & [402], 1737; ed. 6, 14. 1764 [not *Verbena* Dill., 1763, nor Pluk., 1763].—*Verbena* Endl. ex Bocq., Adansonia, ser. 1, 3: 181. 1862.—*Uerbena* Sessé & Moc., Pl. Nou. Hisp. 1: 6. 1887.—*Verbena* [Tourn.] L. ex Migula, Exkursionsfl. Deutschl. 2: 134. 1906.—*Verbenia* L. ex Moldenke, Alph. List Invalid Names Suppl. 1: 28, in syn. 1947; Runner, Rep. Groff Coll. 361. 1961.—*Vervena* Kundu & De, Bull. Bot. Surv. India 10: 399, sphalm. 1968.

Obletia LeMonnier ex Rozier, Introd. Obs. Phys. Hist. Nat. 1: 367. 1771.— *Obletia* Rozier apud Jacks. in Hook. f. & Jacks., Ind. Kew. 2: 323, in syn. 1894.—*Obletia* Lemonn. ex Rozier apud Airy Shaw in Willis, Dict., ed. 7, 784, in syn. 1966.

Patya Neck., Elem. Bot. 1: 296. 1790.

Glandularia J. F. Gmel. in L., Syst., ed. 13, 2 (2): 920. 1791 [not *Glandularia* J. Agardh, 1848, nor P. DC., 1836].—*Glandvlaria* Raeusch., Nom. Bot., ed. 3, 172. 1797.—*Grandularia* Martínez Crovetto & Piccinini, Revista Invest. Agric. 4: 77, sphalm. 1951.—*Glanduria* Troncoso, Biol. Abstr. 46: 7724, sphalm. 1965.

Billardiera Moench, Meth. 369. 1794 [not *Billardiera* Sm., 1793, nor Vahl, 1796].

Shuttleworthia Meisn., Pl. Vasc. Gen. 1: 29 & 2: 198. 1839.—*Shuttelworthia* Steud., Nom. Bot., ed. 2, 2: 575.—*Schuttleworthia* Meisn. apud Schau. in A. DC., Prod. 11: 535, in syn. 1847.—*Shuttleworthia* Walp. apud Schau. in A. DC., Prod. 11: 553, in syn. 1847.—*Shuttlevorthia* Bocq., Adansonia, ser. 1, 2: 126. 1862.

Uwarowia Bunge, Bull. Sci. Acad. Imp. Sci. Saint-Petersbourg 7: 278. 1840.— *Uwarovia* Bocq., Adansonia, ser. 1, 2: 126. 1862.—*Uwarovia* Lindl. ex Pfeiffer, Nom. Bot. 2 (2): 1544, in syn. 1874.

Verbenella Spach, Hist. Nat. Veg. Phan. 9: 237–238. 1840.

Aubletia Jacq. apud Wittstein, Etymolog.-bot. Handwörterb. 85. 1852 [not *Aubletia* Gaertn., 1788, nor Lour., 1790, nor Neck., 1790, nor Rich., 1807, nor Schreb., 1789].—*Aubletia* LeMonnier ex Rozier apud Dandy, Ind. Gen. Vasc. Pl. 121, in syn. 1967.

Helleranthus Small, Fl. Southeast. U.S., ed. 1, 1011 & 1337. 1903.

Canadea Patermann, Beitr. Zytol. Verbenac. 13, 43, & [54], pl. 1, fig. 1 & 2. 1935.

Elissia Barkley, List Ord. & Fam. Anthoph., ed. 2, 76 & 163, in syn. 1965 [not *Ellisia* P. Br., 1756].

Herbs, sometimes slightly woody basally; stems and branches procumbent, ascending, or erect, glabrous or variously pubescent, usually more or less tetragonal; leaves mostly decussate-opposite, rarely whorled, dentate (rarely entire) or variously lobed, incised, or pinnatifid; inflorescence spicate; spike terminal, usually densely many-flowered, often flat-topped and pseudo-umbellate or fasciculate-capitate, sometimes greatly elongate with densely crowded or scattered flowers, rarely also axillary, often greatly elongating only after anthesis; flowers small or medium-sized, each solitary and axillary to a usually narrow bractlet; calyx usually tubular, 5-angled, 5-ribbed, unequally 5-toothed, not at all or but slightly changed in fruit, then herbaceous, mostly ventricose, eventually split, often connivent or contorted apically, thin-textured; corolla salverform or funnelform, the tube cylindric, straight or curved, often slightly ampliate or subinflated apically, usually villous at the stamen-insertion within and barbate at the mouth, the limb flat, spreading or oblique, weakly 2-lipped, the lobes 5, usually elongate, more or less unequal, varying from obtuse or rounded to emarginate apically, the 2 posterior outermost and the anterior innermost in prefloration; stamens 4, didynamous, inserted in the upper half of the corolla-tube, included, the anthers ovate, with 2 parallel or slightly divergent thecae, dehiscing longitudinally, the dorsal connective unappendaged and narrowly muticous or provided with a more or less conspicuous glandular appendage; gynoecium 2-carpellate, the ovary superior, entire or 4-lobed, apically situated on a somewhat lobed annular disk, completely 4-loculate even during anthesis, the ovules 1 per locule, attached laterally at or near the base, erect, anatropous; style usually short and equalling the stamens, somewhat dilated, not sunk in the ovary, shortly 2-lobed or bifid apically, the anterior lobe or branch stigmatiferous and subpulvinate-papillose, the posterior lobe or branch smooth and horny and non-stigmatiferous, not as broad as the anterior one; fruit mostly enclosed by the mature calyx, schizocarpous, the pericarp hard and dry, readily separating at maturity into four, 1-seeded, linear or linear-oblong (rarely elliptic-alate), crustaceous nutlets; seeds 4, erect, oblong, triangular in cross-section, without or with negligible endosperm, the outer face convex, the cotyledons 2, thick, applicate. Chromosomes: $2n = 10$, 14, 20, 28, 30, 42, 65 and 72 as reported in the literature.

A complex genus of about 450 specific, subspecific, and hybrid taxa native to temperate and tropical America, 2 species native to the Mediterranean region and the Near East and introduced elsewhere in the Old World. There are scores of widely cultivated forms and numerous natural and artificial hybrids. Several American species have become naturalized in various parts of Europe, Asia, Africa and Australia. A fossil form is known from the Pliocene in Europe. *Glandularia* is perhaps worthy of generic segregation. Some authors include *Junellia* and *Stylodon* in *Verbena*, thus adding 70 more taxa. *Verbena* is represented in Ceylon by six species.

KEY TO THE SPECIES

1 Anthers unappendaged; corolla usually small and individually not showy; mature calyx usually not much longer than the fruit, usually not constricted nor contorted beyond it.
  2 Bractlets shorter than, only subequalling, or very slightly surpassing the mature calyx.
....1. V. bonariensis

2 Bractlets conspicuously longer than the mature calyx
  3 Leaves leathery, rigid, prickly-toothed; corolla-tube more than twice as long as the calyx, the limb rather large and conspicuous, forming en masse a showy inflorescence
  ....**2. V. rigida**
  3 Leaves herbaceous, soft, not prickly; corolla-tube not twice as long as the calyx, the limb very small and inconspicuous, not at all showy..................**3. V. hispida**
1 Some anther-connectives usually glandular-appendaged; corollas large and very showy; mature calyx usually more than twice as long as the fruit and more or less constricted or contorted beyond it
  4 Leaves thin-textured, deeply trifid, the divisions again deeply incised; corolla-tube to 1.4 cm long, the limb about 1 cm wide
    5 Calyx hairs mostly only strigillose, more or less patent-ascending or only subappressed, grey or sordid-whitish, not silvery nor closely appressed; corolla rose-pink; leaf divisions mostly elliptic or oblanceolate........................**4. V. monacensis**
    5 Calyx hairs mostly closely and antrorsely strigose, silvery-white; corolla vivid purple, violet, or magenta; leaf divisions all uniformly linear or narrow-linear.............
    ....**5. V. tenuisecta**
  4 Leaves very thick-textured, lanceolate or ovate, irregularly incised-dentate but not at all trifid; corolla-tube to 3 cm long, the limb to 2.5 cm wide...........**6. V. x hybrida**

1. Verbena bonariensis L., Sp. Pl. ed. 1, 1: 20. 1753; Alston in Trimen, Handb. Fl. Ceylon 6: 231. 1931; MacMillan, Trop. Plant. & Gard., ed. 5, 192. 1943; Abeywick., Ceylon. J. Sci., Biol. Sci. 2: 217. 1959; Moldenke, Phytologia 8: 246–265, 382–383, & 405–407 (1962), 8: 463 & 9: 194 (1963), 10: 95 (1964), 11: 441–442 (1965), 13: 184–185 & 245 (1966), 14: 289 (1967), 15: 487–488 & 16: 184 (1968), 22: 474–479 & 23: 182, 216–217, 259, & 367 & 24: 20–21 & 216–217 (1972), 28: 114–116, 196, 242, & 346 (1974), & 30: 134–135. 1975; Gunawardena, Gen. Sp. Pl. Zeyl. 147. 1968. Type: Herb. Linnaeus *35/11* from Buenos Aires, Argentina (LINN).

Verbena bonariensis altissima, lavandulae canariensis spica multiplici Dill., Hort. Eltham. 406. 1732.
Verbena elongata Salisb., Prod. 71. 1796.
Verbena trichotoma Moench, Suppl. Meth. 131. 1802.
Verbena quadrangularis Vell., Fl. Flum. 16 (1825) and Ic. 1: pl. 39. 1827.—*V. quadrangularis* Arrab. ex Steud., Nom. Bot., ed. 2, 2: 750. 1841.
Verbena corymbosa Hort. ex Walp., Rep. 4: 19, in syn. 1845 [not *V. corymbosa* Cham., 1832, nor Relh., 1947, nor Ruíz & Pav., 1798].
Verbena bonariensis γ longibracteata Walp., Rep. 4: 20. 1845 [not *V. bonariensis* var. *longibracteata* Kuntze, 1898].
Verbena bonariensis Dill. ex Goncalves de Cunha & Goncalves Sobrinho, Revista Fac. Ci. Univ. Lisboa 3: 10 & 43. 1938 [not *V. bonariensis* Rendle, 1904, nor Schau., 1960].—*Berbena bonariensis* L. ex Moldenke, Alph. List Invalid Names Suppl. 1: 2, in syn. 1947.—*Verbena bonarriensis* L. ex Dhillon & Bajwa, Bull. Bot. Surv. India 11: 241, sphalm. 1969.—*V. bonaviensis* Farnsworth, Pharmacog. Titles 7 (10): xvi, sphalm. 1972.

Verbena hasta L. ex Moldenke, Alph. List Invalid Names Suppl. 1: 24, in syn. 1947.

Cymaria idjenensis Koord. ex Moldenke, Résumé 358, in syn. 1959.

Verbena bonariensis f. *umbrosa* Osten ex Moldenke, Résumé 359, in syn. 1959.

Verbena littoralis H. Betch. ex Moldenke, Résumé 368, in syn. 1959 [not *V. litoralis* Humb., 1829, nor Humb. & Bonpl., 1841, nor H.B.K., 1845, nor Humb. & Kunth, 1843, nor Kunth, 1847, nor L., 1913].

Coarse erect perennial or annual herb, 0.3–2 m tall, usually robust, deep-green throughout, often suffrutescent, sometimes in clumps 1 m wide, with a taproot; stems strict, sharply and conspicuously tetragonal, somewhat sca-brous-pubescent, hispidulous, or subvillous, especially on the angles, often 3-branched at the base, often rather naked above; leaves decussate-opposite, sessile, lanceolate or oblong-lanceolate, 4.5–13 cm long, 0.6–2 cm wide, the lower ones usually 9–13 cm long and 1–1.5 cm wide, all acute at the apex, cor-date and subauriculate to adnate-semiamplexicaul at the base, sharply and unequally serrate along the margins from below the middle or incised-serrate, entire toward the base, rugose and hirtellous above, spreading-pubescent beneath, particularly along the prominently reticulate veins, or hirsute and scabrous on both surfaces, venose, penninerved, the margins revolute; inflo-rescence paniculate, terminal, spicate, fastigiate; spikes many-flowered, com-pact and aggregated, mostly short, eventually cylindric, 4–10 in number, com-monly sessile or subsessile and crowded in dense fasciculate long-pedunculate clusters; bractlets lanceolate, acuminate at the apex, barely equalling or slight-ly surpassing the calyx, pubescent or hirtellous and ciliate, not glanduliferous; flowers very small or even minute; calyx about 3 mm long, pubescent, hispi-dulous on the angles, not glanduliferous, its lobes acute with short subulate tips; corolla varying from blue, bright-blue, reddish-blue, or blue-violet to vio-let, dark violet-purple, purple, bright purple, red-purple, rosy-violet, lavender, rose-lavender, lavender-pinkish, lilac, dark lilac, mauve, or even red, its tube scarcely twice the length of the calyx, pubescent on the outer surface, the limb small and inconspicuous, nearly regular; stamens didynamous, included; fruit splitting into 4 cylindric brown cocci included in the persistent calyx-tube, trigonous, about 2 mm long, mostly striate, slightly raised-reticulate at the apex, the dorsal side 3-striate, slightly cross-striate at one end, the commissur-al faces scarcely reaching the tip of the cocci, muricate-scabrous by being thickly set with strongly bulbous acute strigullae. Chromosome number: $x = 7$, $2n = 28$.

D i s t r. Originally native to the area from Brazil and Bolivia south through Paraguay and Uruguay to Argentina and west to Chile; introduced into and now rather widespread in other parts of South America, the United States, Bermuda, Jamaica, parts of Europe and Africa, tropical Asia, and Pacific Oceanica.

E c o l. In many areas it acts as an aggressive weed in cultivated and other-wise disturbed land. It occurs in cultivation as a specimen plant in many parts of the world and its seeds are offered in the horticultural trade. Its chief use is for mass-planting and cutting. MacMillan (1943) has reported it as natural-ized near up-country gardens in Ceylon.

U s e s. The plant is used in popular medicine in Argentina and in other localities it is a nectar-producing supply for honey-making. The honey is dark in colour, with a pronounced but pleasant flavour. In Brazil a decoction from its leaves is used in the treatment of intermittent fevers and catarrh. It con-tains an alkaloid.

V e r n. Among the 35 vernacular names recorded in various parts of its range are: Purple-top, South American vervain, and Tall verbena.

N o t e s. Its reproduction is often apomictic.

Verbena brasiliensis Vell., a closely related South American species which is now appearing in many of the areas where *V. bonariensis* has been introduc-ed, is to be expected in Ceylon. It differs in its leaves being narrowed to the base and sessile but not at all cordate-auriculate nor amplexicaul. The wide-spread and very variable European *V. officinalis* L., with very slender and much elongate spikes and variously lobed, incised, or 1- or 2-pinnatifid leaves, widespread in India, is also to be expected in Ceylon.

S p e c i m e n s E x a m i n e d. NUWARA ELIYA DISTRICT: Sita Eliya, 29 Aug. 1963, *Amaratunga 695* (PDA); close to vegetable cultivation, Ohiya, 2000 m alt., 1 Nov. 1971, *Balakrishnan NBK. 1038* (PDA, US); in cultivation, Hakgala, 23 Sept. 1897, *s. coll. s.n.* (PDA); common along borders of stream near milepost 55, Hakgala, on the Rendapola to Hakgala road, 2100 m alt., 29 Oct. 1971, *Cramer 3461* (PDA, US); in cultivation, Hakgala, 22 May 1911, *Silva s.n.* (PDA). LOCALITY UNKNOWN: *Silva 48* (NY).

2. Verbena rigida Spreng., Syst. Veg., Cur. Post, 4 (2): 230. 1827; Trimen, Handb. Fl. Ceylon 3: 349. 1895; Willis, Cat. 142. 1911; Alston in Trimen, Handb. Fl. Ceylon 6: 231. 1931; Abeywick., Ceylon J. Sci., Biol. Sci. 2: 217. 1959; Moldenke, Phytologia 11: 62–68 & 80–95 (1964), 11: 478 (1965), 13: 259–260 (1966), 14: 295 (1967), 16: 197–199 (1968), 24: 128–132 & 219–220 (1972), 28: 378–381 (1974), & 30: 167–168. 1975; Gunawardena, Gen. Sp. Pl. Zeyl. 147. 1968. Type: *Sellow s.n.* from Rio Grande do Sul, Brazil.

Verbena venosa Gill. & Hook., Bot. Misc. 1: 167. 1829.
Verbena scaberrima Cham., Linnaea 7: 267–269. 1832.
Verbena rugosa D. Don in Sweet, Brit. Fl. Gard. 7 [ser. 2, 4]: pl. 318. 1836 [not *V. rugosa* Michx., 1947, nor Mill., 1768, nor Muhl., 1809, nor Willd., 1947].—*V. rugosa* G. Don ex Steud., Nom. Bot., ed. 2, 2: 750, in syn. 1841. —*V. rugosa* Sweet apud Walp., Rep. 4: 27, in syn. 1845.—*V. rugosa* Hook. & Grew. ex Kunth, Ind. Sem. Hort. Berol. 7. 1845.

Verbena scabra Marnock, Floric. Mag. & Misc. Gard. 5: 87, pl. 54, fig. 3. 1840 [not *V. scabra* Gray, 1959, nor Muhl., 1825, nor Vahl, 1798].

Verbena doniana Steud., Nom. Bot., ed. 2, 2: 750. 1841.

Buchnera montevidensis Spreng. ex Walp., Rep. 4: 26, in syn. 1845.

Verbena bonariensis γ *rigida* (Spreng.) Kuntze, Rev. Gen. Pl. 3 (2): 255. 1898.

—*V. bonariensis* var. *rigida* Kuntze apud Briq., Annuaire Conserv. Jard. Bot. Genève 7–8: 291. 1904.

Verbena bonariensis f. *robustior* Chodat, Bull. Herb. Boissier, ser. 2, 2: 817. 1902.

Verbena bonariensis var. *venosa* (Gill. & Hook.) Chodat, Bull. Herb. Boissier, ser. 2, 2: 817. 1902.

Verbena bonariensis var. *venosa* f. *robustior* Chodat, Bull. Herb. Boissier, ser. 2, 2: 817. 1902.

Verbena venosa var. *parviflora* Thell. & Zimmerm. ex Hegi, Illustr. Fl. Mittel-Eur. 5 (3): 2240. 1927.

Verbena rigida (L.) Spreng. apud Small, Man. Southeast. Fl. 1138. 1933.

Verbena venusta Hort. ex Moldenke, Alph. List Invalid Names 51, in syn. 1942.

Verbena nervosa Link ex Moldenke, Alph. List Invalid Names Suppl. 1: 25, in syn. 1947 [not *V. nervosa* Scheele, 1843].

Stiff, tufted, rhizomatous or stoloniferous, scabrous-pubescent, perennial herb of erect-spreading habit, usually low, 15 cm to 1 m tall, forming wide spreading clumps, sometimes robust or suffrutescent, with an extensive underground root and rhizome system, the roots fleshy or tuberous, the rhizome creeping or procumbent; stems branched underground, the aerial floriferous ones simple or little branched, usually 2–6.5 dm tall, herbaceous, ascending or erect, decumbent or creeping at the base, acutely tetragonal, very scabrous-hirsutulous, scabrous-pubescent, or hirtous, abundantly foliose to the middle, about 3 mm in diameter at the base, the alternate sides sulcate; internodes sometimes greatly elongate; leaves decussate-opposite or approximate, rather dull pale green, sessile but not connate, remote, somewhat or very rigid, oblong to oblong-lanceolate or narrowly obovate, 7.5–10 cm long, 1–2.5 cm wide, subcuneate and entire at the base on the lower ones, more or less semi-amplexicaul or subcordate and adnate at the base on the upper ones, acute at the apex, unequally and coarsely subincised-serrate with spreading acuminate teeth, with somewhat revolute margins on older leaves, conspicuously venose, penninerved, scabrous and more or less hispidulous on both surfaces or callous-strigose above and rather shiny beneath and hispidulous only on the veins, lineate-rugose above, rough to the touch; midrib and veins impressed above, prominently reticulate beneath, the primary lateral ones excurrent into the teeth; spikes terminal, in 3's or decussately paniculate, disposed in subternate groups, short, sessile or the lateral ones pedunculate, fastigiate, usually dense-flowered and congested at first, eventually cylindric and elongating to 5 cm; foliaceous bracts usually present at the base of the peduncles, lanceolate or lanceolate-subulate, acute, entire; peduncles opposite, 3 or 4 pairs forming a sort of decussate panicle, 6–10 cm long; bractlets lanceolate, acuminate-subulate, usually closely imbricate and longer than the calyx, often 2–3 times as long as the calyx, purple when fresh, mostly glandular-pubescent, ciliate; flowers very showy and handsome en masse, blooming from below upwards in succession, imbricate, usually crowded in heads or spikes; calyx red or green, cylindric, shorter than the subtending bractlet and hidden by it, 4–6 mm long, 5-angled, glandular-pubescent or hirtous, its teeth 5, nearly equal, oblique, red, acute, with short mucronulate-subulate tips; corolla relatively large, mostly about 1 cm long, varying from purple or rose-purple to violet, rose-violet, blue-violet, or mauve, very lightly villosulous or pubescent on the outside, inflated toward the middle, the tube slender, 2–4 times as long as the calyx, curved, downy-pubescent on the upper part outside and within, mostly surpassing the calyx-teeth by 5–8 mm, white below where covered by the calyx, the limb 4–7 mm wide, composed of 5 broad, emarginate, almost bifid segments, the mouth slightly hairy; the 4 stamens inserted below the middle of the corolla-tube; filaments short, white; anthers ovate-lanceolate; style about half as long as the corolla-tube, glabrous, white below, purplish above; stigma subcapitate, with a spur at its base; ovary oval, glabrous; fruiting-calyx closely imbricate, dilated below the fruit; fruit separating into 4 oblong cocci, on one of which the style sometimes remains, and enveloped by the persistent calyx which may be closed at its mouth; cocci trigonous, slightly broader at the base than at the apex, scarcely 2 mm long, bright fuscous outside, raised-reticulate on the upper half, striate toward the base with 5 pairs of dorsal ridges, margined, the apex subareolate, the commissural surface white-leathery, muricately scabrous. Chromosome number : $x = 7$, $n = 21$, $2n = 42$.

D i s t r. Native from central Brazil south to northern Argentina; widely cultivated and naturalized in many parts of North, Central, and South America, the West Indies, Europe, South Africa, Micronesia, India, the Pacific Islands, and Australia. The lilac-flowered var. *lilacina* (Benary & Bodger) Moldenke is to be expected in Ceylon.

E c o l. Alston records the species from grassy places about Nuwara Eliya and Hakgala.

U s e s. *Verbena rigida* contains an irritant principle and is said to cause a form of dermatitis in people allergic to it. In Africa some natives use a decoction of the roots in the treatment of heartburn and colic. It has been suspected of causing sickness in domestic stock. The leaves and stems contain the enzyme, urease, and give a negative antibiotic test.

V e r n. Among some 25 names recorded in various parts of its range are:

hardy verbena, hardy garden verbena, hardy vervain, margarita, stiff verbena, and tuber verbena.

Specimens Examined. KANDY DISTRICT: in cultivation, Royal Botanic Garden, Peradeniya, Dec. 1887, *s. coll. s.n.* (PDA). NUWARA ELIYA DISTRICT: in outdoor cultivation, tending to spread, Farr Inn, Horton Plains, 7000 ft alt., 29 Jan. 1974, *H.N. & A.L. Moldenke, Jayasuriya, & Sumithraarachchi 28290* (LL, PDA, US). BADULLA DISTRICT: in open places at side of railroad track, 2400 m alt., Ohiya station, 12 Dec. 1971, *Balakrishnan NBK. 413* (NY, PDA, US); below Ohiya railroad station, probably escaped from cultivation, 18 May 1968, *Mueller-Dombois 68051848* (PDA, US).

3. Verbena hispida Ruíz & Pav., Fl. Peruv. & Chil. 1: 22–23, pl. 34a, fig. 1–5. 1798; Moldenke, Phytologia 9: 292–299 (1963), 10: 110 (1964), 11: 466 (1965), 13: 201 & 250 (1966), 14: 285–286 (1967), 16: 91–92 (1968), 23: 269–270 (1972), 28: 219–220 & 352–353 (1974), & 30: 148. 1975. Type: *Ruíz 1/34* from sandy soil along torrents, Huánuco, Peru (MA).

Verbena glandulosa Moris, Ann. Storia Nat. 4: 39. 1830.—*V. glandulosa* Morren.

Verbena cuneifolia Hort. ex Walp., Rep. 4: 22, in syn. 1845 [not *V. cuneifolia* Raf., 1808, nor Ruíz & Pav., 1798, nor Wallberg, 1959].

Verbena clandestina Mart. ex Moldenke, Alph. List Invalid Names Suppl. 1: 23, in syn. 1947.

Rough-hairy perennial herb, mostly 25–50 cm tall and decumbent or partially procumbent, rarely suffrutescent and to 1 m tall, greyish or yellowish in drying; stems 1 to many, erect or ascending, often rigid, sometimes trailing or decumbent at the base, sharply 4-angled, hispid, many-branched; branches usually rigid, the lower ones sometimes prostrate and closely appressed to the ground; leaves sessile, decussate-opposite, varying from oblong to ovate-lanceolate or lanceolate, 4–10 cm long, 1.5–2.5 cm wide, acute or acuminate at the apex, cuneate-attenuate to the cordate-clasping base, soft-textured, coarsely and unequally serrate or incised, sometimes trifid or subtrifid, lineate-rugose above, strigose-hispidulous on the venation on both surfaces and hirtellous-pubescent on the lamina beneath, the teeth acuminate, very variable in size and position; venation prominent beneath, the larger parts usually impressed above; spikes terminal, often ternate, very dense and crowded, long- or short-pedunculate, cylindric, 3–8 cm long, glandular-hispid or hirsute throughout; bractlets lanceolate, subulate at the apex, conspicuous, equalling or usually conspicuously surpassing the calyx, glandular-hispidulous; calyx 2–2.5 mm long, glandular-hispidulous, its teeth short, acute or subacute to subulate, hairy; corolla varying from blue or purplish-blue to purple, lilac, lavender, violet, or pinkish-mauve, its tube about twice as long as the calyx, the limb deeply

5-lobed, very small and inconspicuous, the interior of the throat and base of the tube sometimes white, the lobes emarginate; stamens 4; stigma bilobed, the upper lobe obtuse, the lower acute; fruiting-calyx including the fruit, ventricose; seeds 4, oblong, extrorsely convex, sulcate, slightly concave within. Chromosome number: 2n = 14.

D i s t r. Native to Andean Ecuador, Peru, Chile, Bolivia, and Argentina, but also found in Paraguay and Brazil; cultivated in many parts of the United States, Europe, Australia, and elsewhere.

U s e s. The plant contains stachyose and is sometimes used medicinally as a substitute for *V. officinalis* (which has been used medicinally since ancient times in Europe).

V e r n. bristly vervain, hairy vervain, hairy verbena, and several others in various parts of its range.

S p e c i m e n s   E x a m i n e d. NUWARA ELIYA DISTRICT: in cultivation, Hakgala Botanic Garden, Jan. 1888, *s. coll.s.n.* (PDA). BADULLA DISTRICT: in waste places, Haputale, 3 Jan. 1928, *Alston 1603* (PDA).

4. **Verbena monacensis** Moldenke, Phytologia 2: 148–149. 1946; Moldenke, Phytologia 10: 157–158 (1964), 23: 371 (1972), & 28: 257 & 356. 1974. Type: *Herb. Martius s.n.*, cultivated in Munich, Germany, in 1823 (BR).

Herb; stems usually prostrate, ascending toward the tips, branched, sharply tetragonal, brownish, lightly and irregularly pilose, less so in age; branches more sharply tetragonal, often almost submargined and more densely appressed-pubescent; nodes annulate; principal internodes 2–7 cm long; leaves decussate-opposite, often bearing abbreviated and very leafy branchlets in their axils; petioles to 1 cm long, usually much shorter, winged and almost indistinguishable from the rachis of the leaf-lamina, strigose on both surfaces; leaf-blades uniformly green on both surfaces, chartaceous, 2–3.5 cm long, 1–2 cm wide, deeply trifid, the divisions again incised, the individual lobes mostly obtuse at the apex and elliptic or oblanceolate in outline rather than linear or oblong, strigose on both surfaces, the margins slightly revolute, the midrib and secondaries slender, obscure above, prominulous beneath; inflorescence solitary at the end of each stem and branch, at first condensed, later elongating to 4 cm or more, densely many-flowered; peduncles slender, 1.5–6.5 cm long, densely strigose or appressed-pubescent, conspicuously tetragonal like the branches; bractlets lanceolate or short-triangular, about 6 mm long and 1 mm wide at the base, densely short-pubescent with subappressed whitish hairs, densely white ciliate along the margins, long-attenuate at the apex; calyx tubular, 8–9 mm long (including the teeth), strigillose with ascending or more or less appressed grey or sordid-whitish pubescence, 5-costate, its rim shortly 5-toothed, the teeth triangular and usually less than 1 mm long; corolla large, showy, salverform, rose-pink, its tube projecting about 5 mm beyond the calyx, glabrous outside, the limb about 1 cm wide, the lobes shallowly bilobulate at the apex; anther-appendages not exserted.

D i s t r. The species is known thus far only from cultivated material from European and Asian gardens. It is probable that much of the material in Indian literature identified as *V. bipinnatifida* Nutt. is actually *V. monacensis* which we have seen very commonly in Indian gardens.

V e r n. Munich verbena.

S p e c i m e n s E x a m i n e d. KANDY DISTRICT: in outdoor cultivation in the Medical Garden, Royal Botanic Garden, Peradeniya, 1550 ft alt., 18 Jan. 1974, *H.N. & A.L. Moldenke & Jayasuriya 28150* (US). PRECISE LOCALITY UNKNOWN: Dickpitiya, 23 Aug. 1958, *s. coll. s.n.* (PDA).

5. Verbena tenuisecta Briq., Annuaire Conserv. Jard. Bot. Genève 7–8 : 294–296. 1904; Moldenke, Phytologia 2: 167 (1948), 11: 280–287, 290–301, & 481 (1965), 13: 272–273 (1966), 14: 299 (1967), 16: 208–210 (1968), 24: 234–240 (1972), 28: 395–397 (1974), & 30: 172–173. 1975. Type: *Balansa 1025* from La Trinidad, Paraguay, 4 October 1875 (G).

Verbena dissecta Morong apud Briq., Annuaire Conserv. Jard. Bot. Genève 7–8: 294, in syn. 1904 [not *V. dissecta* Poepp., 1847, nor Schau., 1959, nor Spreng., 1959, nor Walp., 1849, nor Willd., 1825].
Glandularia tenuisecta (Briq.) Small, Man. Southeast. Fl. 1139 & 1508. 1933. —*Grandularia tenuisecta* (Briq.) Small ex Martínez Crovetto & Piccinini, Revista Invest. Agric. 4: 77, 181, & 225, sphalm. 1951.
Verbena tenera x *lanceolata* Kellogg ex Moldenke, Publ. Carnegie Inst. Wash. 522: 150, in syn. 1940.
Verbena ericoides Macself in Sanders, Enc. Gard., ed. 21, 457, in syn. 1931.— *V. ericoides* L. ex Roig, Dicc. Bot. 2: 1114. 1953.
Verbena arenicola Reade ex Moldenke, Résumé 357, in syn. 1959.
Verbena bipinnatifolia Wall. ex Moldenke, Résumé 358, in syn. 1959.
Verbena erinoides f. *glabrescens* Regnell ex Moldenke, Résumé 364, in syn. 1959.
Verbena moteana Hor. ex Moldenke, Résumé Suppl. 7: 9, in syn. 1963.

Annual or perennial herb, varying from prostrate and creeping or semi-creeping to procumbent or decumbent, 10–60 cm tall, sometimes of upright habit or suffrutescent at the base; stems usually decumbent, branched at the base, spreading and forming mats; branches mostly prostrate, ascending at the tips, divergent or bent, 20–55 cm long, rooting at the nodes, tetragonal, sparsely pilose with antrorse hairs, becoming glabrescent in age; principal internodes 1.5–3 cm long; vegetative parts aromatic-resinous; leaves decussate-opposite; leaf-blades triangular in outline, 2–3.5 cm long, 2–3 cm wide, green, tripartite-pinnatifid, substrigose above with appressed antrorse hairs, more densely so along the venation beneath, becoming glabrescent, the segments or laciniations all uniformly linear or narrowly linear, 1–3 mm long, entire or dentate, mostly less than 1 mm wide, obtuse (especially on the lower leaves) or sharply acute (especially on the upper leaves) at the apex, flat except for the revolute margins; inflorescence terminal, spicate, showy; spikes pedunculate, solitary, fastigiate, dense and short during anthesis, about 1.5 cm long, ovate-capitate, later elongating to 4 or more cm; flowers resinous-odorous, sessile, at first dense and ascending, later lax and spreading; bractlets subovate-lanceolate, 2–3 mm long, usually about 1/4 as long as the calyx, canescent-puberulent on the back; calyx long-tubular, 8–9 mm long, densely strigose or substrigose-canescent throughout with silvery-white, mostly closely antrorsely appressed hairs appearing as though combed, with a few scattered glands, its tube about 7 mm long, the teeth ovate, 1–2 mm long, filiform-setulose at the apex; corolla hypocrateriform, showy, varying from blue or bluish-purple to vivid purple, violet, magenta, or mauve, often with a minute white "eye", drying blue, the tube glabrous, exserted 3–5 mm from the mouth of the calyx, the limb about 10 mm wide, the lobes broadly obcordate, spreading, 3–4 mm long, 3–4 mm wide above the middle, emarginate to 1–1.5 mm at the apex, ciliate-pilose at the base within; stamens included; anther-connectives appendaged, the appendage glandular, scarcely exserted; style included, 1–1.3 cm long, surpassing the calyx, lasting one day; schizocarp oblong-linear, yellowish, 3–3.5 mm long, prominently reticulate-nervose or -scrobiculate above the middle. Chromosome number: 2n = 10.

D i s t r. This species is native to and very common in the area of southern Brazil, Uruguay, Argentina and Paraguay, extending north as far as Peru. It is extremely widely cultivated in practically all parts of the civilized world, mostly under other scientific names (such as *V. tenera*, *V. dissecta*, *V. erinoides*, etc.).

E c o l. In subtropical and warm temperate areas it tends to escape very rapidly and becomes naturalized along roadsides and in otherwise disturbed ground where it may produce a spectacularly beautiful display of colour.

V e r n. Among some 30 (mostly Spanish) common names is the trade name, Moss verbena.

N o t e. A white-flowered form (var. *alba* Moldenke) and a pink-flowered form (f. *rubella* Moldenke) are to be expected in Ceylon.

S p e c i m e n s E x a m i n e d. KANDY DISTRICT: in outdoor cultivation, Royal Botanic Garden, Peradeniya, 1550 ft alt., 21 Feb. 1938, *Y.W. de Silva 722* (PDA).

6. Verbena x hybrida Voss in Vilm., Fleure Pleine Terre, ed. 1, 936. 1863; Beale, J. Genet. 40: 337–358. 1940; Price & Scott-Moncrieff, J. Genet. 41: 65–74. 1940; Moldenke, Phytologia 9: 305–336 & 351–356 (1963), 11: 466 (1965),

13: 202–203 (1966), 16: 92–94 & 187–188 (1968), 23: 271–278 & 368–369 & 24: 22 & 218 (1972), 25: 220–221 & 28: 244–245 & 353 (1974), & 30: 148–151. 1975. Type: None designated; probably a cultivated plant in the Vilmorin-Andrieux garden in Paris.

Verbena buistii Harrison, Floric. Cab. & florist's Mag. 8: 160, hyponym. 1840.
Verbena hendersonii Hort. ex Harrison, Floric. Cab. & florist's Mag. 8: 160 & 184, hyponym. 1840.
Verbena teucrioides var. *anais* Lem., Hort. Universel 3: 9. 1842.
Verbena melindres latifolia Bohn, Florists' J. 5: 41. 1844.
Verbena hybrida grandiflora elegans Regel, Gartenflora 35: 668. 1887.
Verbena hortensis Vilm. in Vilm. Andr. & Cie, Fleure Pleine Terre, ed. 5, 1126. 1909.
Verbena hybrida Hort. ex Rümpler in Vilm., Illustr. Blumeng., ed. 2, 1045. 1879 [not *V. hybrida* Bicknell, 1941].—*V. hybrida* L. apud Rambo, Pesquisas Bot. 21: 58, sphalm. 1965.—*V. hybrida* Grönl. & Rpl. ex Backer & Bakh., Fl. Java 2: 596. 1965.—*V. hybrida* Vossler ex López-Palacios, Revista Fac. Farm. Univ. Los Andes 15: 89. 1975.
Verbena teucriodes x phlogiflora Voss in Vilm., Blumeng., ed. 3, 1: 827. 1895.
Verbena phlogiflora x coerulea Schwencke, Zytol. Untersuch. Verbenac. 15 & 27. 1931.
Verbena lindleyi Hort. ex Moldenke, Résumé 368, in syn. 1959.
Verbena grandiflora Bodger ex Harrow, J. Roy. Hort. Soc. 61: 399. 1936 [not *V. grandiflora* Michx., 1821, nor Ort., 1797, nor Sessé & Moc., 1889, nor Steud., 1895].
Glandularia hybrida (Vossl.) López-Palacios, Revista Fac. Farm. Univ. Los Andes 15: 89. 1975.

Perennial herb, usually treated as an annual in gardens in temperate climates, half-hardy in protected places, of spreading or compact [var. *compacta* Haage & Schmidt] growth, 15–45 cm tall when in bloom; stems mostly procumbent, trailing or creeping, or ascending in compact forms, sometimes forming perennial mats 1 m wide, slender, tetragonal, usually 30–60 cm long, occasionally to 1 m long, densely hirsute or villous; branches numerous, decumbent or ascending, slender, tetragonal, more or less densely soft-hirsute or villous with spreading hairs; nodes slightly annulate; principal internodes 1–5.5 cm long; leaves decussate-opposite, numerous; petioles slender, abbreviated, 2–7 mm long, densely hirsute with spreading white hairs, margined; leaf-blades chartaceous, usually thick-textured, rather uniformly dark-green on both surfaces or somewhat lighter beneath, often variegated with yellow (var. *variegata* Hort.), rarely entirely chlorotic (f. *chlorina* Winge), those at the tips of the branches smaller, all lanceolate or ovate, 1.3–8.3 cm long, 1–5.8 cm wide, acute at the apex, usually truncate or subtruncate at the base or cuneately narrowed into the petiole, irregularly incised-dentate from the apex to the

base with numerous acute and spreading, often lobe-like and doubly dentate
teeth, more or less densely soft-pubescent or hirsutulous on both surfaces with
rather coarse whitish hairs which are antrorsely strigose above and usually
spreading from the midrib and larger veins beneath; inflorescence terminal,
often large and showy (var. *grandiflora* Haage & Schmidt), varying from an extremely flat corymb to a very long spike (var. *multiflora* Putz), the floriferous
portion 4.5–6.5 cm long, 5.5–9 cm wide, 28–55 flowered; peduncles tetragonal,
3–10 (or more) cm long, densely white-hirsute or -villous like the branches;
spikes at first depressed and corymb- or fascicle-like, later elongating, very
densely many-flowered, the flowers closely imbricate and often more or less
fragrant; bractlets lanceolate, much shorter than the calyx, 5–6 mm long, attenuate at the apex, densely soft-pubescent with whitish hairs; calyx tubular,
0.8–1.5 cm long, 5-costate and 5-plicate, densely white-hirsutulous, its rim
varying from subtruncate and merely undulate to very shortly 5-apiculate;
corolla hypocrateriform, often very large and showy (var. *grandiflora* Haage &
Schmidt), varying from white (var. *alba* Haage & Schmidt) or cream-colour to
practically all shades of pink, rose, red, crimson, scarlet, yellow, maroon, light
vermillion, deep blue, or purple, uniformly coloured (var. *unicolor* Voss) or
more usually with a white, cream, or yellow "eye-spot" of varying diameter in
the centre of the limb (var. *auriculiflora* Hort.) and with or without a coloured
inner rim, sometimes with pink or red and white stripes (var. *striata* Hort.),
the tube 1.5–3 cm long, usually greenish or whitish, glabrous or obscurely
pilosulous on the outside, the limb 1–2.5 cm wide, the young flowers often
with a small white "eye" which is absent from or not so noticeable on older
flowers; anthers often not clearly appendaged; pollen often 38–78 per cent
aborted. Chromosome number: $x = 5$, $2n = 10, 20, 40$.

D i s t r. This is an extremely polymorphic hybrid and is planted for ornament practically throughout the civilized world. It tends to escape from or
persist after cultivation in warmer areas.

V e r n. Among the 50 or more names recorded in various parts of its
range are: Common verbena, Garden verbena.

N o t e. At least 175 scientific names have been proposed for the various
existing forms, in addition to over 400 horticultural names. The exact ancestry of the plant is not certain, but it is supposed to be a multiple hybrid of the
South American *V. platensis* Spreng., *V. phlogiflora* Cham., *V. incisa* Hook.,
and *V. peruviana* (L.) Britton. The first named "parent" is apparently the
source of the white corollas and fragrance seen in the white cultivars; the
second brought in the rosy and purple shades; and the last two are the source
of the red colours as well as the general leaf-shape and procumbent habit of
the plant. A very dwarf form for rock gardens is f. *nana* Beale.

S p e c i m e n s E x a m i n e d. NUWARA ELIYA DISTRICT: in outdoor cultivation at Farr Inn, Horton Plains, 7000 ft alt., 29 Jan. 1974, *H.N. &
A.L. Moldenke, Jayasuriya, & Sumithraarachchi 28291* (PDA, US).

2. LANTANA

L., Sp. Pl., ed. 1, 2: 626. 1753; L., Gen. Pl., ed. 5, 275. 1754. Type species: *Lantana trifolia* L.

Camara Plum., Nov. Pl. Amer. Gen. 21. 1703.—*Camara* L., Gen. Pl., ed. 5, 275, in syn. 1754.—*Camara* Fabr., Enum. Meth. 515, in syn. 1759.— *Kamara* Adans., Fam. Pl. 2: 12. 1763.—*Camara* Adans., Fam. Pl. 2: 199 & 530. 1763.
Myrobatindum Vaill. ex L., Meth. Sex. Gen. Pl. 135 & [293]. 1737.—*Myrobolindum* Vaill. ex L., Gen. Pl., ed. 1, 185 & [396]. 1737.—*Myrobatinium* Vaill. ex Adans., Fam. Pl. 2: 199, in syn. 1763.
Pseudo-viburnum Riv. ex L., Gen. Pl., ed. 1, 185 & [399], in syn. 1737.
Latana Robin, Voy. Louis. 3: 385. 1807.—*Lantuna* Chapm., Fl. South. U.S., ed. 1, 612, sphalm. 1860.—*Lanana* Hunt, Amer. Midl. Naturalist 37: 688, sphalm. 1947.—*Lanthana* Acosta Solis, Publ. Dept. Forest. Ecuador 7: 9, sphalm. 1949.—*Lautana* Briq. ex A. María, Pl. Valle Cochamb. 2: 41, sphalm. 1966.
Charachera Forsk. ex Bartl., Ord. Nat. Pl. 178. 1830.—*Carachera* Juss. ex Airy Shaw in Willis, Dict. ed. 7, 196, in syn. 1966.
Riedelia Cham., Linnaea 7: 240. 1832 [not *Riedelia* Meisn., 1863, nor Oliv., 1883, nor Trin., 1833].—*Riedelia* Schlecht. ex Lindl., Nat. Syst. Bot., ed. 2, 278. 1836.—*Ridelia* Spach, Hist. Nat. Vég. Phan. 9: 227, sphalm. 1840.
Sarcolippia Cham. ex Schau. in A. DC., Prod. 11: 594, in syn. 1847.
Tamonopsis Griseb., Abh. Königl. Ges. Wiss. Göttingen 19: 246. 1874.— *Tamanopsis* Griseb. apud Kuntze, Rev. Gen. Pl. 2: 504. 1891.

Erect herbs or shrubs, sometimes subscandent, scandent, or prostrate, usually more or less scabrous and hirtous-pubescent or tomentose with simple hairs; stems sometimes armed with thorns or prickles; leaves decussate-opposite or ternate (rarely quaternate), usually dentate or serrate, often rugose, often with a characteristic fragrance; inflorescense in dense cylindric spikes or contracted to form heads, usually axillary, pedunculate (sometimes shortly so), mostly quite showy; flowers sessile, borne in the axils of solitary, oblong or lanceolate to ovate, often apically acuminate, and spreading or subimbricate bractlets; calyx small, membranous, truncate and entire or sinuate-dentate; corolla hypocrateriform, red or yellow to purple, blue, or white, the tube narrow-cylindric, slender, equal in diameter throughout or slightly ampliate above, sometimes curvate, the limb spreading, regular or obscurely 2-lipped, 4- or 5-fid, the lobes broadly obtuse or retuse apically; stamens 4, didynamous, inserted at about the middle of the corolla-tube, included; anthers ovate, with parallel thecae; gynoecium 1-carpellary; ovary 2-loculate; ovules 1 per locule, basal and erect or attached laterally near the base of each locule; style usually short; stigma rather thick, oblique or sublateral; fruit drupaceous, the exocarp usually more or less fleshy when mature, rarely dry, the endocarp hard, 2-loculate or splitting into two 1-loculate pyrenes; seeds without endosperm. Chromosomes: $x = 8, 11$.

A complex genus of about 270 specific and subspecific entities, mostly natives of subtropical and tropical America; a few also in tropical Asia and Africa; several are widely cultivated under more than a hundred cultivar names. Interspecific and intervarietal hybridization is probably widespread in the genus; a few species tend to become aggressive weeds in disturbed areas. Many species give off a very characteristic strongly pungent odour.

KEY TO THE SPECIES AND VARIETIES

1 Inflorescences conspicuously elongate and cylindric-spiciform, at least after anthesis; leaves mostly ternate
  2 Corollas pink or lavender to lilac or purple..................**1. L. trifolia f. hirsuta**
  2 Corollas white...**L. trifolia f. albiflora**
1 Inflorescences capitate, not elongate-spiciform, flat or globose in age
  3 Outer bractlets much larger than the rest, broadly ovate, often 5 mm wide, very conspicuously involucrate
    4 Corollas bright magenta or lilac; leaf-blades merely strigillose-puberulent beneath; outer bracts not cordate at base; introduced....................**2. L. montevidensis**
    4 Corollas pink or white; leaf-blades densely white-woolly beneath; outer bracts often cordate at base; native...**3. L. indica**
  3 Outer bracts not much larger than the rest (if at all), narrow-lanceolate, usually only 1-2 mm wide, nor broadly ovate nor conspicuously involucrate
    5 Stems, branches, and branchlets usually more or less densely hispid-hirsute with stiff wide-spreading hairs.......................................**L. camara var. mista**
    5 Stems, branches, and at least the larger branchlets usually not hispid-hirsute
      6 All flower-clusters on a given plant exhibiting the same colour or colour changes
        7 Corollas all white.......................................**L. camara var. alba**
        7 Corollas not white
          8 Corollas mostly opening yellow, deep-yellow, yellow-orange, or orange and changing to orange, deep-orange, or orange-red; youngest parts of the twigs (only) usually temporarily white-hirsute...............**L. camara var. splendens**
          8 Corollas mostly opening yellow, turning to rose, rose-pink, or pink
            9 Branches and branchlets usually conspicuously spiny....**L. camara var. aculeata**
            9 Branches and branchlets usually practically unarmed..**4. L. camara var. camara**
      6 Flower-clusters exhibiting various colour changes in different parts of the same plant (probably a hybrid); some open yellow and remain yellow, others open yellow and change to pink, still others open pinkish-yellow and change to pink............
      ....**L. camara var. varia**

1. Lantana trifolia L.f. **hirsuta** Moldenke, Phytologia 3: 113. 1949; Thw., Enum. Pl. Zeyl. 242. 1861; Clarke in Hook. f., Fl. Br. Ind. 4: 563. 1885; Trimen, Handb. Fl. Ceylon 3: 346. 1895; Willis, Cat. 142. 1911; Alston in Trimen, Handb. Fl. Ceylon 6: 230. 1931; Alston, Kandy Fl. 63 & 64, fig. 341. 1938; Abeywick., Ceylon J. Sci., Biol. Sci. 2: 217. 1959; Gunawardena, Gen. Sp. Pl. Zeyl. 146. 1968; Fonseka & Vinasithamby, Prov. List Local Names Fl. Pl.

Ceylon 50 & 91. 1971; Moldenke in Woodson, Schery *et al.*, Ann. Missouri Bot. Gard. 60: 47, 49, 50, & 146. 1973; Moldenke, Phytologia 28: 436, 455, & 459. 1974; López-Palacios, Revista Fac. Farm. Univ. Los Andes 15: 44, 48, 50, 52, & 54. 1975. Type: *Cuatrecasas 14438* from Valle del Cauca, Colombia (NY).

Cordia microcephala Willd. in Roem. & Schult., Syst. Veg. 4: 801. 1819 [not *Lantana microcephala* A. Rich., 1850].

Lantana pittieri Moldenke, Phytologia 3: 269. 1950.

Perennial herb with woody underground stem or subshrub to 2.5 m tall; above-ground stems and branches spreading-hirsute or densely hirsute-pubescent, the hairs mostly rather stiff and divergent; leaves mostly ternate, usually thin-membranous, oblong-lanceolate to elliptic-lanceolate or ovate, petiolate, 5–12 cm long, acute or acuminate at the apex, crenate-serrate, attenuate basally and decurrent into the petiole, often reticulate-rugose above and scabrous or more or less strigose-pubescent, densely resinous-punctate and puberulent beneath, often fragile in drying; inflorescence spicate, subcapitate when young, later cylindric and elongating to 4.5 cm, densely many-flowered; spikes at first subglobose, 1–1.5 cm in diameter; peduncles slender, usually shorter than or subequalling the subtending leaves, 2–10.5 cm long, densely spreading-hirsute, solitary in each leaf-axil; bractlets herbaceous, green, lanceolate to ovate, the lowest or outermost to 10 mm long and 3 mm wide, cuspidate-acuminate apically, 5-veined, strigose above, loosely imbricate, the upper (or inner) with a cusp about equalling the corolla-tube; corolla pink or lavender to lilac or purple, the tube 5–6 mm long; drupes fleshy, purple or lavender, 2–3 mm in diameter. Chromosome number: 2n=48.

D i s t r. This is the hirsute form of the common West Indian *L. trifolia* L., which has the hairs on the stems, branches, petioles, and peduncles appressed-pubescent or strigose, not spreading-hirsute as in this form. The hirsute form occurs from Mexico and Cuba, through Central America and the West Indies, to Argentina, Bolivia, and Peru. It has been introduced in the Hawaiian Islands, Indonesia, Hong Kong, India, Burma, and elsewhere. In Ceylon Thwaites records it (as *L. trifolia* L.) as a roadside weed extremely common "in some parts of Uva, as near Badulla".

V e r n. Among the several dozen names recorded for the species in various parts of its range are: Cambara, Three-leaved lantana, Wild sage.

N o t e. A form with uniformly opposite, rather than ternate, leaves (f. *oppositifolia* Moldenke) is to be expected wherever the species is found.

S p e c i m e n s E x a m i n e d. KANDY DISTRICT: Asgiriya hill, 18 Jan. 1926, *Alston s.n.* (PDA); along railroad line on earth cutting, fairly common, Peradeniya, 8 Jan. 1968, *Cooray 68010801* (PDA); common roadside weed in clayey-limey soil on open embankment along the Lewella to Wattapuluwa road, about 530 m alt. 17 July 1975, perennial herb to 85 cm tall, corolla mauve with a yellow centre, *Cramer 4496* (NY, US); uncommon weed on University campus, Peradeniya, 10 Nov. 1970, *Fosberg 52705* (LL); on disturbed earth bank, hillside above town, Kandy, 1900 ft alt., 24 June 1972, *Hepper 4490* (PDA, US); along road by river, Gannoruwa, jungle, *Kostermans 24031* (US); locally abundant on moist earthen roadbanks in shade, Kandy, 2400 ft alt., 21 Jan. 1974, corollas pinkish-lavender, *H.N. & A.L. Moldenke, Jayasuriya, & Sumithraarachchi 28195* (PDA, US); on damp shaded roadbank on the Kandy to Annivatta road, 1600 ft alt., 30 Jan. 1974, *H.N. & A.L. Moldenke & Silva 28314* (LL, PDA, US); in shade on steep earthen road banks, scattered, Werellagama, 1400 ft alt., 22 Jan. 1974, *H.N. & A.L. Moldenke & Sumithraarachchi 28198* (AAU, ARIZ, CAI, KARACHI, LL, MO, PDA, UC, US); open places near road, Katugastota, 29 April 1953, *Senaratna 10100* (PDA); very scattered occurrence, Gannoruwa hill, 1700 ft alt. 21 Jan. 1974, flowers purple, *D.B. & D. Sumithraarachchi DBS. 24* (PDA, US). MATALE DISTRICT: Matale, 26 June 1965, *Amaratunga 902 A* (PDA); locally abundant on damp shady roadbank, Alawatugoda, 800 ft alt., 23 Jan. 1974, *H.N. & A.L. Moldenke & Jayasuriya 28203* (AAU, LL, PDA, US); common shrubs, Kandegedara, Wiltshire forest, 2 July 1975, leaves ternate, *Sumithraarachchi DBS. 387* (AAU, LACROSSE). BADULLA DISTRICT: in gravelly soil on open wild slope on way to falls from Diyaluma Estate, Diyaluma, about 200 m alt., 17 May 1975, common abundant herb 78 cm tall, corolla pale pink with a pale yellow centre, *Cramer 4487* (NY, US); common weed on roadside near stream along the Ella to Wellawaya road, about 850 m alt., 26 Jan. 1977, perennial herb, flowers pale mauve with a yellow eye, *Cramer 4835* (NY); roadside near Dowa temple, 24 April 1974, hirsute shrub, flowers purplish. *Sumithraarachchi & Waas DBS. 256* (LL, US). MONERAGALA DISTRICT: wayside bordering savanna between Medagama and Dambagalla, low altitude, 2 May 1975, shrub 1 m tall, heads uniformly pale pinkish-purple, *Jayasuriya 1986* (LL, US). MATARA DISTRICT: Dikwelle, Sept. 1890, *s. coll. s.n.* (PDA).

f. albiflora Moldenke, Phytologia 6: 327. 1958. Type: *Asplund 15821* from Zaruma, El Oro, Ecuador, collected 19 March 1955 (S).

This form differs from the previous form in having white corollas.

Alston in Trimen, Handb. Fl. Ceylon 6: 230. 1931 records this form from Ceylon, probably on the basis of the collection cited below. The form is to be expected throughout the range of the species and has been found already from Mexico to Ecuador.

Specimens Examined. MATALE DISTRICT: Matale, Sept. 1885, *s. coll. s.n.* (PDA).

2. Lantana montevidensis (Spreng.) Briq., Annuaire Conserv. Jard. Bot.

Genève 7–8: 301. 1904; Mart., Fl. Bras. 9: 261. 1851; Nair & Rehm., Bull.
Nat. Bot. Gard. Lucknow 76: 7. 1962; Brilmayer, All About Vines 278–279.
1962; Henderson, Contr. Queensland Herb. 3: 1–4. 1969; R. Bailey, Good
Housk. Ill. Encycl. 9: 1389. 1972. Type: *Sellow s.n.* from Montevideo, Uruguay, collected in 1822 (M. Orro herbarium).

Lippia montevidensis Spreng. in L., Syst., ed. 16, 2: 751. 1825.
Lantana sellowiana Link & Otto, Pl. Sel. Hort. Berol. 107, pl. 50. 1827.—*L.
selloana* Link & Otto ex Voss in Vilm., Blumengärt. 1: 824. 1895.—*L. callowiana* Stribling ex Mattoon, Pl. Buyers Guide, ed. 6, 167. 1958.—*L. callowiana* Monrovia ex Moldenke, Fifth Summ. 1: 364 & 2: 884. 1971.
Lippia megapotamica Spreng. in L., Syst., ed 16 [cur. Post], 4 (2): 231. 1827.
Lantana decumbens Sellow ex Schau. in Mart., Fl. Bras. 9: 261, in syn. 1851.
Lantana delicatissima Poit. ex Gonault, Rev. Hort., ser. 4, 1: 461. 1852.—*L.
delicatissima* Hort. ex Bailey, Man. Cult. Pl. 631, in syn. 1924.—*L. deleca-
tissima* Poit. ex Moldenke, Alph. List Invalid Names 28, in syn. 1942.—*L.
delicata* Hort. ex Moldenke, Alph. List Invalid Names Suppl. 1: 12, in syn.
1947.
Camara sellowiana (Link & Otto) Kuntze, Rev. Gen. Pl. 2: 504. 1891.
Camara montevidensis (Spreng.) Kuntze, Rev. Gen. Pl. 3 (2): 250. 1898.
Camara aculeata α *subinermis* f. *obtusifolia* Kuntze, Rev. Gen. Pl. 3 (2): 250.
1898.—*C. aculeata* f. *obtusifolia* Kuntze ex Moldenke, Lilloa 5: 416, in syn.
1940.
Lantana megapotamica Spreng. ex Moldenke, Suppl. List Invalid Names 4, in
syn. 1941.—*L. megapotamica* (Spreng.) Troncoso, Darwiniana 18: 326.
1974.
Lantana montevidiensis Mattoon, Pl. Buyers Guide, ed. 6, 167. 1958.—*L.
montividensis* Cav., Ind. Pl. Chromos. Numb. 2: 136. 1961.

Suffruticose herb or low shrub, rather unpleasantly aromatic-fragrant,
mostly lax in growth and producing long willowy shoots sometimes to 4 m
long, very variable, mostly a much-branched scrambler or climber, growing
from an underground xylopodium, sometimes to 1 m tall, at other times (in
areas subject to frequent burning) very dwarf and mat-forming with very short
but profusely flowered branches, much more luxuriant in more favourable and
protected areas; stems weak, often to 4 cm in diameter at the base; branches
lopping or trailing, often woody and vine-like, usually quite slender, the older
portions becoming very woody, often prostrate or creeping, rooting at the
nodes when these touch damp soil and sending up more branches from those
nodes, usually 15–45 cm long, without prickles, subterete, often virgately deflexed or decumbent, more or less strigose- or hirtous-pubescent, the pubescence spreading or appressed, soft or rough to touch; leaves decussate-opposite
or ternate, very variable in size and shape, resinous-punctate on both surfaces;
petioles short, usually about 4 mm long; leaf-blades ovate or subovate (the

larger ones) or subrhomboid-oblong or lanceolate (the smaller ones), mostly
1.2–3.5 cm long and 8–16 mm wide (on dwarf forms only 6 mm long and 3
mm wide!), paler beneath, subacute or obtuse apically, coarsely toothed, narrowed to the acute base or cuneate-attenuate into the petiole, lineate or
lineate-rugose and scabrous-pubescent or pilose-hirsute above, strigose on
the reticulation beneath, sometimes much more densely pubescent; inflorescence at first capitate and hemispheric, 2.5 or more cm wide, later elongating
and finally oblong in fruit; peduncles long, filiform, surpassing the subtending
leaves; bractlets thin-herbaceous, concave, ciliate, with deflexed margins apically, resinous-punctate, the outer ones broadly ovate or ovate-oblong, acuminate, not more than half as long as the corolla-tubes, subinvolucrate, the
outermost slightly larger, eventually spreading, strigose-hirtellous; flowers
sessile in the head, about 1.25 cm long; calyx about 2 mm long, obsoletely 4-
or 5-dentate, subvillous-pubescent, resinous-punctate; corolla infundibular,
slightly irregular, varying from pink, lilac, or lavender to violet, rose, purple,
or magenta, paler on the outside, the tube slender, about twice as long as the
subtending bractlets, 8–10 mm long, conspicuously exserted in anthesis, almost straight, slightly ampliate above, subvillous-pubescent, resinous-punctate, whitish below, the inner ones (younger ones) often with a white-edged
yellow "eye", the throat yellow, the limb spreading, about 6 mm wide, 4- or
5-lobed; drupes dark-violet, globose, about 4 mm long and wide, fleshy, half
enclosed by the hyaline fruiting-calyx; endocarp woody, 2-locular, splitting
into 2 halves septicidally, the septum-walls thin; seeds incrassate dorsally.
Chromosome numbers: for the sterile exclusively garden form, 2n (3x)=36;
for the fertile wild form now widely naturalized, 2n (4x)=48.

D i s t r. A native of the area from southern Brazil, through Uruguay,
and Paraguay, to Argentina; now very widely cultivated in almost all civilized
countries and tending to escape quickly and become naturalized in subtropical and tropical lands.

U s e s. *Lantana montevidensis* contains camphor, menthol, and bornyl
acetate. In South America it is employed in native medicine in the treatment
of broncho-pulmonary diseases, headaches, sunstroke, and fevers and is often
carried in amulets by the superstitious natives. It is very valuable as a screen
to cover piles of stones or other low objects, on walls, fences, and embankments, and in hanging baskets.

V e r n. Among some 20 recorded vernacular names are: polecat-gera-
nium, Trailing lantana, and Weeping lantana.

N o t e s. There is an as-yet unnamed very pubescent form and an especially large-flowered form; the rare white-flowered form is f. *albiflora*
Moldenke. The similar prostrate yellow- or orange-flowered "var. *aurea*"
Mattoon or "*L. callowiana* var. *aurea*" Mattoon seems to be a horticultural
development of the native Floridian *L. depressa* Small. It has been observed

in cultivation in urns and hanging baskets and window-boxes in Thailand and Pakistan and is to be expected in Ceylon.

The *"Verbena montevidensis* Spreng." cited by some authors as the basionym for *Lantana montevidensis* actually does *not* belong in its synonymy at all! Rather, it is a true and valid species of *Verbena* native to temperate South America and now appearing as an introduction in as diverse areas as the southern United States.

S p e c i m e n s E x a m i n e d. KANDY DISTRICT: in outdoor cultivation in the Rock Garden, Royal Botanic Garden, Peradeniya, 1550 ft alt., 18 Jan. 1974, *H.N. & A.L. Moldenke & Jayasuriya 28151* (US); locally very abundant on earthen roadcut banks, Hunnasgiriya, 1700 ft alt., 19 Jan. 1974, corollas rose-tinted lavender, *H.N. & A.L. Moldenke & Sumithraarachchi 28182* (AAU, ARIZ, CAI, KARACHI, LL, MO, PDA, UC, US); abundant roadside weed along edge of tea estate at Hunnasgiriya and the Kandy to Mahiyangane road, 2000 ft alt., 19 Jan. 1974, small plants, leaves small and more roundish, flowers purple, *Sumithraarachchi, A.L. & H.N. Moldenke, & Jayasuriya DBS. 17* (US). NUWARA ELIYA DISTRICT: cultivated as an ornamental hedge plant in compound of house, Yatiwalla, about 1300 m alt., 18 July 1975, perennial herb diffusely branched, corolla pale pink with a yellow centre, fading to white with age, *Cramer 4514* (NY).

3. Lantana indica Roxb., Hort. Beng., 46, hyponym. 1814; Roxb., Fl. Ind., ed. 1 [Carey & Wall.] 3: 89–90. 1832; Thw., Enum. Pl. Zeyl. 242. 1861; Trimen, Cat. 68. 1885; Clarke in Hook. f., Fl. Br. Ind. 4: 562. 1885; Trimen, Handb. Fl. Ceylon 3: 346. 1895; Willis, Cat. 68. 1911; Abeywick., Ceylon J. Sci., Biol. Sci. 2: 217. 1959; Gunawardena, Gen. Sp. Pl. Zeyl. 146. 1968. Type: *Wallich 1823/B*, cultivated in the Botanical Garden, Calcutta, from seed sent by Heyne from Mysore, India, East India Company herbarium (K).

Lantana collina Decaisne in Jacquem., Voy. Ind. 4 (Bot.): 136, pl. 141. 1836.
Lantana rubra Perr., Mém. Soc. Linn. Paris 3: 124. 1825.
Lantana radula Wight ex Wall., Num. List 87, no. 1823/D, hyponym. 1831 [not *L. radula* Baker, 1965, nor Gmel., 1947, nor Sw., 1788].
Lantana stricta Wight ex Wall., Num. List 87, no. 1823/D, hyponym. 1831 [not *L. stricta* Sw., 1788].
Lantana salvifolia Wight ex Wall., Num. List 87, no. 1823/D, hyponym. 1831 [not *L. salvifolia* Auct., 1962, nor DeWild., 1947, nor Jack, 1956, nor Jacq., 1798, nor L., 1759].
Lantana latifolia Tausch, Flora 19: 391. 1836.
Lantana trifolia f. *indica* Roxb. ex Voss in Vilm., Blumengärt 1: 824. 1895.
Lantana trifolia f. *indica rosea* Voss in Vilm., Blumengärt 1: 824. 1895.
Lantana alba Brandis, Indian Trees 502. 1906 [not *L. alba* L., 1947, nor Link,

1947, nor Mill., 1768, nor Mill. & Benth., 1971, nor Mill. ex Link, 1901, nor Schau., 1895].

Woody fast-growing shrub, 1–1.9 m tall, not prickly; branches long, rambling, tetragonal, appressedly scabrid-pubescent or (toward the tips) densely pubescent with fulvous and strigose or spreading hairs; leaves decussate-opposite or ternate, 2.5–7.5 cm long, 2.5–4 cm wide, mostly unequal; petioles about 6 mm long; leaf-blades ovate or lanceolate, generally acute (not rounded) apically, crenate-serrate, rugose and softly hairy above, more or less woolly beneath; inflorescences axillary, numerous; peduncles 2.5–7.5 cm long, usually 2 per node, usually equalling or shorter than the subtending leaves; heads ovoid, usually 1.5–2 cm wide, spicate and cylindric and sometimes 6–7.5 cm long in fruit; bractlets ovate or elliptic to lanceolate, 6–8 mm long, the lower (outer) ones involucrate, the upper (inner) ones smaller, acuminate apically, typically cordate basally, softly and loosely pubescent; flowers sessile; calyx less than 2 mm long, pubescent outside; corolla hypocrateriform, usually pink or pale-purple to dull-purple, about 8 mm long, hairy outside, the tube yellowish, the limb about 6 mm wide; drupes 3–8 mm in diameter, purple, enclosed by the thin transparent fruiting-calyx. Chromosome number: n = 11 [Cave], 2n = 22, 44 [Sahni], or 72 [Baghaven & Arora].

D i s t r. This is a very perplexing species, variously interpreted by different authors, a fact which probably explains the discrepancies in chromosome count reports by cytologists. It appears to be native to parts of Afghanistan, Pakistan, India, and Burma. Reports of its being in the Hawaiian Islands are erroneous, being based on palpable misidentifications.

U s e s. In India *L. indica* is believed by some country folk to "generate malarial fevers". Children often eat the fleshy fruits. In Assam it is sometimes used in the treatment of snakebites. Its ash is a fairly good source of potassium.

V e r n. In India it is known as Coffee-weed and in Burma as Tase-hnit-yathi.

N o t e s. A var. *albiflora* Wight [probably the "*Lantana alba* Mill." of Thwaites and of Trimen], with consistently white corollas and smaller leaves (only 5–19 mm long) which are obtuse and with outer bractlets which are only ovate and minutely appressed-pubescent, may or may not prove distinct.

The name, *L. indica*, has very often been misapplied by authors and collectors to material of *L. camara* L., *L. dubia* Wall., and *L. tiliaefolia* Cham. The *L. gochana* Buch.-Ham. [*L. gochana* Wall. or *L. goschana* Buch.-Ham.], often included in the synonymy of *L. indica*, seem, rather, to belong to that of *L. dubia* Wall. The true *Lantana alba* Mill., referred to above, actually is the basionym for *Lippia alba* (Mill.) N. E. Br.; *Lantana alba* Schau., *L. alba* Mill. & Benth., *L. leucantha* Hort., and *L. wightiana* Wall., names all sometimes regarded as being involved here, seem actually to belong to the synonymy of

L. indica var. *albiflora* Wight; *L. alba* Link and *L. alba* Mill. ex Link seem better placed in the synonymy of *L. rugosa* Thunb.; and *L. dubia* Royle is definitely *L. trifolia* L.

The plants with "yellow or orange flowers", referred to *L. indica* by some Indian authors, certainly must be *L. camara* or one of its varieties, and the same is true of the "aggressive weed threatening the teak plantations" identified by some Indian writers as *L. indica*, a species which appears to be very scattered in its distribution and probably even rare, certainly not aggressive. Material of *L. indica* has even been confused by some Indian authors with the West Indian *L. involucrata* L. and the Mexican *L. velutina* Mart. & Gal.

Specimens Examined. RATNAPURA DISTRICT: Galagawa, April 1856, *s. coll. C.P. 498* [G. Gardner coll.] (PDA).

4. **Lantana camara** L., Sp. Pl., ed. 1, 2: 627. 1753 var. **camara**. Schau. in Mart., Fl. Bras. 9: 256. 1851; Clarke in Hook. f., Fl. Br. Ind. 4: 562. 1885; Trimen, Handb. Fl. Ceylon 3: 346–347. 1895; Gamble, Man. Indian. Timb. 524. 1902; Cooke, Fl. Pres. Bombay, ed. 1, 3: 419. 1905; Brandis, Indian Trees 502. 1906; Petch, Indian J. Bot. 2: 302–306. 1921; Turbet, Agric. J. (Suva) 2: 34. 1929; West & Emmel, Univ. Florida Agr. Exp. Sta. Bull. 468: 21–24. 1950; Connor & Adams, Poison. Pl. N. Zealand 105–106, fig. 35. 1951; Lampe & Fagerström, Pl. Toxicity & Dermat. 172–174, fig. 57. 1968; Mueller-Dombois & Perera, Ceylon J. Sci., Biol. Sci. 9: 14. 1971; Ahmed, Shoaib, Wassel & El-Sayyad, Pl. Medic. 21: 282–288. 1972; Thaman, Micronesica 10: 17–39. 1974; Vivekanandan, Sri Lanka Forester, ser. 2, 11: 99, 123, 127, & 128. 1974. Type: *Herb. Linnaeus 783/4*, probably collected from cultivated material in the University garden at Uppsala, Sweden (LINN).

Lantana mutabilis Weigel, Physiogr. Sälsk. Handl. 1: 46. 1776.
Lantana scabrida Soland. in Ait., Hort. Kew, ed. 1, 2: 352. 1789.
Lantana antillana Raf., Sylv. Tellur. 82. 1838.
Camara vulgaris Benth., Bot. Voy. Sulphur 154. 1846.
Lantana mexicana Turner, Flor. Kingd. 181. 1876.
Camara aculeata var. *subinermis* Kuntze, Rev. Gen. Pl. 1: 503. 1891.
Lantana viburnoides Blanco ex Liu, Ill. Nat. & Introd. Lign. Pl. Taiwan 2: 1223. 1962 [not *L. viburnoides* Baker, 1942, nor Schau., 1902, nor Vahl, 1851, nor (Forsk.) Vahl, 1790].

Branching shrub, to 3 m tall; stems and branches mostly unarmed or only slightly prickly, usually minutely and inconspicuously pubescent; leaves decussate-opposite; petioles 7–12 mm long; leaf-blades chartaceous, ovate to oblong-ovate, 2–12 cm long, 2–4.5 cm wide, acute or short-acuminate (rarely obtuse) apically, crenate-serrate, acutely narrowed or abruptly rounded to a subcuneiform cuneation basally, more or less reticulate-rugose and decidedly scabrous or scabrellous above, usually only sparsely pilosulous or strigillose beneath (mostly only on the venation) with canescent or brownish hairs, sometimes glabrescent; inflorescence axillary, varying from shorter than or equalling to surpassing the subtending leaves; heads always capitate, hemispheric, to 3 cm wide, not elongating after anthesis, many-flowered; peduncles slender, 2–9 cm long, more or less appressed-pilose or puberulent; bractlets usually not conspicuous, not plainly involucrate, oblong or lanceolate, mostly equal, 4–7 mm long, 1–1.5 mm wide, subulate or acute apically, rarely a few larger ones also present, appressed strigose-pubescent, usually about as long as the corolla-tube; calyx small, inconspicuous, about 3 mm long, thin-textured; corolla hypocrateriform, mostly opening yellow and turning to rose, rose-pink, or pink, sometimes orange or orange-yellow to red or scarlet in age, the tube about 10 mm long, barely enlarged above the middle, slightly curved, puberulent, the limb 6–8 mm wide; drupes fleshy, purple or black, about 3 mm in diameter. Chromosome numbers: 2n=22, 32, 33, 44, or 66 [Natajan & Ahuja].

D i s t r. A very variable and much misinterpreted species, the typical form probably native to the West Indies, now widely distributed in subtropical and tropical America from Florida, through the West Indies and South America to Argentina, Bolivia, and Peru; less common in Central America; introduced and naturalized in many other warmer parts of the world.

U s e s. The powdered roots in milk are given to children in the treatment of colic and stomach-ache; an infusion of the whole plant is used in treating catarrh and bronchitis. A leaf-decoction is used in treating constipation, as a febrifuge, and as a diaphoretic, externally for ophthalmia and festering sores, and in baths and hot fomentations for dropsy. In Colombia it is used as an emenagogue and diaphoretic and in Brazil in baths as an anti-rheumatic.

A quinine-like alkaloid, lantanine, occurs in this plant and is used medicinally as an antispasmodic. A toxic substance, lantadene, causes "pink-nose", a photo-sensitivity disease in cattle and sheep. It also contains myristic, palmitic, arachidic, and linoleic acids, α-amyrin, β-sitosterol, and 1-triacontanol, as well as the carbohydrates glucose, maltose, and rhamnose, and the essential oils α-phellandrene, dipentene, α-terpeneol, geraniol, linaleol, cineol, eugenol, citral, furfural, and phellandrone.

V e r n. Of more than 150 names used in various parts of its range are: Camará, Cinco negritos, English sagebush, Red sagebush, Tres colores, Wild sage, and yellow sage.

N o t e s. Sahni claims that only the chromosome count of 2n=33 applies to the true L. camara var. camara, 22 applies to var. alba, 44 to L. indica, and 66 to L. trifolia. Obviously, the cytological work will have to be repeated on more carefully identified (and preserved!) material.

The variety obviously hybridizes readily with other varieties and other related species when these grow in proximity, so intermediate and puzzling forms are very common.

The name, *L. camara*, has been so loosely applied by collectors and authors to so many diverse species that much of the recorded information in botanical, horticultural, ecological, medical, pharmaceutical, and anthropological literature is completely unreliable, much of it probably incorrect, unless it can be verified by consultation of preserved herbarium voucher specimens.

S p e c i m e n s E x a m i n e d. KANDY DISTRICT: in waste area of grass, shrubs and herbs on old rubber estate, soil red-brown sandy loam, University grounds, Peradeniya, 504 m alt., 16 Oct. 1967, *Comanor 477* (LL, PDA); in outdoor cultivation in Students' Garden, Royal Botanic Garden, Peradeniya, 1550 ft alt., 18 Jan. 1974, corolla opening yellow with a deep-yellow eye, turning to rose-pink with an orange eye, buds coral-red, *H.N. & A.L. Moldenke & Jayasuriya 28159* (LL, PDA, US). KEGALLE DISTRICT: common along roadside fencerows, Karawanella, 12 Feb. 1974, flowers open yellow, turning pink, low altitude, *H.N. & A.L. Moldenke, Dassanayake, & Jayasuriya 28334* (AAU, ARIZ, CAI, KARACHI, LL, MO, PDA, US). TRINCOMALEE DISTRICT: in sand along margin of inlet among low woody coastal vegetation on the north side of the inlet at milepost 13 north of Trincomalee along the road to Mullaittivu, 1 m alt., 13 Oct. 1974, shrub 3 m tall, flowers carmine-red, *Davidse 7543* (LL, US). HAMBANTOTA DISTRICT: in discontinuous scrub in a brown loamy-sand soil, Block I, Ruhuna National Park, on the road to Patanagala Beach, about 3 m alt. 30 Nov. 1967, long-stemmed shrub, arching to 3 m, abundant, flowers yellow-orange and red orange, pollen collected, *Comanor 611* (AAU, US); Ruhuna National Park, Block I, Rakinawala, Plot R 33, 22 Oct. 1968, *Cooray 68102215R* (LL, PDA); Patanagala, Ruhuna National Park, 16 Nov. 1969, shrub 2 m tall, flowers orange in colour, fruits green when young, black when ripe, edible, common, *Cooray 69111634R* (AAU, PDA, US).

var. **alba** Moldenke, Phytologia 5: 132. 1955; Moldenke, Phytologia 28: 438, 445, & 450. 1974. Type: *V.M. Sahni s.n.* from cultivated material at Kharacpur, West Bengal, India (Moldenke herbarium).

Camara aculeata var. *subinermis* f. *nivea* Kuntze, Rev. Gen. Pl. 2: 503. 1891 [not *C. aculeata* var. *normalis* f. *nivea* Kuntze, 1891, nor *L. nivea* Vent., 1803].
Lantana mehraii Sahni ex Moldenke, Résumé 306, in syn. 1959.
Lantana mehraii var. *alba* Sahni ex Moldenke, Résumé 306, in syn. 1959.

This variety differs from the typical form of the species in having its corollas white in bud, opening with the tubes yellow, a yellow "eye", and the limb white, in age completely white, the inner (younger) flowers often showing the yellow tubes while the outer (older) ones are already completely white. The stems and branches are usually unarmed or with only minute prickles. The leaves are usually narrower than in the other varieties, often elongate-lanceolate. Chromosome number: 2n = 22 [Sahni].

V e r n. White lantana.

N o t e. This plant is very often confused with and identified as *L. nivea* Vent. or *L. camara* var. *nivea* (Vent.) Bailey, but that variety is most distinct in having its stems and branches very copiously and viciously armed with very stout strongly hooked prickles.

S p e c i m e n s E x a m i n e d. ANURADHAPURA DISTRICT: locally common in roadside hedgerows and fencerows at turnoff to Wilpattu, 24 Jan. 1974, low altitude, flowers open white with a yellow eye, turning completely white, no large thorns, *H.N. & A.L. Moldenke & Jayasuriya 28233* (AAU, LL, PDA, US). KANDY DISTRICT: Royal Botanic Garden, Peradeniya, March 1887, *s. coll. s.n.* (PDA); in outdoor cultivation, Students' Garden, Royal Botanic Garden, Peradeniya, 1550 ft alt., 29 Jan. 1974, shrub, flowers open white with a yellow eye, turning completely white, no spines, *H.N. & A.L. Moldenke & Jayasuriya 28173* (LL, PDA, US). MATALE DISTRICT: abundant shrubs in roadside hedgerows, Palapatwela, 600 ft alt., 23 Jan. 1974, flowers open white with a yellow eye, turning completely white, no large spines, *H.N. & A.L. Moldenke & Jayasuriya 28207* (AAU, ARIZ, CAI, LL, MO, PDA, US). KEGALLE DISTRICT: small colony in roadside shrubbery and fencerows, Kegalle, 600 ft alt., 12 Feb. 1974, corollas white, *H.N. & A.L. Moldenke, Dassanayake & Jayasuriya 28347* (AAU, ARIZ, CAI, KARACHI, LL, PDA, US).

var. **splendens** (Medic.) Moldenke, Phytologia 33: 130. 1976; Medic., Hist. & Commentat. Acad. Elect. Sci. Theod.-Palat. 3: 226–227. 1775; Clarke in Hook. f., Fl. Br. Ind. 4: 563. 1885. Type: *Dillenius s.n.* from James Sherard's garden at Eltham, England (OXF).

Lantana splendens Medic., Hist. & Commentat. Acad. Elect. Sci. Theod.-Palat. 3: 226–227. 1775.

Lantana crenulata Otto & Dietr., Allg. Gartenzeitung 9: 363. 1841.

This variety differs from the other varieties of this species in its corollas mostly opening yellow, deep-yellow, yellow-orange, or orange and changing to orange, deep-orange, or orange-red and the youngest parts of the twigs (only) usually temporarily white-hirsute.

It appears to be a native of the tropical and subtropical parts of America from Florida and the Bahama Islands, through the West Indies and Central America, to various parts of South America and has been widely introduced elsewhere in the world where it often escapes and becomes naturalized.

Material has been most widely confused with var. *camara* and especially with var. *mista* (L.) Bailey; in the latter the older branchlets, branches, and

224   VERBENACEAE

stems are more or less scattered-hispid and the corollas open yellow and change to purple; in the former there are no bristly hairs anywhere and the corollas are usually finally pink or red.

In Ceylon this appears to be the commonest and most widespread form of the species.

Specimens Examined. KURUNEGALA DISTRICT: common along hedgerows and fencerows, Panirendawa, 25 Jan. 1974, flower-buds red, opening orange, turning orange-red, shrubs at edge of jungle, *H.N. & A.L. Moldenke & Jayasuriya 28253* (LL, PDA, US). PUTTALAM DISTRICT: scattered in sandy field at sea level, Puttalam lagoon, 25 Jan. 1974, shrubs, flowers opening orange, turning orange-red, *H.N. & A.L. Moldenke & Jayasuriya 28248* (AAU, LL, PDA, US). ANURADHAPURA DISTRICT: very common on trunk road A-12 at milepost 54/2 about 4 miles east of Anuradhapura, outskirts of Mihintale, 200–300 m alt., 1 May 1970, heads of orange and yellow flowers, *Gould & Cooray 13639* (US); abundant along roadside hedgerows 4 miles south of Wilpattu, low altitude, 24 Jan. 1974, sprawling shrubs with widespreading branches, flower-buds orange-red, opening yellow-orange, turning deep-orange, *H.N. & A.L. Moldenke & Jayasuriya 28232* (AAU, ARIZ, CAI, KARACHI, LL, MO, PDA, US). COLOMBO DISTRICT: very common in Colombo district, Dewalapola, 31 Oct. 1969, *Amaratunga 1936* (PDA); abundant in waste ground along roadside on the Peliyagoda to Negombo road, low altitude, 15 Jan. 1974, low spreading shrubs, 2 ft tall, the branches 5 ft long, flowers open deep yellow, turning orange, *H.N. & A.L. Moldenke & Jayasuriya 28116* (AAU, ARIZ, CAI, KARACHI, LL, MO, PDA, US); abundant along roadside in hedgerows and fencerows, Madampella, 16 Jan. 1974, buds deep orange, opening light orange, turning deep orange, *H.N. & A.L. Moldenke, Jayasuriya & Sumithraarachchi 28123* (AAU, ARIZ, CAI, KARACHI, LL, PDA, US). KANDY DISTRICT: abundant along roadsides and fencerows, Haragama, 1500 ft alt., 19 Jan. 1974, flower-buds red, opening and remaining deep orange, *H.N. & A.L. Moldenke, Jayasuriya & Sumithraarachchi 28178* (AAU, ARIZ, CAI, KARACHI, LL, MO, PDA, US); common along roadsides and fencerows at milepost 18/14 south of Kandy and the Nuwara Eliya road, 2000 ft alt., 30 Jan. 1974, flower-buds coral-red, opening yellow-orange, turning deep orange, in roadside shrubbery, *H.N. & A.L. Moldenke, Jayasuriya & Sumithraarachchi 28313* (AAU, ARIZ, CAI, KARACHI, LL, MO, PDA, US); in dry patana above University Circuit Bungalow, Peradeniya, 1000 m alt., 9 Nov. 1967, scattered among *Cymbopogon* and *Themeda* grass cover, only 70 cm tall, collected as voucher for ecological studies, *Mueller-Dombois 67110910* (US). MATALE DISTRICT: abundant along roadsides and hedgerows, Alawatugoda, 800 ft alt., 23 Jan. 1974, flower-buds red, opening light-orange, turning deep-orange, *H.N. & A.L. Moldenke & Jayasuriya 28202* (AAU, LL,

PDA, US). NUWARA ELIYA DISTRICT: common along roadsides and hedgerows at milepost 26/10 beyond Pusselawa, 3200 ft alt., 28 Jan. 1974, flower-buds red, opening orange and remaining orange, stems hairy, prickly, and reddish, hybrid?, *H.N. & A.L. Moldenke, Jayasuriya, & Sumithraarachchi 28261* (AAU, ARIZ, CAI, KARACHI, LL, MO, PDA, US); at milepost 29/4, flower-buds red, opening and remaining orange, *28262* (AAU, LL, PDA, US). KEGALLE DISTRICT: abundant along roadside fencerows, no other variety present, Kalugahatenna, 500 ft alt., 12 Feb. 1974, all plants uniform in flower colour for many miles of roadside, corollas opening orange, turning orange-red, *H.N. & A.L. Moldenke, Dassanayake, & Jayasuriya 28331* (AAU, CAI, KARACHI, LL, PDA, US). RATNAPURA DISTRICT: scattered along roadside fencerows, low altitude, Ratnapura, 12 Feb. 1974, corollas opening yellow, turning orange, all uniform on many plants, *H.N. & A.L. Moldenke, Dassanayake, & Jayasuriya 28338* (ARIZ, PDA, US). TRINCO-MALEE DISTRICT: in dry zone near coast forest, broken canopy, soil light, not common in this habitat, Irrakkakandi, 3–4 m alt., 15 Jan. 1968, *Comanor 800* (AAU, PDA). HAMBANTOTA DISTRICT: common in tall semi-open scrub, Patanagala, Ruhuna National Park, 1–2 m alt., 6 April 1968, shrub 2 m tall, sparsely branched, flowers yellow, turning scarlet, *Fosberg 50375* (US), *50376* (PDA, US). AMPARAI DISTRICT: member of thicket surrounding large rock outcrop area, southeast corner on dry land, Lahugula tank, 36 m alt., 25 July 1967, voucher for ecological observations, *Mueller-Dombois & Comanor 67072541* (US).

var. **aculeata** (L.) Moldenke, Torreya 34: 9. 1934; Thw., Enum. Pl. Zeyl. 242. 1861; Clarke in Hook. f., Fl. Br. Ind. 4: 562. 1885; Trimen, Handb. Fl. Ceylon 3: 346. 1895; Gamble, Man. Indian Timb. 524. 1902; Brandis, Indian Trees 502. 1906; Willis, Cat. 142. 1911; Petch, Indian J. Bot. 2: 302–306. 1921; Alston in Trimen, Handb. Fl. Ceylon 6: 229 & 230. 1931; Alston, Kandy Fl. 63 & 64, fig. 340. 1938; MacMillan, Trop. Plant. & Gard., ed. 5, 450. 1943; Abeywick., Ceylon J. Sci., Biol. Sci. 2: 217. 1959; Sastri, Wealth India 6: 31–34. 1962; Gaussen, Viart, Legris & Labroue, Trav. Sect. Scient. Techn. Inst. Franç. Pond. Hors 5: 35. 1965; Burkill, Dict. Econ. Prod. Malay Penins. 2: 337–339. 1966; Gunawardena, Gen. Sp. Pl. Zeyl. 146. 1968; Fonseka & Vinasithamby, Prov. List Local Names Fl. Pl. Ceylon 14, 24, 49, 50, 78, & 92. 1971; Moldenke in Woodson, Schery, *et al.*, Ann. Missouri Bot. Gard. 60: 58. 1973; Sultanbawa, Weerasekara & Balasubramaniam, Gloss. Sinhala & Tamil Names 1974. Type: *Herb. Linnaeus 786/6* cultivated at the University of Uppsala Botanical Garden (LINN).

Viburnum americanum odoratum, urticae foliis latioribus, spinosum, floribus miniatis Plukenet, Alm. 285, pl. 223. fig. 5. 1696.
Myrobatindum viburnifolium spinosum, floribus coccineis Vaill., Act. 276. 1722.

Lantana aculeata L., Sp. Pl., ed. 1, 2: 627. 1753.—*L. aculeata* Ait. in Presl,
Wseobecny Rostlinop. 2: 1202. 1846.—*Lanthana aculeata* Farnsworth,
Pharmacog. Titles 5 (4): vii. 1970.
Camara aculeata (L.) Kuntze, Rev. Gen. Pl. 1: 503. 1891.
Camara aculeata var. *normalis* Kuntze, Rev. Gen. Pl. 1: 503. 1891.
Lantana aculeata ssp. *normalis* Voss in Vilm., Blumengärt. 1: 873. 1895.
Lantana spinosa L. ex LeCointe, Amaz. Bras. III Arvor. & Pl. Uteis 83. 1934.
Lantana camara Auct. ex Santapau, Pl. Saurashtra 31, in syn. 1953 [not *L.
camara* L., 1753].—*L. camara* Griseb. ex Moldenke, Résumé 303, in syn.
1959.
Lantana camara aculeata L. ex Raju, Trop. Ecol. 7: 121. 1966.

This variety differs from the typical form of the species in usually having
its stems, branches, and branchlets conspicuously armed with rather stout and
recurved prickles, being more generally half-climbing in habit or even completely scandent to 12 m, and the corollas generally opening yellow or orange
and turning to rose, rose-pink, or pink. Chromosome number: 2n=44.

D i s t r. The variety, whose nomenclatural history extends back at least as
far as 1696, is probably originally native to the West Indies, but is now very
widely distributed in practically all the subtropical and tropical regions of the
earth. It is by far the most common form of the species. Because of its very
aggressive nature, it has become a most troublesome "weed" in the Hawaiian
Islands, Australia, India, and elsewhere, leading to some of its common
names. Vast sums of money have been expended in eradication attempts and
the literature on this subject is large (with the plant mostly identified merely
as *L. camara*). Entomologists have searched the tropics to find insect enemies
that might be introduced to combat it.

In some parts of the West Indies, at least, this variety is quite distinct
from the other varieties, not only in the colour of its flowers, but in its habit
and even in its habitat; elsewhere many intermediate forms are found which
probably represent hybrids. It has been cultivated for ornament in Europe as
early as 1692. In Italy it has been trained to grow as a tree and may attain a
height of 8 metres, with a trunk diameter of 10–12 cm at the base.

E c o l. According to MacMillan it is "Perhaps the most familiar plant in
Ceylon, introduced about 1826 as an ornamental plant" and growing there as
"a weed in waste and neglected ground only", especially in semi-dry districts,
to altitudes of up to 5000 feet.

U s e s. The strong characteristic smell of the plant is due to a volatile oil
containing a sesquiterpene (probably caryophyllene), 1-α-phellandrene, alde-
hydes, and alcohols, which has been distilled experimentally in several
laboratories but is not commercial. The smell is somewhat like that of sage,
but is not exactly pleasant; it varies considerably with the age of the leaves
and possibly other factors.

Although this plant is usually regarded as a pest it may prove beneficial under certain conditions in forests. It improves the fertility of exhausted areas and of rocky, gravel, or hard laterite soils. It enriches the soil and serves to retain humus in deforested areas and checks soil erosion. It may serve as a nurse plant for sandalwood seedlings if not too dense and in the Pacific islands is used as support for yam vines. In India the leaves and twigs are often used as green manure (mulch) in forest areas and for paddy crops; they can also be composted along with other materials. Lantana ash is rich in soluble potassium salts and manganese and is useful for manuring coconut trees. The entire plant is bitter because of an active principle called "lantanin". In Brazil it is used as a tonic and sudorific. The leaves are sometimes used in India as a substitute for tea; the fermented leaves give off a mild not unpleasant odour and yield an inferior beverage. The leaves contain a powerful oxidase, as well as a catalase, amylase, invertase, lipase, tannase, and glucosidase; also some tannins, sugar, and a resin containing a crystalline glucoside. The leaves, however, also contain a toxic principle, lantadene A, which causes acute photosensitization and severe icterus in sheep. They also contain lantadene B and a steroid, lantamarone, which is a fish poison and is cardioactive. The bark of the stems and roots contains a quinine-like alkaloid, lantanine, with strong antipyretic and antispasmodic properties. Acid extracts from the shoots exhibit antibacterial activity.

The plant is not readily eaten by cattle, but may be browsed when pasturage is very scarce and may then result in symptoms of severe jaundice, exfoliation of the skin near the muzzle, profuse salivation, severe dermatitis, copious lachrymation, and loss of appetite in the cattle.

The ripe fruits are eaten by childern in many lands and can be employed as a flavouring. The stems are used as a toothbrush and the leaves for polishing wood. In Guyana and Réunion the plant is considered to be a vulnerary, diaphoretic, carminative, and antispasmodic. It is used in the treatment of fistulas, pustules, and tumors. A decoction is given in tetanus, rheumatism, malaria, and atony of the visceral muscles. In the Philippines a decoction of the fresh roots is used as a gargle for toothache. In Tanzania the leaves, soaked in water, are employed against fevers in cattle and the leaves pounded into a paste are used in the treatment of stomach-ache. In Malaya and Java the paste is applied to cuts, ulcers, and swellings, and a decoction of the leaves and fruits as a lotion on wounds. A leaf infusion is taken internally against bilious fevers and catarrhal afflictions. Externally it is used as a lotion or fomentation in treating eczema and rheumatism. An infusion of the flowers is used as a pectoral for children. The stems have been tried in India as raw material for paper pulp suitable for wrapping-paper, cardboard, and even printing and writing paper. In Java a decoction of the leaves acts as an emetic. It will grow through the pestiferous "lalang" and suppress it.

V e r n. Ganda-pana, Garda-pana, Genda-pana, Katu-hinguru, Rata-hinguru, Ton-kinna (S); also over 150 other names in various parts of its range, including Common lantana, Curse-of-India, Lantana, Lilac lantana, Prickly lantana, Scourge-of-India, and Wild sage (E).

Specimens Examined. JAFFNA DISTRICT: in empty weedy lot 9 miles northeast-north of Jaffna along the road to Palai, 6 m alt., 6 Dec. 1974, 1 m tall shrub, buds red, corollas orange, *Davidse & Sumithraarachchi 9098* (US). PUTTALAM DISTRICT: scattered in sandy fields, Puttalam lagoon, 25 Jan. 1974, flower-buds coral-red, opening pale yellow with deeper yellow eye, turning rose-pink with orange eye, shrub, *H.N. & A.L. Moldenke & Jayasuriya 28247* (AAU, LL, PDA, US). ANURADHAPURA DISTRICT: occasional along roadsides and hedgerows, Nochchiyagama, 24 Jan. 1974, shrubs, flowerbuds coral yellow, opening yellow, turning rose, *H.N. & A.L. Moldenke & Jayasuriya 28234* (AAU, LL, PDA, US). COLOMBO DIS-TRICT: abundant in waste ground along roadside on the Peliyagoda to Negombo road, 15 Jan. 1974, flowers opening yellow, turning to rose-pink, slender branching shrubs, erect, 5 ft tall, with small prickles, *H.N. & A.L. Moldenke & Jayasuriya 28115* (AAU, ARIZ, CAI, KARACHI, LL, PDA, US). KANDY DISTRICT: weed, Royal Botanic Garden, Peradeniya, 1550 ft alt., July 1887, *s. coll. s.n.* (PDA); abundant at base of Kabaragala mountain behind Raxawa Tea Estate east of Dolosbage, 1400 m alt., 7 Aug. 1969, *Grupe 145* (PDA, US). MATALE DISTRICT: abundant along roadsides and fencerows, Dambulla, 400 ft alt., 23 Jan. 1974, flower-buds coral yellow, opening yellow, turning pink with an orange throat, *H.N. & A.L. Moldenke & Jayasuriya 28218* (AAU, ARIZ, CAI, KARACHI, LL, MO, PDA, US). NUWARA ELIYA DISTRICT: dry patana, 2000 ft alt., 24 Jan. 1964, *Carrick 1280* (KLU); abundant along roadsides and fencerows at milepost 27/10 beyond Pusselawa, 3200 ft alt., 28 Jan. 1974, very prickly stems, flower-buds rose-red, opening yellow with a slightly deeper yellow eye, turning pink with a yellow eye, *H.N. & A.L. Moldenke, Jayasuriya, & Sumithraarachchi 28263* (AAU, ARIZ, CAI, KARACHI, LL, MO, PDA, UC, US).

var. **varia** (Kuntze) Moldenke, Phytologia 2: 105, nom. nud. 1944; 29: 503. 1974. Type: *Kuntze s.n.* from Buitenzorg, Java, (NY).

Camara aculeata α *subinermis* f. *varia* Kuntze, Rev. Gen. Pl. 2: 503. 1891.
Lantana aculeata ssp. *subinermis* f. *varia* (Kuntze) Voss in Vilm., Blumengärt. 1: 823. 1895.

This variety differs from the typical form of the species in having flower-heads with corollas of several colour combinations on the same plant; described originally as yellow turning to orange and sulphur-yellow turning to purple or violet. In Ceylon I have tentatively referred here the plants where some heads have corollas opening yellow and remaining yellow and other heads with corollas opening yellow and turning true pink, pinkish, or pinkish-yellow.

Other colour variations of this species to be expected in Ceylon are var. *flava* (Medic.) Moldenke, practically unarmed, the corollas remaining bright yellow or opening sulphur-yellow and changing to saffron; var. *hybrida* (Neubert) Moldenke, very dwarf cultivated plants used for edging flower beds with low bushy growth and yellow or yellowish corollas; var. *multiflora* (Otto & Dietr.) Moldenke, an unarmed shrub, the youngest parts of the stem his-pidulous, and the corollas all lilac or pink; var. *mutabilis* (Hook.) Bailey, with leaves usually somewhat narrower and longer and more finely crenulate and the corollas opening white, then turning yellowish, and finally rose or lilac; var. *rubella* Moldenke, conspicuously armed and the corollas all pink; var. *sanguinea* (Medic.) Bailey, with all the corollas opening saffron-yellow and turning bright red and var. *rubra* Mosty, with all the corollas red. There is also a f. *parvifolia* with unarmed stems and small leaves, about 1–2.5 cm long and 1–2 cm wide when mature, the internodes only 1–2 cm long, and the peduncles only 1–2 cm long; and a var. *ternata* Moldenke with ternate leaves.

V e r n. Harlequin lantana.

S p e c i m e n s   E x a m i n e d. KURUNEGALA DISTRICT: in hedge-rows, Dambadeniya, 16 Jan. 1974, some corollas open yellow and remain yellow, others turn pinkish, pinkish-yellow, or true pink, *H.N. & A.L. Moldenke, Jayasuriya, & Sumithraarachchi 28127* (AAU, ARIZ, CAI, KARA-CHI, LL, MO, PDA, US).

var. **mista** (L.). Bailey, Cyclop. Amer. Hort. 884. 1900; Medic., Hist. & Com-mentat. Acad. Elect. Sci. Theod.-Palat. 3: 227–228. 1775; Schau. in A. DC., Prod. 11: 600. 1847; Thw., Enum. Pl. Zeyl. 242. 1861; Clarke in Hook. f., Fl. Br. Ind. 4: 562. 1885; Trimen, Handb. Fl. Ceylon 3: 346. 1895. Type: culti-vated specimen from garden of J. Sherard at Eltham, England, collected about 1726 (OXF).

Viburnum americanum urticae foliis Com., Hort. 1: 151, pl. 78. 1697.
Camara lamii albi folio, flore misto Dill., Hort. Elth. 64, pl. 56, fig. 64. 1732.
Lantana mista L., Syst., ed. 12, 417. 1767.—*L. mixta* Medic., Hist. & Com-mentat. Acad. Elect. Sci. Theod.-Palat. 3: 227. 1775.—*L. mista* Bailey apud Sasaki, List Pl. Formos. 352. 1928.
Lantana coccinea Lodd. ex G. Don in Loud., Hort. Brit. 245. 1830.
Lantana mutabilis Lippold ex Otto & Dietr., Gartenzeitung 10: 314. 1842 [not *L. mutabilis* Salisb., 1796, nor Weigel, 1776].
Lantana aculeata Hort. ex Schau. in A. DC., Prod. 11: 600, in syn. 1847 [not *L. aculeata* L., 1753].
Camara aculeata var. *subinermis* f. *mista* (L.) Kuntze, Rev. Gen. Pl. 1: 503. 1891.
Camara aculeata var. *normalis* f. *mista* Kuntze, Rev. Gen. Pl. 1: 503. 1891.

Lantana craigii Hort. ex Moldenke, Suppl. List Invalid Names 4, in syn. 1941.

Lantana camara f. *cubensis* Baker ex Moldenke, Suppl. List Invalid Names 4, in syn. 1941.

Lantana camara var. *mixta* L. E. Bailey apud Pittier, Cat. Fl. V nez. 2: 331. 1947.

This variety differs from the typical form of the species and all other named forms in having most of the twigs, branchlets, and upper stems rather densely spreading-hirsute, rather than appressed-puberulent, the stiff yellowish hairs rather easily breaking off in age.

D i s t r. The variety has approximately the same geographic distribution as the species as a whole, i.e., from Bermuda and Florida, through the West Indies and Central America, to Argentina; also in tropical Asia and Africa as an introduced "weed". It is rather widely cultivated for ornament under several horticultural names.

U s e s. In Brazil the juice of the leaves and flowers, mixed with an equal part of water, is used as a cough remedy. An infusion of the leaves is also used in treating intermittent fevers and as an ointment for contusions. The dried leaves are also used to make a tea substitute. In the Philippines a decoction from the fresh roots is gargled to relieve toothache; the pounded leaves are also used to reduce inflammations and a lotion from them is employed in treating rheumatism. The active principle is said to be lantanine, an alkaloid that acts like quinine in reducing fever and slowing circulation. In the Tongan Islands the leaves are chewed until thoroughly mixed with saliva and then applied to cuts. A variation of this treatment is warming the leaves over a fire and then squeezing out the juices directly on to the cut or wound.

V e r n. Among the 30 or more names recorded are: Cambara, Dona Ana, Filigrana, English sage bush, Hairy lantana, red sage, Rock sage, and Wild sage.

N o t e s. The corolla colour is quite variable, but typically begins as yellow and changes to purple. The plant is often galled and is also attacked by the parasitic fungus, *Prospodium tuberculatum* (Speg.) Arth.

The assortment of flower colours given by Mueller-Dombois on the label of his collection, cited below, and which he identified as *L. indica*, probably refers to colours seen on various plants observed by him in this ecologic habitat and taken by him to represent the same taxon, rather than to one individual plant, inasmuch as his specimen was intended only as a voucher for ecological observations. Plants of this species apparently hybridize freely when growing in proximity (as they very often do). Two such hybrids are probably represented by the *Moldenke et al. 28303* and *28304* collections, also cited below. In the former of these some heads exhibited flower-buds coral-pink, opening yellow with a deeper yellow "eye", turning pink [the almost normal form], while other heads had the buds coral, opening pale pink with an orange "eye", and turning magenta-pink with a deeper "eye". In the latter the buds were orange-yellow, opening all yellow, then turning orange and finally rose-tinted.

Specimens Examined. JAFFNA DISTRICT: empty weed lot 9 miles northeast-north of Jaffna along the road to Palai, 6 m alt., 6 Dec. 1974, shrub 1 m tall, buds red, corolla orange, *Davidse & Sumithraarachchi 9098* (MOLDENKE). KURUNEGALA DISTRICT: scattered shrubs in roadside hedgerows, Dambadeniya, 16 Jan. 1974, stems hairy, flower-buds pinkish, opening pale-yellow with deeper yellow eye, turning to rosy pink with orange eye, *H.N. & A.L. Moldenke, Jayasuriya, & Sumithraarachchi 28128* (AAU, CAI, LL, PDA, US). POLONNARUWA DISTRICT: in shade, Polonnaruwa Sacred Area, 61 m alt., 6 Oct. 1971, macaques eat the fruit, *Dittus WD. 71100601* (US). NUWARA ELIYA DISTRICT: a single plant among normal form on roadbank, Boragas, 5800 ft alt., 30 Jan. 1974, buds orange-yellow, opening all yellow, turning orange and eventually rose-tinted, stems hairy, hybrid?, *H.N. & A.L. Moldenke, Jayasuriya, & Sumithraarachchi 28304* (AAU, ARIZ, CAI, KARACHI, LL, MO, PDA, UC, US); growing gregariously on roadside on highway between Hakgala and Nuwara Eliya, 1760 m alt., voucher for ecologic observations, *Mueller-Dombois 67090107* (PDA). RATNAPURA DISTRICT: on clay slopes near paddy, common, gregarious, between Boralanda and Pelmadulla, 460 m alt., 20 March 1968, 1 m tall, *Comanor 1122* (PDA, US). BADULLA DISTRICT: common along roadsides and edge of forest, Warwick Tea Factory between Hakgala and Ambewela, 5800 ft alt., 30 Jan. 1974, some flower-buds coral-pink, opening yellow with deeper yellow eye, turning pink, other buds coral, opening pale pink with orange eye, turning magenta-pink with deeper eye, stems spreading-hairy, *H.N. & A.L. Moldenke, Jayasuriya & Sumithraarachchi 28303* (AAU, ARIZ, CAI, KARACHI, LL, MO, PDA, UC, US).

3. ALOYSIA

Ortega ex Pers., Syn. Pl. 2: 139. 1806. Type species: *Verbena triphylla* L' Hér. [= *Aloysia triphylla* (L'Hér.) Britton].

Aloysia Ortega & Palau ex L'Hér., Stirp. 21, hyponym. 1786; Jacks. in Hook. f. & Jacks., Ind. Kew. 1: 89, in syn. 1895.—*Aloisia* Ortega apud Perez-Arbelaez, Pl. Med. Colomb. 240. 1937.

Usually sweet-aromatic shrubs or low trees; leaves decussate-opposite or whorled, simple, exstipulate, deciduous, short-petiolate, the blades entire or toothed, not pinnatifid nor deeply lobed, glabrous or pubescent, mostly resinous-punctate; inflorescence centripetal (racemose), in the form of axillary, usually numerous, slender, mostly elongate, often loosely flowered spikes or racemes, rarely abbreviated and dense; flowers perfect, hypogynous, each subtended by a usually narrow and inconspicuous (rarely broad and conspicuous) bract; calyx gamosepalous, tubular-campanulate, usually spreading-hirsute or -villous (rarely only puberulent), not incrassate nor inflated at maturity, its tube angled, not flattened, the limb 4-lobed, the lobes slender, nearly equal; corolla gamopetalous, zygomorphic, hypocrateriform, 2-lipped, the upper lip and the lobes of the lower lip nearly equal, white or yellow to pink or lavender; stamens 4, didynamous, inserted at about the middle of the corolla-tube, included; anthers 2-celled, unappendaged, the thecae parallel; pistil one, included; ovary 2-celled, each cell 1-ovulate; ovules erect; fruit small, dry, composed of 2 thin-walled nutlets; seeds without endosperm. Chromosome number: x=9.

A genus of about 58 species, varieties, and named forms, ranging from the southwestern part of the United States through much of Mexico and also from Brazil and Ecuador south to Chile and Argentina; the type species introduced in the West Indies, widely cultivated elsewhere and often tending to escape. In Ceylon the genus is represented by only a single species.

Aloysia triphylla (L'Hér.) Britton, Scient. Surv. Puerto Rico & Virg. Isles. 6: 140. 1925; Junell, Symb. Bot. Upsal. 4: 32, 35, & 177–178. 1934; Roig y Mesa, Pl. Medic. 718–719. 1945; Arctander, Perf. & Flav. Mat. Nat. Orig. 648. 1960; Enare, Ornament. Shrubs Calif. 168. 1962; Sastri, Wealth India 6: 142. 1962; Montes, Valenzuela, Wilkomirsky & Arrivé, Pl. Medic. 23: 119–124. 1973; Hylton, Rodale Herb Book 492–494. 1974. Type: *C.L. L'Héritier de Brutelle s.n.* from a cultivated plant in the Jardin des Plantes, Paris, grown from seed sent by Commerson from Montevideo, Uruguay (P).

Verbena triphylla L'Hér., Stirp. Nov. 21–22, pl. 11. 1784.—*V. trifolia* L'Hér. ex Fedde & Schust. Just's Bot. Jahresber. 58 (2): 329, nom. nud. 1938.—*V. triflora* Peter ex Moldenke, Alph. List Invalid Names Suppl. 1: 27, in syn. 1947.—*V. triphila* Willd. ex Moldenke, Résumé 377, in syn. 1959.—*V. triphyla* Willd. ex Moldenke, Résumé 377, in syn. 1959.—*V. trifoliata* L'Hér. ex Moldenke, Résumé Suppl. 6: 11, in syn. 1963 [not *V. trifoliata* P. Beauv., 1960].

Aloysia citrodora Ort. & Palau ex L'Hér., Stirp. Nov. 21, in syn. 1784.—*A. citriodora* Ort. ex Pers., Syn. Pl. 2: 139. 1807.—*A. citrodora* Ort. apud H.B.K., Nov. Gen. & Sp., ed. folio, 2: 269, in syn. 1817.—*A. citriodora* Pers. ex Bojer, Hort. Maurit. 255. 1837.—*A. citriodora* (H.B.K.) Ort. ex Walp., Rep. 4: 41. 1845.—*A. citriodora* Ort. & Palau apud Schau. In A. DC., Prod. 11: 574, in syn. 1847.—*Aloisia citrodora* Ort. apud Perez-Arbelaez, Pl. Medic. Colomb. 240. 1937.—*Aloysia citroidora* Ort. ex Moldenke, Prelim. Alph. List Invalid Names 55, in syn. 1940.—*Alloysia citriodora* Ort. ex Moldenke, Alph. List Invalid Names Suppl. 1: 2, in syn. 1947.

Zapania citrodora Lam., Tabl. Enc. 1: 59. 1791.—*Z. citriodora* Lam. apud
Steud., Nom. Bot., ed. 2, 2: 54. 1840.—*Zappania citriodora* Lam. ex Steud.,
Nom. Bot., ed. 2, 2: 797. 1840.
Lippia citrodora (Lam.) H.B.K., Nov. Gen. & Sp., ed. folio, 2: 269. 1817.—*L.
citriodora* Kunth apud Spreng. in L., Syst., ed. 16, 2: 753. 1825.—*L. citriodora* Humb. & Kunth ex D. Dietr., Syn. Pl. 3: 599. 1843.—*L. citriodora*
(Lam.) Kunth ex Briq. in Pflanzenfam., ed. 1, 4 (3a): 151. 1894.—*L. citriodora* H.B.K. ex Jacks. in Hook. f. & Jacks., Ind. Kew. 2: 95. 1894. —*L. citroidora* H.B.K. ex Moldenke, Prelim. Alph. List Invalid Names 56, in syn.
1940.—*L. citriodora* (Lam.) H.B.K. ex Moldenke, Lilloa 10: 338, in syn.
1944.—*L. citridora* H.B.K. ex Rageau, Pl. Medic. Nouv. Caled. 81, sphalm.
1957.—*L. citrodora* Kunth ex Maria, Pl. Vall. Coch. 38. 1962.—*L. citriodera*
H.B.K. ex Rau, Bull. Bot. Surv. India 10, Suppl. 2: 62. 1969.—*L. citriodora*
(Ort.) H.B.K. ex Encke & Buchheim in Zander, Handwörterb. Pfl.-Nam.,
ed. 10, 100, in syn. 1972.
Aloysia triphylla Royle, Illustr. Bot. Himal. 299, nom. nud. 1839; Jacks. in
Hook. f. & Jacks., Ind. Kew. 4: 1264, in syn. 1895.—*A. triphylla* (Lam.)
Royle ex Moldenke, Suppl. List Invalid Names 1, in syn. 1941.—*A. trih-
hylla* (L'Hér.) Britton ex Roig y Mesa, Pl. Medic. 794, sphalm. 1945.—*A.
triphylla* Britton ex Watt & Breyer-Brandwijk, Medic. & Poison. Pl. S.
Africa., ed. 2, 1046. 1962.
Lippia citrata Schlecht. ex Bedevian, Illustr. Polyglott. Dict. 365. 1936 [not
L. citrata Willd., 1832, nor Cham., 1847].
Verbena citriodora Ort. ex Moldenke, Résumé 362, in syn. 1959.

Tender aromatic-odorous shrub, 1–5 m tall, with a spread of 1–1.5 m;
stems rugose puberulent above, much branched; branches slender, smooth,
striate; branchlets slender, stramineous, striate and more or less sulcate, minutely scabridous-puberulous or glabrescent, not twiggy; nodes annulate; principal internodes 1–6 cm long; leaves strongly aromatic, caducous, whorled in
groups of 3 or 4, spreading, numerous, with a lemon-like scent; petioles very
slender, short, 2–9 mm long, very obscurely and minutely puberulous or glabrate, canaliculate above; leaf-blades membranous or submembranous,
uniformly bright green on both surfaces or somewhat lighter beneath, narrow-
lanceolate or oblong, 2.5–9.5 cm long, 6–23 mm wide, acute or acuminate apically, acutely narrowed basally, entire or more or less serrate at or near the
middle or from the base to the apex, often scabrous along the margins, glabrous or usually minutely scabridous above, glabrous and densely resinous-
punctate beneath; midrib very slender, flat above, prominulous beneath;
secondaries filiform, 12–30 per side, very close together, almost straight and
subparallel, not anastomosing, flat and often obscure above, prominulous
beneath; veinlet reticulation mostly indiscernible; inflorescence spicate,
whorled, axillary in the upper leaf-axils and 3 or 4 per node, or aggregate in

naked terminal panicles, often dull purple throughout when immature, the spikes slender, loose, many-flowered, 3–10 cm long, 7–11 mm wide; peduncles filiform, 2–6 mm long, pilosulous; rachis slender, angled, striate, pubescent or pilosulous; foliaceous bracts usually absent or in 1 or 2 whorls at the base of the terminal panicle; bractlets subtending the individual spikes and flowers exiguous, lanceolate-ovate, c. 1 mm long, acuminate, often caducous, minutely puberulous; flowers sessile, fragrant, small, crowded or distant on the rachis; calyx tubular, purple, about 2 mm long and 1 mm wide, striate, pubescent or densely puberulent, angulate, subbilabiate, its rim short-toothed, the teeth 4, acute, nearly equal; corolla hypocrateriform, white or pale-violet, or else the tube lavender and the lobes white, the tube slender, 3–4 mm long, minutely puberulous apically outside, slightly longer than the calyx, the limb 2-lipped, about 2 mm wide, the lobes nearly equal; stamens 4, didynamous, included or equalling the corolla-tube; pollen 3-zonicolporate, spheroidal, 24μm (range 19–25μm) in diameter, the endocolpium faint, the exine significantly thin (1μm thick), the ectine not well differentiated from the endine, psilate; style included or equalling the corolla-tube; ovary 2-loculate; nutlets 2, their integument thin; fruiting-calyx including the fruit. Chromosome number: 36.

D i s t r. This very well known garden plant is widely cultivated in the warmer parts of southern Europe, North America, the West Indies, South America, Madeira, Mauritius, and many other areas, and has escaped and become naturalized in many warm countries. It is apparently originally native to Uruguay and north-eastern Argentina, inhabiting riverbanks, especially rocky ones, and "quebrados", blooming practically throughout the year, at altitudes of 700 to 2400 m, but in Ecuador has been cultivated successfully as high as 2670 m and in Peru at almost 3000 m.

U s e s. An essence is distilled from the leaves of this plant and this, under the name "verbena oil", is highly valued in perfumery and is sometimes drunk, either hot or cold, and in Spain, sweetened or with mint added, used as a substitute for tea. In Ecuador the leaves are boiled and the resulting liquid is drunk with bicarbonate of soda to alleviate lower abdominal pains; in Colombia it is used as an expectorant and antispasmodic. Pharmacopoeias list it as a repellant and antiseptic under the names "herba aloysiae", "herba lippiae citriodorae", and "herba verbenae odoratae". Its reputed medicinal uses include being an aromatic, digestive, nervine, diaphoretic, stomachic, carminative, and tonic; said to be of value in the treatment of intermittent fevers, stomach-ache, constipation, nervous diseases, melancholia, hypochondria, insomnia, stomach bleeding, colds, vomiting, and diarrhoea. It is said to act as a gentle balm for certain cardiac conditions and to serve as a general panacea. It is widely cultivated merely for the fragrance of its flowers and foliage and is interspersed among showy flowers in Hawaiian leis. In the preparation of the tea the leaves must be steeped in boiling water for at least 10 minutes, but a prolongation of the time does not add to the flavour.

The greenish-yellow volatile oil produced is a combination of β-citral, linalyl acetate, 1-limonene, geraniol, verbenalin, verbenone, methylheptone, citronellol, isovalerianic acid, cineol, and d-sesquiterpene, with traces of acetic acid, pyrrols, and alcohols. Oil-of-verbena has an agreeable odour resembling that of lemongrass, but more delicate. This "true oil of verbena" should not be confused with "Spanish verbena oil", which is derived from *Thymus hiemalis*, or "Indian verbena oil" from *Cymbopogon citratus* and *C. flexuosus*.

This plant is attacked by several fungi, notably *Coniothyrium fuckelii* Sacc., *Diplodina aloysiae* Grove, *Hendersoniella trabicola* Sacc., and *Phomopsis citriodora* Grove, and by a lepidopteran, the omnivorous looper, *Sabulodes caberata*. On the other land, experiments have shown that the essential oil is useful as an insecticide in spraying against mites and aphids; concentrations of 1–2 per cent may kill 67 per cent of the mites and 93 per cent of the aphids; higher concentrations scorch the plants.

V e r n. Among the over 100 names are: Cidrón, Herba-Luisa, Herva-cidreira, Lemon-scented verbena, Lemon verbena, Limoneto, Sweet-scented verbena, Té cedrón, and Yerba Maria Luisa.

S p e c i m e n s E x a m i n e d. KANDY DISTRICT: Castlereagh Estate garden, 15 May 1927, *Alston 1084* (PDA). LOCALITY UNKNOWN: *Buysman s.n.* (PDA).

4. PHYLA

Lour., Fl. Cochinch. ed. 1, 66. 1790. Type species: *Phyla chinensis* Lour. [=*P. nodiflora* (L.) Greene].

Zapania Scop. ex A.L. Juss., Ann. Mus. Natl. Hist. Nat. 7: 72. 1806 [not *Zapania* Juss., 1841, nor Lam., 1791].

Platonia Raf., Med. Repos. 5: 352. 1808 [not *Platonia* Kunth, 1829, nor Mart., 1829, nor Raf., 1810].

Diototheca Raf., Fl. Ludov. 74. 1817.—*Diolotheca* Raf. ex Airy Shaw in Willis, Dict., ed. 7, 358. 1966.

Bertolonia Raf., Amer. Monthly Mag. & Crit. Rev. 2: 267. 1818 [not *Bertolonia* DC., 1812, nor Moc. & Sessé, 1825, nor Raddi, 1820, nor Spinola, 1809, nor Spreng., 1821].

Blairia Gaertn. apud Steud., Nom. Bot., ed. 1, 111. 1821 [not *Blairia* Adans., 1763, nor Gled., 1751, nor Houst., 1737, nor L., 1737, nor Spreng., 1966].

Piarimula Raf., Fl. Tellur. 2: 102. 1836.

Pilopus Raf., Fl. Tellur. 2: 102. 1836.

Panope Raf., Fl. Tellur. 2: 102. 1836.

Cryptocalyx Benth., Ann. Nat. Hist., ser. 1, 2: 446. 1839.

Hippia Delchev., Rev. Hortic. 44: 316, sphalm. 1872 [not *Hippia* Bourgeau, 1947, nor Kunth, 1968, nor L., 1767].

Phylla Greene ex Vyas, J. Indian Bot. Soc. 44: 153, sphalm. 1965.

Lipia Sessé & Moc. ex Moldenke, Prelim. Alph. List Invalid Names 30, in syn. 1940.—*Lipparia* Hort. ex Moldenke, Résumé 310, in syn. 1959.

Mostly perennial and usually procumbent or creeping herbs, rarely annual in temperate climates; stems trailing or ascending (rarely erect), sometimes slightly woody basally, usually more or less incanous throughout with appressed-strigose, mostly malpighian (medifixed) hairs, rarely with simple hairs or subglabrous; leaves decussate-opposite, often fleshy, flat or pinnately to palmately plicatulate, petiolate; inflorescence spicate, axillary, usually at first capitate, later cylindric, densely many-flowered, usually greatly elongate in fruit, solitary, paired, or ternate, never aggregated into corymbs nor panicles; flowers small, sessile, borne singly in the axils of small cuneate-obovate or flabelliform bractlets, usually not at all 4-ranked; calyx small, membranous, ovoid-campanulate or compressed and 2-carinate or -winged, the rim 2- or 4-fid or 4-dentate; corolla hypocrateriform, irregular, mostly white or lavender to purple, the tube straight or incurved, slender, slightly exserted from the calyx, equal in diameter throughout or slightly ampliate apically, the limb oblique, spreading, somewhat 2-lipped, 4-parted, the lobes broad, often retuse apically, the posterior one entire, emarginate, or bifid to about the middle, the lateral ones exterior, the anterior one often larger; stamens 4, didynamous, included or slightly exserted, the anthers unappendaged; ovary 2-locular, the ovules 1 per locule, the stigma incrassate, oblique or recurved; fruit small, dry, included by the mature calyx and sometimes adnate to it, dividing into 2 pyrenes at maturity, the pericarp leathery and hard, the exocarp membranous and rarely distinct from the pyrenes. Chromosome number: $x = 9$.

A very difficult genus of about 20 species and subspecific entities, widely distributed in subtropical and tropical America, with one or two in the warmer parts of the Old World. Some forms are widely cultivated for lawns or as soil-binders. One species in Ceylon, *Phyla nodiflora* (L.) Greene.

KEY TO THE VARIETIES

1 Venation of leaf-blades very obscure or almost indiscernible on both surfaces..........
....var. **nodiflora**
1 Larger venation usually quite distinct and subprominulous on the lower leaf-surface..
....var. **reptans**

Phyla nodiflora (L.) Greene, Pittonia 4: 46. 1899 var. **nodiflora**. Hermann, Mus. Zeyl., ed. 1, 56. 1717; Moon, Cat. 1: 45. 1824; Thw., Enum. Pl. Zeyl. 241. 1861; Clarke in Hook. f., Fl. Br. Ind. 4: 563. 1885; Trimen, Cat. 68. 1885; Trimen, Handb. Fl. Ceylon 3: 347. 1895; Willis, Cat. 68. 1911; Reynier, Bull.

Soc. Bot. France 62: 205. 1915; Hallier, Meded. Rijks-Herb. 37: 19. 1918; Moldenke in Lundell, Fl. Texas 3 (1): 60–61. 1942; Abeywick., Ceylon J. Sci., Biol. Sci. 2: 217. 1959; Grindal, Everyday Gard. India, ed. 16, 51. 1960; Gaussen, Viart, Legris, & Labroue, Trav. Sect. Scient. Techn. Inst. Franç. Pond. Hors 5: 24. 1965; Gunawardena, Gen. Sp. Pl. Zeyl. 146. 1968; Maiti, Bull. Bot. Soc. Bengal 22: 74. 1968; Fonseka & Vinasithamby, Prov. List Local Names Fl. Pl. Ceylon 30, 31, & 73. 1971; Moldenke in Woodson, Schery *et al.*, Ann. Missouri Bot. Gard. 60: 59–65, fig. 3. 1973; Vivekanandan, Sri Lanka Forester, ser. 2, 11: 107, 140, & 148. 1974. Type: *Clayton 448* from "Virginia" (LINN).

Verbena nodiflora C. Bauhin, Pinax 269. 1623.—*V. nodiflora* L., Sp. Pl., ed. 1, 1: 20. 1753.—*V. nodiflora* Petagn. ex Moldenke, Résumé Suppl. 2: 12, in syn. 1960.

Verbenaca nodiflora J. Bauhin, Hist. Pl. Univ. 3: 444. 1650.—*V. nodiflora* Imperato, Hist. Nat. 673. 1672.

Verbenaca repente Imperato, Hist. Nat. 674. 1672.

Hirimanadaetta Hermann, Mus. Zeyl., ed. 1, 56. 1717.

Sherardia repens nodiflora Vaill., Serm. 49. 1718.

Verbena folio verticaliter ovatis, spicis globosis L., Hort. Cliff. 11. 1737.—*V. foliis verticaliter ovatis, spicis solitariis ovatis* Royen, Fl. Leyd. Prod. Lugd. 327. 1740.

Verbena capitata Forsk., Fl. Aegypt.-arab. 10. 1775.—*V. capitata* Blume ex Walp., Rep. 4: 33, in syn. 1845.

Blairia nodiflora (L.) Gaertn., Fruct. 1: 266, pl. 56. 1788.

Phyla chinensis Lour., Fl. Cochinch., ed. 1, 66. 1790.

Zapania nodiflora (L.) Lam., Tabl. Enc. 1: 59, pl. 17, fig. 3. 1791.

Lippia nodiflora (L.) Michx., Fl. Bor.-Amer. 2: 15. 1803.—*L. nodiflora* (L.) Eich. ex Oppenh. & Evenari, Bull. Soc. Bot. Genève 31: 363. 1940.—*L. nodiflora* Rich. ex Hieron., Bol. Acad. Ci. (Córdoba) 4: 69. 1881.—*Lippea nodiflora* Mich. apud Anon., Bull. Bot. Surv. India 2: 242. 1960.—*Lippia nodiflora* (C. Bauhin, L.) Michx. ex Fournier, Quatre Fl. France 807. 1961.— *L. nodiflora* (L.) L.C. Rich. ex Michx. apud Jafri, Fl. Karachi 286. 1966.— *L. nodiflora* L. ex Fosberg & Tenvoize, Atoll Res. Bull. 136: 170. 1970.

Verbena repens Bertol., Rar. Ital. Pl. Dec. 2: 27. 1806.—*V. repens* Petagu. ex Spreng. in L., Syst. ed. 16, 2: 752. 1825.—*V. repens* Sav. ex Spreng. in L., Syst. ed. 16, 2: 752, in syn. 1825.

Platonia nudiflora Raf., Med. Repos. 5: 352. 1808.

Verbena sarmentosa Willd., Enum. Hort. Berol. 632. 1809.

Zapania repens (Bertol.) Bertol., Rar. Ital. Pl. Dec. 3: 27. 1810.

Bertolonia crassifolia Raf., Chloris Aetn. 5. 1815.

Bertolonia scabra Raf. ex McMurtie, Sketch Louisv. 214. 1819.

Lippia sarmentosa (Willd.) Spreng. in L., Syst., ed. 16, 2: 752. 1825.

Lippia repens Spreng. in L., Syst., ed. 16, 2: 752. 1825.

Zapania crassifolia (Raf.) Raf., Herb. Raf. 66. 1833.

Piarimula chinensis (Lour.) Raf., Fl. Tellur. 2: 102. 1836.

Lippia nodiflora α *vulgaris* Walp., Rep. 4: 49. 1845.

Lippia nodiflora var. *sarmentosa* (Willd.) Schau. in A. DC., Prod. 11: 585. 1847.

Lippia nodiflora var. *repens* (Bertol.) Schau. in A. DC., Prod. 11: 586. 1847.

Lippia nodosa Bocq., Adansonia, ser. 1, 2: 121. 1862.

Lippia nodiflora α *normalis* Kuntze, Rev. Gen. Pl. 2: 508. 1891.

Lippia nodiflora α *normalis* f. *brevipes* Planch. ex Kuntze, Rev. Gen. 2: 508. 1891.

Lantana repens Larrañ., Escrit. 2: 188. 1923.

Phyla nodiflora Lour. ex Hartl. Beitr. Biol. Pflanzen 37: 294. 1962.—*Phylla nodiflora* (L.) Greene ex Vyas, J. Indian Bot. Soc. 44: 153, sphalm. 1965.

Tough perennial creeping herb; stems prostrate, mostly rooting at the nodes, usually 30–90 cm long; branches slender, procumbent or ascending, densely appressed-strigillose to minutely puberulent or glabrate; leaves decussate-opposite, variable; petioles 2–8 mm long or obsolete, often so broadly cuneate-margined as to appear as though a part of the blade; leaf-blades thick-textured, fleshy when fresh, usually uniformly green on both surfaces, spatulate or oblanceolate to obovate, sometimes elliptic or cuneiform, 1–7.2 cm long, 0.6–2.5 cm wide, rounded or obtuse (rarely subacute) apically, narrowed into a long- or short-cuneate base, sharply serrate above the middle with acute or acuminate mostly appressed or subappressed antrorse teeth, entire basally, minutely or densely strigillose-puberulent on both surfaces or glabrous, the venation usually indiscernible on both surfaces or at least inconspicuous and not prominent; inflorescence solitary in the upper leaf-axils, at first globose-capitate, later cylindric, often greatly elongating in age, 1–2.5 cm long when mature and 6–9 mm in diameter, densely many-flowered; peduncles solitary in each axil, slender, often much elongate, usually much longer than the subtending leaves, 1–11.5 cm long, densely or sparsely appressed-puberulent or strigose with antrorse canescent hairs or glabrous; bractlets closely imbricate, obovate or subrhomboid-cuneate, subequalling the corolla-tube, often broadly membranous-margined apically, mucronate-acuminate or muticous, glabrous or finely ciliate; flower-buds purple; calyx hyaline-membranous, flattened, about equalling the corolla-tube, deeply 2-cleft, slightly 2-carinate, the keels puberulent, the lobes lanceolate; corolla purple or pink to white, often opening white and turning lavender with a deeper red-purple spot at the base of the lower lip, 2–2.5 mm long, the mouth often yellow and the throat pink-brown, slightly surpassing the subtending bractlets, the limb exiguous, slightly strigillose; pollen-grains 3-colporate, subprolate to spheroidal, $25–26 \times 24–31\,\mu m$, amb circular, circular-lobate, or subangular, colpi short, $13–14 \times 2\,\mu m$,

aperture of drop type, ora transversely parallel, exine 2μm thick, tectum psilate, sexine reticulate, with OL pattern, maxine as thick as the sexine; fruit
dry, about 2 mm long, splitting at maturity into 2 nutlets, each 1-seeded,
planoconvex, glabrous. Chromosome number: 9, 18, or 36.

D i s t r. A very common and well-known plant found in moist or wet soil
of fields, lawns, hillsides, clearings, savannas, beaches, dry riverbeds, the
edges of ponds, and thickets, widely distributed throughout the subtropical
and tropical portions of both the Eastern and Western Hemispheres, being especially abundant in moist sandy soil and capable of standing much abuse. It
is an extremely polymorphic and variable species. Although widely described
by authors as an "annual", it most certainly is perennial in tropical climates;
perhaps it acts as an annual at the northern and southernmost borders of its
range.

U s e s. This plant is valued as a lawn plant in Egypt and elsewhere. It
makes an excellent ground-cover, withstanding walking and tramping very
well. It is said to use up less water in a given area than grass would. Its most
valuable use is to prevent water and/or wind erosion. It is said that its fresh
leaves are sometimes eaten in Ceylon as a vegetable. An infusion is widely
drunk as a tea in the Philippines. Its reputed medicinal values are considerable and varied. The Hindus employ it as a febrifuge, emollient, and diuretic;
with cummin seed it is used to treat gonorrhoea; applied as a paste it promotes
suppuration; as a poultice it serves as a good maturant for boils, swollen cer-
vical glands, erysipelas, and chronic indolent ulcers. It is said to be useful in
the treatment of blennorrhoea, lithiasis, ischury, constipation, and pain in the
knee-joints; an infusion is used to treat the febrile stage of colds and children's
indigestion and it is drunk by women after childbirth. An alcoholic extract of
the leaves shows anti-bacterial activity against *Escherichia coli*. In Vietnam it
is used in treating bronchitis and other respiratory ailments.

V e r n. Among its more than 250 common names in various parts of its
range are: Cape-weed, Cidron, Fog-fruit, Godet's-weed, Link-weed, Lippia-
grass, Sprain bush, Mat-grass, and Turkey-tangle (E). In Ceylon, Harimena-
kola, Herimanadatta, Hiramanadetta, Hirimandatta (S); Podutalai (T); Raala
in Portuguese.

N o t e s. Chemically, *Phyla nodiflora* has been found to contain the flavone
glucosides, lippiflorin-A and lippiflorin-B, as well as nodiflorin-A, nodiflorin-
B, and nodefloretin, a non-glucoside bitter substance, an essential oil, resin,
free lactose, maltose, fructose, and xylose, and a large amount of potassium
nitrate.

This plant is subject to attack by the fungus, *Meliola durantae*, and the
leafspot fungus, *Cercospora lippiae*.

S p e c i m e n s E x a m i n e d. JAFFNA DISTRICT: in sand of seashore
by Ferry, 12 Oct. 1975, fleshy herb, stoloniferous, stems green, more or less

angular, leaves opposite, fleshy, deeply serrate, inflorescence in erect dense glomerules, globose or oblong, florets pale purple-violet, *Bernardi 15317* (US); on sand dunes, Nagarkovil, 23 Oct. 1973, *Waas 242* (US). MANNAR DISTRICT: Talaimannar, 17 July 1916, *J.M. Silva s.n.* (PDA). KURUNEGALA DISTRICT: Mawatagama, 26 June 1967, flowers very pale mauve, *Amaratunga 1347* (PDA). PUTTALAM DISTRICT: Palavi, 7 Dec. 1961, flowers violet-pink, *Amaratunga 119* (PDA); seashore, Chilaw, near Rest House, 30 May 1931, very fleshy, 30 May 1931, very fleshy, *Simpson 8170* (PDA); Kalpitiya, Aug. 1883, *Collector undetermined s.n.* (PDA); mat-forming in sand just back of water's edge, sea-level, Puttalam lagoon, 25 Jan. 1974, corollas lavender, *H.N. & A.L. Moldenke & Jayasuriya 28245* (AAU, LL, PDA, US). ANURA-DHAPURA DISTRICT: trailing then erect, forming a mat on black clay soil, roadside weedy area in full sun, 150 m alt., on Dambulla to Habarana road, 7 May, 1968, herbaceous, petals white, throat pink-brown or yellow, *Comanor 1209* (AAU, PDA); procumbent at edge of tank, Malawa-Wewa, Kekirawa, 24 Jan. 1974, corollas lavender, *H.N. & A.L. Moldenke & Jayasuriya 28227* (AAU, ARIZ, CAI, KARACHI, LL, PDA, US); procumbent in low moist ditches, Rajangana, 25 Jan. 1974, corolla lavender, *H.N. & A.L. Moldenke & Jayasuriya 28237* (AAU, LL, PDA, US); forming dominant cover on moist soil near coast west of Wilpattu, in centre area of Sinna Uppu Villu, 27 April 1969, *Mueller-Dombois, Wirawan, Cooray, & Balakrishnan 69042713* (LL, PDA, UC, US); common in plot W. 9, Kali Villu, Wilpattu National Park, 8 July 1969, flowers violet, later white, *Wirawan, Cooray, & Balakrishnan 991* (ARIZ, PDA). COLOMBO DISTRICT: bordering a water pool, Talahena, 8 Feb. 1963, *Amaratunga 500* (PDA); prostrate, Uswetakeiyawa, 13 Dec. 1968, flowers pale violet, *Amaratunga 1688* (PDA); Colombo, Jan. 1885, *Grunow s.n.* (W); waste ground, Mount Lavinia, 17 April 1970, flowers pale purplish-pink, *Amaratunga 2062* (PDA); forming mats in sandy soil at fish hatchery, Pitipana, 3 Feb. 1974, corollas lavender, *H.N. & A.L. Moldenke, Sumithraarachchi, & Waas 28317* (AAU, ARIZ, CAI, KARACHI, LL, MO, PDA, US); mixed with grass close to lagoon water, Pitipana, 10 August 1974, *Waas 711* (US). KANDY DISTRICT: prostrate in Medical Garden, Royal Botanic Garden, Peradeniya, 1550 ft alt., 18 Jan. 1974, corollas lavender, *H.N. & A.L. Moldenke & Jayasuriya 28146* (US). MATALE DISTRICT: forming a close mat in open grassy area near edge of tank, sandy and heavily grazed, Sigiriya tank, 15 July 1973, *Nowicke, Fosberg, & Jayasuriya 370* (US). GALLE DISTRICT: beach area, Koggala, on Galle to Matara road, 19 Nov. 1973, creeping herb, flowers purple, *Sohmer, Waas, & Eliezer 8880* (LAC-ROSSE, NY, US). HAMBANTOTA DISTRICT: uncommon in damp places on sand flat back of beach, prostrate, 1 m alt., Ruhuna National Park, Pata-nagala, 6 April 1968, *Fosberg 50340* (PDA, US); locally common on high dunes of loose sand partly bound by vegetation, Yala sand dunes at mouth of Menik Ganga, Ruhuna National Park, 5 Jan. 1969, flowers white, *Fosberg,*

Mueller-Dombois, Wirawan, Cooray & Balakrishnan 51071 (PDA, US). BAT-
TICALOA DISTRICT: common and abundant beside pond by railroad
tracks, sea-level, Kalkudah, 6 Nov. 1969, flower-heads pinkish, *Cramer 2730*
(PDA, US); in resthouse compound near shore, Kalkudah, 9 June 1974, pro-
strate herb, whitish-pink flowers, *Waas 640* (US). TRINCOMALEE DIS-
TRICT: prostrate herb, Foul Point, 7 April 1974, tiny whitish flowers,
Sumithraarachchi & Jayasuriya DBS. 239 (LACROSSE, US). LOCALITY
UNKNOWN: *J. Fraser 164* (DS, US), "Zeylona", *Herb. Schmiedelian s.n.*
(M), Ana-coluppa, *Herb Schreber s.n.* (M), *s. coll. C.P. 1947* in part (BO,
PDA).

var. **reptans** (Spreng.) Moldenke, Torreya 34: 9. 1934; Gay, Fl. Chil. Bot. 5:
33. 1849; Schau. in Mart., Fl. Bras. 9: 238. 1851; Thistelt.-Dyer, Fl. Cap. 5:
194. 1912; Moldenke, Publ. Carnegie Inst. Wash. 522: 173–174. 1940; Moldenke in Lundell, Fl. Texas 3 (1): 61–62. 1942. Type: *Burman s.n.* from "locis
arenosis Coromandeli", India.

Verbena fruticosa Mill., Gard. Dict., ed. 8, no. 14 (in part) 1768.—*V. fruteosa*
   Mill. & Houst. apud Steud., Nom. Bot. Phan., ed. 1, 873. 1821.—*V. fruti-
   cosa* Houst. & Mill. apud Steud., Nom. Bot. Phan., ed. 2, 2: 750. 1841.
Zapania reptans Spreng., Pl. Min. Cog. Pugill. 2: 70. 1813.
Verbena reptans Loisel. ex Spreng., Pl. Min. Cog. Pugill. 2: 70, in syn. 1813.
Zapania nudiflora Juss. ex Spreng., Pl. Min. Cog. Pugill. 2: 70, in syn. 1813.
Diototheca repens Raf., Fl. Ludov. 75. 1817.
Lippia reptans H.B.K., Nov. Gen. & Sp., ed. quarto, 2: 263. 1818.—*L. reptans*
   Humb. apud Spreng. in L., Syst. ed. 16, 2: 751. 1825.
Hippia aegyptiaca Delchev., Rev. Hortic. 44: 316–317. 1872.—*Lippia aegyp-
   tiaca* Carr. apud Jacks. in Hook. f. & Jacks., Ind. Kew. 2: 95. 1894.
Lippia nodiflora var. *reptans* (H.B.K.) Kuntze, Rev. Gen. Pl. 2: 508. 1891.—
   L. nodiflora var. *repanda* (H.B.K.) Kuntze ex Moldenke, Alph. List In-
   valid Names Suppl. 1: 15, in syn. 1947.
Lippia lanceolata Rose apud B. L. Rob., Proc. Amer. Acad. Sci. 51: 332, in
   syn. 1916 [not *L. lanceolata* Michx., 1803].
Lippia nodiflora Rob. & Greenman apud B. L. Rob. Proc. Amer. Acad. Sci.
   51: 532, in syn. 1916.—*L. nodiflora* Millsp. apud Standl., Publ. Field Mus.
   Nat. Hist., Bot. Ser. 3: 402, in syn. 1930 [not *L. nodiflora* (L.) Michx.,
   1803].
Lippia canescens Rob. apud B. L. Rob., Proc. Amer. Acad. Sci. 51: 532, in
   syn. 1916 [not *L. canescens* H.B.K., 1818].

This variety differs from var. *nodiflora* in usually having the leaves much
larger in size, often 3–4.5 cm long and 1.5–2.5 cm wide, the teeth often more
spreading, and the larger venation (midrib and secondaries) quite firm, distinct, and prominulous on the lower surface.

D i s t r. The variety may be found almost throughout the range of the species, more especially in wetter and more protected situations, suggesting that it may be an edaphic form.

V e r n. Among a dozen or more recorded names are: Buttonweed and Largeleaf fogfruit and, in India, Mallei-cajan-tagare.

N o t e. Its leaves are sometimes attacked by the leaf fungus, *Meliola ambigua* Pat. & Gaill.

S p e c i m e n s E x a m i n e d. ANURADHAPURA DISTRICT: Minneri, Sept. 1885, *s. coll. s.n.* (PDA). HAMBANTOTA DISTRICT: in borrow pit in bund of tank, in shade, Tissamaharama, 12 Aug. 1932, *Simpson 9931* (PDA). LOCALITY UNKNOWN: *Ploem 185* (BR).

5. SVENSONIA

Moldenke, Feddes Repert. Spec. Nov. Regni Veg. 41: 129–136. 1936. Type species: *Bouchea pterygocarpa* Schau. [= *Svensonia laeta* (Fenzl) Moldenke].

Perennial herbs, often woody at the base, or shrubs, abundantly branched; leaves opposite or subopposite, simple, exstipulate, deciduous, petiolate, the blades penninerved and dentate; inflorescence spicate, terminal, elongate, the spikes simple, straight, short-pedunculate, densely many-flowered or sometimes only few-flowered, the flowers (except for the lowest) mostly closely appressed to the rachis and imbricate, the rachis straight, often striate but not sculptured or excavated; pedicles absent or obsolete; bractlets numerous, sessile, lanceolate, mostly closely appressed to the calyx and only 1/4–3/4 as long as the calyx; calyx closely appressed to the rachis but not impressed in it, tubular, erect, straight, slightly zygomorphic, the abaxial side slightly surpassing the adaxial side, slightly ampliate apically, conspicuously 5-costate and 5-plicate, the rim more or less bilabiate, unequally 5-dentate or 5-apiculate, the abaxial lobe 2-apiculate, the adaxial lobe 3-apiculate; corolla zygomorphic, hypocrateriform, mostly white or pink to purple, conspicuously surpassing the calyx, glabrous on the outer surface, its tube narrowly cylinddric, slightly widened and infundibular apically, the adaxial side slightly surpassing the abaxial side, straight or plainly curvate, not twisted, often venose, pilose within among the stamens; corolla-limb zygomorphic, 5-lobed, 2-lipped, the lobes imbricate in bud, the adaxial lip 2-lobed with small lobes, the abaxial lip 3-lobed with the 2 lateral lobes larger and the central lobe largest, or 4 of the lobes very small, oblong- or elliptic-lingulate, and the 5th lobe very large, ovate or obovate; stamens 4, didynamous, inserted below the mouth of the corolla-tube, the 2 lower ones inserted on the adaxial lip and the 2 superior ones on the abaxial lip, included or slightly exserted from the corolla-tube; staminode absent; anthers bilocular, dorsifixed above the base (the 2 lower ones smaller), the thecae dehiscing by means of a longitudinal slit, introrse, the connective unappendaged, slightly thickened; pistil one; style terminal, smooth, long-persistent, bent apically and bilobed, the ventral lobe elongate and stigmatiferous, the dorsal lobe abortive, tooth-like, and non-stigmatiferous; stigma elliptic-capitate or oblique; ovary narrowly oblong, glabrous, 1-carpellary, 2-locular, 2-ovulate; ovules basal, anatropous; fruiting-calyx splitting from apex to base; fruit a schizocarp, the cocci dry, subspatulate, the margins and apex usually more or less conspicuously and broadly alate, not rostrate nor reticulate.

A small genus of three known species ranging from southwestern India through southern Arabia, Sudan, and Ethiopia to Somaliland, Kenya, and Tanzania. Only one species is known from Ceylon and that has not been collected in recent years.

Svensonia hyderobadensis (Walp.) Moldenke, Feddes Repert. Spec. Nov. Regni Veg. 41: 139–143. 1936; Thw., Enum. Pl. Zeyl. 2: 241. 1861; Trimen, Cat. 68. 1885; Clarke in Hook. f., Fl. Br. Ind. 4: 566. 1885; Trimen, Handb. Fl. Ceylon 3: 347–348. 1895; Willis, Cat. 68. 1911; Abeywick., Ceylon J. Sci., Biol. Sci. 2: 217. 1959; Gunawardena, Gen. Sp. Pl. Zeyl. 146. 1968; Mukherjee, Trans. Bose Res. Inst. Calcutta 35: 38–42. 1972. Type: *Rottler s.n.* from Hyderabad, India (Herb. Wallich 6318), probably (B).

Verbena hyderobadensis Rottl. ex Wall., Num. List 215, no. 6318, hyponym. 1832.—*V. hyderabadensis* Rottl. ex Moldenke, Feddes Repert. Spec. Nov. Regni Veg. 41: 139, in syn. 1936.—*V. hydrabadensis* Rottl. ex Moldenke, Feddes Repert. Spec. Nov. Regni Veg. 41: 139, in syn. 1936.

Verbena hyderobadensis β maysorensis Wight ex Wall., Num. List 215, no. 6318b, in syn. 1832.—*V. hyderobadensis β mysorensis* Wight ex Steud., Nom. Bot., ed. 2, 2: 750, nom. nud. 1841.

Bouchea? *hyderobadensis* Walp., Rep. 4: 12. 1845.—*Bouchea hyderabadensis* Walp. apud Thw., Enum. Pl. Zeyl. 2: 241. 1861.—*B. hyderobadensis* (Rottl.) Walp. ex Moldenke, Torreya 34: 9, in syn. 1934.—*B. hyderabadensis* (Rottl.) Walp. ex Moldenke, Feddes Repert. Spec. Nov. Regni Veg. 41: 139, in syn. 1936.—*B. hyderabadensis* Wall. ex Moldenke, Feddes Repert. Spec. Nov. Regni Veg. 41: 139, in syn. 1936.—*B. hyderabaadensis* Walp. ex Razi, Half-yearly J. Mysore Univ. 7 (4): 63. 1946.

Verbena myssorensis Wight ex Walp., Rep. 4: 34, in syn. 1845.—*V. mysoorensis* Wight ex Walp., Rep. 4: 12 & 794, in syn. 1845.—*V. mysorensis* Wight apud Jacks. in Hook. f. & Jacks., Ind. Kew. 2: 1179, in syn. 1895.—*V. maysorensis* Wight ex Moldenke, Feddes Repert. Spec. Nov. Regni Veg. 41: 139, in syn. 1936.—*V. mysuriensis* Wight ex Moldenke, Feddes Repert. Spec. Nov. Regni Veg. 41: 139, in syn. 1936.

Chascanum hyderobadense (Rottl.) Moldenke, Torreya 34: 9. 1934.—*C. hyderobadense* (Walp.) Moldenke, Feddes Repert. Spec. Nov. Regni Veg. 41: 139, in syn. 1936.

Svensonia hyderabadensis (Walp.) Moldenke ex Abeywick., Ceylon J. Sci., Biol. Sci. 2: 217. 1959.

Perennial, semi-shrubby herb, often bushy, to about 1 m tall, usually abundantly branched; branches and branchlets medium-slender, obtusely tetragonal, brownish, the youngest parts purplish or nigrescent in drying, sparsely strigillose-pubescent throughout with short scattered hairs, glabrescent in age; nodes distinctly annulate, the annulation often slightly more densely strigillose; principal internodes 0.7–4.5 cm long, sometimes elongate to 8 cm or on young shoots more abbreviated; leaves decussate-opposite; petioles slender, 0.7–2.9 cm long, convex beneath, flattened and canaliculate above, rather sparsely or densely strigillose like the adjacent branchlets, slightly ampliate basally; leaf-blades thin-chartaceous, rather uniformly dark green on both surfaces or somewhat lighter beneath, the younger ones often brunnescent or nigrescent (especially above) in drying, ovate or ovate-lanceolate to lanceolate, 2.5–10.7 cm long, 1.6–5 cm wide, acute apically, acuminate basally and often prolonged into the petiole, uniformly and deeply serrate with acute broadly triangular antrorse teeth (1–5 mm long and 3–5 mm wide basally) from just below the widest part to the apex, very sparsely and obscurely strigillose or glabrate on both surfaces or pubescent only on the larger veins beneath or on both surfaces; inflorescence terminal, spicate, indeterminate, blooming from the bottom upwards, straight, 11.5–35 cm long, to 3 cm wide (including the corollas) or slightly less than 1 cm wide (excluding the corollas), very densely many-flowered with closely imbricate flowers (except toward the base where the first few flowers are scattered and often distant); peduncles (1–3 cm long) and rachis similar to the adjacent branchlets in texture, colour, and pubescence, the rachis often striate, not sculptured; bractlets numerous, one subtending each flower, linear or lanceolate, sessile, 4–6 mm long, 1–1.5 mm wide basally, tapering regularly to the sharply acute apex, 1/3–1/2 the length of the calyx during anthesis (the basal ones often to 3/4 the length of the calyx after anthesis), sparsely strigillose on the back; calyx light and herbaceous, tubular, zygomorphic, straight, 12.2–13 mm long on the abaxial and 9.8–11.9 mm long on the adaxial side, about 1.5 mm wide basally, slightly ampliate to 2.6 mm apically, closely appressed to but not at all sunken into the rachis, 5-ribbed and decidedly plicate, thickened on the ribs, very thin-membranous or subtranslucent between them, strigillose with very short, c. 0.1 mm long, straight, distinct, and rather distant, whitish, antrorse hairs on the ribs outside, glabrous within, the rim irregularly 5-apiculate, more or less bilabiate, minutely ciliolate, the abaxial lip with two 1–2.1 mm long apiculations, the adaxial lip with the 2 lateral apiculations 0.3–1.3 mm long and the small central one 0.15–0.26 mm long, all very narrowly lanceolate and sharply attenuate, minutely ciliolate, and strigillose on the back; corolla bright-pink, glabrous outside, the tube 17–18 mm long on the adaxial and slightly longer on the abaxial side, straight in bud but sharply curvate just above the top of the calyx during anthesis, venose, the limb oblique, spreading, the 2 axial lobes each 2–4.6 mm long and 1.8–3.3 mm wide, the 2 lateral abaxial lobes each 2.6–6.2 mm long and 2–5.2 mm wide, the central abaxial lobe 3.1–5.7 mm long and 2.8–7.8 mm wide, the 4 smaller lobes oblong- or elliptic-lingulate, the largest lobe decidedly ovate, all rounded at the apex and scattered-pilose with irregular hairs just above the base; stamens included, the filaments 1.3 and 1.8 mm long; lower anthers 0.6 mm long and 1 mm wide, upper pair 1.5–1.8 mm long and 1.6 mm wide; pollen-grains 3-colpate, the colpa short, slit-like, sometimes provided with margo, c. 27.5μm (range 21–34μm) $\times 0.5\mu$m, mean intercolpial distance c. 30.5μm, amb convex, circular, crassimarginate, mean apocolpium diameter c. 32μm, spheroidal diameter c. 77μm (range 50–94μm), exine about 6μm thick, sexine c. 5μm thick (sometimes the exine forms a lobe at one side of the equatorial region where it is then c. 10μm thick and the sexine 9μm thick), punctitegillate supratectal processes perceptible in LO-analysis, tectum thick, bacula simple but somewhat heteromorphic in respect to length (which perhaps accounts for the reticuloid appearance), nexine c. 1μm thick, NPC classification 343; style capillary, about 14.5 mm long; ovary 2–2.3 mm long, 0.5–0.6 mm wide, glabrous, not lobed; seeds without endosperm; fruiting-calyx only slightly enlarged, to 15 mm long and 4 mm wide, scarious, slightly strigillose on the ribs, glabrous within; fruit released when the calyx splits, the cocci remaining joined until they are shed, after which they separate easily, each mature coccus subspatulate, 7.5–8 mm long, c. 1 mm wide basally and 2 mm apically, viewed dorsally the central portion (seed) is linear and greatly elevated, about 6 mm long and 1 mm wide, hard and woody, prominently parallel-ridged, glabrous, broadly winged with a membranous chestnut-brown wing which begins at the very base on one side and c. 1 mm above the base on the other side and is there very narrow, gradually widening until it is c. 1 mm wide on each side at the widest part, projecting 2 mm beyond the seed and rounded or slightly subapiculate apically, glabrous and shiny, viewed ventrally the seed is somewhat prominulent, light-grey or whitish, margined on the sides and top by a very dense band of minute projections, the whole margined and surpassed by the membranous brown and shiny wing which is often very slightly revolute, excavated basally.

D i s t r. Native of peninsular India and apparently (formerly, at least) Ceylon, ascending to altitudes of 10,000 feet in India.

V e r n. In India the plant is called "Curroo-poovanroonee".

N o t e. About 4 flowers bloom at a time and the lowest part of the spike is usually in fruit while the upper part is still in anthesis. In India curious, perhaps virus-infested specimens of *Stachytarpheta jamaicensis* (L.) Vahl occur which have by some been regarded as natural hybrids between that species and *Svensonia hyderobadensis* and by others as a monstrous form of the latter. In Ceylon *S. hyderobadensis* has not been collected during the past 115 years and may well be extinct.

Specimens Examined. KANDY DISTRICT: on a patana between Mcdamahanuwara and Alutnuwara, Bintenna, February 1858, *s. coll. C.P. 3574* (B, BM, BO, G, K, NY, P, PDA, W).

6. STACHYTARPHETA

Vahl, Enum. Pl. 1: 205. 1805 [nom. cons.] Type species: *Verbena jamaicensis* L. [=*Stachytarpheta jamaicensis* (L.) Vahl].

Sherardia Mill., Gard. Dict. Abridged ed. 4. 1754 [not *Sherardia* Boehm., 1760, nor Dill., 1754, nor L., 1753].—*Sherardia* Vaill. ex Adans., Fam. Pl. 2: 198. 1763.—*Sherardia* Adans. apud Briq., Internat. Rules Bot. Nom. 106. 1935 [nom. rejic.].

Serarda Adans., Fam. Pl. 2: 12. 1763.

Verbena Plukenet ex Adans., Fam. Pl. 2: 198 in syn. 1763 [not *Verbena* (Dorst.) L., 1749, nor Endl., 1862, nor Tourn., 1737, nor (Tourn.) L., 1906].

Valerianoides Boerh. ex Medic., Phil. Bot. 1: 177. 1789 [nom. rejic.].—*Valerianodes* Medic. apud Kuntze, Rev. Gen. Pl. 1: 509. 1891.—*Valerianodes* Boerh. apud Millsp., Publ. Field Mus. Nat. Hist. Bot. Ser. 1: 41. 1895.— *Valerianoides* Medic. apud Jacks. in Hook. f. & Jacks., Ind. Kew. 2: 1168 1895.—*Valerianodes* Kuntze apud Dalla Torre & Harms, Gen. Siphonog. 431. 1904.

Abena Neck., Elem. 1: 296. 1790.

Vermicularia Moench, Meth. Suppl. 150. 1802 [nom. rejic.; not *Vermicularia* Tode, 1790].

Cymburus Salisb., Parad. Lond. pl. 49. 1806.

Sarcostachya Juss., Dict. Sci. Nat. 50: 379, nom. provis. 1827.—*Sarcostachys* Juss. ex Airy Shaw in Willis, Dict. ed. 7, 1003, in syn. 1966.

Melasanthus Pohl, Pl. Bras. Ic. 1: 75, pl. 60. 1827.

Stachytarpha Link, Enum. Hort. Berol. 1: 18. 1827.—*Stachytarpha* Vahl apud Schau. in A. DC., Prod. 11: 560. 1847.—*Stachytarpha* St. apud Thw., Enum. Pl. Zeyl. 241. 1861.—*Stachytapenta* Parham, Names Few Fijian Pl. 2, 5, 6, & 10. 1935.—*Stachytarpetha* Fedde, Just's Bot. Jahresber. 57 (2): 890, sphalm. 1938.—*Stachytarphaeta* Steyerm., Bol. Soc. Venez. Ci. Nat. 10: 279. 1946.—*Stachytarfetta* Vahl ex Barroso, Rodriguésia 32: 70. 1957.—*Stachytarphetta* Vahl apud Angely, Liv. Gen. Bot. Bras. 35 & 55. 1960.—*Stachitarpheta* Hocking, Excerpt. Bot. A. 5: 45, sphalm. 1962.—*Stachytarphaeta* Vahl ex Steyerm., Acta Bot. Venez. 3: 156. 1968.—*Stachytarpheia* Auct. ex Airy Shaw in Willis, Dict. ed. 8, 1092, in syn. 1973.—*Satchytarpheta* El-Gazzar, Egypt. J. Bot. 17: 75, sphalm. 1974.

Tarpheta Raf., Fl. Tellur. 2: 103. 1836.

Annual or perennial herbs or low shrubs, glabrous throughout or variously pubescent or villous with simple hairs; leaves opposite or alternate, mostly dentate, often rugose; inflorescence terminal, spicate, the spikes mostly elongate, sometimes greatly abbreviated, densely or loosely many-flowered, occasionally few-flowered, the flowers sessile or semi-immersed in furrows or excavations in the rachis, rarely pedicellate, each solitary in the axil of a bract; bracts small and narrow, appressed or spreading, or sometimes large and ovate or lanceolate, often rigid and imbricate, especially on immature spikes, persistent; flowers opening a few at a time, blooming from the bottom of the spike upwards; calyx long, narrowly tubular, membranous or herbaceous, 5-lobed or 5-dentate at the apex, 5-costate, the teeth equal or unequal, mostly unchanged in fruit or sometimes variously split in age; corolla white, blue, purple, or red, gamopetalous, usually hypocrateriform, the tube cylindric, straight or incurved, slender throughout or ampliate apically, the limb spreading, 5-parted, the lobes broad, often orbicular, obtuse or retuse at the apex, equal or somewhat unequal; perfect stamens 2, anterior, inserted above the middle of the corolla-tube, included; filaments short; anthers unappendaged, the thecae divergent and dehiscing in one continuous line; staminodes 2, posterior, small or minute; ovary 2-loculate, each locule 1-ovulate; ovules attached laterally near the base of the locule; style elongate, filiform; stigma terminal, orbicular, capitate or subcapitate; fruit schizocarpous, dry, oblong-linear, included by the fruiting-calyx, splitting at maturity into 2 long, hard, narrow, truncate, 1-seeded cocci; seeds erect, linear, without endosperm.

A genus of about 140 specific and infraspecific entities, widely distributed in subtropical and tropical America, with a few (mostly naturalized) in tropical Asia, Africa, and Oceania. Several species tend to become quite weedy and spread rapidly when introduced into proper environments. King (Weeds of the World 272. 1966) notes that these aggressive species were not known in Pacific Oceania before the time of the first explorations by Europeans, but apparently came in with them, spread, and rapidly took over, using each island as a stepping stone to the next. Sauer (Plants & Man Seych. 57, 63, & 106. 1967) avers that in the Seychelles Islands they were introduced through local botanical gardens. Probably both agencies were responsible in Ceylon.

Merrill (Ind. Raf. 204. 1949) and Airy Shaw (in Willis, Dict. ed. 7, 664. 1966) claim that the genus *Lomake* Raf. also belongs in the synonymy of *Stachytarpheta*, but this is incorrect; it is a synonym of *Bouchea* Cham.

Stachytarpheta is represented in Ceylon by 4 species, 3 named forms, and 3 natural hybrids, with 2 other species reported (probably erroneously).

KEY TO THE SPECIES, FORMS AND HYBRIDS

1 Leaf-blades mostly ovate, oval, or broadly elliptic, not lanceolate nor narrowly elongate-elliptic

2 Inflorescence spikes about 1 cm wide after anthesis
  3 Leaf-blades densely pubescent beneath; rachis densely spreading-pubescent; plants to 2 m tall
    4 Corollas pink, rose-red, or bright red...............**1. S. mutabilis** var. **mutabilis**
    4 Corolla blue or violet...............................**S. mutabilis** var. **violacea**
  3 Leaf-blades sparsely pilose beneath; rachis sparingly short-pubescent; plants 1–1.5 m tall..**2. S. × trimeni**
2 Inflorescence spike less than 1 cm wide after anthesis
  5 Rachis in fruit stout and firm, deeply excavated, conspicuously wider than the furrows
    6 Rachis to 7 mm wide; plants low and more or less wide-spreading; teeth on leaf-margins mostly antrorsely appressed; corollas light-blue
      7 Corollas 8–11 mm long, limb 8 mm wide, in anthesis.........................**4. S. jamaicensis** f. **jamaicensis**
      7 Corollas about 5 mm long, the limb 4 mm wide, in anthesis...................**S. jamaicensis** f. **parviflora**
    6 Rachis 3–4 mm wide; plant upright-erect; teeth on leaf-margins slightly divergent; corollas dark lavender-blue to violet-purple
      8 Rachis subglabrous or sparsely pilose; leaf-blades mostly elliptic; corolla violet-purple..**3. S. × adulterina**
      8 Rachis plainly (often densely) pilose; leaf-blades mostly ovate; corolla dark lavender-blue..**5. S. × intercedens**
  5 Rachis slender, weak and flexible, to 2.5 mm wide, about as wide as the furrows, not deeply excavated
    9 Leaf-blades glabrous beneath, bullate above when fresh, broad, the marginal teeth widely divergent
      10 Corollas dark purple-blue.....................**6. S. urticaefolia** f. **urticaefolia**
      10 Corollas white...................................**S. urticaefolia** f. **albiflora**
    9 Leaf-blades pilosulous beneath, not bullate above when fresh, the teeth antrorsely appressed
      11 Corollas blue...................................**7. S. dichotoma** f. **dichotoma**
      11 Corollas white..................................**S. dichotoma** f. **albiflora**
1 Leaf-blades lanceolate or narrowly lanceolate-ovate; marginal teeth very coarse and obliquely wide-spreading...**8. S. indica**

1. Stachytarpheta mutabilis (Jacq.) Vahl, Enum. Pl. 1: 209. 1804 var. **mutabilis.** Trimen, Cat. 68. 1885; Trimen, Handb. Fl. Ceylon 3: 349. 1895; Willis, Cat. 142. 1911; Alston, Kandy Fl. 64. 1938; Nair & Rehman, Bull. Nat. Bot. Gard. Lucknow 76: 11. 1962; Gunawardena, Gen. Sp. Pl. Zeyl. 146. 1968; Vajravelu et al., Bull. Bot. Surv. India 10: 78. 1968. Type: *Jacquin s.n.*, from a cultivated plant in the Hortus Schönbrunnensis (W).

Verbena orubica teucriifolio primulae veris flore siliquis & seminibus longissimis Hermann, Parad. Bot. Prod. 383. 1689.—*V. orubica teucriifolio, primulae veris flore, siliquis & seminibus longissimis, cauda muris vulgo* Parkins. ex R. Morison, Pl. Hist. Univ. Oxon. 3: 419. 1699.—*V. orubica tenui folia* Plukenet apud J. Hill, Brit. Herb. 356, in syn. 1756.—*V. orubica, teucrii fol. etc.* Plukenet apud Peterm., Cod. Bot. Linn. Ind. Alph. 196, in syn. 1840.

Verbena americana, veronicae foliis, flore coccineo spicato breynii Comm.,
Hort. 2: 223. 1901.—*V. americana, veronicae foliis, flore coccineo spicato*
Breyn. ex Ray, Hist. Pl. 3: suppl. 286. 1704.—*V. americana veronicae foliis,*
flore coccineo spicato Breyn. ex Vaill., Serm. Struct. Fl. 49, in syn. 1718;
Breyn., Prod. Fasc. Rar. Pl., ed. 2, 2: 104. 1739.—*V. americana flore cocci-*
neo spicato Breyn., Prod. Fasc. Rar. Pl., ed. 2, 2: 104. 1739.
Sherardia teucriifolio, flore coccineo Vaill., Serm. Struct. Fl. 49–50. 1718.
Verbena mutabilis Jacq., Collect. 2: 334–335. 1788.
Zapania mutabilis (Jacq.) Lam., Tabl. Enc. 59. 1791.—*Zappania mutabilis*
Lam. ex Moldenke, Prelim. Alph. List Invalid Names 55, in syn. 1940.
Cymburus mutabilis (Jacq.) Salisb., Parad. Lond. 1: 49. 1805.
Stachytarpheta zuccagni Roem. & Schult. in L., Syst. ed. 15, 1: 205. 1817.
Verbena americana frutescens etc. Breyn. apud Peterm., Cod. Bot. Linn. Ind.
Alph. 196, in syn. 1840.
Stachytarpha mutabilis Vahl apud Schau. in A. DC., Prod. 11: 565. 1847.—
S. mutabilis Schau. apud Danser, Ann. Jard. Bot. Buitenzorg 40: 11, in syn.
1929.—*Stachytarpetha mutabilis* Fedde, Just's Bot. Jahresber. 57 (2): 890,
sphalm. 1938.—*Stachitarpheta mutabilis* Vahl ex Moldenke, Alph. List
Invalid Names Suppl. 1: 20, in syn. 1947.
Stachytarpheta elegans Welw., Apont. Phyto-geogr. Angola 588. 1858.
Valerianodes mutabilis (Jacq.) Kuntze, Rev. Gen. Pl. 2: 510. 1891.—*Valeria-*
noides mutabilis (Jacq.) Kuntze apud Hill, Ind. Kew. Suppl. 9: 293, in syn.
1938.
Stachytarpheta cayennensis var. *schiedeana* Loes., Bot. Jahrb. Syst. 23: 119 &
129. 1896.—*S. cayennensis* var. *schiediana* Loes. ex Moldenke, Prelim.
Alph. List Invalid Names 42, in syn. 1940.
Stachytarpheta variabilis Saunders, Floral Morphol. 2: 446. 1939.—*S. varia-*
bilis Schau. ex Moldenke, Alph. List Invalid Names Suppl. 1: 21, in syn.
1947.
Verbena imbricata Sessé & Moç. ex Moldenke, Prelim. Alph. List Invalid
Names 46, in syn. 1940 [not *V. imbricata* Woot. & Standl., 1913].

Suffrutescent herb or slender straggling shrub, usually 1–2 m (rarely to 5
m) tall, mostly incanous-pubescent throughout; stems stout, sometimes to 2
cm in diameter basally, roughish-pubescent, the wood often very firm and
solid; branches tetragonal, strict, tomentose-villous; leaves decussate-opposite,
petiolate; leaf-blades usually rather thick-chartaceous or sometimes almost
leathery, ovate or oval-oblong, varying to oblong-lanceolate or subcordate-
ovate, 5–10 cm long, acute or acuminate apically, narrowed basally and decurrent into the petiole, uniformly crenate or serrate from just above the base
to the apex with broad mucronate teeth, often rugose and sparsely villous and
scabridous above, densely and persistently canescent-tomentose or -villous
and velutinous beneath; spikes elongate, strict, 1–6 dm long, usually very

stout, to 6 mm in diameter (excluding the corollas), terete; rachis stout, densely strigose-pubescent or hirtellous throughout, rarely very hirsute, shallowly excavated opposite the flowers; bracts herbaceous or membranous, rigid, striate, lanceolate or oblong-lanceolate, 8–12 mm long, subulate-acuminate or cuspidate apically, hirtellous-pubescent toward the margins and there ciliate, the awn-like acumination often divergent or reflexed; calyx tubular, compressed, 8–12 mm long, subequalling or longer than the subtending bract, recurved during anthesis, then erect, finally completely immersed in the furrows of the incrassate rachis, unequally 4-subulate-dentate, the teeth minute; corolla large, showy, hypocrateriform, at first varying from scarlet, crimson, red, or bright red to rose-red, carmine, or magenta, fading to dull brick-rose, rose, rose-pink, bright pink, deep pink, or salmon-pink, sometimes rose-carmine with a white throat and a rose-magenta ring surrounding it, its tube nearly twice as long as the calyx, curvate, dilated at the throat, the limb 8–12 mm wide, unequally 4-parted; cocci shorter than the calyx, cylindric, glabrous.

D i s t r. This species is rather widespread in the American tropics from Mexico and Cuba, through Central America and the West Indies, to northern South America and central Brazil. It has been introduced in Angola, Madagascar, Mauritius, Réunion, India, Pahang, the Lingga Archipelago, Java, Amboina, Fiji, and elsewhere. It is widely cultivated in Europe (since 1801), America, and Australia. In the American tropics it is often employed to make fences or hedges. Lord (Shrubs & Trees Austral. Gard., rev. ed., 314. 1964) asserts that it was originally imported to Australia to serve as an adulterant to tea. Ridley reports that in Malaya it persists for a short time after being thrown out from a garden, but does not seem to establish itself permanently.

U s e s. In Java, according to Heyne (Nutt. Plant. Ned. Ind. 1310. 1927), a decoction of the leaves, along with the leaves of *Aerua sanguinolenta*, is drunk to alleviate painful menstruation. Pounded with lime, the leaves may be applied to swollen wounds and sores. Van Dongan (Bekn. Overz. Geneesmidd. Ned. Oost. Ind. 152. 1913) describes it as an abortifacient.

V e r n. Among several hundred names in various parts of its vast range are: Pink snakeweed and Verbena rosada.

N o t e. *Stachytarpheta mutabilis* is not a hybrid as inferred by Gunawardena (1968).

S p e c i m e n s E x a m i n e d. KANDY DISTRICT: cultivated, Royal Botanic Garden, Peradeniya, April 1887, *s. coll. s.n.* (PDA); in outdoor cultivation, Botany Department gardens, University, Peradeniya, 1550 ft alt., 21 Jan. 1974, shrubs 6 ft tall, corollas red, *H.N. & A.L. Moldenke, Jayasuriya, & Sumithraarachchi 28197* (AAU, ARIZ, CAI, KARACHI, LL, MO, PDA, US); along roadside, Ganegoda, between Peradeniya and Doluwa, 1600 ft alt. 9 Feb. 1974, *A.L. & H.N. Moldenke & Albert 28321* (AAU, ARIZ, CAI, KARACHI, LL, MO, PDA, US); locally abundant, seedlings present, 14th milepost from Kandy to Galagedara, 21 June 1940, *Senaratne 3140* (PDA); Gurukala, at 13/8 milepost along the Kandy to Galaha road, 19 Feb. 1974, wild shrub 4–7 ft tall, very hairy stems and leaves, flowers pink, *Sumithraarachchi DBS. 92* (NY, US).

var. **violacea** Moldenke, Phytologia 1: 436–437. 1940. Type: *Skutch 4224* from San José, Costa Rica (NY).

This variety differs chiefly in having the corollas blue or violet. It is found sporadically in many parts of the range of the species.

S p e c i m e n s E x a m i n e d. KANDY DISTRICT: rare in remnants of forest 1 mile south of Herondale, c. 80° 29' E. 7° 03' N., 2200 ft alt., 8 March 1977, subshrub 2 metres tall, *Bremer & Bremer 1022* (PDA, S, US).

2. **Stachytarpheta** × **trimeni** Rech., Feddes Repert. Spec. Nov. Regni Veg. 11: 189. 1912; Trimen, Handb. Fl. Ceylon 3: 348. 1895; Danser, Ann. Jard. Bot. Buitenzorg 40: 20–24. 1929; Alston in Trimen, Handb. Fl. Ceylon 6: 230. 1931; Alston, Kandy Fl. 64. 1938; Moldenke, Amer. Midl. Naturalist 59: 341. 1958. Type: *Rechinger 2285*, from Kandy, Ceylon (W).

Stachytarpheta indica × *mutabilis* Rech., Feddes Repert. Spec. Nov. Regni Veg. 11: 189, in syn. 1912.—*S. indica* × *S. mutabilis* Trimen ex Alston, Handb. Fl. Ceylon 6: 230. 1931.—*Stachytarpetha indica* × *mutabilis* Fedde, Just's Bot. Jahresber. 57 (2): 890, in syn. 1938.
Stachytarpheta speciosa Danser, Ann. Jard. Bot. Buitenzorg 40: 20–24, pl. 1, fig. 9, & pl. 10. 1929 [not *S. speciosa* Pohl, 1847].
Stachytarpheta jamaicensis × *mutabilis* Danser, Ann. Jard. Bot. Buitenzorg 40: 20, in syn. 1929.
Stachytarpetha trimeni Fedde, Just's Bot. Jahresber. 57 (2): 890, sphalm. 1938.
Stachytarpheta zeylanica × *mutabilis* Hort. ex Moldenke, Phytologia 28: 463, in syn. 1974.

This natural hybrid is very similar to *S. mutabilis* in its general characters, but the plant is usually lower in growth, the leaves are usually smaller, often more obtuse apically, and less densely pubescent, the rachis is only sparingly short-pilose, and the corollas vary from purplish-pink to purple, deep purple, or dark violet and are very hairy within. It is actually a hybrid between *S. urticaefolia* (Salisb.) Sims and *S. mutabilis* (Jacq.) Vahl—the ancestry given by Rechinger, by Danser, and by Trimen is incorrect because Danser consistently misused the name "*S. jamaicensis*" for what is actually *S. urticaefolia*, while Trimen, Rechinger, and Alston misused the name *"S. indica"* for the same plant!

The hybrid has a more slender but stronger stem than does *S. mutabilis*, and with a little pruning can be trained to form a small treelet which will bloom profusely all year and make a splendid addition to tropical gardens. Its pollen is more fertile than one would expect from parental species so very different in appearance. Pistil fertility, however, is not as good—usually only 2 or 3 seeds are formed on an entire spike and from 150 seeds only 5 seedlings were secured by Danser. These he was able to grow to maturity in Java and found that they differed notably from each other, with the two sets of parental characters present in different degrees and combinations in each.

The hybrid is known in the wild also from India (Mysore), Java, Amboina and the Hawaiian Islands and in cultivation from Java.

Specimens Examined. KANDY DISTRICT: growing among both parents near Kandy, *Rechinger 2285* (W). MATALE DISTRICT: Galbodde, Ambagamwa, 1884, *Ferguson s.n.* (PDA).

3. Stachytarpheta × adulterina Urb. & Ekm., Ark. Bot. 22A (17): 105. 1929; Danser, Ann. Jard. Bot. Buitenzorg 40: 17, pl. 1, fig. 8, & pl. 9. 1929; Alston in Trimen, Handb. Fl. Ceylon 6: 230. 1931; Moldenke, Amer. Midl. Nat. 59: 338–339. 1958. Type: *N.L. Britton 3241* from Jamaica (NY).

Valerianoides jamaicensis × mutabilis Britton, Bull. Torrey Bot. Club 37: 356.
1910.—*Valerianodes jamaicensis × mutabilis* Britton ex Moldenke, Résumé 356, in syn. 1959.
Stachytarpheta mutabilis × S. jamaicensis Lam & Brink ex Alston in Trimen, Handb. Fl. Ceylon 6: 230. 1931.—*S. jamaicensis × mutabilis* Britton ex Moldenke, Prelim. Alph. List Invalid Names 42, in syn. 1940.

This natural hybrid between *S. jamaicensis* (L.) Vahl and *S. mutabilis* (Jacq.) Vahl has the height of *S. mutabilis*, but the general facies of *S. jamaicensis*. Danser (1929) gives a detailed description of its variable morphologic characters, but unfortunately uses the name, *S. trimeni* Rech., for it by mistake. Both Danser and Rechinger described their respective plants as hybrids between *"S. indica"* and *S. mutabilis*. However, Rechinger's *"S. indica"* was actually *S. urticaefolia* (Salisb.) Sims, while Danser's was *S. jamaicensis*. Danser's plant, therefore, was not *S. trimeni*, but was *S. adulterina*.

Danser notes that the description of Rechinger's plant does not agree in all particulars with his plant, but that the curators of the Rechinger herbarium in Vienna regarded both plants as the same when he submitted some material of his plant to them. Danser never found *S. adulterina* wild in Java; he produced his plants by artificial pollination in 1926. He predicts, however, that the hybrid is likely to be found wherever the two parental species grow in proximity, either in the wild or in cultivation. He secured no fruit when he pollinated *S. mutabilis* pistils with *S. jamaicensis* pollen, but the reciprocal cross was very successful, yielding 30 plants. Of these, 14 were typical *S. jamaicensis* and 16 were the hybrid.

The hybrid is shrubby, 60 cm–1.8 m tall, the dull-green leaves not as bullate as those of *S. mutabilis*, and the corollas variable in colour, but usually some shade of violet or purple, although some collectors have referred to them as "pinkish-lilac" or even "medium-blue". It has been found wild in Jamaica, Sumatra, Haiti, Cuba, the Seychelles Islands, Queensland, and New Zealand. In New Zealand it is thought to have been introduced from the Seychelles with guano used there to top-dress paddocks. In Ceylon it is known only from a rather ambiguous record by Alston (1931), apparenly not backed by any herbarium material at Peradeniya.

4. **Stachytarpheta jamaicensis** (L.) Vahl, Enum. Pl. 1: 206. 1804 f. **jamaicensis**. Hermann, Mus. Zeyl., ed. 1, 1. 1717; Moon, Cat. 1: 4. 1824; J. Grah., Pl. Bombay 154. 1839; Voigt, Hort. Suburb. Calc. 471. 1845; Thw., Enum. Pl. Zeyl. 241. 1861; Trimen, Cat. 68. 1885; Clarke in Hook. f., Fl. Br. Ind. 4: 564–565. 1885; Trimen, Handb. Fl. Ceylon 3: 348–349. 1895; Cooke, Fl. Pres. Bombay ed. 1, 3: 421. 1905; Willis, Cat. 69. 1911; Alston in Trimen, Handb. Fl. Ceylon 6: 230–231. 1931; Alston, Kandy Fl. vii & 64, fig. 342 & 343. 1938; Kanjilal *et al.*, Fl. Assam 3: 461 & 558. 1939; Cooke, Fl. Pres. Bombay ed. 2, 2: 501. 1958; Abeywick., Ceylon J. Sci., Biol. Sci. 2: 217. 1959; Maheshwari, Fl. Delhi 285. 1963; Chopra, Badhwari, & Ghosh, Poison. Pl. India 2: 700. 1965; Ellis, Bot. Surv. India 8: 337. 1966; Gunawardena, Gen. Sp. Pl. Zeyl. 146. 1968; Fonseka & Vinasithamby, Prov. List Local Names Fl. Pl. Ceylon 5, 18, & 63. 1971; Moldenke in Woodson, Schery, *et al.*, Ann. Missouri Bot. Gard. 60: 74–76. 1973. Type: *P. Browne s.n.* from Jamaica [*Herb. Linnaeus 35/2*] (LINN).

Karalhaebo Hermann, Mus. Zeyl., ed. 1, 1. 1717.
Verbena jamaicensis L., Sp. Pl., ed. 1, 1: 19. 1753.
Zapania jamaicensis (L.) Lam., Tabl. Enc. 1: 59. 1791.
Vermicularia decurrens Moench, Suppl. Meth. Pl. 150. 1802.
Stachytarpheta marginata Vahl, Enum. Pl. 1: 207. 1804.
Stachytarpheta pilosiuscula H.B.K., Nov. Gen. & Sp. Pl., ed. folio, 2: 226. 1817.
Stachytarpheta mexicana Steud., Nom. Bot. Phan., ed. 1, 873, nom. nud. 1821.
Verbena decurrens Moench ex Steud., Nom. Bot. Phan., ed. 1, 807 & 873, in syn. 1821 [not *V. decurrens* (Cham.) Kuntze, 1898].
Stachytarpheta bogoriensis Zoll. & Mor. in Mor., Syst. Verz. Zoll. 52. 1845.
Stachytarpheta indica var. *jamaicensis* (L.) Vahl ex Trimen, Cat. 68. 1885.—
S. indica var. *jamaicensis* Trimen ex Willis, Cat. 69. 1911.—*S. indica* var.

jamaicensis (L.) Razi, J. Mysore Univ. 7 (4): 63. 1946.
Valerianodes jamaicense (L.) Kuntze, Rev. Gen. Pl. 2: 509. 1891.
Valerianodes jamaicense α *sloaneanum* Kuntze, Rev. Gen. Pl. 2: 509. 1891.
Valerianodes jamaicense β *indicum* f. *strigosum* Kuntze, Rev. Gen. Pl. 2: 509. 1891.
Valerianodes jamaicense β *indicum glabrum* Kuntze, Rev. Gen. Pl. 2: 510. 1891.
Valerianodes jamaicense γ *spathulatum* Kuntze, Rev. Gen. Pl. 2: 510. 1891.
Valerianodes jamaicense γ *spathulatum* f. *glabrum* Kuntze, Rev. Gen. Pl. 2: 510. 1891.
Abena jamaicensis (L.) Hitchc., Ann. Rep. Missouri Bot. Gard. 4: 117. 1893.
Stachytarpheta surinamensis Miq. ex Pulle, Enum. Pl. Surin. 402. 1905.
Stachytarpheta friedrichsthalii Hayek, Feddes Repert. 3: 272. 1907.
Stachytarpheta cayennensis Millsp. & Loes. apud Standl., Publ. Field Mus. Nat. Hist., Bot. Ser. 3: 403, in syn. 1930 [not *S. cayennensis* (L.C. Rich.) Vahl, 1804].
Verbena officinalis Cuevas apud Standl., Publ. Field Mus. Nat. Hist. Bot. Ser. 3: 403, in syn. 1930 [not *V. officinalis* L., 1753].
Stachytarpheta dichotoma Heller apud Degener, Fl. Hawaii. fam. 315 sub *S. jamaicensis*, in syn. 1938 [not *S. dichotoma* H.B.K., 1817, nor Humb. & Kunth, 1846, nor (Ruíz & Pav.) Vahl, 1804].
Stachytarpheta strigosa Griseb. ex Moldenke, Résumé 349, in syn. 1959 [not *S. strigosa* Vahl, 1804].

Low and usually spreading herb, 6–12 dm tall, shiny, often purplish throughout, sparingly pubescent or glabrate throughout, sometimes slightly woody basally; stems and branches dichotomous, subtetragonal, usually more or less depressed-spreading, usually glabrate except for the lanuginous-pilose nodes; leaves alternate or opposite, rather fleshy and bluish- or greyish-green when fresh, flat, thin-chartaceous or membranous in drying, oblong or oval or ovate (rarely rounded), 2–8 cm long, 1.2–5 cm wide, obtuse or acute apically, rather coarsely serrate along the margins with acute mostly antrorsely appressed teeth and more or less ciliate-scabrous, cuneately narrowed basally and prolonged into the petiole (which is as long as or shorter than the blade), glabrous on both surfaces or slightly pilosulous on the veins beneath, not usually blackening in drying; spikes terete, stout, stiff, often flexuous, 1.5–5 dm long, glabrous throughout; rachis conspicuously incrassate, to 7 mm wide, the deep furrows much narrower than the rachis itself, especially at maturity; flowers at first erect, later immersed in the thickened rachis furrows; bracts medium-size or comparatively small, lanceolate or oblong-lanceolate, 5–8 mm long, about 2 mm wide, aristate-acuminate apically, striate, scabridous, the margins scarious and obscurely ciliolate; calyx compressed, about 5 mm long or about as long as the subtending bract, its rim bifid, the teeth triangular or triangular-

ovate, completely immersed in the furrows of the rachis in fruit; corolla hypocrateriform, mostly light-blue, 8–11 mm long, the tube slightly curved, the
limb about 8 mm wide; style included; pollen-grains very flattened, peroblate-
oblate, the largest equatorial diameter 110–140μm. Chromosome number:
2n = 160.

D i s t r. This is an almost pantropic "weed" widely distributed in both
tropical and subtropical America from Alabama (U.S.A.), through the West
Indies, Mexico, and Central America, to Ecuador and Brazil; introduced in
parts of tropical Africa, Madagascar, the islands of the Indian Ocean, tropical
Asia, Australia, and Oceania. It has been widely confused with *S. indica* (L.)
Vahl and *S. urticaefolia* (Salisb.) Sims. It hybridizes readily with the latter
species when they grow in close proximity, as well as with other species in the
genus.

U s e s. The juice of the leaves, roots, or the entire plant is used in many
countries as a tonic, emetic, expectorant, sudorific, cathartic, anthelmintic,
emmenagogue, stimulant, antihepatic, purgative, depurative, emollient, and
cooling agent. It is used locally in various parts of its range in the treatment of
headaches, earaches, malaria, tertian fever, yellow fever, amenorrhoea, gonorrhoea, diarrhoea, syphilis, erysipelas, dropsy, jaundice, contusions and wounds
caused by blows, liver troubles, stomach affections, indolent ulcers, intestinal
worms, and nervous pains. It is widely used in the treatment of dysentery. In
Africa the natives use its juice in the treatment of eye troubles such as catar-
acts and of sores in children's ears and the leaves in the treatment of heart-
troubles and as an adulterant in tea. In Java it is fed to horses and cattle as
fodder. In Indonesia the stem-tips are eaten as a flavouring. The dried leaves
are used in many areas to make a poor grade of tea which is sometimes sold
even in Europe as "Brazilian tea". In Malaya a decoction of the leaves is employed against ulcers in the nose and as an antiperiodic in cases of malaria.
In Cuba the juice is used as a bath in treating skin diseases and to bathe
babies during the first six days after birth. In Venezuela a decoction of the
leaves is used against jaundice and in treating sheep poisoning. It is employed
as an abortifacient in India. Saponins, tannins, and a glucoside are present
in the plant. In Jamaica it is used to treat stomach-ache, administered as an
enema, and as a poultice with onion to treat dropsy and ulcers; the expressed
juice is used as a cooling purge in cases of children's fevers and worms. Native
doctors there use it to treat obstruction in menstruation. In fact, writers
assert that in Jamaica "It is very much in repute among the Indian and negro
doctors for the cure of most diseases".

V e r n. Balu-nakuta, Rata-nil-nakuta (S); Nay-uranchi, Simainavirunji
(T). Among its 100 or more other names in various parts of its range are:
Berbena, Blue porterweed, Blue snakeweed, Common snakeweed, Gervão,
Jamaica vervain, Porterweed, Rinchão, Verbena azúl, Verbena cimarrona,

Verbena manza, Verbena morada, and Vervain. The name Karalhaebo is also recorded from Ceylon.

N o t e. The flowers often become deformed by the galls produced by an itonid insect, *Hyperdiplosis producta*, in South America; in India the inflorescences become deformed due to the virus, *Chlorogenus santali*. It is also often attacked by the following fungi: *Asteridiella callista*, *Cercospora stachytarphetae*, *Endophyllum stachytarphetae*, *Micropuccinia urbaniana*, and *Puccinia lantanae*. Biologic control is possible by a snail, *Marisa* sp.

S p e c i m e n s E x a m i n e d. JAFFNA DISTRICT: on heavily grazed dry land among rice fields near Ampan, 14 Jan. 1970, *Clayton 5238* (PDA, US). ANURADHAPURA DISTRICT: Siyambalagastanne, 9 Dec. 1926, *Alston s.n.* (PDA); abundant along roadsides, Rajangana, 25 Jan. 1974, low altitude, corolla lavender-blue, *H.N. & A.L. Moldenke & Jayasuriya 28236* (AAU, ARIZ, CAI, KARACHI, LL, MO, PDA, US). COLOMBO DISTRICT: in coconut plantation, Badalgama, low altitude, 16 Jan. 1974, plants low, spreading, leaves pale-green, flat, corollas lavender-blue, *H.N. & A.L. Moldenke, Jayasuriya, & Sumithraarachchi 28125* (AAU, ARIZ, CAI, KARACHI, LL, MO, PDA, US). KANDY DISTRICT: Peradeniya, mixed with *S. urticaefolia*, Aug. 1884. *s. coll. s.n.* (PDA); scattered on dry sandy road shoulders, Haragama, 1500 ft alt., 19 Jan. 1974, plants low, spreading, leaves light grey-green, flat, corollas lavender-blue, *H.N. & A.L. Moldenke, Jayasuriya, & Sumithraarachchi 28179* (LL, PDA, US). MATALE DISTRICT: 1 mile north of Naula at road-marker 35/9, 500 feet altitude, 23 Jan. 1974, plants low, spreading, leaves grey-green, flat, corollas pale lavender-blue, *H.N. & A.L. Moldenke & Jayasuriya 28214* (AAU, ARIZ, CAI, KARACHI, LL, MO, PDA, US). MONERAGALA DISTRICT: common on roadsides, Kirindi-oya. 13 Aug. 1932, *Simpson 9962* (PDA). AMPARAI DISTRICT: on floodplain, Hatpatha, southern shore of Senanayake Samudra, Gal-oya National Park, low altitude, 5 May 1975, low herb, corolla purplish-blue, *Jayasuriya 2079* (PDA, US); not common on eastern side of drier grassland fringe, Lahugula tank, 25 July 1967. *Mueller-Dombois & Comanor 67072518* (PDA, US). TRINCOMALEE DISTRICT: 3 miles west of the Mahaweli-Ganga ferry road, Kantalai, 23 Nov. 1975, coarse herb, becoming woody, flowers blue, *Sohmer & Sumithraarachchi 10791* (NY). HAMBANTOTA DISTRICT: near fishing village at Patangala, Ruhuna National Park, Block I, 22 April 1969, *Cooray 69042206R* (LL, PDA, US). LOCALITY UNKNOWN: *Fraser 4* (US), *101* (US); *Simpson 8446* (BM).

f. **parviflora** Moldenke, Phytologia 28: 304. 1974. Type: *Fosberg & Stoddart 54896* from Canton Island (US).

This form differs from the typical form of the species in having its corollas only about half as large during anthesis. It apparently occurs sporadically in various parts of the range of the species.

Specimens Examined. PUTTALAM DISTRICT: in shady roadside at edge of jungle, Wanniyagama, 25 Jan. 1974, corolla 1/2 normal size, pale-blue, *H.N. & A.L. Moldenke & Jayasuriya 28240* (MOLDENKE, PDA, US).

5. **Stachytarpheta × intercedens** Danser, Ann. Jard. Bot. Buitenzorg 40: 16–17, pl. 1, fig. 7. 1929; Alston, Kandy Fl. 64. 1938; Moldenke, Amer. Midl. Nat. 59: 340–341. 1958.

Stachytarpheta indica × jamaicensis Danser, Ann. Jard. Bot. Buitenzorg 40: 16, in syn. 1929.

Stachytarpheta intercedens Fedde, Just's Bot. Jahresber. 57 (2): 890, sphalm. 1938.

Stachytarpheta jamaicensis (L.) Vahl × *S. urticaefolia* (Salisb.) Sims ex Moldenke, Résumé 349, in syn. 1959.—*S. urticaefolia* (Salisb.) Sims × *S. jamaicensis* (L.) Vahl ex Moldenke, Résumé 349, in syn. 1959.

This is a natural hybrid between *S. jamaicensis* and *S. urticaefolia* found rather commonly where the ranges of both parental species overlap and the plants grow in close proximity. The plants are weakly upright-erect in growth, the leaf-blades mostly ovate, their marginal teeth slightly divergent, the rachis plainly (often densely) pilose, the corollas dark lavender-blue, and pollen-grains seldom formed in the anthers. When growing among its parents it is easily distinguishable in the field. Danser (1929) gives a detailed description of this hybrid in comparison with its parents, but unfortunately misidentified the parents—what he calls *S. indica* is actually *S. jamaicensis* and what he calls *S. jamaicensis* is *S. urticaefolia*. In general the hybrid resembles *S. jamaicensis* more closely than it does *S. urticaefolia*, but the corollas are larger and darker in colour than those of *S. jamaicensis*, the habit is more erect, and the leaves are more ovate and darker green, with slightly more divergent teeth.

Specimens Examined. COLOMBO DISTRICT: Scattered in coconut plantation, dry sandy soil, growing between parents, Nahalla, 500 ft alt., 16 Jan. 1974, corollas dark lavender-blue, darker than *S. jamaicensis*, *H.N. & A.L. Moldenke, Jayasuriya, & Sumithraarachchi 28126* (AAU, ARIZ, CAI, KARACHI, LL, MOLDENKE, PDA, US). KANDY DISTRICT: occasional among parents along roadside and on road shoulders 4 miles east of Hunnasgiriya, 1700 ft alt., 19 Jan. 1974, *H.N. & A.L. Moldenke, Jayasuriya, & Sumithraarachchi 28183* (AAU, ARIZ, CAI, KARACHI, LL, MO, PDA, US). MATALE DISTRICT: scattered among parents on roadside, limestone area, at milepost 36 on Kandy to Dambulla road, 400 ft alt., 23 Jan. 1974, *H.N. & A.L. Moldenke & Jayasuriya 28215* (AAU, CAI, LL, PDA, US).

6. **Stachytarpheta urticaefolia** (Salisb.) Sims, Bot. Mag. 43: pl. 1848 [as "*urticifolia*"]. 1816 f. **urticaefolia** [mostly as "*S. indica*"]. Moon, Cat. 1: 4. 1824;

Thw., Enum. Pl. Zeyl. 241. 1861; Clarke in Hook. f., Fl. Br. Ind. 4: 564–565.
1885; Trimen, Cat. 68. 1885; Prain, Bengal Pl. 826. 1903; Cooke, Fl. Pres.
Bombay, ed. 1, 3: 421. 1905; Duthie, Fl. Up. Ganges Pl. 2: 229. 1911; Haines,
Bot. Bihar & Orissa 4: 707. 1922; Gamble, Fl. Pres. Madras 6: 1090. 1924;
Alston in Trimen, Handb. Fl. Ceylon 6: 229–231. 1931; Alston, Kandy Fl. vii
& 64, fig. 342. 1938; Kanjilal *et al.*, Fl. Assam 3: 461 & 558. 1939; Rao, J.
Indian Bot. Soc. 31: [297], 299–301, & 311–314, fig. 10. 1952; Bor & Raizada,
Some Beaut. Indian Climb. 137, 138, & 188, fig. 87, pl. 52. 1954; Cooke, Fl.
Pres. Bombay, ed. 2, 2: 501. 1958; Abeywick., Ceylon J. Sci., Biol. Sci. 2: 217.
1959; Bose, Handb. Shrubs 90. 1965; Chopra, Badhwari & Ghosh, Poison. Pl.
India 2: 695 & 700, fig. 178. 1965; Maheshwari & Singh, Dict. Econ. Pl. India
149. 1965; Duthie, Fl. Up. Ganges p. 9: 43. 1967; Gunawardena, Gen. & Sp.
Pl. Zeyl. 146. 1968; Fonseka & Vinasithamby, Prov. List Local Names, Fl. Pl.
Ceylon 5, 18, 62, 63, & 65. 1971. Type: an Isaac Swainson collection from
cultivated material near London in or before 1806 (BM).

Cymburus urticaefolius Salisb., Parad. Lond. pl. 53. 1806.—*Cimburus urtici-*
folius Salisb. apud Jiménez, Cat. Fl. Doming. Suppl. 1: 220, in syn. 1966.
Stachytarpheta urticifolia Sims, Bot. Mag. 43: pl. 1848. 1816.—*S. urticaefolia*
Sims ex Voigt, Hort. Suburb. Calc. 472. 1845.—*S. urticifolia* (Salisb.) Sims
ex Moldenke, Résumé Suppl. 3: 35, in syn. 1962.—*Stachytarphaeta urti-*
caefolia (Salisb.) Sims apud Venkatareddi, Bull. Bot. Surv. India 11: 258.
1969.
Verbena violacea Walker ex Sims, Bot. Mag. 43: pl. 1848, in syn. 1816.
Zapania urticifolia Poir., Enc. Méth. Bot. 5: 520. 1817.
Valerianoides urticaefolia Buswell ex Moldenke, Alph. List Invalid Names
Suppl. 1: 22, in syn. 1947.
Stachytarpheta jamaicensis sensu Alston ex Abeywick., Ceylon J. Sci., Biol.
Sci. 2: 217, in syn. 1959 [not *S. jamaicensis* (L.) Vahl, 1804].
Stachytarpheta indica Auct. ex Raizada, Indian Forester 92: 324, in syn. 1966
[not *S. indica* (L.) Vahl, 1804].
Stachytarpheta zeylanica Hort. ex Moldenke, Phytologia 28: 463, in syn. 1974.

   A rather coarse herb or subshrub, 0.8–2 m tall, mostly weakly erect,
intricately branched, with a long tap-root; branches mostly quite slender, ascending or spreading, glabrous or the younger parts rather obscurely pilosulous; internodes often quite elongate; leaves decussate-opposite; petioles 5–20
mm long, cuneately winged and not distinct from the base of the blade, obscurely pilosulous or glabrate; leaf-blades membranous, not fleshy, usually
dark glossy-green above when fresh, lighter beneath, plainly bullate-rugose
above when fresh, oval or ovate to broadly elliptic, 4–8 cm long, 2–4.5 cm
wide, rather abruptly acute apically, cuneately acuminate into the petiole
basally, glabrous on both surfaces, the margins from the apex to the start of
the basal acumination regularly and sharply serrate with antrorse, divergent

(often widely so) triangular teeth; midrib sometimes deep vinous-purple in fresh leaves; spikes elongate, many-flowered, mostly terminating the branches or rarely a few in the upper leaf-axils, erect or nutant, 14–40 cm long, slender, short-pedunculate; peduncles 1–2 cm long, minutely and obscurely pilosulous or subglabrate; rachis slender, about 2.5 mm in diameter, often weak and flexible during anthesis, stiffer in fruit, not deeply excavated, about as wide as the furrows; flowers imbricate, opening centripetally a few at a time, each lasting only one day; bracts lanceolate, conspicuous, about equalling the subtending calyx, 7 mm long, 2 mm wide at the base, glabrate or microscopically puberulent, scarious only on the wide basal portion and there often microscopically ciliolate, long-aristate apically; calyx cylindric, about 7 mm long and 2 mm wide, closely appressed to ther achis, 5-costate, glabrate, the rim shortly 5-toothed, the teeth about 0.5 mm long, apiculate; corolla hypocrateriform, usually dark purple-blue with a lighter-coloured or white central "eye"; stamens and style white; stigma yellowish-white.

D i s t r. This much-misunderstood species has a widespread distribution. It is probably native to tropical Asia from India, through Burma, Thailand, Indo-China, and Malaya to Hong Kong, north to the Ryukyu Islands and Formosa and east through the Philippines, Marianas and Palau Islands, and Indonesia, to the islands of the far Pacific; widely introduced now in Florida (U.S.A.), the Greater and Lesser Antilles, Tobago, and South America from Venezuela and the Guianas south to Brazil and in Africa from the Sudan through Kenya, Tanzania, and Zaire to South Africa, Madagascar, and the Seychelles Islands. It tends to become a common roadside "weed", spreading also into areas of secondary vegetation, sand dunes, and coconut plantations.

U s e s. In the Samoan Islands the natives regard this plant as good only as food for goats, and of questionable value at that. In the Society Islands the juice is mixed with coconut oil and taken as a laxative; in Sabah it is also employed in native medicine. In Venezuela the leaves are used to make tea.

V e r n. Bala-nakuta, Balloona-koota, Balu-nakuta, Batu-nakuta, Nil-nakuta (S), Naioriji, Naioring, Nay uranch, Nay uranchi, Nil-nakuta (T). Among its 50 or more other vernacular names in various parts of its range are: Aaron's-rod, Blue rat's-tail, Dog's-tail, false vervain, Nettle-leaved cymburus, Nettle-leaved bastard vervain, and Snake-weed.

N o t e s. In the Fiji Islands it is reported that the stamens and pistils of this species and of *S. mutabilis* (Jacq.) Vahl are fed on by the hymenopterous parasite, *Scolia ruficornis*, which parasitizes the coconut rhinoceros beetle, *Oryctes rhinoceros*, which is so destructive to cultivated coconut trees.

This species has been confused very widely in literature and herbaria and misidentified as *S. cayennensis* (L.C. Rich.) Vahl, *S. dichotoma* (Ruíz & Pav.) Vahl, *S. orubica* (L.) Vahl, *S. jamaicensis* (L.) Vahl, and especially *S. indica* (L.) Vahl, from all of which taxa it is abundantly distinct. In fact, Salisbury himself (1806) thought that this was Linnaeus' *Verbena jamaicensis*, which he cited as a synonym. However, since he gives a Latin diagnosis for his *Cymburus urticaefolius* differing from that of Linnaeus, his binomial has legal standing and his specific epithet must be adopted with its original spelling. His colour illustration is not very accurate and his statement of where the species is native and was collected applies equally well to *S. jamaicensis* and was probably copied from Linnaeus. The colour illustration given by Sims (1816), on the other hand, is very excellent and his description unmistakable. He enumerates his reasons very clearly for regarding it as distinct from *S. jamaicensis*. In the field the two species are easily distinguished. In *S. urticaefolia* the growth is mostly erect, the leaves are thinly membranous, dark green and bullate when fresh, the marginal teeth are plainly divergent, the bracts are scarious only at their base, and the corollas are mostly dark purplish-blue. In *S. jamaicensis* the growth is mostly low and wide-spreading, the leaves are greyish- or bluish-green, fleshy, and flat, the marginal teeth are appressed, the bracts are scarious for their entire length or even mostly apically, and the corollas are light blue. A hybrid is often found where the two species grow in proximity (*S.* × *intercedens* Dans.). Plants with fasciated spikes are sometimes seen.

Specimens Examined. KURUNEGALA DISTRICT: Very common along roadsides and the edges of woodland, 400 ft alt., 25 Jan. 1974, plants erect, leaves dark green, bullate, corollas dark purple-blue, *H.N. & A.L. Moldenke & Jayasuriya 28258* (CAI, KARACHI, PDA, US). ANURADHAPURA DISTRICT: Siyambalagastenne, 9 Dec. 1926, *Alston s.n.* (PDA). COLOMBO DISTRICT: abundant along roadside near fences, Madampella, low altitude, 16 Jan. 1974, corollas purple-blue, leaves dark-green, bullate, plants erect, *H.N. & A.L. Moldenke, Jayasuriya, & Sumithraarachchi 28124* (AAU, ARIZ, CAI, KARACHI, LL, MO, PDA, US). KANDY DISTRICT: along slope, "shrub height 8 m in higher areas to 2–3 m when rooted at stream edge", Upper Hantana Road, University Peradeniya, 545 m altitude, 15 May 1967, *Comanor 309* (NY, PDA, US); on roadside slope toward cliff in lateritic clay soil, Lower Hantana Road, University, Peradeniya, near waterfall above church, 29 Dec. 1967, *Comanor 686* (AAU, MICH, NY, PDA); Peradeniya, *Alston E. 2* (PDA), *E. 3* (PDA); Peradeniya, mixed with *S. jamaicensis*, Aug. 1884, *s. coll. s.n.* (PDA); in roadcut on steep mountainside in forest cover about 5 miles south on Ginigathena, north of Adam's Peak, 1000 m altitude, 25 April 1930, *Gould 13592* (PDA); Udawatte, 28 Sept. 1970, *Kundu & Balakrishnan 120* (US); in outdoor cultivation, Students' Garden, Royal Botanic Garden, Peradeniya, 1550 ft alt., 18 Jan. 1974, plants 3 ft tall, corollas bluish-purple, *H.N. & A.L. Moldenke & Jayasuriya 28157* (AAU, PDA, US); abundant on roadsides and road shoulders, Haragama, 1500 ft alt., 19 Jan. 1974, plants erect, leaves dark-green, bullate, corollas purple-blue, *H.N. & A.L. Moldenke, Jayasuriya, & Sumithraarachchi 28180* (AAU, CAI, KARACHI, LL,

PDA, US); Peradeniya, 1572 ft alt., 12 June 1930, flowers blue, "balu-nakuta", S., *J.M. Silva 201* (NY); Bible Rock, 2618 ft alt., 19 March 1974, *Sumithraara-chchi & Fernando DBS. 130* (US). MATALE DISTRICT: at edge of roadside forest patch, low forest border, before milepost 44/A9 on Matale to Dambulla road, 215 m altitude, 12 Jan. 1968, *Comanor 720* (AAU, NY, PDA); locality abundant along shady roadside, Alawatugoda, 800 ft alt., 23 Jan. 1974, plants erect, leaves dark-green, bullate, corollas dark purple-blue, *H.N. & A.L. Moldenke & Jayasuriya 28205* (AAU, LL, PDA, US); very abundant along road-sides, Naula, 500 ft alt., 23 Jan. 1974, plants erect, leaves dark green, bullate, corollas dark purple-blue, *H.N. & A.L. Moldenke & Jayasuriya 28213* (AAU, LL, PDA, US). NUWARA ELIYA DISTRICT: on dry patana, January, *Carrick 1300* (KLU); abundant on road shoulders and banks in shaded areas at road-marker 31/5 beyond Pussellewa, 3200 ft alt., 28 Jan. 1974, 4 ft tall, leaves dark green, bullate, corollas dark purple-blue, *H.N. & A.L. Moldenke, Jayasuriya, & Sumithraarachchi 28265* (AAU, ARIZ, CAI, KARACHI, LL, MO, PDA, US); abundant in shady places at edge of forest, Ramboda, 3200 ft alt., 30 Jan. 1974, plants erect, leaves dark green, bullate, corollas dark-purple, *H.N. & A.L. Moldenke, Jayasuriya, & Sumithraarachchi 28308* (AAU, ARIZ, CAI, KARACHI, LL, MO, PDA, US). KEGALLE DISTRICT: common on hill-side around rock fences above railroad track 1/2 mile west of Kadugannawa between tunnels 10 and 11, 500 m alt., 5 Sept. 1969, *Grupe 203* (PDA, US); abundant on shady roadsides, Kalugahatenne, 500 ft alt., 12 Feb. 1974, leaves dark green, bullate, corollas dark purple-blue, plants erect, *H.N. & A.L. Moldenke, Dassanayake, & Jayasuriya 28330* (AAU, ARIZ, CAI, KARACHI, LL, MO, PDA, US); common, Meliganga River near "Bridge on River Kwai", 23 April 1972, *Mueller-Dombois & Balakrishnan 72042304* (US). MONERAGALA DISTRICT: wayside weed. Rathugala off Mullegama, low altitude, 4 May 1975, corollas purplish-blue, *Jayasuriya 2054* (LL, US). MATARA DISTRICT: Urapola, 27 Sept. 1969, *Amaratunga 1858* (PDA).

f. **albiflora** Moldenke, Phytologia 4: 182. 1953. Type: *Danser 6655* from Tjiandjoer along the roadside near Soekaboemi, Res. Priangan, Java, collected 30 May 1927 (BO).

This form differs from the typical form in having pure white corollas. It is found sporadically throughout the range of the species, being known from Java, Amboina, the Samoan and Hawaiian Islands, and Martinique, as well as in cultivation. In Ceylon it is thus far known only from cultivated material.

Specimens Examined. KANDY DISTRICT: Economic Nursery, Royal Botanic Garden, Peradeniya, 8 Nov. 1940, flowers pure white, *Y.W. de Silva 826* (PDA).

7. **Stachytarpheta dichotoma** (Ruíz & Pav.) Vahl, Enum. Pl. 1: 207. 1804 f.

dichotoma. Alston in Trimen, Handb. Fl. Ceylon 6: 231. 1931; St. John & Hosaka, Univ. Hawaii Res. Publ. 6: 128–129. 1932; Junell, Symb. Bot. Upsal. 4: 24, 27, & 29, fig. 30–35, 37–41, & 50–52. 1934; Kuhlmann & Kühn, Fl. Distr. Ibiti 116 & 182. 1947; Weiss & O'Brien, Ind. Pl. Diseases U.S. 5: 1176. 1953; Darlington & Wylie, Chromos. Atlas, ed. 2, 324. 1956; León & Alain, Fl. Cuba 4: 295 & 296. 1957; Neal, Gard. Hawaii, ed. 2, 723 & 725, fig. 276c. 1965; Pope, Man. Wayside Pl. 192–194. 1968; Howes, Dict. Useful Pl. 255. 1974; López-Palacios, Revista Fac. Farmac. Univ. Los Andes 15: 79–81. 1975. Type: A Ruíz & Pavon collection from "in silvis Cuchero at Chinchao", Peru, (probably MA).

Verbena dichotoma Ruíz & Pav., Fl. Peruv. & Chil. 1: 23, pl. 34b. 1798.
Stachytarpheta hirta H.B.K., Nov. Gen. & Sp. Pl., ed. folio, 2: 226. 1817.
Stachytarpheta umbrosa H.B.K., Nov. Gen. & Sp. Pl., ed. folio, 2: 227. 1817.
—*S. umbrosa* Kunth ex Voss in Vilm., Blumengärt., 1: 825, in syn. 1895.—
S. umbrosa Hort ex Moldenke, Alph. List Invalid Names 21, in syn. 1947.
Verbena jamaicensis Vell., Fl. Flum. 16. 1825; Ic. 1: pl. 37. 1827 [not *V. jamaicensis* L., 1753].
Stachytarpheta gibberosa Reichenb., Ic. Bot. Exot. 2: 15, pl. 138. 1828.
Stachytarpha cajanensis Cham. apud Schau. in A. DC., Prod. 11: 562. 1847 [not *Stachytarpheta cajanensis* Vahl, 1804].—*Stachytarpheta cayennensis* Briq., Ark. Bot. 2, no. 10: 21, in syn. 1904 [not *S. cayennensis* (L.C. Rich.) Vahl, 1804].
Stachytarpha dichotoma Vahl apud Schau. in A. DC., Prod. 11: 561. 1847.—
Stachytarpheta dichotoma Vahl ex Voss in Vilm., Blumengärt. 1: 825. 1895.
—*S. dicotoma* Vahl ex Harris, Physico-chem. Prop. Pl. Saps 134. 1934.—
S. dicotoma Hastings ex Moldenke, Prelim. Alph. List Invalid Names 42, in syn. 1940.—*Stachytarphetta dichotoma* Vahl ex Barroso, Rodriguesia 32: 70. 1957.—*Stachytarpheta dichotoma* Wahl. ex Moldenke, Résumé Suppl. 12: 12, in syn. 1965 [not *S. dichotoma* Heller, 1938, nor H.B.K., 1817, nor Humb. & Kunth, 1846].—*S. dichotyma* MacDaniels ex Moldenke, Phytologia 26: 376, in syn. 1973.
Stachytarpha jamaicensis Gardn. apud Schau. in A. DC., Prod. 11: 561–562, in syn. 1847.—*Stachytarpheta jamaicensis* Gardn. apud. Jacks. in Hook. f. & Jacks., Ind. Kew. 2: 974, in syn. 1895 [not *S. jamaicensis* (L.) Vahl, 1804].
Valerianodes dichotoma Kuntze ex Voss in Vilm., Blumengärt 1: 825. 1895.
—*V. dichotomum* (R. & P.) Cook & Collins ex Moldenke, Prelim. Alph. List Invalid Names 44, in syn. 1940.
Verbena jamaicensis var. *campestris* Griseb. ex Seckt, Revista Univ. Nac. Cordoba 17: 90. 1930.
Bouchea dichotoma Mohr [in part] ex Moldenke, Prelim. Alph. List Invalid Names 7, in syn. 1940.
Stachytarpheta australis Moldenke, Prelim. Alph. List Invalid Names 42, hy-

ponym. 17 March 1940; Phytologia 1: 470. 25 November 1940.—*S. austra-lis* Mild. ex Reitz, Sellowia 11: 50, sphalm. 1959.

Zapania dichotoma (Ruíz & Pav.) Mirb. ex Moldenke, Prelim. Alph. List In-valid Names 54, in syn. 1940.

Stachytarpheta guianensis Good ex Moldenke, Résumé Suppl. 18: 14, in syn. 1969.—*S. guyanensis* Vattuoni & Bianchi ex Moldenke, Fifth Summ. 2: 630, in syn. 1971.

Shrubby annual or perennial subshrub, branching, 25 cm to 2 m tall, the base becoming woody; stems and branches dichotomous, slender, rather ob-tusely tetragonal, light-grey, the upper internodes usually sharply margined, the youngest portions usually sublanuginous at the nodes, glabrous or sub-glabrescent in age; branchlets very slender, brownish, more or less densely short pubescent; leaves decussate-opposite, small, pale green; petioles very slender, 3–8 mm long, appressed-pubescent; leaf-blades membranous or chart-aceous, brunnescent above in drying, somewhat lighter beneath, elliptic to ovate-oblong or ovate, 1.5–10 cm long, 1–5 cm wide, acute or acuminate api-cally, regularly serrate or coarsely crenate-serrate from almost the base to the apex with small, sharply acute or subacuminate, antrorse teeth, cuneately nar-rowed basally and decurrently prolonged into the petiole, usually densely puberulent and scabrellous above, varying to strigillose or glabrate, not at all rugose nor bullate, slightly scabridous along the margins, more or less substri-gose-hirsutulous or appressed-pubescent beneath with short hairs often more dense on the larger venation, rarely glabrate except for the venation; spikes terminal, slender, flaccid, 15–45 cm long, densely many-flowered, sometimes almost black, more or less densely hirsutulous throughout, sometimes fasciat-ed; rachis very slender, scarcely or very slightly incrassate, more or less densely whitish-pilose, its furrows about as broad as the rachis; bracts lanceolate, about 5 mm long, long-attenuate or much narrowed to subulate-aristate api-cally, striate, scarious and more or less pilose-ciliate along the margins; flowers small, somewhat but not deeply embedded in the rachis, subrecurved-spread-ing or later erect during anthesis; calyx light-green, compressed, about 6 mm long, 4-costate and 4-plicate, pilose, its rim 4-dentate, about equalling or sur-passing the subtending bracts, the lobes often violet-tipped; corolla hypocra-teriform, varying from blue, light blue, or sky-blue to blue-violet, light violet, violet, rose, lilac, mauve, pale purplish, or purple, sometimes lavender with a white throat and mouth, the tube slightly curvate, scarcely surpassing the calyx, the limb medium-size; filaments white; anthers dark brown; style in-cluded, white; stigma greenish; fruiting-calyx erect, half immersed in the rachis-furrow. Chromosome number: 2n = 18 (Baldwin) or "c. 112" (Junell).

D i s t r. A widely distributed species apparently native from Cuba and Mexico south to Argentina and Peru; introduced and now spreading in Assam, Ceylon, Java, New Guinea, New Caledonia, the Hawaii Islands, and elsewhere.

U s e s. In Brazil *S. dichotoma* is much esteemed in popular medicine in all the areas of agricultural and/or sheep-raising activity; it is also used in native medicine in Argentina.

V e r n. Among its 20 recorded vernacular names in various parts of its range are: Brazilian tea, Cuturuguay, False vervain, Gervão, Owi, Timbo, Verbena azul, Vervain, and Yerbon.

N o t e. It is very closely related to (and possibly better regarded as a variety of) *S. cayennensis* (L.C. Rich.) Vahl, which is glabrous or subglabrate throughout, but is also widely confused with *S. indica* (L.) Vahl, *S. jamaicensis* (L.) Vahl, *S. lythrophylla* Schau., and *S. strigosa* Vahl. Some authors place *S. urticaefolia* (Salisb.) Sims in the synonymy of *S. dichotoma*, but the two taxa are abudantly distinct.

It may be noted here that the original description of *Verbena dichotoma* Ruíz & Pav. (1798) calls for the branches to be hairy only at the articulations (=nodes), but the illustration accompanying the description plainly shows scattered hairs on the entire length of the branches, petioles, and lower leaf-surface, but the inflorescence completely glabrous.

S p e c i m e n s E x a m i n e d. KANDY DISTRICT: main Police Station at turnoff to Bahirawakanda, Kandy, 21 May 1969, common, flowers purple, collected as voucher for ecologic observations, *Cooray 69052101R* (PDA); single plant on roadbank at milepost 18/14 south of Kandy on the Nuwara Eliya road, 2000 ft alt., 30 Jan. 1974, corollas very pale-bluish, *H.N. & A.L. Moldenke, Jayasuriya, & Sumithraarachchi 28309* (AAU, ARIZ, CAI, KARACHI, LL, MO, PDA, US).

f. **albiflora** (Moldenke) Moldenke, Phytologia 28: 102. 1974. Type: *H.N. & A.L. Moldenke 19654* from low wet soil near edge of lake, Interlagos, São Paulo, Brazil, collected 25 September 1948 (NY).

Stachytarpheta australis f. *albiflora* Moldenke, Phytologia 3: 63. 1949.

This form differs from the typical form only in having white corollas. It occurs sporadically throughout the range of the species, being known from Jamaica, Venezuela, Brazil, Argentina, Bolivia, Ceylon, Malaya, Java, New Caledonia, and the Samoan and Hawaiian Islands.

V e r n. Cola de tatu, tatu-ruguay, and yerbon.

S p e c i m e n s E x a m i n e d. KANDY DISTRICT: along roadside, Lady Blake's Drive Kandy, 1550 ft alt., 27 Jan. 1974, only one plant seen, all corollas white, *H.N. & A.L. Moldenke & S. de Silva 28259* (AAU, CAI, KARACHI, LL, PDA, US); growing wild, Royal Botanic Garden, Peradeniya, 26 June, 1974, shrubs, flowers white, *Sumithraarachchi DBS. 382* (LACROSSE), *DBS. 383* (AAU, LL).

8. Stachytarpheta indica (L.) Vahl, Enum. Pl. 1: 206. 1804; L., Syst. ed. 10, 2: 851. 1759; L., Sp. Pl., ed. 2, 27. 1762; Jacq., Obs. 4: 7, pl. 86. 1771; Moon, Cat. 1: 4. 1824; Bojer, Hort. Maurit. 255. 1837; Schau. in A. DC., Prod. 11: 564. 1847; Thw., Enum. Pl. Zeyl. 241. 1861; Trimen, Cat. 68. 1885; Trimen, Handb. Fl. Ceylon 3: 348. 1895; Baker in Thiselt.-Dyer, Fl. Trop. Africa 5: 284. 1900; Willis, Cat. 69. 1911; Hallier, Meded. Rijks-Herb. 37: 20–21. 1918; Danser, Ann. Jard. Bot. Buitenzorg 40: 5. 1929; Alston in Trimen, Handb. Fl. Ceylon 6: 231. 1931; Alston, Kandy Fl. vii & 64, fig. 342 & 343. 1938; Abeywick., Ceylon J. Sci., Biol. Sci. 2: 217. 1959; Gaussen, Viart, Legris, & Labroue, Trav. Sect. Scient. Techn. Inst. Franç. Pond. Hors 5: 35 & 43. 1965; Balasubramaniam, Ceylon J. Sci., Biol. Sci. 7: 116–123. 1967; Gunawardena, Gen. Sp. Pl. Zeyl. 146. 1968; Fonseka & Vinasithamby, Prov. List Local Names Fl. Pl. Ceylon 5, 62, 63 & 65. 1971; Vivekanandan, Sri Lanka Forester ser. 2, 11: 114 & 132. 1974. Type: Herb. Linnaeus 35: 1, cultivated at Uppsala, Sweden, seeds supposedly sent from Ceylon.

Verbena indica Bondt, Hist. Nat. Med. Ind. Orient. 150–151. 1658; Hermann, Mus. Zeyl., ed. 1, 1, in syn. 1717.—*Verbena indica bontii* Hermann ex Moldenke, Phytologia 31: 411, in syn. 1971.
Amaranthus spicatus Boccone ex Hermann, Mus. Zeyl., ed. 1, 1, in syn. 1717.
Verbena indica L., Syst. ed. 10, 2: 851. 1759.
Zapania indica (L.) Lam., Tabl. Enc. [Illustr.] 1: 59. 1791.
Verbena caudata Salisb., Prod. 71. 1796.
Vermicularia lancifolia Moench, Suppl. Meth. Pl. 150–151. 1802.
Verbena ellipticifolia Stokes, Bot. Mat. Med. 1: 38. 1812.
Verbena ellipticifolia α *acuta* Stokes, Bot. Mat. Med. 1: 38. 1812.
Stachytarpheta ciliata Kunze, Del. Sem. Hort. Lips. 9. 1840.
Verbena lancifolia Moench ex Steud., Nom. Bot., ed. 2, 2: 750, in syn. 1841.
   —*Verbena lancifolia* Steud. ex H.J. Lam, Verbenac. Malay. Arch. 369, in syn. 1919.
Valerianodes jamaicense β *indicum* Kuntze, Rev. Gen. Pl. 2: 509–510. 1891.
Stachytarpheta indica L. ex Patermann, Beitr. Zytol. Verbenac. 20–23. 1935.—*Stachytarpheta indica* Trimen ex Alston, Kandy Fl. vii, in syn. 1938.—*Stachytarpetha indica* Fedde in Just's Bot. Jahresber. 57 (2): 890. 1938.

This is an extremely poorly understood taxon, whose nomenclature is inordinately confused. The binomial *Stachytarpheta indica* has been applied variously by botanists in the past and is even today variously applied to *S. jamaicensis*, *S. urticaefolia*, and *S. angustifolia*.

The name is based on *Verbena indica* L., first published by Linnaeus in his Syst. ed. 10, in 1759. His description is, unfortunately, very brief ["V. diandra, spicis longissimis carnosis nudis, fol. lanceolato-ouatis oblique dentatis, caule laeui"] and he cites no illustrations, no previous descriptions and no specimens. However, in the Linnean Herbarium [Linnean Society, London] there is preserved a good specimen (consisting of a larger and a smaller branch) which I have examined and photographed, the larger part of which I regard as the type specimen.

B.D. Jackson, in his "Index to the Linnean Herbarium", p. 149 (1917), asserts that the specimen in question [genus 35, specimen 1] was actually in Linnaeus' herbarium in the third (1767), but not in the second (1755), enumeration. Thus there is nothing in regard to the date of its acquisition by Linnaeus to preclude its being regarded as his 1759 type. J.E. Smith, in Rees' Cyclopaedia (1816), asserts that seeds of this material were sent to Linnaeus by his correspondent, David van Royen, who received them from Ceylon and that the species is [therefore] native to Ceylon. He says that Linnaeus planted the seeds and raised the plants in his "stove" at Uppsala. The aforementioned sheet in the Linnean Herbarium actually is inscribed "indica" and "UP" in Linnaeus' own hand and "Stachytarpheta indica Smith in Rees' Cyclop. n. 2" in Smith's handwriting [cfr. Savage, Cat. Linn. Herb. Lond. 4. 1945], so there is no doubt that this is the plant and, indeed, the actual specimen, referred to by Smith in Rees' work. Smith goes on to say that "Jacquin [Obs. Bot. 4: 7, pl. 86. 1771] represents the leaves more narrow and acute, with more regular serrations than in the Linnean specimen, which came from the Uppsala garden, and is accompanied by a branch [apparently applied later to the sheet since it in some places lies above parts of the other branch] with narrower leaves. This latter, evidently a mere variety, may be similar to what Vahl had from the same garden, and took for Miller's *Verbena angustifolia*."

Careful examination of the two parts of the Linnean specimen show that the earlier (on the right-hand side of the sheet) larger branch agrees perfectly in all respects with Linnaeus' original 1759 description with its plainly lanceolate-ovate leaves and salient obliquely spreading teeth. I regard this as the type specimen of *S. indica*. The later smaller (left-hand) branch agrees with Jacquin's illustration and doubtless truly is *S. angustifolia* (Mill.) Vahl. That these so very similar taxa represent two separate species is not likely, and I tend to agree with Smith that Vahl's *S. angustifolia* [based on Miller's *Verbena angustifolia*] should probably be reduced to varietal status under the older *S. indica*.

The illustration of Bondt's *Verbena indica* shows leaves much like those of the Linnean specimen or of *S. angustifolia* or even of *Elytraria imbricata* (Vahl) Pers. [of the West Indies]; certainly nothing at all like those of *S. jamaicensis* or *S. urticaefolia*.

Thus far I have seen no material of either *S. indica* or *S. angustifolia* that was definitely from Ceylon and the doubt naturally persists as to whether Royan's seeds actually originated in Ceylon or were merely dispatched to Royan from there. Both *S. indica* and *S. angustifolia* appear to be native to northwestern Africa, the latter also to northeastern South America [where it now passes mostly as *S. angustifolia* f. *elatior* (Schrad.) López-Palacios].

Louis 2014, from Zaire, is a perfect match for the Linnean type of *S. indica*.

It should be noted that Moon (1824) lists three species of *Stachytarpheta* from Ceylon. Of these he says one, *S. indica*, was native, and two, *S. jamaicensis* and *S. urticaefolia*, were introduced. He even records the Sinhala name for *S. indica* as "nil-nakuta" and that for *S. jamaicensis* as "rata-nil-nakuta". He lists no native name for *S. urticaefolia*, apparently implying that it was introduced too recently to have earned a native name.

That later works by Linnaeus compare *S. indica* and *S. jamaicensis* and since the latter species occurs so commonly in Ceylon, this has led some authorities to equate the two taxa; others have supposed, rather, that *S. indica* applies to the other common Ceylon species, *S. urticaefolia*. Hallier (1918) went so far as to reduce both *S. jamaicensis* and *S. urticaefolia* to synonymy under *S. indica*. There is nothing in the original description to support any of these views. The *Stachytarpheta marginata* Vahl, *S. pilosiuscula* H.B.K., *S. villosa* Turcz., and *Zapania marginata* Mirb., sometimes regarded as synonyms of *S. indica*, seem, rather, to belong to the synonymy of *S. jamaicensis*.

Vern. Nil-nakuta (S).

7. PRIVA

Adans., Fam. Pl. 2: 505. 1763. Type species: *Verbena lappulacea* L. [=*Priva lappulacea* (L.) Pers.].

Blairia Houst. ex L., Gen. Pl., ed. 1, 334, in syn. 1737; Adans., Fam. Pl. 2: 12 & 198. 1763; Gaertn., Fruct. 1: 265, pl. 56. fig. 1, in part. 1788 [not *Blairia* Gled., 1751, nor Gaertn., 1821, nor L., Oct. 1737, nor Spreng., 1966].
Burseria Loefl., Iter Hisp. 194. 1758 [not *Burseria* Jacq., 1763].
Scorodonia Sloane ex Adans., Fam. Pl. 2: 505, in syn. 1763.
Verbena Dill. ex Adans., Fam. Pl. 2: 198, in syn. 1763 [not *Verbena* (Dorst.) L., 1749, nor L., 1753, nor Plukenet, 1763, nor Tourn., 1737, nor (Tourn.) L., 1906].
Phryma Forsk., Fl. Aegypt.-arab. cxv, nom. nud. 1775 [not *Phryma* L., 1751].
Zapania Lam., Tabl. Enc. 1: 58. 1791 [not *Zapania* Scop., 1806, nor Schau., 1847).—*Zappania* Zuccagni apud Jacks. in Hook. f. & Jacks., Ind. Kew. 2: 1248. 1895 [not *Zappania* Scop., 1786].
Streptium Roxb., Pl. Corom. 2: 25, pl. 146. 1798.—*Steptium* Roxb. apud Boiss., Fl. Orient. 4: 533, sphalm. 1879.
Tortula Roxb. ex Willd. in L., Sp. Pl., ed. 4, 3: 359. 1801 [not *Tortula* Hedw., 1782].—*Tortula* Willd. ex Bartl., Ord. Nat. Plant. 178–180. 1830.—*Tertula* "Roxb. ex Willd." apud Brenan, Mem. New York Bot. Gard. 9: 37, sphalm. 1954.
Prina Adans ex Moldenke, Prelim. Alph. List Invalid Names 38, in syn. 1940.

Herbaceous caulescent perennials, harshly pubescent throughout; leaves decussate-opposite or subopposite, thin-membranous; stems, branches, and branchlets more or less tetragonal, often decumbent; inflorescence terminal and axillary, indeterminate, racemiform, often subspicate in anthesis, narrow, pedunculate, erect or subflexuous; flowers small, solitary in the axil of a small bractlet, arranged in a spirally alternate or pseudosecund manner on an elongate rachis, never whorled; calyx tubular in anthesis, 5-ribbed, slightly 5-plicate, slightly zygomorphic or nearly actinomorphic, terminating in 4 short, equal or subequal teeth, persistent, enlarging with and investing the fruit; corolla more or less zygomorphic, hypocrateriform or infundibular, surpassing the calyx, its tube straight or somewhat curved, more or less ampliate at the apex, the limb spreading, oblique, more or less bilabiate, the abaxial lip 3-lobed with 1 large central and 2 medium-sized lateral lobes, the axial lip 2-lobed, with usually very small lobes; fertile stamens 4, didynamous, the upper pair better developed and usually inserted slightly above the middle of the corolla-tube, the lower pair inserted approximately at the middle of the tube, all included or subequalling the tube; filaments slender; anthers erect, ovate or oblong, 2-celled, dorsifixed at or below the middle, introrse, the connective usually conspicuously thickened and sagittate, unappendaged, the thecae parallel or divergent at the base, opening by a lateral longitudinal slit; the fifth (posterior) stamen reduced to a minute staminode or absent; style usually equalling the lower stamens, 2-lobed at the apex, the anterior lobe longer and recurved or erect, stigmatiferous at the apex, the posterior lobe reduced, very minute and tooth-like, not stigmatiferous; ovary 4-celled or (by abortion) 2-celled; ovules basal, erect, anatropous, solitary in each cell; fruit a dry, often woody schizocarp included by the fruiting-calyx, composed of 2 usually similar, 2- (or by abortion 1-) celled cocci, which separate easily on maturity; pericarp hard, the dorsal surface echinate, scrobiculate, or ridged, the commissural surface excavated, concave or plane; seeds without endosperm; Chromosome number: $x = 6$.

A genus of about 26 recognized species and varieties of tropical and subtropical Asia, Asia Minor, Africa, and America. In Ceylon represented by only the following species.

Priva cordifolia (L. f.) Druce, Bot. Soc. Exch. Club Brit. Isles 4: 641. 1917; Hook. f., Fl. Br. Ind 4: 565. 1885; Trimen, Cat. 68. 1885; Trimen, Handb. Fl. Ceylon 3: 349. 1895; Cooke, Fl. Pres. Bombay, ed. 1, 3: 422. 1905; Willis, Cat. 69. 1911; Gamble, Fl. Pres. Madras 6: 1091. 1924; Alston in Trimen, Handb. Fl. Ceylon 6: 231. 1931; Sebastine, Bull. Bot. Surv. India 1: 95. 1959; Abeywick., Ceylon J. Sci., Biol. Sci. 2: 217. 1959; Nair & Rehman, Bull. Nat. Bot. Gard. Lucknow 76: 8, 9, & 23, fig. 14 a & b, pl. 1, fig. 4. 1962; Gunawardena, Gen. Sp. Pl. Zeyl. 147. 1968. Type: *J.G. König 77* from the Coromandel coast, Madras, India (LINN).

Büchnera cordifolia L. f., Suppl. 287. 1781.—*Buchnera cordifolia* L. f. apud

Jacks. in Hook. f. & Jacks., Ind. Kew. 1: 350. 1893.—*Buechnera cordifolia*
L. f. ex Moldenke, Feddes Repert. Spec. Nov. Regni Veg. 41: 42, in syn.
1936.
Streptium asperum Roxb., Pl. Corom. 2: 25, pl. 146. 1798.—*Strepium asperum*
Roxb. apud Boiss., Fl. Orient. 4: 533, in syn. 1879.
Tortula aspera Roxb. ex Willd., Sp. Pl. 3: 359. 1801.—*Tertula aspera* "Roxb.
ex Willd." apud Brenan, Mem. New York Bot. Gard. 9: 37, sphalm.
1954.
Verbena forskaelaei Vahl ex Rottl., Ges. Naturf. Freunde Berlin Neue Schriften 4: 222. 1803 [not *V. forskaelei* Vahl ex Willd., 1797].
Priva leptostachya A.L. Juss., Ann. Mus. Natl. Hist. Nat. 7: 70. 1806 [not *P.
leptostachys* Auct., 1962, nor Aitches., 1879, nor Kobuski, 1929, nor L.,
1940, nor H.H.W. Pearson, 1966].
Verbena aspera Hügel ex Moldenke, Feddes, Repert. Spec. Nov. Regni Veg.
41: 42, in syn. 1936 [not *V. aspera* Gill. & Hook., 1829, nor Kunze, 1845].

Herb to 1 m tall; stems erect, mostly branching, sharply tetragonal, strigillose-puberulent or becoming subglabrate in age, brown or purplish in drying;
nodes annulate, often decussately contracted; branches usually more densely
strigillose; petioles 0.5–4.1 cm long, strigillose-pubescent or puberulent; leaf-
blades papery, dark green above, somewhat lighter beneath, ovate, 2–9.5 cm
long, 1.3–7.5 cm wide, abruptly acute apically, rather uniformly serrate from
the widest part to the apex with rather large rounded or acute teeth, subtruncate or subcordate basally, the very centre of the base usually prolonged
slightly into the petiole, more or less strigillose above, usually more densely
so and also puberulent beneath; inflorescence terminating the stems and
branchlets, subspicate in anthesis, racemiform in fruit, many-flowered, 9.5–36
cm long; peduncles continuous with the stems or branchlets and similar to
them in all respects, but usually more densely strigillose; rachis similar to the
peduncle in all respects, the flowers distinctly spiral-alternate, but often appearing pseudosecund in pressing; bractlets linear-subulate, 1–4 mm long,
strigillose, one subtending each flower; pedicels obsolete in anthesis, to 3 mm
long and wide-spreading in fruit, puberulent-strigillose; calyx c. 7.8 mm long
and 3.1 mm wide, usually widest below the middle, densely short-tomentose
with uncinate hairs c. 0.1 mm long and interspersed among them scattered
straight hairs c. 0.5 mm long, its rim very obscurely 5-apiculate; corolla pure
white, glabrous throughout on both surfaces, its tube decidedly twisted, c.
11.9 mm long on the abaxial and 13.5 mm long on the axial side, 2 mm wide
at the base, ampliate to 3.6 mm below the apex, the central abaxial lobe c.
3.6 mm long, 3.1 mm wide, the 2 lateral abaxial lobes each c. 2.6 mm long and
3.8 mm wide, the 2 axial lobes each 3.1 mm long and 2.8 mm wide, all broadly elliptic-lingulate and rounded; upper pair of fertile stamens inserted c. 7.2
mm and the lower pair 5.9 mm above the base of the corolla-tube; filaments

0.7 mm long, pilose throughout; anthers ovate, c. 0.5 mm long and 0.2 mm wide, dorsifixed at about the middle; staminode obsolete; style capillary, c. 6.2 mm long, glabrous, somewhat ampliate at base and very much so at apex; ovary glabrous; fruiting-calyx thin-membranous, inflated, shortly rostrate apically, 5.5–7 mm long, 7–8 mm wide, densely hirsutulous with uncinate whitish hairs and sometimes with interspersed longer straight ones; cocci glabrous or subglabrous throughout, the dorsal surface echinate with 2 parallel longitudinal marginal bands of straight sharp spines, each band consisting of 2 or more rows of spines, the spines 0.4–1.6 mm long, plainly separate basally, the area between the bands of spines scrobiculate-reticulate or sometimes also more or less echinate with shorter scattered spines, the sides scrobiculate-reticulate on the half adjoining the bands of spines, the remainder transversely parallel-ridged with long slender ridges, the commissural surface deeply excavated and widely thin-margined, the apex of the margins usually involute and not ridged.

D i s t r. This species in its typical form is found from Baluchistan to southern peninsular India, north to Nepal, and east to Upper Burma, inhabiting jungles, grassy plains, riverbanks, and open places, ascending to 2000 feet in India. In Ceylon it is said by Trimen (1895) to be "very rare" in the dry region, flowering there in December.

U s e s. The native medicinal usage ascribed to *P. cordifolia* by some writers actually applies to the African varieties and species instead, but in view of the close relationship of the taxa in this genus may be worth repeating here: the Zulus apply a cold infusion of the leaves to inflammations of the eyeball and a paste of the groundup seeds (said to contain tannin) to sores and wounds.

V e r n. In India, Enkami and Obeera.

N o t e. The *Priva forskälaei* E. Mey., *P. dentata* A.L. Juss., *Verbena forskålaei* Vahl, and *Zapania arabica* Poir., regarded by Alston and others as belonging to the synonymy of *P. cordifolia*, actually are synonymy of the Arabian and east African *P. adhaerens* (Forsk.) Chiov.

S p e c i m e n s E x a m i n e d: HAMBANTOTA DISTRICT: not common near camp, Patanagala, Ruhuna National Park, 14 Nov. 1969, herb 40 cm tall, probably a perennial, flowers white, deciduous, collected as voucher for ecologic studies, *Cooray 69111407R* (US); rare in disturbed ground in cleared area in scrub forest on sandy loam soil back of beach, Smithsonian Camp, Patanagala, Ruhuna National Park, 2–3 ft alt., 5 April 1968, erect, branched from base, flowers white, *Fosberg 50229* (LL, PDA); Tissamaharama Tank, 19 Dec. 1882, *Trimen s.n.* (BM, K, PDA).

8. PETREA

Houst. ex L., Sp., Pl., ed. 1, 626. 1753; L., Gen. Pl., ed. 5, 275. 1754. Type species: *Petrea volubilis* L.

Petraea L. apud A.L. Juss., Gen. Pl., ed. 1, 108. 1789.—*Petroea* L. apud
Lam., Enc. Ill. 3: pl. 539. 1797.—*Petrea* L. apud Steud., Nom. Bot., ed. 1,
606. 1821.—*Petraea* Houst. apud Meisn., Pl. Vasc. Gen. 291. 1839.—*Petraea* B. Juss. apud Jacks. in Hook. f. & Jacks., Ind. Kew. 2: 477, in syn.
1894.—*Petraeae* L. apud Augusto, Fl. Rio Grande do Sul 227, sphalm.
1946.—*Petrae* Nees apud F.C. Hoehne, Relat. Annual Inst. Bot. 1951: 100,
sphalm. 1955.—*Pehoia* L. ex Moldenke, Prelim. Alph. List Invalid
Names 33, in syn. 1940.—*Peraea* L. ex Moldenke, Prelim. Alph. List Invalid Names 33, in syn. 1940.—*Pitrea* L. ex Moldenke, Prelim. Alph. List
Invalid Names 36, in syn. 1940.

Shrubs, trees, or woody vines; leaves opposite or whorled, deciduous, exstipulate, pinnately net-veined, often roughened and with prominent venation; inflorescence axillary or terminal, indeterminate, racemiform, the
racemes mostly elongate, many-flowered; bractlets and prophylla small, numerous, caducous; torus swollen; flowers hypogynous, perfect, alternate on the
rachis, often distant, each subtended by 1 or more prophylla; calyx gamosepalous, mostly actinomorphic, its tube cylindric or campanulate, mostly ribbed,
membranous during anthesis, its rim normally 5-lobed, the lobes mostly
equal, blue or violet to purple or white, mostly longer than the tube, alternate
with the corolla-lobes, bearing on its ventral surface at the base of the lobes
a thin-membranous calicinal crest, which is either in the form of a narrow
sinuate or 5-toothed coronet or is 5-cleft to the base, the teeth alternate with
the calyx-lobes, erect during anthesis; corolla gamopetalous, hypocrateriform,
mostly darker blue or purple than the calyx, or white, mostly slightly zygomorphic, its tube cylindric, urceolate, or infundibular, the basal portion mostly
narrow, the upper portion mostly abruptly and widely ampliate, its limb
rotate, 5-lobed, the lobes mostly of 2 sizes, the anterior largest (rarely of 5
sizes, with the 2 posterior ones smallest), mostly much shorter than the calyx-lobes and alternate with them, the posterior ones outside in prefloration; stamens 4, didynamous, inserted close together near the middle of the corolla-tube, included; filaments very short and slender; anthers oblong or ovate,
dorsifixed near the base, 2-celled, each theca opening by means of a longitudinal slit, introrse, the connective mostly enlarged, often surpassing the
thecae; staminode present or absent; pistil one, compound but 1-carpellary
through the abortion of one carpel, included by the corolla-tube; style single,
terminal; stigma capitate, mostly oblique, more or less distinctly bilobed;
ovary subglobose or oblong, borne on a more or less conspicuous disk, more
or less completely 2-celled, each cell 1-ovulate; ovules lateral, ascending, hemianatropous or imperfectly anatropous, or pendent and orthotropous; fruiting-calyx incrassate, its tube not much accrescent, mostly losing its blue colour,
but becoming very hard and tough and mostly plicate-ribbed, its lobes greatly
accrescent, stiffened, reticulate-veined, divergent, acting as wings for floating

the fruit, the calicinal crest very callose, mostly curving inwards and converging, thus completely closing the mouth of the calyx-tube; fruit drupaceous, completely enclosed by the mature calyx, the exocarp leathery or fleshy, the endocarp hard, more or less completely 2-celled, forming 2 pyrenes, not easily separating, each pyrene 1-seeded, or by abortion the fruit 1-pyrened and 1-seeded; seeds laterally or apically attached, without endosperm.

A genus of about 40 living species and varieties of tropical and subtropical America, extending from the southernmost United States, Cuba, and Jamaica, through the West Indies, and from northern Mexico through Central America to southern Brazil, Paraguay, and Peru; one species has become naturalized in Java; many are cultivated and tend to escape; fossil species are known from the United States and Europe. In Ceylon there are only the three following cultivated taxa.

KEY TO THE SPECIES AND VARIETIES

1 Leaves sessile or subsessile..**1. P. arborea**
1 Leaves distinctly petiolate
 2 Mature leaf-blades more or less pubescent beneath..........**P. volubilis** var. **pubescens**
 2 Mature leaf-blades glabrous or subglabrate beneath........**2. P. volubilis** var. **volubilis**

1. Petrea arborea H.B.K., Nov. Gen. & Sp., ed. folio, 2: 228 [as *"Petraea"*]. 1817; Moldenke, Feddes Repert. Spec. Nov. Regni Veg. 43: 22–26. 1938; Menninger, Flow. Trees World pl. 413. 1962. Type: *Humboldt & Bonpland s.n.* from near Guacara, at Hacienda de Cure, and near Cura, Venezuela (P).

Petrea arborea Humb. & Bonpl. ex Steud., Nom. Bot., ed. 1, 606. 1821.—*P. arborea* Humb. ex Spreng. in L., Syst., ed. 16, 2: 761. 1825.—*Petroea arborea* H.B.K. ex Neumann, Ann. Fl. Pomone 1837–38: 254–255. 1838.— *Petrea arborea* Kunth ex Schau. in A. DC., Prod. 11: 619, in syn. 1847.— *Petraea arborea* Kunth ex Moldenke, Prelim. Alph. List Invalid Names 34, in syn. 1940.—*Petraea arborea* L. ex Moldenke, Prelim. Alph. List Invalid Names 34, in syn. 1940.—*Petrea arbirea* H.B.K. ex Moldenke, Phytologia 2: 173, in syn. 1946.—*Petraea arborea* Rich. ex Moldenke, Résumé 330, in syn. 1959.—*Petrea arborea* Turcz. ex López-Palacios, Revista Fac. Farm. Univ. Los Andes 16: 64–66, fig. 13. 1975.

Petrea erecta Hort. ex Steud., Nom. Bot., ed. 2, 2: 309. 1841.—*P. erecta* Lodd. ex Schau. in A. DC., Prod. 11: 619, in syn. 1847.

Petrea vincentina Turcz., Bull. Soc. Imp. Naturistes Moscou 36 (2): 212. 1863. —*P. vincentiana* Turcz. ex Moldenke, Phytologia 7: 431, in syn. 1961.

Petrea splendens Landsbergen ex Moldenke, Feddes Repert. Spec. Nov. Regni Veg. 43: 22, in syn. 1938.—*P. splendes* López-Palacios, Revista Fac. Farm. Univ. Los Andes 15: 66, sphalm. 1975.

Verbena arborea H.B.K. ex Beltrán, Cat. Sem. Hort. Bot. Univ. Valentin. 1948: 26. 1948 [not *V. arborea* Hort., 1959].

Shrub or low tree, sometimes subscandent; branchlets rather slender, greyish, conspicuously lenticellate, obtusely tetragonal or subterete, more or less densely short-pubescent, glabrescent in age; leaves mostly sessile or subsessile, petioles (if present) 1–3 mm long, very inconspicuous, mostly hidden by the somewhat clasping leaf-bases; leaf-blades firmly chartaceous, slightly scabridous on both surfaces, elliptic, 6.5–16 cm long, 2.5–7.7 cm wide, obtuse or slightly retuse apically, entire but usually more or less undate-crimped along the margins, sometimes with a very few, scattered, appressed teeth near the middle, cordate or subcordate at the base and usually more or less clasping, very obscurely asperous on both surfaces, not at all pubescent; inflorescence axillary, rather abundant, appearing with or usually after the leaves, ascending or nutant, 4–16 cm long; peduncles 5 mm long or less, densely short-pubescent; pedicels about 5 mm long, densely spreading short-pubescent; torus expanded; calyx firm in anthesis, its tube 3–5.2 mm long, ampliate to 3.5–4.2 mm apically, obscurely 10-ribbed, not verruculose, densely spreading-pubescent, the lobes oblong, 9.5–12.5 mm long, 3–3.5 mm wide, rounded apically, sparsely puberulent outside, glabrous within except for the sparsely pilose midrib; calicinal lobes 1.2–1.5 mm long, 1.8–2.5 mm wide basally, erect, blunt and minutely fringed apically; corolla-tube about 7 mm long, 3–3.5 mm wide apically, the lower 3/4 glabrous, the upper 1/4 minutely spreading-puberulent outside, densely long-pubescent from the apex to just below the stamens within, the hairs densest among the stamens, anterior lobe of limb suborbicular, about 4.2 mm long, 4.5–5 mm wide, rounded, irregularly sinuate, glabrous outside, minutely puberulent within, the hairs longer and denser basally, remaining lobes smaller, 3–3.5 mm long and 4 mm wide; stamens inserted about 4 and 4.8 mm above the base of the corolla-tube; filaments about 1 mm long, glabrous; anthers oblong, about 1 mm long and 0.25 mm wide, the stout connective not surpassing the thecae, sparingly pilose; staminode obsolete; style about 1.8 mm long, thickened basally, glabrous; ovary glabrous; disk about 1 mm long and 1.5 mm wide; fruiting-calyx tough, the tube to 7 mm long and 5.5 mm wide, its lobes to 18 mm long and 8 mm wide.

D i s t r. This is a much misunderstood species, widely confused with *P. volubilis* L. and other species. It occurs naturally only from Colombia and Venezuela to Guyana and Trinidad, but occurs sparingly in cultivation.

E c o l. In its native haunts it is partial to light cool forests, rocky gorges, hedges, pastures, and savannas, ascending to at least 1000 m in Venezuela.

V e r n. Among horticulturists in various parts of the world known as: blue-petrea, Blue-wreath, Lilac, and Tree petrea, but from its native haunts these names have been recorded: Liane St. Jean, Nacareno, Opptizimin, Tostatido, and Totopostillo.

S p e c i m e n s   E x a m i n e d. KANDY DISTRICT: Royal Botanic

Gardens, Peradeniya, Section R, July 1895, probably cultivated, *s. coll. s.n.*
(PDA, TRIN).

2. Petrea volubilis L., Sp. Pl., ed. 1, 626. 1753 var. **volubilis.** Voigt, Hort.
Suburb. Calc. 471. 1845; Mart., Fl. Bras. 9: 273. 1851; Naire, Fl. Pl. West.
India 249. 1894; Woodrow, Gard. Trop., ed. 6, 442. 1910; Duthie, Fl. Up.
Gang. Pl. 2: 229. 1911; Haines, Bot. Bihar & Orissa 4: 708. 1922; Gamble,
Fl. Pres. Madras 6: 1106. 1924; Junell, Symb. Bot. Upsal. 4: 43–46, fig.
80–86. 1934; Moldenke, Feddes Repert. Spec. Nov. Regni Veg. 43: 32–44.
1938; Bor & Raizada, Some Beautiful Indian Climb. 140–142, pl. 54 & 55.
1954; Cooke, Fl. Pres. Bombay, ed. 2, 2: 518. 1958; Moldenke, Phytologia
7: 446–451. 1961; MacMillan, Trop. Plant. & Gard., ed. 5, 122. 1962; Cowen,
Fl. Trees & Shrubs India, ed. 4, 134. 1965; Sen & Naskar, Bull. Bot. Surv.
India 7: 53. 1965; Santapau, Bull. Bot. Surv. India 8: 39. 1967; Rau, Bull.
Bot. Surv. India 10, Suppl. 2: 62. 1969. Type: *Herb. Linnaeus 781/1* cultivated in the George Clifford garden at Hartecamp, Holland, between 1735 and
1737 (BM).

Petraea volubilis Gaertn., Fruct. 2: 471, pl. 177, fig. 5. 1791.—*Petraea volubilis*
L. apud H.J. Lam, Verbenac. Malay. Arch. 26. 1919.—*Petroea volubilis*
Hort. ex Neumann, Ann. Fl. Pomone 1837–38: 254–255, pl. 31. 1838.—
Petrea volubilis Gaertn. ex Schau. in A. DC., Prod. 11: 618, in syn. 1847.—
Petrea volubilis Schiede ex Standl., Contrib. U.S. Nat. Herb. 23: 1237, in
syn. 1924.—*Petrea volubilis* Millsp. ex Standl., Field Mus. Nat. Hist. Bot.
Ser. 3: 403, in syn. 1930.—*Petraea volubilis* Jack ex Daniel, Verb. Cent.
Antioq. 5. 1947.—*Petrea volubilis* H.B.K. ex Moldenke, Alph. List Invalid
Names Suppl. 1: 18, in syn. 1947.—*Petraeae volubilis* L. ex Augusto, Fl.
Rio Grande Sul 227, sphalm. 1946.—*Petraea volubilis* Haust. ex Datta &
Majumdar, Bull. Bot. Soc. Bengal 20: 106. 1966.
Petraea (volubilis?) mexicana Cham., Linnaea 7: 367. 1832.—*Petrea volubilis*
var. ? *mexicana* Schlecht. ex Steud., Nom. Bot., ed. 2, 2: 309, in syn. 1841.—
Petraea volubilis var. *mexicana* Schiede ex Moldenke, Feddes Repert. Spec.
Nov. Regni Veg. 43: 33, in syn. 1938.
Petraea mexicana Willd. ex Cham., Linnaea 7: 367, in syn. 1832.—*Petrea me-
xicana* Willd. ex Steud., Nom. Bot., ed. 2, 2: 309, in syn. 1841.
Petrea stapelsiae Paxt., Mag. Bot. 4: 199–200. 1838.—*Petrea stapeliae* Paxt.
apud Steud., Nom. Bot., ed. 2, 2: 309. 1841.—*Petraea stapelsiae* Paxt. apud
Britton & P. Wils., Sci. Surv. Porto Rico 6: 370. 1926.—*Petrea staphylea*
Hort. ex Moldenke, Feddes Repert. Spec. Nov. Regni Veg. 43: 33, in syn.
1938.
Petrea sub-serrata Bárcena, Notic. Cienc. Estad. Hidalg. 31–32. 1877 [not *P.
subserrata* Cham., 1832].—*Petrea subserrata* Bárcena apud Jacks. in Hook.
f. & Jacks., Ind. Kew. 2: 478. 1894.

Petraea ovata Mart. & Gal., Bull. Acad. Roy. Sci. Bruxelles 11 (2): 328. 1844.
—*Petrea ovata* Mart. & Gal. ex Schau. in A. DC., Prod. 11: 619, in syn.
1847.
Stachytarpheta volubilis Vesque, Ann. Sci. Nat. (Paris) ser. 7, 1: 337, 341, &
343, pl. 15, fig. 4. 1885.
Petraea arborea (Kunth) Smith & Wiles in Forbes, Wand. Nat. East. Arch. 2:
78–79 & 514. 1885; H.J. Lam, Verbenac. Malay. Arch. addenda. 1919 [not
P. arborea H.B.K., 1817].
Petraea scandens Jacq. ex Moldenke, Feddes Repert. Spec. Nov. Regni Veg.
43: 33, in syn. 1938.—*Petrea scandens* Heller ex Moldenke, Feddes Repert.
Spec. Nov. Regni Veg. 43: 33. 1938.
Petrea guranensis Cham. ex Moldenke, Feddes Repert. Spec. Nov. Regni Veg.
43: 33, in syn. 1938.
Petrea arborescens Pesman, Meet Fl. Mex. 266. 1962.

Woody vine or subshrub, to 13 m tall; branches and branchlets slender, greyish or brownish, prominently lenticellate, rather densely short-pubescent or puberulent with mostly subappressed brownish hairs (on older wood) or spreading subhirsute hairs (on young shoots), very obtusely tetragonal or subterete; leaf-scars large and prominent, borne on very conspicuous corky sterigmata; petioles 4–13 mm long, short-pubescent or puberulent; leaf-blades rather firmly chartaceous, very scabrous on both surfaces, elliptic, 3–21 cm long, 1.4–10.6 cm wide, mostly acute or short-acuminate apically (rarely obtuse or emarginate), mostly entire (rarely sparsely dentate) with margins often more or less undate or subrevolute, acute or obtusely narrowed basally (rarely rounded or subcordate), densely asperulous on both surfaces, glabrate or subglabrate beneath; racemes axillary, very abundant, erect or nutant to pendent, solitary in each leaf-axil, often clustered near the tips of the branches or branchlets, 8–29 cm long, rather loosely many-flowered; pedicels in anthesis about 8 mm long, obscurely puberulent; torus expanded, not ribbed; calyx-tube about 3 mm long, ampliate to 3 mm apically, not ribbed, densely pubescent, its lobes membranous, oblong, 13–18 mm long, 4–6 mm wide, rounded apically, glabrous on both surfaces, lobes of the calicinal crest about 1 mm long and wide, sparsely ciliate, acute; corolla-tube 6–8 mm long, conspicuously ampliate to 4–5 mm apically, the lower 3/4 glabrous, upper 1/4 densely puberulent outside, puberulent within and densely villous-pubescent among the stamens, the anterior lobe broadly elliptic, 5–6.5 mm long, 4–4.5 mm wide, slightly sinuate along the margins, densely puberulent on both surfaces, the other lobes similar but only 4–6 mm long and about 4 mm wide; stamens inserted 4.5 and 5 mm above the base of the corolla-tube; staminode obsolete; ovary glabrous; fruiting-calyx tough, to 4 mm long, densely long-pubescent, the lobes stiff, to 22 mm long and 7 mm wide, divergent. Chromosome number: 2n = 34.

D i s t r. This species is native from Mexico through Central America to Panama and in the Greater Antilles, introduced in southern Florida, parts of the Lesser Antilles, India, China, Java, and elsewhere, widely cultivated in subtropical and tropical countries throughout the world and there sometimes escaped. Its nomenclatural history is very involved, chiefly because it was early confused with the typically South American *P. arborea* H.B.K.

U s e s. The plant serves well on trellises and for covering an arbor or roof; in its native haunts it climbs into tall trees and spreads over the crown. In many parts of the tropics it will bloom 2–4 times per year, the individual flowers lasting about 10 days, but the racemes remaining very showy long afterwards because of the highly coloured fruiting calyces. The pollen is described and illustrated in Erdtman, Pollen Morph. & Pl. Tax., ed. 2, 448 & 449, fig. 256 F (1966). In Mexico the tough stems are often used by the natives as a rope. In Indo-China the juice is employed as a diaphoretic and excitant and the sandpapery leaves for polishing and cleaning metals, ivory, and animal horns and hooves. In cultivation its purple-blue inflorescences blend well with *Bougainvillea*.

V e r n. In India it is called Kudirai valuppu; among its 50 other names elsewhere are: Purple-wreath, Queen's-wreath, Sandpaper-vine, Adolfina, Bejuco de caballo, Flor de Jesús, Flor de Santa Maria, Jazmín azul, Lengua de vaca, and Raspa sombrero.

S p e c i m e n s E x a m i n e d: KANDY DISTRICT: in outdoor cultivation on arbor in Pergola Garden, Royal Botanic Garden, Peradeniya, 1550 ft alt., 18 Jan. 1974, profusely blooming, calyx and corolla blue, leaves rough above, *H.N. & A.L. Moldenke & Jayasuriya 28131* (AAU, CAI, KARACHI, LL, PDA, US); University of Sri Lanka Botany Department gardens, 1600 metres altitude, 12 Dec. 1973, 2–4 m tall, flowers blue, *D.B. & D. Sumithra-arachchi DBS. 77* (US). KEGALLE DISTRICT: isolated plant in outdoor arbour cultivation, Pelwadiya, low altitude, 12 Feb. 1974, calyx and corolla purplish-blue, *H.N. & A.L. Moldenke, Dassanayake, & Jayasuriya 28344* (LL, PDA, US).

var. **pubescens** Moldenke, Feddes Repert. Spec. Nov. Regni Veg. 43: 45–46. 1938; Moldenke, Phytologia 2: 108 (1946), 2: 198 (1946), 2: 501 (1948), and 7: 451. 1961; Moldenke in Woodson, Schery, *et al.*, Ann. Missouri Bot. Gard. 60: 82, 87, & 147. 1973. Type: *J.B. Edwards P. 601* from cut-over valley lands, San Louis, Honduras, 6 May 1933 (US).

Petrea mexicana H.B.K. ex Mart. & Gal., Bull. Acad. Roy. Sci. Bruxelles 11 (2): 329. 1844 [not *P. mexicana* Willd., 1841].
Petraea consanguinea Klotzsch ex Moldenke, Feddes Repert. Spec. Nov. Regni Veg. 43: 45, in syn. 1938.—*Petrea consanguinea* Klotzsch apud E.J. Salisb., Ind. Kew. Suppl. 10: 168, in syn. 1947.

This variety differs from the typical variety only in its leaf-blades being conspicuously and more or less densely pubescent on both surfaces when immature or only beneath when mature.

It occurs sporadically among the typical form almost throughout the range of the latter and has also been cultivated in various parts of the subtropics and tropics. In India it appears to have become naturalized.

V e r n. Among the names recorded from various parts of its range are: Chorreque, Cuera de zapo, Flor de Jesus, and Raspa-guacal.

S p e c i m e n s E x a m i n e d. KANDY DISTRICT: Royal Botanic Garden, May 1887, *s. coll. s.n.* (PDA); Rest harrow, Kandy, 2120 ft alt. 78 inch rainfall, Sept. 1960, *Worthington 6967* (P, PDA), on label: "This is an experiment to preserve colour: dried immediately in cotton wool, colour gone in a month, a failure!"

9. DURANTA

L., Sp. Pl., ed. 1, 637. 1753; L., Gen. Pl., ed. 5, 284. 1754. Type Species: *Duranta erecta* L. [=*D. repens* L.].

Castorea Plum. ex L., Gen. Pl., ed. 1, 373, in syn. 1737; Mill., Gard. Dict. Abridg. ed. 4. 1754.—*Castorea* Mill. apud Druce, Bot. Exch. Club Brit. Isles Rep. 3: 430. 1913.
Ellisia P. Browne, Hist. Pl. Jamaic. 262. 1756 [not *Ellisia* L., 1763].
Hoffmannia Loefl., Iter Hisp. 194. 1758 [not *Hoffmannia* Sw., 1788. nor Willd., 1789].
Durantia L. apud Mill., Gard. Dict., ed. 8. 1768.—*Dvranta* Scop., Introd. Hist. Nat. 170. 1777.—*Durantha* Jacq. ex Griseb., Cat. Pl. Cubens. 216, sphalm. 1866.—*Durandea* Houard, Zoocéd. Pl. Amer. Sud 344. 1933 [not *Durandea* Planch., 1847].—*Durantha* Jacq. ex Patermann, Beitr. Zytol. Verbenac. 25–27, pl. 2, fig. 18–21. 1935.—*Durant* Fletcher, Bull. Misc. Inform. 1938: 408, sphalm. 1938.—*Durantea* Post & Kuntze apud Caro, Revista Argent. Agron. 23: 3, in syn. 1956.—*Durante* L. ex Moldenke, Alph. List Invalid Names 9, in syn. 1947.—*Durantha* Acosta Solis ex Moldenke, Resumé 284, in syn. 1959.—*Durantia* Scop. ex Airy Shaw in Willis, Dict. ed. 7, 385. 1966.—*Duranata* Dennis, Kew Bull. Addit. Ser. 3: 414, sphalm. 1970.
Darbyana A.M. Murr., Letters 305. 1856.

Glabrous or pubescent, often spinose shrubs; leaves decussate-opposite, whorled, simple, entire or dentate, deciduous; inflorescence mostly terminal, rarely axillary or abbreviated, indeterminate, racemiform, elongate; flowers often showy, mostly pedicellate, each borne in the axil of a small bractlet; calyx gamosepalous, subplicate, tubular or subcampanulate, 5-costate, mostly truncate apically, each rib terminating in a short subulate tooth, the posterior tooth smallest; corolla gamopetalous, hypocrateriform, mostly blue, purple, or white, the tube cylindric, straight or curved above, exserted from the calyx, the limb spreading, regular or oblique, 5-parted, mostly pubescent at the mouth, the lobes rounded, usually unequal, mostly pubescent on the inner surface; stamens 4, didynamous, included, inserted at or above the middle of the corolla-tube; filaments very short; anthers sagittate, dorsifixed, erect, with parallel thecae; style terminal, shorter than or equalling the lower stamens, the stigma obliquely subcapitate, very shortly and unequally 4-lobed; ovary more or less completely 8-celled, composed of four 2-celled carpels, each cell 1-ovulate; fruiting-calyx accrescent, flask-shaped, usually surpassing and closely appressed to the fruit, but not coalesced with it, usually coarctate-rostrate apically; fruit drupaceous, mostly completely included by the mature calyx, the exocarp fleshy, the endocarp hard; pyrenes 4, each 2-celled and 2-seeded. Chromosome number: $x = 12$.

A genus of about 53 species and varieties, widespread in subtropical and tropical America from Florida and Bermuda through the West Indies, Mexico, and Central America, to Argentina; one species is doubtfully native in Thailand, several are widely cultivated and frequently escape and become more or less naturalized. In Ceylon it is represented by only one species, *D. repens*, with two varieties.

KEY TO THE VARIETIES

1 Corolla blue to lilac, violet, or purple.................................**1.** var. **repens**
1 Corolla white..**2.** var. **alba**

Duranta repens L., Sp. Pl., ed. 1, 637. 1753, var. **repens**. Willis, Cat. 143. 1911; Haines, Bot. Bihar & Orissa 4: 709. 1922; Gamble, Fl. Pres. Madras 6: 1106. 1924; Domin, Biblioth. Bot. 89: 1106–1107. 1928; Ali, J. Bombay Nat. Hist. Soc. 35: 597. 1932; Junell, Symb. Bot. Upsal. 4: 50–52, fig. 93 & 94. 1934; Alston, Kandy Fl. 63. 1938; Moldenke, Publ. Carnegie Inst. Wash. 522: 196–197. 1940; Moldenke in Lundell, Fl. Tex. 3 (1): 76. 1942; Sastri, Wealth India 23: 117. 1952; Cooke, Fl. Pres. Bombay, ed. 2, 2: 518. 1958; Abeywick., Ceylon J. Sci., Biol. Sci. 2: 218. 1959; Srinivasan & Agarwal, Bull. Bot. Surv. India 5: 80. 1963; Maheshwari, Fl. Delhi 279. 1963; Prain, Bengal Pl. 2: 617. 1963; Puri *et al.*, Rec. Bot. Surv. India 19: 108. 1964; Maheshwari & Singh, Dict. Econ. Pl. India 61. 1965; Chopra *et al.*, Poison. Pl. India 2: 694 & 697, fig. 176. 1965; Cowen, Fl. Trees & Shrubs India, ed. 4, 114, pl. 43. 1965; Santapau, Bull. Bot. Surv. India 8: 38. 1967; Banerjee, Bull. Bot. Soc. Bengal 23: 168. 1969; Moldenke in Wiggins & Porter, Fl. Galáp. Isls. 486–490, fig. 128. 1971; Inamdar, Indian Forester 97: 328. 1971; Shah & Unnikrishnan, Bot. Gaz. 132: 81–91. 1971. Type: Based on *Castorea repens*, *spinosa* Plum.; *Herb. Linnaeus 806/1* (LINN).

Castorea repens, spinosa Plum., Nov. Pl. Amer. Gen. 30, pl. 17. 1703.—*C. repens spinosa* Plum. ex L., Sp. Pl., ed. 1, 2: 637, in syn. 1753.

Duranta erecta L., Sp. Pl., ed. 1, 637. 1753.

Duranta ellisia Jacq., Enum. Pl. Carib. 26. 1760.

Duranta plumieri Jacq., Select. Stirp. Amer. Hist. 186, pl. 176, fig. 76. 1763.—*Durantia plumeiri* Mill., Gard. Dict., ed. 8. 1768.—*Duranta plumieri* L. apud H.B.K., Nov. Gen. & Sp. ed. folio, 2: 254. 1817.

Durantia racemosa Mill., Gard. Dict., ed. 8. 1768.—*Duranta racemosa* Mill. ex Moldenke, Prelim. Alph. List Invalid Names 25, in syn. 1940.

Duranta angustifolia Salisb., Prod. 108. 1796.

Duranta latifolia Salisb., Prod. 108. 1796.

Duranta dentata Rich. ex Pers., Syn. Pl. 2: 142. 1806.

Duranta xalapensis H.B.K., Nov. Gen. & Sp. ed. folio, 2: 206. 1817.

Duranta spinosa L. apud Schau. in A. DC., Prod. 11: 615, in syn. 1847.—*D. spinosa* Mill. ex Crevost & Pételot, Bull. Econ. Indo-chine 37: 1289. 1934.

Duranta inermis L. apud Schau. in A. DC., Prod. 11: 615, in syn. 1847.

Castorea racemosa L. apud Schau. in A. DC., Prod. 11: 615, in syn. 1847.—*C. racemosa* Plum. ex Moldenke, Prelim. Alph. List Invalid Names 15, in syn. 1940.

Ellisia acuta L. apud Schau. in A. DC., Prod. 11: 615, in syn. 1847.

Ellisia frutescens P. Br. apud Schau. in A. DC., Prod. 11: 615, in syn. 1847.

Duranta plumieri var. *strigillosa* Schau. in Mart., Fl. Bras. 9: 271. 1851.

Darbyana integrifolia A.M. Murr., Letters 306. 1856.

Duranta bonardi Guillard ex Bocq., Adansonia, ser. 1, 2: 112. 1862.

Duranta plumieri var. *ellisia* (L.) Hort. ex Woodrow, Gardening Ind. 420. 1889.

Duranta plumieri var. *glabra* Hieron. ex Hiederl., Bol. Mens. Mus. Prod. Argent. 3 (31): 322. 1890.

Duranta repens var. *acuta* (L.) Kuntze, Rev. Gen. Pl. 2: 507. 1891.

Duranta repens var. *glabrifolia* Kuntze, Rev. Gen. Pl. 2: 507. 1891.

Duranta repens α *multidentata* Kuntze, Rev. Gen. Pl. 2: 507. 1891.

Duranta repens β *paucidentata* Kuntze, Rev. Gen. Pl. 2: 507. 1891.

Duranta rostrata Hort. ex Wehmer, Pflanzenst., ed. 2, 2: 1023. 1931.

Duranta macrophylla Hort. ex Moldenke, Résumé Suppl. 11: 6, in syn. 1964. —*D. macrophylla* Bose ex Moldenke in Woodson, Schery, *et al.*, Ann. Missouri Bot. Gard. 60: 90, in syn. 1973.

Duranta repens Auct. ex Caro, Revista Argent. Agron. 23: 6, in syn. 1956.—*Durante repens* L. apud Watt & Breyer-Brandwijk, Med. & Poison. Pl. S. & East. Africa, ed. 2, 1387. 1962.

Duranta ligustrosa Isert ex Moldenke, Prelim. Alph. List Invalid Names 25, in syn. 1940.

An extremely variable and polymorphic shrub or small tree to 7 m tall;

branches slender, arching, often drooping or trailing, unarmed or spiny, sometimes scandent or semiscandent, usually glabrate, sometimes obscurely appressed-strigillose; branchlets tetragonal; leaves decussate-opposite, numerous, very variable in shape, size, and texture, ovate-elliptic or ovate to obovate, 1.5–5 cm long, 1–4 cm wide, obtuse or acute to acuminate apically, sometimes apiculate, basally cuneate into the petiole, margins entire or coarsely serrate above the middle, occasionally coarsely dentate throughout (especially on sterile shoots), mostly thin-textured, often almost membranous, glabrate on both surfaces; petioles slender, 1–8 mm long; inflorescence racemose, terminal and axillary, usually concentrated at or near the tips of the branches, loosely many-flowered, erect or (usually) recurved, often paniculate, 5–30 cm long; bractlets minute, occasionally subfoliaceous; pedicels 1–5 mm long; flowers sweet-scented with the odour of vanilla; calyx tubular, 3–4.5 mm long, angled, appressed-strigillose, sometimes decidedly canescent, the teeth minute, subulate apically for 1 mm or less; corolla blue, lilac, violet, or light violet-blue to lavender or purple, sometimes mauve or purplish with a white tube and with or without two purplish stripes on the tube, the tube surpassing the calyx by 2–3 mm, densely puberulent outside above the calyx, the limb 7–9 mm wide, densely puberulent on both surfaces, especially outside and toward the throat within, the puberulence often canescent in bud; fruiting-calyx yellowish, glabrous, shiny, prolonged into a curved beak beyond the fruit; fruit yellow or orange-yellow, globose, 7–11 mm in diameter, completely enclosed by the fruiting-calyx. Chromosome number: n = 24, 32, 36.

Distr. A common plant of woods, thickets, hedgerows, fencerows, and roadsides almost throughout subtropical and tropical America from the southernmost United States to Argentina; introduced and often firmly naturalized in many parts of tropical Africa, Asia, Australia, and Oceania. It is widely cultivated in all warm portions of the civilized world and numerous varietal and horticultural names have been proposed, some of which may prove worthy of retention. On the other hand, some names placed in the synonymy of typical *D. repens* by some writers definitely do not belong here.

Uses. This plant is very widely used as a hedge because it withstands clipping well and tends to sucker from the base; most browsing animals refuse to eat it except under stress of extreme hunger. It is suspected of killing livestock that eats it, yet the fruit is eaten by many birds. In some areas stimulant properties are ascribed to the flowers and the fruits are used as a febrifuge. In some countries an infusion of the leaves and the juice of the fruit is employed as a diuretic, yet it has been shown that these parts contain hydrocyanic acid. The bark contains a glucoside, the leaves are known to contain saponin, and the fruit has been reported by various investigators to contain saponin and durantin (an alkaloid analogous to narcotine). Various parts of the plant are reported to have a depressant property which may be toxic, containing β sisterol, ursolic acid, triterpenes, alkaloids, fatty substances, and a fixed oil. Consuming the fruit is said to have caused the illness (marked by sleepiness, fever, and convulsions) and even death of children in Queensland. The macerated fruit yields a juice which even in dilutions of 1 part to 100 parts of water is lethal to mosquito larvae in ponds and swamps, the action being somewhat less pronounced on culicine larvae. In Mexico the Mayans drank a decoction of this plant in the treatment of jaundice and biliousness.

V e r n. Among its 75 recorded vernacular names in various parts of its range are: Brazilian skyflower, Golden-dewdrop, Heliotrope-bush, pigeonberry, Skyflower, Adonis morado, Celosa cimarrona, Cuenta de oro, Espina de paloma, Fruta de iguana, Jupiter cimarron, and Lora.

N o t e. The plant is attacked by a number of parasitic fungi, including *Asteridiella pittieri* (Toro) Hansf., *Didymosphaeria durantae* Srin., *Phyllachora fusicarpa* Seaver, and *Sporodesmium durantae* Pat. Seedlings are subject to attack by a blight caused by *Sclerotium rolfsii* Sacc. The species is also abundantly attacked by a cecidiomyid gall-wasp which disfigures the fruit, and by red spiders or mites. In India it serves as host to the mistletoe, *Dendrophthoë falcata* (L.f.) Ettingsh.

S p e c i m e n s E x a m i n e d. COLOMBO DISTRICT: Bandarawatta, on the Yakkala to Gampaha road, 8 July 1971, flowers pale blue with white throat, mature fruit globose, orange, commonly used as a hedge plant, *Amaratunga 2301* (PDA). KANDY DISTRICT: Golf Club, Peradeniya, 2 Feb. 1952, flowers light pink, *Appuhamy s.n.* (PDA); in outdoor cultivation in Students' Garden, Royal Botanic Garden, Peradeniya, 1550 ft alt., 18 Jan. 1974, shrub about 7 ft tall, sprouts from severely pruned-back stump, *H.N. & A.L. Moldenke & Jayasuriya 28170* (PDA, US); abundantly cultivated as trailside hedge, Lagamuwa Temple, Poilakanda, Kadugannawa, 1900 ft. alt., 22 Jan. 1974, shrub 8 ft tall, branches arching, corolla pale bluish-lavender, leaves almost all entire, *H.N. & A.L. Moldenke & Sumithraarachchi 28201* (AAH, ARIZ, CAI, KARACHI, LL, MO, PDA, US); in outdoor cultivation, Katugastota, 1500 ft alt., 3 Feb. 1974, a single specimen shrub in fruit, leaves mostly all entire, *H.N. & A.L. Moldenke & Dassanayake 28315* (AAU, LL, PDA, US); Royal Botanic Garden, March 1887, *s. coll. s.n.* (PDA). NUWARA ELIYA DISTRICT: abundant on roadsides and fencerows, Boragas, 5800 ft alt., 30 Jan. 1974, interlacing shrubs 8 ft tall, corollas blue, *H.N. & A.L. Moldenke, Jayasuriya, & Sumithraarachchi 28305* (AAU, ARIZ, CAI, KARACHI, LL, MO, PDA, US); common in hedgerows and fencerows, road marker 36/9 south of Ramboda, 28 Jan. 1974, interlacing shrubs 8 ft tall, flowers blue, *H.N. & A.L. Moldenke, Jayasuriya, & Sumithraarachchi 28626* (AAH, ARIZ, CAI, KARACHI, LL, PDA, US). RATNAPURA DISTRICT: roadside between Balangoda and Belihul-oya, 650 m alt., 3 March 1968, hedge probably planted, flowers blue-purple, *Comanor 1106* (LL, NY); in outdoor cultivation as hedge plant, Pelwadiya, low altitude, 12 Feb. 1974, corollas blue, *H.N. &*

A.L. Moldenke, Dassanayake, & Jayasuriya 28346 (ARIZ, MO, PDA, US). BADULLA DISTRICT: cultivated as hedge, Haputale, at Monamaya, 1500 ft alt., 18 April 1973, flowers lavender, 2 petals with a darker central line, "lignum-vitae", *Stone 11210* (US).

var. **alba** (Masters) Bailey in L.H. & E.Z. Bailey, Hortus 225. 1930; Moldenke in Lundell, Fl. Texas 3: 76–77. 1942; Kuck & Tongg, Mod. Trop. Gard. 112 & 235, 1955; Grindal, Everyday Gard. India, ed. 16, 48. 1960; Wyman, Gard. Enc. 331. 1971; Stewart in Nasir & Ali, Fl. West Pakistan 606. 1972; Moldenke in Woodson, Schery, *et al.*, Ann. Missouri Bot. Gard. 60: 92. 1973. Type: Woodrow material probably sent from India in or before 1888 to Dr. M.T. Masters in England.

Duranta plumieri var. *alba* Masters, Gard. Chron. 63 [ser. 3, 3]: 44, fig. 9. 1888.

Duranta repens f. *alba* Matuda, Amer. Midl. Naturalist 44: 576, hyponym. 1950.

Duranta erecta var. *alba* (Masters) Caro, Revista Argent. Agron. 23: 11. 1956.

This variety differs from the typical variety in having white corollas.

The variety occurs sporadically throughout the range of the species and is widely cultivated in subtropical and tropical regions, sometimes escaping. Its chromosome count is reported to be 34. Usually it is less common, both in the wild and in cultivation, than the blue-flowered variety. Gardeners assert that it is not as strong-growing and is more susceptible to red spider (mite) attack in the dry season and therefore less desirable as a hedge. We have personally seen an example in Hawaii that was 25 ft tall. Usually it is nearly or completely thornless.

V e r n. Among the dozen recorded from various parts of its range are: heliotropio blanco [white heliotrope], lluvia [rain], no-me-olvides [forget-me-not], varita de San José [rod of St. Joseph], velo de novia [sweetheart's veil], corona de la novia [bride's crown], and white skyflower.

S p e c i m e n s   E x a m i n e d. TRINCOMALEE DISTRICT: Trincomalee, 28 March 1963, flowers white, *Amaratunga 544* (PDA).

10. CITHAREXYLUM

Mill. ex L., Sp. Pl., ed. 1, 625. 1753; L., Gen. Pl., ed. 5, 273 [as "*Citharexylon*"]. 1754. Type species: *Citharexylum spinosum* L.

Citarexylon L., Syst. ed. 6, ind. 2. 1748.—*Citharexylon* B. Juss. ex L., Amoen. Acad. 1: 406. 1749.—*Citharexylum* Mill., Gard. Dict., ed. 6, App. 175. 1752.—*Citharoxylon* L., Syst. ed. 11, 2: ind. q. 3. 1760.—*Citharexylon* Pluk. ex Adans., Fam. Pl. 2: 200. 1761.—*Kitarexulon* Adans., Fam. Pl. 2: 12. 1763.—*Citharoxylum* Mill. ex Hildt, Beschr. In- und Ausl. Holzart. 45.

1798.—*Citharexylon* L. ex Steud., Nom. Bot., ed. 1, 202. 1821.—*Cytharexylum* Mill. ex Sessé & Moc., Naturaleza, ser. 2, 1: 103. 1889.

Rauwolfia Ruíz & Pav., Fl. Peruv. & Chil. 2: 26, pl. 152. 1799 [not *Rauwolfia* L., 1913, nor *Rauvolfia* Plum., 1737 & 1753].

Scleroon Benth. ex Lindl., Bot. Reg. 29: Misc. 65–66. 1843.

Cacocalyx S. Wats., Proc. Amer. Acad. Arts 24: 67. 1889.

Marexylon Zucc. ex Moldenke, Prelim. Alph. List Invalid Names 32, in syn. 1940.—*Merexylon* Zucc. ex Moldenke, Phytologia 6: 243, in syn. 1958.

Hadongia Gagnep. in Humbert, Not. Syst. 14: 30. 1950.

Turncasa Ruíz & Pav. ex Moldenke, Phytologia 6: 243, in syn. 1958.

Trees or shrubs, rarely climbing; branches and branchlets usually tetragonal, sometimes spiny; leaf-scars mostly large, corky, and elevated, borne on more or less prominent sterigmata; leaves deciduous, decussate-opposite, ternate or verticillate, rarely approximate, subopposite, or even alternate, entire or dentate, usually bearing a pair of prominent glands at the base of the blade, petiolate or sessile, the petioles rarely myrmecophilous at the apex, exstipulate; inflorescence axillary and terminal, indeterminate, racemiform or spicate. mostly simple, occasionally sparsely branched, mostly elongate and many-flowered, rarely reduced to only a few flowers, erect or nutant; flowers small, each subtended by a usually tiny and inconspicuous bractlet; calyx tubular or cyathiform, regular or somewhat zygomorphic, thin, accrescent, apically truncate and entire or 5-toothed or -lobed; corolla infundibular or hypocrateriform, mostly yellow or white, varying to blue, violet, or lilac, the tube narrow-cylindric and regular, the limb spreading, usually 5-parted, rarely 4- or 6-parted, with broad, slightly irregular lobes, the 2 hindmost outermost in prefloration, mostly more or less pubescent in the throat; stamens 4, mostly didynamous, inserted at or above the middle of the corolla-tube, included, a fifth stamen represented by a rudimentary staminode, or occasionally stamens 5 or even 6, the filaments very short, the anthers ovate or sagittate, introrse, erect, with 2 parallel thecae opening by longitudinal slits and with a thickened connective which often surpasses the thecae in length; style terminal, included, often thickened upwards, the stigma shortly bifid; ovary perfectly or imperfectly 4-celled, 2-carpellate, each cell with 1 lateral anatropous ovule; fruit drupaceous, with a juicy exocarp and hard endocarp, the 2 pyrenes each 2-celled and 2-seeded, often separated by a median fissure; fruiting-calyx conspicuously enlarged and indurated, cupuliform or patelliform, shorter than the fruit.

A genus of about 145 species and infraspecific taxa, ranging from Bermuda and the southernmost United States through Mexico, Central America, and the West Indies to Argentina and Uruguay. Many species are cultivated for ornament in various parts of the world. Several fossil forms are known from the Tertiary of the United States, Colombia, and Italy. In Ceylon only two cultivated species are known.

KEY TO THE SPECIES

1 Leaf-blades very firmly chartaceous and stiff, the vein and veinlet reticulation very prominent and conspicuous on both surfaces..........................**1. C. fruticosum**
1 Leaf-blades thinly subchartaceous or membranous, not stiff, the vein and veinlet reticulation usually not conspicuously elevated on either surface............**2. C. spinosum**

1. Citharexylum fruticosum L., Syst. ed. 10, 2: 1115 [as *'fruticos.'*]. 1759; Sandm., Fl. Jamaic. 18. 1759; O.E. Schulz in Urb., Symb. Ant. 6: 61. 1909; Moldenke, Phytologia 6: 354–366 (1958), 7: 75 (1959), 13: 287–289 (1966), 14: 433–434 & 507 (1967), 31: 356–360 & 448 (1975), and 32: 49. 1975. Type: *James Reed s.n.* from Barbados, deposited in Sloan Herbarium (BM).

Citharexylon cinereum L., Sp. Pl., ed. 2, 2: 872. 1763 [not *C. cinereum* Spreng., 1851].—*Citharexylum cinereum* L., Syst. ed. 12, 416. 1767 [not *C. cinereum* Jacq., 1789, nor Donn. Sm., 1907, nor Lam., 1975, nor "sens. Mayc.", 1965].—*Cytharexylum cinereum* L. ex Jacq., Amer. Gew. 2: 44. 1787.— *Citharexylum cinereum* Sessé & Moc. ex D. Don, Edinburgh New Philos. J. 11 [Jan.–Mar.]: 238, in syn. 1831; Sessé & Moc., Fl. Mex., ed. 1, 152. 1894. — *Citarexylum cinereum* L. apud Alain in León & Alain, Fl. Cuba 4: 300, in syn. 1957.
Citharexylum coriaceum Desf., Tabl. Ecole Bot., ed. 2, 65, nom. nud. 1815; Desf., Cat. Pl. Hort. Reg. Paris, ed. 3, 91 & 392. 1829. — *Citharexylon coriaceum* Desf. ex Steud., Nom. Bot., ed. 1, 202. 1821.
Citharexylum caudatum Sagra apud O.E. Schulz in Urb., Symb. Ant. 6: 61, in syn. 1909 [not *C. caudatum* L., 1763, nor *Citharexylon caudatum* Sw., 1821].
Citharexylum quadrangulare Griseb. (in part) apud O.E. Schulz in Urb., Symb. Ant. 6: 62, in syn. 1909 [not *C. quadrangulare* L., 1786, nor Schau., 1864, nor Sessé & Moc., 1894, nor Millsp., 1907, nor Boutelou, 1909, nor Jacq., 1909, nor A. Rich., 1909, nor Hort., 1911, nor Hort. Madrit., 1806, nor *Citharexylon quadrangulare* Jacq., 1760].
Citharexylum villosum Griseb. apud O.E. Schulz in Urb., Symb. Ant. 6: 62, in syn. 1909 [not *C. villosum* Jacq., 1781].—*C. villosum* Chapm. apud Small, Fl. Miami 161, in syn. 1913.
Citharexylum spicatum Ryan ex Moldenke, Prelim. Alph. List Invalid Names 17, in syn. 1940 [not *C. spicatum* (Jacques) Sprague, 1924, nor *Citharexylon spicatum* Rusby, 1900].
Citharexylum villosum var. *glaberrimum* C. Wright ex Moldenke, Prelim. Alph. List Invalid Names 18, in syn. 1940.

Shrub or graceful, slender, semi-deciduous, small or medium-sized tree, to 16 m tall; trunk to 21 cm in diameter at breast height; branches medium-stout, grey, obtusely or rather acutely tetragonal, glabrous; bark on old trees pale-brown or grey, smooth or with very shallow furrows, on young trees light-brown; branchlets more slender, acutely tetragonal, often ribbed, glabrous;

leaf-scars borne on stout ascending sterigmata which on larger branches become very corky and to 5 mm long and 4 mm wide; leaves decussate-opposite; petioles slender or stoutish, orange when fresh, 1–2.5 cm long, more or less margined, canaliculate above, glabrous; leaf-blades very firmly chartaceous and stiff, often subcoriaceous, bright- or yellow-green on both surfaces or somewhat darker above, very shiny and glossy (especially above), oblong or elliptic (occasionally sublanceolate, oblanceolate, or obovate), 4.5–21 cm long, 1.5–8 cm wide, varying from acute or very shortly acuminate to obtuse or rounded at the apex (rarely emarginate), entire (or coarsely serrate on seedlings and sprouts), cuneate or narrow-cuneate at the base, with 1–3 pairs of glands at the very base, one pair of which is always much elongated and parallel to the petiole, reticulate, very glabrous on both surfaces or very rarely punctate beneath and obsoletely puberulent along the venation when immature, the younger ones appearing as though varnished; midrib sharply prominulous above and prominent beneath; the 5–8 pairs of secondaries sharply prominulous on both surfaces, usually hardly at all or very obscurely anastomosing; veinlet reticulation very abundant, fine, sharply prominulous on both surfaces, especially above; racemes axillary and (mostly) terminal, 3.5–26.5 cm long, 1–1.7 cm wide, the axillary ones usually abbreviated, the terminal ones sometimes branched with 1 or 2 short branches near the base, mostly lax, nutant or pendent, many-flowered, often dense; peduncles slender, brown, 0.5–1.5 cm long, glabrous; rachis similar to the peduncles; pedicels filiform, to 1 mm long or obsolete, glabrate; bractlets setaceous or linear, 1–2 mm long; flowers fragrant, often at least functionally dioecious; calyx cyathiform, 2.5–4 mm long, glabrous, its rim truncate or very light 5-repand-dentate and ciliate; corolla white or greenish-white, subhypocrateriform, its tube 2–6 mm long, externally glabrous, villous within (especially at the mouth), its limb 5-parted, about 5 mm wide, the lobes suborbicular or elliptic-lingulate, 2–3 mm long, apically rounded; fruiting-calyx indurated, shallowly cupuliform, 2–3 mm long, 5–6 mm wide, glabrous, its rim shallowly and more or less irregularly scarious-lobed; fruit oblong or subglobose, fleshy, to 13 mm long and 12 mm wide, apiculate by the persistent style when immature, much wrinkled in drying, dull or subnitid, 2-lobed, varying from pink or red to orange, orange-red or scarlet when immature, purplish or black when ripe; seeds 2, thin, saucer-shaped.

D i s t r. This species is native from southern Florida in the U.S.A. through all of the West Indies to northern South America and occurs in cultivation (mostly as specimen plants in botanical gardens or fine collections) in various parts of the world.

U s e s. It is reported to be used medicinally in the Dominican Republic, where its stems are also employed as living fenceposts. In other countries of the West Indies its wood is used for making charcoal. The physico-chemical properties of the sap are discussed by Harris (Physico-chem. Prop. Plant Saps 143. 1934). The wood is used commercially in Cuba, being very hard, heavy, and strong, with a specific gravity of 0.7. In Puerto Rico it is highly regarded for fenceposts and in various places the wood has been used for making furniture, in house construction, and for making violins, guitars, and other musical instruments. It is sometimes planted along highways and fences and in gardens as an ornamental and as a source of nectar for honey, but is subject to attack by several parasitic fungi and by caterpillars which fasten the leaves together in bundles and cause leaf-fall, reducing the ornamental value.

V e r n. Among its 65 recorded common names are: Black fiddlewood, Cutlet, Fairytree, Old-woman's-bitter, Pendula, Savanna-wattle, Susannatree, and White fiddlewood.

S p e c i m e n s E x a m i n e d. KANDY DISTRICT: in outdoor cultivation in Section E, Royal Botanic Garden, Peradeniya, 1550 ft alt., 18 Jan. 1974, tree about 35 ft tall, numbered E. 274, *H.N. & A.L. Moldenke & Jayasuriya 28137* (AAU, LL, PDA, US).

2. Citharexylum spinosum L., Sp. Pl., ed. 1, 2: 625. 1753; Hallier, Meded. Rijks-Herb. 37: 23. 1918; Moldenke, Phytologia 7: 33–46 & 77 (1959), 13: 313–315 (1966), 14: 510–511 (1967), and 32: 192–200 & 218. 1975. Type: *James Reed s.n.* from Barbados, collected before 1700, deposited in the Sloan Herbarium (BM).

Citharexylum americanum Mill., Gard. Dict., ed. 6, app. 1752.

Citharexylum quadrangulare Jacq., Enum. Syst. Pl. Carib. 26. 1760.—*C. quandrangulare* Jacq. ex Murr. in L., Syst., ed. 13, 472. 1774.—*C. quadrangulare* L. apud Lam., Enc. 2: 133, in syn. 1786.—*C. quadrangulare* Willd. apud Pers., Syn. Pl. 2: 142. 1806.—*Citharexylon quadrangulare* Jacq. ex Richter, Linn. Op. 603. 1835.—*Citharexylum quadrangulare* Schau. apud Griseb., Fl. Brit. W. Ind. 497, in syn. 1861.

Citharexylum teres Jacq., Select. Stirp. Amer. Hist. 185, pl. 118. 1763.— *Citharexylon teres* Jacq. ex Sw., Obs. Bot. 234, in syn. 1791.

Citharexylum cinereum Jacq. ex J.F. Gmel. in L., Syst. ed. 13, imp. 1, 2: 942. 1789 [not *C. cinereum* Donn. Sm., 1907, nor L., 1767, nor Sessé & Moc., 1831, nor Spreng., 1893, nor *Citharexylon cinereum* L., 1763, nor Spreng., 1851].—*Citharexylum cinereum* "sensu Mayc." apud Gooding, Loveless, & Proctor, Fl. Barbados 356, in syn. 1965.—*C. cinereum* Lam. apud López-Palacios, Revista Fac. Farm. Univ. Los Andes 15: 21, in syn. 1975.

Citharexylon caudatum Sw. apud Steud., Nom. Bot., ed. 1, 202, in syn. 1821 [not *C. caudatum* L., 1763, nor *Citharexylum caudatum* L., 1774, nor Seem., 1861, nor Sieb., 1896, nor Donn. Sm., 1907, nor Sagra, 1909, nor Cham. & Schlecht., 1940].—*Citharexylum caudatum* Sw. apud Schau. in D. DC., Prod. 11: 611, in syn. 1847.

Citharexylon cinereum var. *β* Lam. ex Steud., Nom. Bot., ed. 1, 202. 1821.
Citharexylon spinosum L. ex Richter, Linn. Op. 603. 1835 [not *C. spinosum*
Kunth, 1825, nor H. & B., 1840, nor H.B.K., 1845, nor *Citharexylum spi-
nosum* H.B.K., 1817, nor Kunth, 1847].
Citharexylum surrectum Griseb. (in part), Fl. Brit. W. Ind. 497. 1861.
Citharexylum laevigatum Hostm. ex Griseb., Fl. Brit. W. Ind. 497, in syn.
1861.
Citharexylum lucidum Griseb. (in part) apud O.E. Schulz in Urb., Symb. Ant.
6: 65, in syn. 1909 [not *C. lucidum* Schlecht. & Cham., 1830, nor D. Don,
1831, nor Cham., 1861, nor C. DC., 1942].
Citharexylum caudatum var. *obtusifolium* Hornemann ex Moldenke, Prelim.
Alph. List Invalid Names 16, in syn. 1940.
Citharexylum hostmannii Klotzsch ex Moldenke, Prelim. Alph. List Invalid
Names 16, in syn. 1940.
Hadongia eberhardtii Gagnep. in Humbert, Not. Syst. 14: 30. 1950.

Shrub or tree, to 16 m tall; trunk to 35 cm in diameter; crown narrow;
wood pithy, brittle; branches and branchlets medium-slender, usually acutely
tetragonal, grey or stramineous, glabrous; leaf-scars borne on large, ascending, corky sterigmata to 4 mm long; leaves decussate-opposite, but sometimes
only one of a pair developed or one greatly reduced; petioles slender, 0.7–
2.4 cm long, orange when fresh, mostly canaliculate above, glabrous; leaf-
blades thinly subchartaceous or membranous, not stiff, usually rather dull
rich-green above and pale-green beneath or uniform in colour on both surfaces, often more or less brunneous in drying, elliptic or elliptic-oblong to oblong, rarely subovate, 3.5–29 cm long, 1.3–11.3 cm wide, mostly larger, varying
from obtuse (rarely emarginate) to acute to short-acuminate at the apex,
entire (or rarely irregularly and coarsely dentate with large teeth on watersprouts), acute or subacuminate at the base and usually bearing 1 or 2 black
glands of varying dimensions there, glabrous on both surfaces or sparsely
barbellate along the sides of the midrib and in the axils of the secondaries
beneath; midrib and 5–8 pairs of secondaries plane or very slightly prominulent above, prominent beneath; veinlet reticulation rather distant, mostly
obscure on both surfaces or only slightly prominulent beneath; racemes axillary and (mostly) terminal, simple or compound with 1–5 pairs of basal
branches, 2.5–35 cm long, to 2 cm wide during anthesis, rather loosely many-
flowered, nutant; peduncles and the pale-green rachis slender, very sparsely
and minutely pulverulent or glabrous, the former brown, 1.5–2.5 cm long,
usually with a bractlet-bearing node near the middle; pedicles very slender,
1.5–4 mm long, glabrate; large foliaceous bracts sometimes present; bractlets
linear, to 1 cm long, the upper 1–2 mm long; flowers very fragrant; calyx cyathiform, 3–4 mm long, pale-green, glabrous, its rim ciliate and obsoletely
5-dentate; corolla varying from white or whitish to cream-colour or reddish-

white, subhypocrateriform or hypocrateriform to infundibular, its tube 4–6 mm long, externally glabrous, white-villous at the mouth within, the limb 5-parted, the lobes suborbicular-lingulate, 2–3 mm long, rounded apically, sparsely ciliate; fruiting-calyx indurated, cupuliform or broadly cupuliform, 3–4 mm long, 5–6 mm wide, orange when fresh, often venose, glabrous, shiny, its rim irregularly erose or shallowly and irregularly lobed and more or less scarious; fruit drupaceous, oblong, about 8 mm long and 6 mm wide, very fleshy, brownish- or reddish-black to black, shiny and very much wrinkled in drying, often apiculate when immature. Chromosome number: $2n = 76$.

D i s t r. The species is very widely distributed in the West Indies and northern South America, and is very widely cultivated, and sometimes naturalized, in other warm portions of the world.

U s e s. Its wood is used commercially in Cuba and elsewhere, being close-grained and very tough, useful for mill-rollers and frames, carriage-wheels, window-frames, doors, beams, etc. It is also reputedly used in the manufacture of stringed musical instruments.

In some regions this species is used with others to form windbreaks to protect sugarcane fields, but alone it does not serve well because the wood will not withstand hurricane winds. It requires protection from frost. In Hawaii it is used as a street tree. The fruits are eaten by various birds.

V e r n. Among the 50 common names recorded are Cutlet, Fairy, Fiddle-wood, Juniper-berry, Penda, Savanna-wattle, Susanna tree, White fiddlewood, and Zither-wood.

N o t e s. The leaves usually turn a russet-gold before falling. The bark and wood are often attacked by the fungus, *Polyporus marasmioides* (Pat.) Sacc. & D. Sacc., and the leaves by *Gloeosporium cytharexyli* Scalia. The pollen has been described by Nair & Rehman in Bull. Nat. Bot. Gard. Lucknow 76: 10 & 23, pl. 1, fig. 6, text-fig. 16 (1962).

S p e c i m e n s   E x a m i n e d. KANDY DISTRICT: cultivated, Royal Botanic Garden, Peradeniya, 1550 ft alt., 27 June 1904, flowers reddish-white, *Hallier C. 237* (HBG; L); April 1880, *s. coll. s.n.* (PDA); April 1887 (PDA); seeds from South America, *s. coll. s.n.* (PDA); River Drive, May 1894, *s. coll. s.n.* (PDA); along river behind Royal Botanic Garden, Peradeniya, 500 m alt., 21 May 1973, tree 8 m tall, diameter 10 cm, bark smooth, grey, flowers white, very fragrant, *Kostermans 24918* (AAU); in outdoor cultivation, section E. 275, Royal Botanic Garden, Peradeniya, 1550 ft alt., 18 Jan. 1974, tree 15 ft tall, *H.N. & A.L. Moldenke & Jayasuriya 28136* (CAI, LL, PDA, US); in outdoor cultivation, section E. 229, Royal Botanic Garden, Peradeniya, 1550 ft alt., 18 Jan. 1974, tree 20 ft tall, leaves on sprouts coarsely dentate, *H.N. & A.L. Moldenke & Jayasuriya 28143* (AAU, PDA, US); Royal Botanic Garden, Peradeniya, 1600 ft alt., 26 June 1974, tree 7 m tall, flowers yellow, *Waas 703* (US).

11. AEGIPHILA

Jacq., Obs. Bot. 2: 3. 1764. Type species: *Aegiphila martinicensis* Jacq.

Manabea Aubl., Hist. Pl. Guian. 1: 61. 1775.—*Manabaea* Aubl. ex J.F. Gmel. [ed. Turton] in L., Gen. Syst. Nat. 5: 219, in syn. 1802.—*Manabaea* Hedw. f. apud Dalla Torre & Harms, Gen. Siphon. 432. in syn. 1900.

Aegyphila Jacq. apud Planer, Gatt. Pfl. 1: 87–88. 1775.—*Aeegiphila* Sw., Nov. Gen. & Sp. Pl. Prod. 31: 1788.—*Aegephila* Vell., Fl. Flum. Ic. 1: 89. 1827.— *Aegiphyla* L. apud Steud., Nom. Bot., ed. 2, 1: 29. 1840.—*Aegiphyla* Steud. ex Pfeiffer, Nom. Bot. 1 (1): 64, in syn. 1873.

Omphalococca Willd. ex Roem. & Schult., Mant. 3: 10. 1827.

Amerina P. DC., Prod. 9: 512–513. 1845 [not *Amerina* Noronha, 1790, nor Raf., 1838].

Distigma Klotzsch ex Walp., Rep. 4: 123, in syn. 1845.

Brückea Klotzsch & Karst., Ausw. Neu. Gew. Venez. 31. 1848.—*Bruckea* Klotzsch & Karst. ex Bocq., Adansonia, ser. 1, 2: 83 & 130. 1862.—*Brueckia* Klotzsch & Karst. apud Jacks. in Hook. f. & Jacks., Ind. Kew., imp. 1, 1: 46, in syn. 1893.—*Brueckea* Klotzsch & Karst. apud Jacks. in Hook. f. & Jacks., Ind. Kew., imp. 1, 1: 345, in syn. 1893.—*Brueckia* Karst. ex Briq. in Pflanzenfam. 4 (3a): 116, in syn. 1895.

Pseudaegiphila Rusby, Mem. New York Bot. Gard. 7: 339. 1927.

Woody plants, mostly shrubs or trees, sometimes scandent; branches and branchlets tetragonal or subterete, glabrous or variously pubescent; leaves simple, usually decussate-opposite, rarely subopposite or ternate, deciduous, exstipulate, mostly petiolate, glabrous or variously pubescent, entire or dentate; inflorescence cymose, determinate, the cymes often paniculate, umbellate, or reduced to a few or even solitary flowers, axillary or terminal; flowers actinomorphic, hypogynous, hermaphroditic but usually conspicuously diclinous, sometimes at least functionally dioecious; calyx gamosepalous, more or less campanulate, cyathiform, or tubular, apically truncate and entire or 4- or 5-toothed or -lobed, accrescent, greatly incrassate and indurated in fruit; corolla gamopetalous, infundibular or hypocrateriform, mostly white or yellow, the tube cylindric, the limb equally 4- or 5-parted, the lobes imbricate in prefloration; stamens 4 or 5, equal, isomorphic, inserted below the mouth of the corolla-tube, included or exserted, alternate with the corolla-lobes; filaments mostly filiform; anthers often reduced but sometimes still polleniferous in pistillate flowers; pistil one, the style terminal or subterminal, single, capillary, mostly glabrous, the stigma bifid, its branches elongate and awl-shaped; ovary superior, perfectly or imperfectly 4-celled, each cell 1-ovulate, the ovules lateral or sub-apical, hemianatropous; fruit drupaceous, mostly fleshy, globose or subglobose, 4-seeded or sometimes fewer by abortion; seeds without endosperm.

A complex genus of about 175 species and infraspecific taxa of subtropical and tropical America, ranging from Cuba and Mexico, through the West Indies and Central America, to Peru and northern Argentina. One species is introduced in southern Florida. Several species are sometimes cultivated as specimen plants in botanical gardens and fine collections. Only the following species is known from Ceylon.

Aegiphila martinicensis Jacq., Obs. Bot. 2: 3, pl. 27. 1764; Hallier, Meded. Rijks-Herb. 37: 34. 1918; Moldenke, Brittonia 1: 377–382. 1934; Moldenke, Phytologia 1: 235–237 (1937), 1: 293 (1938), 1: 393 (1940), 2: 440 (1948), 4: 398–400 (1953), 7: 486–488 (1961), 13: 331–332 (1966), and 27: 84–88 & 295. 1973. Type: *N.K. von Jacquin s.n.* from the margins of mountainous woods and among bushes on Martinique (W).

Aegiphila martinicensis L., Pflanzensyst. 3: 124. 1773.—*Aegiphyla martinicensis* L. apud Steud., Nom. Bot., ed. 2, 1: 29. 1840.
Aegiphila dumosa Salisb., Prod. 67. 1796.
Aegiphila macrophylla Hort. ex Desf., Tabl. Ecole Bot., ed. 1, 53. 1804 [not *A. macrophylla* Humb., 1818, nor Humb. & Bonpl., 1821, nor Humb. & Kunth, 1839, nor H.B.K., 1817, nor Kunth, 1847, nor Sieber, 1847].—*A. macrophylla* Desf. ex Steud., Nom. Bot., ed. 1, 1: 16. 1821.—*Aegiphyla macrophylla* Desf. ex Steud., Nom. Bot., ed. 2, 1: 29, in syn. 1840 [not *A. macrophylla* Humb. & Bonpl., 1840].
Aegiphila diffusa Andr., Bot. Rep. 9: 578. 1809.—*Aegiphyla diffusa* Andr. apud Steud., Nom. Bot., ed. 2, 1: 29. 1840.
Aegiphila glabra Poir., Enc. Suppl. 1: 150. 1810.
Aegiphila straminea Hoffmgg., Verz. Pfl. Nachtr. 3: 18. 1826.—*Aegiphyla straminea* Hoffmgg. apud Steud., Nom. Bot., ed. 2, 1: 29. 1840.
Psychotria corymbosa Sieber in P. DC., Prod. 4: 523. 1830.
Aegiphyla magnifolia Steud., Nom. Bot., ed. 2, 1: 29. 1840.—*Aegiphila magnifolia* Steud. apud Schau. in A. DC., Prod. 11: 655. 1847.
Aegiphila grandifolia Walp., Rep. 4: 121. 1845.
Aegiphila variabilis Moldenke, Brittonia 1: 377, in syn. 1934.

Shrub or slender tree, 1–5 m tall; branches and branchlets obtusely tetragonal or the larger subterete, brachiate, the younger ones usually ampliate and compressed at the nodes, softly strigose-puberulent, becoming glabrous in age; bark light grey; leaf-scars accrescent, becoming oblique and applanate protuberances; leaves decussate-opposite, spreading, very variable; petioles slender, weak, 5–14 mm long, minutely puberulent; left-blades usually membranous, sometimes chartaceous, bright-green and shiny above, pale beneath, varying from oblong-lanceolate to oblong, 8–25 cm long, 3–10 cm wide, acuminate or coarctate-attenuate into a narrow and abrupt point at the apex, entire, varying from narrowed and acute to obtuse and rounded at the base, usually very glabrous and smooth on both surfaces, sometimes faintly puberulent or glandular-punctate; midrib usually rather prominent beneath, sometimes prominulent above; secondaries 8–12 pairs, more or less anastomosing near the margins; veinlet reticulation delicate and inconspicuous; inflorescence axillary and terminal; cymes solitary, opposite, corymbose or sometimes subcomposite, spreading, many-flowered, more or less trichotomous, half as long as or equalling the subtending leaves, the uppermost often gradually diminishing into the terminal thyrse; panicle terminal, thyrsoid, often pyramidal, to 17 cm long and 13 cm wide, leafy, its sympodia fastigiate, medium-stout, puberulent or glabrate; flowers inodorous; peduncles 2.5–7.5 cm long, terete, puberulent; pedicles slender, 2–4 mm long, minutely puberulent, often 2-bracteolate below the middle, not much thickened in fruit; bractlets and prophylla linear or subulate, 1–2 mm long, puberulent; calyx narrow-campanulate or turbinate-infundibular, widening from an acute and hemispheric base to a cupuliform limb, 2–3 mm long, 1.5–3 mm wide, lax around the corolla-tube, minutely puberulent or glabrate, its rim truncate, subentire or 4-mucronulate; corolla hypocrateriform, white or pale-yellow, its tube narrow-cylindric, 2–6 mm long, ampliate above, the lobes 4 (rarely 5), spreading, ovate-lingulate, 3.2–6.5 mm long, 1.7–3.7 mm wide, apically obtuse, often minutely puberulent on the outside; stamens 4 (rarely 5), inserted 1–3 mm below the mouth of the corolla-tube, exserted or included; filaments filiform, 0.6–7.2 mm long, glabrous; anthers quadrate; pistil included or exserted; style capillary, 3–9 mm long, glabrous; stigma-branches 1–4 mm long; ovary subglobose, 1–1.5 mm long and wide, flattened above, 4-sulcate, glabrous; fruiting-calyx greatly enlarged and indurated, very shallowly cupuliform or patelliform, very lax and spreading, about 6 mm wide, its rim irregularly lobed with large rounded lobes, often very venose, scarious along the margins; fruit subglobose or ovoid, 8–10 mm wide, 5–13 mm long, varying from yellow to red with maturity, umbilicate at both ends, with very little soft pulp, blackening and becoming deeply 4-lobed and -sulcate and roughened in drying, hardly at all invested at the base by the mature calyx, 4-seeded.

D i s t r. This is a common species throughout the West Indies, with very closely related forms in Central America and northern South America; occasionally cultivated elsewhere as a specimen plant mostly in botanical gardens or fine collections.

U s e s. In Cuba a diuretic medicinal tea is made from the leaves of this species and a syrup is made from it that is used in the treatment of asthma. On the island of Dominica torches are made from its wood.

V e r n. Among its 35 recorded popular names are: Bastard white-root, Bois chandelle, Goatwood, Lengua de vaca, Spirit-weed, Sylvania, and Wild-jasmine.

N o t e s. The flowers are decidedly diclinous and essentially dioecious. The leaves are often attacked by two parasitic fungi, *Hobsonia ackermanni* Pat. and *Guignardia prominens* Earle, the latter causing the leaves to become thickly dotted with tiny, black, elevated structures resembling stalked glands.

Specimens Examined. KANDY DISTRICT: Royal Botanic Garden, Peradeniya, 13 June 1896, *s. coll. s.n.* (PDA), 12 Aug. 1900, *s. coll. s.n.* (PDA); cultivated, Royal Botanic Garden, Peradeniya, 1550 ft alt., 27 June 1904, flowers waxy-yellow, *Hallier C. 240* (HBG, L); KALUTARA DISTRICT: Kalutara, *MacRae & Gardner s.n. [C.P. 2895]* (PDA); *J.M. Silva 49–08* (PDA).

12. CALLICARPA

L., Sp. Pl., ed. 1, 1: 111. 1753; L., Gen. Pl., ed. 5, 50. 1754. Type species: *Callicarpa americana* L.

Tomex L., Nov. Pl. Gen. Diss. Dassow 5. 1747; L., Sp. Pl., ed. 1, 1: 118. 1753; L., Gen. Pl., ed. 5, 54. 1754 [not *Tomex* Forsk., 1775, nor Thunb., 1783].— *Tomox* L. apud Adans., Fam. Pl. 2: 446, in syn. 1763.—*Tomea* L. apud Jacks. in Hook. f. & Jacks., Ind. Kew. 1: 386, in syn. 1893.—*Tometax* L. apud Raizada, Indian Forester 72: 304, in syn. 1966.

Spondylococcos Mitch., Acta Phys.-Med. Acad. Caes. Leop.-Carol. Nat. Cur. 8 (app.): 218. 1748.—*Sphondylococcos* Mitch. apud L., Sp., Pl., ed. 1, 1: 111, in syn. 1753.—*Spondylococeus* Mitch. apud P. Mill., Gard. Dict., ed. 7, in syn. 1759.—*Spondylococcus* Mitch. apud P. Mill., Gard. Dict., ed. 8, in syn. 1768.—*Sphondylococcum* Mitch. apud Endl., Gen. Pl. 637, in syn. 1838.— *Sphondylococcus* Mitch. apud Walp., Rep. 4: 137, in syn. 1845.—*Spondylococcum* Wittst. apud Pfeiffer, Nom. Bot. 2 (2): 1244. 1874.—*Spondylococca* Mitch. apud Benth. in Benth. & Hook. f., Gen. Pl. 2 (2): 1150, in syn. 1876.

Burcardia Heist. ex Duham., Trait. Arb. & Arbust. 1: 111–112, pl. 44. 1755 [not *Burcardia* Raf., 1838, nor Schreb., 1789].—*Burcardia* Duham. apud Lam., Enc. 1: 563, in syn. 1783.—*Burchardia* Heist. apud Reichard in L., Gen. Pl., ed. 8, 56, in syn. 1778.—*Burchardia* (Heist.) Duham. ex Jacks. in Hook. f. & Jacks., Ind. Kew., imp. 1, 1: 386, in syn. 1893.

Johnsonia T. Dale ex P. Mill., Gard. Dict., ed. 7. 1759.—*Johnsonia* Mill. apud L., Sp. Pl., ed. 2, 1: 161, in syn. 1762.—*Johnsonia* Catesby apud Endl., Gen. Pl. 637, in syn. 1838.—*Jonsonia* Garden in L., Corresp. 1: 364. 1821.

Illa Adans., Fam. Pl. 2: 446 & 565. 1763.

Callacarpa P. Mill., Gard. Dict., ed. 8, in syn. 1768.—*Callicarpus* Beckm., Lex. Bot. 44. 1801.—*Callicarpa* Willd. ex Moon, Cat. 1: 10. 1824.—*Callicarpus* L. apud Hassk., Cat. Pl. Hort. Bot. Bogor. 136. 1844.—*Callicarpus* Hassk. apud Miq., Fl. Ind. Bat. 2: 884, in syn. 1857.—*Calycarpa* L. apud Featherm., Rep. Bot. Surv. South. Cent. La. 99. 1891.—*Calocarpus* L. apud Post &

Kuntze, Lex. 91. 1904.—*Calocarpus* Post & Kuntze apud Airy Shaw in Willis, Dict. ed. 7, 179, in syn. 1966.
Porphyra Lour., Fl. Cochinch., ed. 1, 1: 69. 1790 [not *Porphyra* C. Agardh, 1822].
Amictonis Raf., Sylv. Tellur. 161. 1838.

Shrubs or trees; leaves mostly decussate-opposite, simple, deciduous, exstipulate; inflorescence cymose (determinate), axillary or supra-axillary, sometimes polygamous; flowers actinomorphic; calyx gamosepalous, tubular or campanulate to cyathiform, 4-toothed to 4-fid, sometimes entire, rarely 5-toothed; corolla gamopetalous, infundibular or hypocrateriform, the tube straight, usually broadly cylindric, ampliate above, the limb 4- (rarely 5-) parted, the lobes lingulate, isomorphic, spreading; stamens 4 (rarely 5), equal, inserted at or near the base of the corolla-tube, alternate with the corolla-lobes, usually more or less exserted; filaments filiform, separate, glabrous; anthers oblong or elliptic, dorsifixed near the base, 2-celled, the thecae parallel and opening extrorsely by longitudinal slits or rarely by terminal pores; pistil single, terminal, compound, absent from staminate flowers; style single, capillary, glabrous; stigma depressed-capitate or peltate; ovary single, hypogynous, compound, usually subglobose and more or less pubescent, 4-celled, composed of two 2-celled carpels, each cell with one high-lateral ovule, rudimentary or absent in staminate flowers; fruit drupaceous, more or less globose or depressed-globose, with fleshy and variously coloured or white exocarp and hard endocarp, the latter separating into 4 (or through abortion fewer) stony pyrenes, each containing a single seed; embryo straight, with scanty or no endosperm; fruiting-calyx usually unchanged, patelliform. Chromosome number: $x = 8$ or 9.

A complex genus of about 205 specific and infraspecific taxa, widely distributed in tropical and subtropical America, Asia, and Oceanica, a few species ranging north into temperate Asia and America. Some species are widely cultivated for ornament in various parts of the world, others as specimen plants. In Ceylon there are one native and three cultivated species.

KEY TO THE SPECIES

1 Leaf-blades mostly rounded or subtruncate at the base
  2 Cymes during anthesis very large, loose, and spreading; peduncles to 8 cm long; leaf-blades to 22 cm long..**1. C. nudiflora**
  2 Cymes during anthesis small, dense, not loosely spreading; peduncles to 2.5 cm long; leaf-blades to 14.5 cm long, usually smaller......................**2. C. pedunculata**
1 Leaf-blades acute or acuminate at the base
  3 Leaf-blades distinctly serrate, oblong or narrowly oblong-ovate; mature fruit white....
  ....**3. C. macrophylla**
  3 Leaf-blades entire, repand, or minutely denticulate, broadly ovate; mature fruit purple
  ....**4. C. tomentosa**

1. Callicarpa nudiflora Hook. & Arn., Bot. Beech. Voy. 206, pl. 46. 1836; Roxb., Fl. Ind., ed. 1, 1: 408 (1820) and ed. 2, 1: 394. 1832; Hook. f., Fl. Br. Ind. 4: 568. 1885; King & Gamble, J. Asiat. Soc. Bengal 74 (2): 805–806. 1908; H.J. Lam, Verb. Malay. Arch. 65. 1919; P'ei, Verb. China 42–44. 1932; Moldenke, Phytologia 21: 341–347 (1971), 22: 203 (1971), and 33: 500. 1976. Type: *Millett s.n.* from Canton, China (lectotype).

Callicarpa acuminata Roxb., Hort. Beng. [10], hyponym. 1814; Roxb., Fl. Ind., ed. 1: 408–409. 1820 [not *C. acuminata* H.B.K., 1817].—*C. acuminata* Wall. ex Mehra & Bawa, Evolution 23: 466. 1960.
Callicarpa reevesii Wall., Num. List. 50, hyponym. 1829.—*C. reewvesii* Wall. ex Briq. in Pflanzenfam.; ed. 1, 4 (3a): 166. 1895.—*C. reveesii* Wall. apud Bakh. in Lam & Bakh., Bull. Jard. Bot. Buitenzorg, ser. 3, 3: 22. 1921.
Callicarpa nudiflora Hook. ex Pritz., Ic. Bot. Ind. 1: 188. 1866.
Callicarpa macrophylla var. *sinensis* Clarke in Hook. f., Fl. Br. Ind. 4: 568. 1885.
Callicarpa acuminata var. *angustifolia* Metc., Lingnan Sci. J. 11: 407. 1932.

Shrub or tree, to 9 m tall; branches obtusely tetragonal or subterete, flattened at the nodes, densely flavescent- or canescent-furfuraceous or short-tomentose, the older ones conspicuously lenticellate, often more or less sulcate, glabrescent in age; leaves decussate-opposite; petioles rather stout, 6–21 mm long, densely furfuraceous or short-tomentose like the branchlets; leaf-blades thin-chartaceous, dark green above (blackening in drying), lighter beneath, oblong or elliptic-oblong, varying to oblong-lanceolate, 7.5–22 cm long, 2.5–8 cm wide, acute or acuminate apically, irregularly serrate (sometimes coarsely, often obscurely) along the margins except at the base, more or less bluntly subacute or rounded (often inequilateral) at the base, densely furfuraceous above when immature, becoming merely rugulose-puberulent or even glabrate in age (often retaining the furfuraceous tomentum on the midrib and secondaries), densely short-pubescent with canescent many-branched hairs beneath, becoming merely lightly furfuraceous on the venation, densely resinous-punctate; secondaries slender, 7–12 per side, arcuate-ascending, prominent beneath, rather obscurely anastomosing at the margins; inflorescence axillary or supra-axillary, large; cymes opposite, solitary, to 17 or more cm long and 15 cm wide, loosely many-flowered, spreading, many times dichotomous, the branches usually ascending at an acute angle, bracteolate; peduncles stout, 3–8 cm long, densely furfuraceous or tomentose, becoming glabrous in age; pedicels very slender, 1–2 mm long or subobsolete; bractlets linear, 1–5 mm long, densely furfuraceous; calyx campanulate, about 1.3 mm long and wide, 4-costate, loosely pubescent or merely puberulent, its rim very shortly 4-toothed; corolla infundibular or hypocrateriform, pink, its tube broadly cylindric, 1.3–1.5 mm long, ampliate above, the limb 4-parted, the lobes ovate-lingulate, c. 1.3 mm long and 1 mm wide, subacute or bluntish apically; stamens 4, inserted at the very base of the corolla-tube, long-exserted; filaments filiform, 6 mm long, glabrous; anthers oblong, 0.9 mm long, 0.5 mm wide; pistil long-exserted and about equalling the stamens; ovary subrotund, c. 0.5 mm long and wide, densely granulose-pulverulent; fruiting-calyx shallowly cupuliform or subpatelliform, 1.5–2 mm wide, puberulent or glabrate, its rim subtruncate, more or less shortly 4-toothed; fruit subglobose, 1.5–2 mm long and wide, glabrous, purple or black when ripe.

D i s t r. This species is rather widely distributed in China, Hong Kong, Hainan, Maçao, and Malaya, westward through Indo-China and Burma to India and Bangladesh.

U s e s. It has long been cultivated in Indian gardens and, usually as a specimen plant, in botanical gardens and fine collections elsewhere. In parts of China it is said to be employed in medicine in the treatment of wounds or injuries.

V e r n. Only three Chinese vernacular names are recorded.

S p e c i m e n s E x a m i n e d. KANDY DISTRICT: in outdoor cultivation, Royal Botanic Garden, Peradeniya, 1550 ft alt., 18 Jan. 1974, shrub 8 ft tall, numbered E. 276, *H.N. & A.L. Moldenke & Jayasuriya 28139* (MOLDENKE, PDA, US); Royal Botanic Garden, Peradeniya, 26 June, 1974, tree 20 ft tall, bark brown-greyish, cracked, leaves opposite; flowers purple, *Sumithraarachchi DBS. 377* (LACROSSE, LL).

2. **Callicarpa pedunculata** R. Br., Prod. Fl. Nov. Holl. 1: 513. 1810; Roxb., Fl. Ind., ed. 1, 1: 409. 1820; Clarke in Hook. f., Fl. Br. Ind. 4: 569. 1885; H. J. Lam, Verb. Malay. Arch. 55–58. 1919; Bakh., Bull. Jard. Bot. Buitenzorg, ser. 3, 3: 23–25. 1921; Moldenke, Phytologia 21: 387–388 & 448–455 (1971), 22: 204 (1971), and 33: 502–503. 1976. Type: *R. Brown s.n.*, from northern Australia.

Callicarpa cuspidata Roxb., Hort. Beng. [83], hyponym. 1814; Roxb., Fl. Ind. 1: 409. 1820 [not *C. cuspidata* Bakh., 1932, nor Hassk., 1921, nor Lam & Bakh., 1951].—*Callicarpus cuspidata* Roxb. ex Hassk., Cat. Pl. Bot. Bogor. Cult. Alt. 136. 1844.
Callicarpus dentata Roth ex Roem. & Schult. in L., Syst. ed. 15, 3: 98. 1818.—*Callicarpa dentata* Roth., Nov. Pl. Sp. 81–82. 1821 [not *C. dentata* Pav., 1936, nor Roxb., 1831, nor Sessé & Moc., 1940].
Callicarpa lanata Zipp. ex Span., Linnaea 15: 330. 1841 [not *C. lanata* Gamble, 1893, nor Hosséus, 1912, nor L., 1771, nor H.J. Lam, 1940, nor Lam., 1821].—*C. lanata* Vahl ex Schau. in A. DC., Prod. 11: 644. 1847.—*C. lanata* Schau. apud Benth. & F. Muell., Fl. Austral. 5: 57, in syn. 1870.—*C. lanata* Walp. apud Bakh. in Lam & Bakh., Bull. Jard. Bot. Buitenzorg, ser. 3, 3: 24, in syn. 1921.
Callicarpus oblongifolia β *acuminatissima* Hassk., Cat. Pl. Bot. Bogor. Cult.

Alt. 136. 1844.—*Callicarpa oblongifolia* var. *acuminatissima* Hassk. apud Miq., Fl. Ind. Bat. 2: 887, in syn. 1856.

Callicarpa cana Wall (in Part) apud Bocq., Adansonia, ser. 1, 3: 192. 1863 [not *C. cana* Dalz. & Gibs., 1919, nor Gamble, 1889, nor L., 1771, nor Spreng., 1866, nor Vahl, 1866].

Callicarpa tiliaefolia Teijsm. & Binn. ex Clarke in Hook. f., Fl. Br. Ind. 4: 569, in syn. 1885.

Callicarpa pedunculata var. *typica* H. J. Lam, Verb, Malay. Arch. 56–57. 1919.

Callicarpa pedunculata Roth ex Schwenke, Zytol. Untersuch. Verbenac. 27 & 28. 1931.

Shrub; branches rather slender, obtusely tetragonal, flattened at the nodes, yellowish- or greyish-furfuraceous; branchlets similar but often subterete, varying from very densely furfuraceous to sordid-pilose or yellowish-tomentose with many-branched hairs; leaves decussate-opposite; petioles usually comparatively stout, 3–10 mm long, very densely yellowish- or fuscous-tomentose like the branchlets; leaf-blades chartaceous or membranous, frequently not much or not at all darker above than beneath, oblong or oblong-elliptic, 5.5–14.5 cm long, 2.5–5.8 cm wide, usually long-acuminate (rarely only subacute) apically, rather regularly sharp-serrate along the margins except at the apex and base, acute or rounded (occasionally truncate) at the base, rather densely pilose-pubescent and scabrous above, rather densely stellate-tomentose or -furfuraceous with greyish or yellowish hairs beneath, the midrib usually densely tomentose above (especially toward the base); secondaries 5–13 per side, anastomosing near the margins beneath; inflorescence axillary or supra-axillary; cymes solitary, decussate, rather numerous, 2–4 cm long, 1.5–4.5 cm wide, many-flowered, rather small and dense in anthesis, often quite loose and spreading in fruit, conspicuously dichotomous, bracteolate, their branches densely yellowish or fuscous throughout; peduncles slender, 1–2.5 cm long, densely yellowish- or fuscous-tomentose; pedicels slender, 1 mm long and tomentose or absent; bractlets linear or setaceous, 1–3 mm long, tomentose; calyx campanulate, 1.2–1.3 mm wide, rather densely spreading-pubescent and more or less granulose-pulverulent, the rim conspicuously 4-toothed; corolla infundibular or hypocrateriform, pale-purple, its tube broadly cylindric, c. 2.1 mm long, the limb 4-parted, the lobes very shortly ovate-lingulate, about 0.8 mm long and 1 mm wide, blunt apically; stamens inserted at the very base of the corolla-tube, exserted; filaments filiform, 3.4–3.6 mm long, glabrous; anthers broadly oblong, about 0.8 mm long and 0.5 mm wide; pistil exserted and surpassing the stamens; style 5–5.2 mm long, glabrous; ovary depressed-globose, about 0.5 mm long and 0.7 mm wide, sparingly granulose-pulverulent or glabrate; fruiting-calyx patelliform, about 2 mm wide, densely pubescent or tomentose, the rim usually entire; fruit depressed-subglobose, usually deep-lilac or purple when ripe, small, smooth.

D i s t r. This species is native to tropical northern Australia and Indonesia, west to Malaya, Assam, and Sikkim, and north to southeastern China.

U s e s. It is occasionally cultivated as a specimen plant in botanical gardens and fine collections, but is subject to attack by the parasitic fungus, *Uredo callicarpae* Petch. In the Solomon islands when a small baby in arms is sick the fruits of this plant are chewed with a betel-nut and spat into the baby's mouth.

V e r n. Among the dozen common names reported are: Beauty-berry and Wild-heliotrope.

S p e c i m e n s E x a m i n e d. KANDY DISTRICT: in outdoor cultivation in Section E, Royal Botanic Gardens, Peradeniya, 1550 ft alt., 18 Jan. 1974, slender shrubby tree, 15 ft tall, numbered E. 22 (2), *H.N. & A.L. Moldenke & Jayasuriya 28145* (MOLDENKE, PDA, US).

3. Callicarpa macrophylla Vahl, Symb. Bot. 3: 13, pl. 53. 1794; Roxb., Fl. Ind., ed. 1, 407–408 (1820) and ed. 2, 1: 393–394. 1832; Clarke in Hook. f., Fl. Br. Ind. 4: 568. 1885; Watt, Dict. Econ. Prod. India 2: 26–27. 1889; Gamble, Man. Indian Timb., ed. 2, 525–526. 1902; Prain, Bengal Pl., ed. 1, 827 & 828. 1903; Bakh., Bull. Jard. Bot. Buitenzorg, ser. 3, 3: 23. 1921; Parker, Forest Fl. Punjab, ed. 2, 397. 1924; P'ei, Verb. China 23–25. 1932; Maheshwari, Fl. Delhi 280–281. 1963; Subramanian *et al.*, Phytochemistry 13: 306–307. 1974; Moldenke, Phytologia 21: 214–226, 336, 376, & 447 (1971), 22: 202–203 (1971), 33: 495–497 (1976), and 34: 156. 1976. Type: *König s.n.* "Habitat in India orientali", probably (C).

Callicarpa tomentosa König ex Vahl, Symb. Bot. 3: 13, in syn. [as "*Callicarpae tomentosae*"]. 1794; Jacks. in Hook. f. & Jacks., Ind. Kew., imp. 1, 1: 386, in syn. 1893 [not *C. tomentosa* Auct., 1962, nor Bakh., 1932, nor Hook. & Arn., 1918, nor "L. ex Moldenke", 1959, nor "L. ex Spreng.", 1825, nor "L. ex Willd.", 1783, nor Murr., 1893, nor Thunb., 1959, nor Willd., 1809, nor "sensu auct. Japon.", 1965, nor "sensu Matsum.", 1964, nor "sensu Matsum. & Hayata", 1963].—*C. tomentosa* Vahl apud H.J. Lam, Verb. Malay. Arch. [371]. 1919.

Callicarpa incana Roxb., Hort. Beng. [10], hyponym. 1814; Roxb., Fl. Ind. 1: 407–408. 1820 [not *C. incana* (Turcz.) Moldenke, 1934, nor "(F.) Moldenke", 1953].

Callicarpa macrophylla Roxb. ex Voigt, Hort. Suburb. Calc. 467. 1845.

Callicarpa roxburghii Wall., Num. List 49–[50]. 1829 [not *C. roxburghii* H. J. Lam, 1948, nor Schau., 1890, nor "Wall. ex Schau.", 1968, nor "Wall. ex Walp.", 1968].

Callicarpa cana Gamble ex Clarke in Hook. f., Fl. Br. Ind. 4: 568, in syn. 1885 [not *C. cana* Dalz. & Gibs., 1919, nor L., 1771, nor Spreng., 1966, nor Vahl, 1866, nor Wall., 1863].

Callicarpa macrophylla var. *incana* Roxb. ex Kuntze, Rev. Gen. Pl. 2: 503. 1891.

Callicarpa dunniana Léveillé, Feddes Repert. Spec. Nov. Regni Veg. 9: 456. 1911.

Callicarpa macrophylla var. *kouytchensis* Léveillé, Fl. Kouy-Tchéou 440, hyponym. 1915.

Shrub, to 3.5 m tall; branchlets stout, obtusely tetragonal or subterete, very densely matted-tomentose with canescent many-branched hairs, becoming glabrate in age, with scattered elliptic and prominently elevated lenticels, often bearing many old fruiting cymes at the nodes; leaves decussate-opposite; petioles very stout, 6–20 mm long, canaliculate above, densely matted-tomentose; leaf-blades membranous, rather dark green above, whitish beneath, oblong or oblong-ovate, 6–23 cm long, 2.5–9.7 cm wide, acute or acuminate apically, rather uniformly and more or less shallowly serrate with rather sharp teeth except at the base, acute or somewhat cuneate basally, roughened-pilose above with minute hairs (or tomentose when very immature), occasionally somewhat areolate, very densely greyish- or sordid-tomentose with matted many-branched hairs beneath; midrib somewhat tomentose (especially-basally) above; secondaries 7–15 or more per side; vein and veinlet reticulation conspicuous; inflorescence axillary, large; cymes decussate, solitary, often very numerous, 4–8 or more cm long, 7–11 cm wide, densely many-flowered, very spreading-dichotomous (often to 8 times furcate), very angulate, often forming a dense mass around the branchlets by the spreading and more or less reflexed dichotomies, bracteolate; peduncles stout (often incrassate in fruit), 1.3–2.6 cm long, densely matted-tomentose, becoming merely furfuraceous in age; pedicels essentially obsolete or exceedingly short; bractlets broadly linear to setaceous, 3–10 mm long, densely sordid-tomentose; calyx oblong-campanulate, 1.3–1.6 mm long, 1–1.3 mm wide, loosely pubescent and granulose-pulverulent, its rim conspicuously 4-toothed; corolla hypocrateriform, lilac or purple, its tube narrowly cylindric, 1–2 mm long, the limb 4-parted, the lobes ovate-lingulate, about 0.9 mm long and 0.8 mm wide, subacute apically; stamens inserted at the very base of the corolla-tube, exserted; filaments filiform, about 3.6 mm long, glabrous; anthers broadly oblong, about 0.5 mm long and 0.4 mm wide; pistil exserted and surpassing the stamens; ovary subrotund, about 0.7 mm long and wide, densely granulose-pulverulent; fruiting-calyx very shallow; cupiliform or practically patelliform, about 2 mm wide, loosely pubescent, the rim 4-toothed; fruit small, white, subglobose, about 2 mm long and wide, pulverulent or glabrate. Chromosomes: $2n = 34$.

D i s t r. This species is widespread in northern and eastern India, north and east into southern China, Hong Kong, Hainan, Burma, and Thailand.

U s e s. It is cultivated as a specimen plant in various parts of the world, chiefly in botanical gardens or fine collections; apparently introduced on Réunion and Madagascar. Wood characters are provided by Gamble (1881). Extracts of the dry leaves have yielded luteolin, apigenin, and calliterpenone and its monoacetate diterpenes.

In various portions of its range this plant is regarded as a good fodder for livestock; a paste made from its leaves is used to treat mouth ulcers; heated leaves are applied to rheumatic joints. In Delhi it is employed as a hedge plant around gardens.

V e r n. Among some 35 names are: Urnfruit beautyberry, Urn-fruit tree, and, in India, Bá-pattra, Bauna, Budhi-ghasit, Daya, Den, Drúss, Mathara, Mattrauja, Muttura, Shiwali, Súmáli, Thar, and Tondi-teregam.

N o t e. Its pollen is described by Nair & Rehman, Bull. Nat. Bot. Gard. Lucknow 76: 13. 1962.

S p e c i m e n s E x a m i n e d. KANDY DISTRICT: in outdoor cultivation in Section E, Royal Botanic Garden, Peradeniya, 1550 ft alt., 18 Jan. 1974, shrub or tree, 10–15 ft tall, with epiphytic *Dendrophthoë* sp. as parasite on branches, peduncles longer than the petioles, cymes wide-spreading, numbered E. 27, *H.N. & A.L. Moldenke & Jayasuriya 28138* (AAU, CAI, KARACHI, LL, PDA, US).

4. Callicarpa tomentosa (L.) Murr. in L., Syst. ed. 12 ["13"], 130. 1774; Hermann, Mus. Zeyl., ed. 1, 11. 1717; Burm., Thes. Zeyl. 26. 1739; Dassow, Nov. Gen. Pl. Zeyl. 5. 1747; Roxb., Fl. Ind., ed. 1, 1: 406 (1820) and ed. 2, 1: 391–392. 1832; Moon, Cat. 1: 10. 1824; Thw., Enum. Pl. Zeyl. 243. 1861; Gamble, List Trees Darj. Dist. 60. 1878; Trimen, Cat. 68. 1885; Clarke in Hook. f., Fl. Br. Ind. 4: 567–568. 1885; Watt, Dict. Econ. Prod. India 2: 26. 1889; Nairne, Fl. Pl. West. India 247. 1894; Trimen, Handb. Fl. Ceylon 3: 350. 1895; Cooke, Fl. Pres. Bombay ed. 1, 423 (1905) and ed. 2, 502–503, 1967; Willis, Cat. 69. 1911; H.J. Lam, Verb. Malay. Arch. 79–82. 1919; Bakh., Bull. Jard. Bot. Buitenzong, ser. 3, 3: 20–22. 1921; Alston, Kandy Fl. 64, fig. 344. 1938; Abeywick., Ceylon J. Sci., Biol. Sci. 2: 217. 1959; Raizada, Indian Forester 92: 304. 1966; Deb *et al.*, Bull. Bot. Soc. Bengal 22: 199. 1968; Gunawardena, Gen. Sp. Pl. Zeyl. 147. 1968; Fonseka & Vinasithamby, Prov. List Local Names Fl. Pl. Ceylon 32. 1971; Moldenke, Phytologia 22: 27–28, 131–132, 196, 199, & 207–209 (1971), 22: 281–283 (1972) and 34: 162–165. 1976. Type: *Burman 26* from Ceylon.

Tondi teregam Rheede, Hort. Mal. 4: 123–124. Pl. 60 [as "Tóndi-teregam"]. 1683.
Illa Hermann, Mus. Zeyl., ed. 1, 11. 1717.
Arbor malabarica Illa dicta Burm., Thes. Zeyl. 26. 1739.
Tomex tomentosa L. ex Dassow, Nov. Gen. Pl. Zeyl. 5. 1747; L., Syst., ed. 10, 2: 897 [as "*tomentos.*"]. 1759.

Callicarpa lanata L., Mant. Alt. 331. 1767 [not *C. lanata* Gamble, 1889, nor Hosséus, 1912, nor H.J. Lam, 1940, nor Lam., 1840. nor Ridl., 1966, nor Schau., 1870, nor Vahl, 1847, nor Walp., 1921, nor Zipp., 1841].—*C. lanata* Willd. ex Ainslie, Mat. Ind. 2: 180–182. 1826.—*C. lanata* Roxb. ex J. Grah., Cat. Pl. Bombay 156. 1839.—*C. lanata* Wall. ex Miq., Fl. Ned. Ind. 2: 890. 1856.

Cornutia corymbosa Lam., Dict. Enc. Bot. 1: 54–55. 1783 [not *C. corymbosa* Burm. f., 1768].

Callicarpa integrifolia L. ex [Retz.], Nom. Bot. 35. nom. nud. 1772; Retz., Obs. Bot. 5: 2. 1789 [not *C. integrifolia* Champ., 1890, nor Forbes & Hemsl., 1932, nor Jacq., 1780].

Callicarpa tomex Poir. in Lam., Enc. Suppl. 2: 32. 1811.

Callicarpa tomentosa Murr. ex Steud., Nom. Bot., ed. 1, 137. 1821.—*C. tomentosa* L. ex E. Balf., Cyclop. Ind., ed. 3, 1: 550. 1885.—*C. tomentosa* (L.) Santapau ex Sen & Naskar, Bull. Bot. Surv. India 7: 38. 1965.—*C. tomentosa* Merr. ex Arora, J. Indian Bot. Soc. 45: 134. 1966.

Callicarpa farinosa Roxb. ex Wall., Num. List 87. 1831 [not *C. farinosa* Sieb., 1865 nor Sieb. & Zucc., 1971].

Callicarpa coja Hamilt. ex Wall., Num. List 87. 1831.

Callicarpa gongalo Hamilt. ex Wall., Num. List 87. 1831.

Callicarpa wallichiana Walp., Rep. 4: 125. 1845.—*C. wallichiana* Miq. ex Bakh. in Lam & Bakh., Bull. Jard. Bot. Buitenzorg, ser. 3, 3: 21. 1921.

Callicarpa arborea Miq. ex Clarke in Hook. f., Fl. Br. Ind. 4: 567. 1885 [not *C. arborea* Merr., 1940, nor Roxb., 1814, nor Wall., 1829].—*C. arborea* L. ex Burkill, Dict. Econ. Prod. Malay Penins. 1: 408. 1966.

Callicarpa lobata Clarke in Hook. f., Fl. Br. Ind. 4: 566. 1885.

Callicarpa cana Dalz. & Gibs. ex Watt, Dict. Econ. Prod. India 2: 26. 1889 [not *C. cana* Gamble, 1889, nor L., 1771, nor Spreng., 1866, nor Vahl, 1866, nor Wall., 1863].

Callicarpa lanata var. *typica* H.J. Lam, Verbenac. Malay. Arch. 81. 1919.

Callicarpa tomentosa var. *lanata* (L.) Bakh. in Lam & Bakh., Bull. Jard. Bot. Buitenzorg, ser. 3, 3: 21–22. 1921.

Callicarpa tomentosa var. *typica* Bakh. in Lam & Bakh., Bull. Jard. Bot. Buitenzorg, ser. 3, 3: 21. 1921.

Tometax tomentosa L. apud Raizada, Indian Forester 92: 304. 1966.

A tall shrub or small, slender, and bushy tree, branching, rather straggly, 2–12 m tall; trunk sometimes 12 cm in diameter; wood white to brownish- or reddish-white; bark grey or light brown, thin, rough, corky, aromatic, bitter; young branches stout, cylindric or subtetragonal, closely covered by a thick easily detachable felt of grey or fulvous stellate hairs; leaves decussate-opposite, crowded toward the ends of the branches; petioles cylindric, 2.5–7.5 cm long, stout, densely tomentose; leaf-blades subcoriaceous-chartaceous, ovate or elliptic-lanceolate to lanceolate, 15–23 cm long, 7.5–15 cm wide, dark green above, grey beneath, apically acuminate or attenuate-acuminate, basally rounded, often cordate or even acute at the very base, entire or slightly repand and minutely denticulate along the margins, glabrous (except on the larger veins) and shiny above but reticulate-rugose, densely stellate-tomentose with grey or white pubescence beneath; secondaries 6–9 pairs, impressed above, very prominent beneath; inflorescence axillary, cymose, bipartite, divaricately dichotomous, many-flowered, short-pedunculate, densely stellate-tomentose throughout; peduncles about half as long as the petioles; flowers sessile, fragrant; bractlets linear, scarcely 1.5 mm long; calyx campanulate, about 2.5 mm long, densely stellate-tomentose outside, its rim truncate or very faintly 4-lobed; corolla hypocrateriform, varying from pink, lavender, or violet to mauve, pale red, reddish-purple, purple, or lilac, petals white, glabrous, the tube about 2.5 mm long, the lobes 4, subequal, subquadrate, about 1.5 mm long, apically rounded; stamens much exserted; anthers white or light yellow-orange; style and ovary glabrous; fruit drupaceous, globose, scarcely 2 mm in diameter, at first green, later dark purple or black, smooth, shiny; pollen described by Nair & Rehm., Bull. Nat. Bot. Gard. Lucknow 76: 13 (1962). Chromosomes: $n=68$ or $2n=40$.

Distr. This is a widely distributed species, found from Nepal, Bhutan, and Sikkim through most of India, Ceylon, and Bangladesh, east through Burma, Thailand, and Malaya to the Philippines, Celebes, Java, Sumatra, Timor, and New Guinea, and north to Hong Kong and Chekiang. It has also been introduced into cultivation in various parts of Europe, tropical Asia, and Mauritius.

Uses. In India the wood is used as fuel and to make charcoal. In Malaya the pounded roots are made into a poultice for cutaneous afflictions and open sores, the juice is given internally in the treatment of stomach-ache, and the plant is regarded as a diuretic. In Java it is regarded as an emollient. The Sinhalese chew the somewhat aromatic and bitter bark as a substitute for betel leaves, and Trimen reports the leaves, roots, and bark are used locally in the treatment of various skin diseases.

Vern. Eela-gass and Illa (S); Koat-komal (T). Among over 50 other vernacular names in various parts of its range are: Bastra, Guenla, Iswar, Khalema, Meras, Tondi-karavatti, and Tondi-teregam.

Note. Unfortunately, it has been widely confused by taxonomists in the past and this may account for the discrepancy in reported chromosome counts.

Specimens Examined. DISTRICT UNKNOWN: Northern Ceylon, *Wight 37* (PDA). KURUNEGALA DISTRICT: Doluwa Kanda, 7°37′ N., 80°25′ E., 1000 ft alt. 14 Feb. 1975, shrub 6 m tall, *Sumithraarachchi DBS. 646* (US). COLOMBO DISTRICT: Mirigama, 7 June 1927, "eela-gas" S., *Als-*

ton 680 (PDA). KANDY DISTRICT: in open sunlight near forest margin, Hantana hill, 1 Feb. 1973, small branching rather straggling tree about 20 ft tall, flowers purple, *Burtt & Townsend 47* (US); edge of forest and patana, steep mountain slope west of the road 3 miles below and north of Corbet's Gap, 750 m alt. 10 Nov. 1974, small tree 4 m tall, lower leaf surface with white pubescence, corolla purple, fragrant, anthers light yellow-orange, fruit black, *Davidse 8338* (LL, US); on roadcut on steep mountainside in forest cover about 5 miles south of Ginigathena, north of Adam's Peak, 1000 m alt. shrub to 2 m tall, flowers purple, *Gould 13591* (PDA, US); evergreen woods, Nilambe, Hantana ridge near Kandy, 700 m alt. 25 April 1969, tree 8 m tall, trunk diameter 12 cm, bark light-brown, thin, flowers violet, *Kostermans 23285* (AAU, NY); Corbet's Gap, 1500 m alt. 13 May 1967, tree 4 m tall, flowers violet, *Kostermans 23520* (US); at edge of jungle at milepost 24/14, 4 miles east of Hunnasgiriya, 1700 ft alt. 19 Jan. 1974, occasional tree in hedgerows and fencerows, low tree about 12 ft tall, corollas and filaments magenta, *H.N. & A.L. Moldenke, Jayasuriya, & Sumithraarachchi 28185* (AAU, ARIZ, CAI, KARACHI, LL, MO, PDA, US); in roadside shrubbery at milepost 67 on the road from Ginigathena to Kitulgala, 1200 ft alt. 12 Feb. 1974, isolated shrubs, *H.N. & A.L. Moldenke, Jayasuriya, & Dassanayake 28328* (AAU, ARIZ, CAI, KARACHI, LL, MO, PDA, US); Hantana, 24 May 1924, *J.M. Silva s.n.* (PDA); on the Kandy to Galaha road, 19 Feb. 1974, flowers purple, *Sumithraarachchi DBS. 93* (US); Bible Rock, 2618 ft alt. 19 March 1974, 25 ft tall, flowers purple, *Sumithraarachchi & Fernando DBS. 162* (US); in secondary montane forest near Maha-oya, Kaikawala, 2500 ft alt. 2 Feb. 1975, tree 10 m tall, 70 cm girth, flowers purplish-blue, *Waas 1076* (US); Ambagamuwa, *s. coll. C.P. 722* (PDA); Kadugannawa, 1800 ft alt. Feb. 1940, rainfall 85 inches, *Worthington 793* (PDA). MATALE DISTRICT: Aluvihare, 26 June 1967, a small tree, flowers mauve, "illa" Sinhala, *Amaratunga 1341* (PDA); common in border of submontane forest beside the Rattota to Illukumbara road, Rattota, 1000 m alt. 4 March 1977, shrub or small tree, about 6.5 m tall, outer bark fissured, panicles conspicuous, corolla 4-lobed, pinkish-mauve, flowers scented, *Cramer 4864* (NY); NUWARA ELIYA DISTRICT: Rikilligaskada, 16 June 1965, small tree, flowers pale mauve, "illa" Sinhala, *Amaratunga 878* (PDA); scattered shrubs on roadbanks and edge of forest at milepost 29/4 beyond Pussellawa, 3200 ft alt. 28 Jan. 1974, shrubs about 6 ft tall, *H.N. & A.L. Moldenke, Jayasuriya, & Sumithraarachchi 28264* (AAU, ARIZ, CAI, KARACHI, LL, MO, PDA, US). RATNAPURA DISTRICT: rare along roadside on the road from Maskeliya to Balangoda, Kotiyagala mountain, between Bogawantalawa and Maratenna, 1400 m alt. 13 Dec. 1975, only seen once, tree 6 m tall, *Solanum*-like, leaves ovate, large, white-woolly beneath, cymes many-flowered, flowers small, violet, *Bernardi 15983* (NY); in shade of forest on cliff at milepost 67 about 13 miles northeast of Deniyaya along highway A. 17 to Ratnapura, 1050 m alt. 22 Oct. 1974, slender tree 4 m tall, lower leaf surface with white pubescence, petals purple, fruit green, *Davidse 7902* (LL, US); in roadside thicket about 2–3 miles southwest of Weddagala on the road to Sinharaja forest, 28 Oct. 1976, shrub 4 m tall, flowers light-purple, fruit black, *Fosberg 56591* (LL); by a waterfall, Bulutota Pass from Rakwana, 2500 ft alt. 29 June 1972, small tree about 3 m tall, perhaps more, leaves grey beneath, green above, flowers pinkish-mauve, *Hepper, Maxwell, & Fernando 4565* (PDA, US); in secondary forest close to temple, Kukulawa Viharakanda, 16 Feb. 1974, shrub 2 m tall, *Waas 267* (US). GALLE DISTRICT: rare in tropical rainforest near stream, Kanneliya Forest Reserve, low elevation, 2 Aug. 1974, small slender tree 5 m tall, *Jayasuriya 1525* (PDA, US); in wet zone at forest edge, Kanneliya Forest Reserve, 200 ft alt. 3 May 1951, flowers mauve, not the narrow leaf, "illa", *Worthington 5266* (PDA). LOCALITY UNKNOWN: *Fraser 122* (DS, US); *Macrae 20* (NY); *J.M. Silva 199* (NY); March 1836, *Wight 767* (PDA).

13. TECTONA

L. f., Suppl. 20 & 151. 1781 [Nom. Cons.]. Type species: *Tectona grandis* L. f.

Jatus Rumpf, Herb. Amboin. 3: 34, pl. 18. 1743.—*Iatus* Rumpf ex Moldenke, Prelim. Alph. List Invalid Names 28, in syn. 1940.—*Jatus* Kuntze ex Airy Shaw in Willis, Dict. ed. 7, 582. 1966.
Theka Adans., Fam. Pl. 2: 445. 1763 [nom. rejic.].—*Theka* Rheede ex Reichb., Consp. Reg. Veg. 1: 117. 1828.—*Theca* Juss. ex Benth. in Benth. & Hook. f., Gen. Pl. 2 (2): 1152. 1876.
Nautea Noronha, Verh. Batav. Genootsch. Kunst. V, ed. 1, art. 4: 3. 1790.
Tectonia Spreng., Anleit. 2: 893. 1818.—*Tectonia* L. f. ex Endl., Gen. Pl. 636. 1838.—*Tectonia* L. ex Schnitzl., Ic. Fam. Nat. Reg. Veg. 2: 137 Verb. 1856. —*Tectoma* Acosta Solis, Proc. Inter-Amer. Conf. Conservation Renewable Resources 329. 1948.—*Techona* Nielsen, Introd. Fl. Pl. W. Afr. 163. 1965. —*Tektona* L. f. ex Moldenke, Prelim. List Invalid Names 43, in syn. 1940; Liogier, Rhodora 67: 350. 1965.
Cajatana Thunb. ex Moldenke, Prelim. List Invalid Names 9. 1940.

Tall trees with soft bark and more or less tetragonal branches and branch-lets; leaves deciduous, decussate-opposite or ternate, mostly very large and broad, petiolate or subsessile, entire or denticulate, rarely irregularly lobed; inflorescence cymose, the cymes numerous, many-flowered, borne in massive terminal panicles, sometimes smaller axillary cymes in the upper leaf-axils; flowers actinomorphic, small; calyx gamosepalous, campanulate, shortly 5–7-lobed, persistent, in fruit greatly enlarged and often inflated, enveloping the fruit and closed above it; corolla gamopetalous, hypocrateriform, white or blue, the tube short-cylindric, the limb patent or reflexed, 5–7-parted, the lobes subequal, overlapping in bud; stamens 5 or 6, inserted in the corolla-tube, exserted; the anthers ovate or elliptic-oblong, 2-celled, dorsifixed, the thecae parallel, opening by longitudinal slits; pistil single, elongate; style terminal, capillary; stigma very shortly bifid, its branches subequal; ovary compound, 2-carpellate, completely 4-celled (each carpel 2-celled), each cell 1-ovulate; ovules lateral or high-lateral, hemianatropous; fruit drupaceous, rounded or weakly 4-lobed, completely enveloped by the enlarged fruiting-calyx, with a thin subcarneous exocarp, a thick bony 4-celled endocarp, and a small central cavity between the cells; seeds without endosperm.

A small but commercially very important genus of 8 specific and infraspecific taxa, native to tropical southern and eastern Asia from India, Burma, and Thailand to the Philippines and Indonesia; widely cultivated. Only a single species, *T. grandis* L. f., known from Ceylon where it is not considered to be native.

KEY TO THE FORMS

1 Leaf-blades not noticeably black-punctate beneath.............**1. T. grandis f. grandis**
1 Leaf-blades noticeably and regularly black-punctate beneath...**2. T. grandis f. punctata**

1. Tectona grandis L. f., Suppl. 151. 1781. f. **grandis**. Moon, Cat. 1: 16. 1824; Schau. in A. DC., Prod. 11: 629. 1847; Clarke in Hook. f., Fl. Br. Ind. 4: 570–571. 1885; Trimen, Cat. 68. 1885; Trimen, Handb. Fl. Ceylon 3: 350. 1895; Gamble, Man. Indian Timb., ed. 2, 526–534. 1902; Brandis, Indian Trees 502 & 505–506. 1906; Willis, Cat. 143. 1911; Alston, Kandy Fl. 63. 1938; Abeywick., Ceylon J. Sci., Biol. Sci. 2: 218. 1959; Worthington, Ceylon Trees 344. 1959; Fernando, Ceylon Forester, ser. 2, 7: 54–56. 1965; Gunawardena, Gen. Sp. Pl. Zeyl. 148. 1968; Fonseka & Vinasithamby, Prov. List Local Names Fl. Pl. Ceylon 87–90. 1971; Vivekanandan, Sri Lanka Forester, ser. 2, 11: 116, 129, & 146. 1974. Type: *König s.n.* from "prope Madras & aliis locis in hortis".

Tekka Rheede, Hort. Mal. 4: 57. pl. 27. 1683.
Jatus s. caju jati Rumph., Herb. Amboin. 3: 34, pl. 18. 1743.
Tectona theka Lour., Fl. Cochinch., ed. 1, 137. 1790.
Theka grandis (L. f.) Lam., Tabl. Enc. 2: 111. 1793.—*Theka grandis* L. ex Fr. de Montholou, Notic. Indie 60. 1837.
Tectonia grandis L. f. ex Walp., Rep. 4: 98. 1846.—*Tectona grandis* L. ex Britton & P. Wils., Sci. Surv. Porto Rico 6: 152. 1930.—*Tectoma grandis* Acosta Solis, Proc. Inter-Amer. Conf. Conservation Renewable Resources 329. 1948.
Jatus grandis (L. f.) Kuntze, Rev. Gen. Pl. 2: 508. 1891.—*Jatus grandis* Kuntze apud Durand & Jacks., Ind. Kew. Suppl. 1: 229. 1903.
Tectona asiatica Hort. ex Moldenke, Prelim. Alph. List Invalid Names 43, in syn. 1940.
Tectona grandis var. *glabrifolia* Moldenke, Phytologia 5: 140. 1955.

Large tree, to 50 m tall; branches and branchlets stout, tetragonal, with large quadrangular pith, the younger parts usually with more obtuse angles and drying more or less sulcate between the angles, densely furfuraceous-tomentellous with cinereous or ochraceous tomentum; nodes distinctly annulate, usually with a circumferential corky layer and denser tomentum; leaves very large, drooping, deciduous, with a clasping base, firmly chartaceous, broadly elliptic, 11–95 cm long (or to 1 m on watersprouts), 6–50 cm wide, apically acute or short-acuminate, entire or repand-denticulate, basally abruptly acute or long-acuminate and prolonged into the alate petiole or clasping at the base, dark green and shiny above, usually lighter and not so shiny beneath, densely squamose and rugose or bullate above, glabrescent and often silvery beneath; petioles short or wanting, more or less margined or alate, densely ochraceous-furfuraceous; inflorescences in the uppermost leaf-axils and terminal, massive, the terminal panicles often many decimeters long and wide but mostly about 40 cm long and 35 cm wide, with distant, opposite, widely divaricate, many-branched, many-flowered cymes, densely cinereous- or ochraceous-furfuraceous throughout; peduncles and sympodia continuous with the branchlets and similar in texture, colour and pubescence, often elongate; pedicles stoutish or slender, 1–4 mm long, furfuraceous; a pair of large foliaceous bracts subtending each pair of cymes, resembling the leaves but much smaller; bractlets numerous, lanceolate-linear, to 15 mm long and 4 mm wide at the base, sessile, ochraceous-furfuraceous, apically attenuate; prophylla oblong or linear-lanceolate, to 5 mm long and 1 mm wide; calyx light yellow or light green, 4–4.5 mm long, 3–3.5 mm wide, densely furfuraceous-tomentellous, 5–7-toothed or -lobed, the teeth ovate or ovate-oblong, 1.5–2.5 mm long, often reflexed, obtuse; corolla white or sometimes rosy on the lobes, short-hypocrateriform, glabrous on both surfaces, the tube broadly cylindric, 1.5–3 mm long, about 1.5 mm wide, the limb 5–7-parted, the lobes obovate-elliptic, 2.5–3 mm long, about 2.3 mm wide, apically rounded, overlapping, erect or reflexed, inserted 1.3 or more mm below the mouth of the corolla-tube; filaments white, 2.5–4 mm long, glabrous, ampliate and flattened below; anthers yellow, ovate or oblong; style white, 3.6–5.2 mm long, more or less pubescent with branched hairs; ovary ovate or conic, 1.2–2 mm long, densely pubescent; fruit subglobose or tetragonally flattened, to 1.5 cm long and wide, densely tomentose with irregularly branched light brown or ochraceous hairs, umbilicate and 4-lobed at the apex; seeds oily; fruiting-calyx to 2.5 cm long and wide, chartaceous, light-brown and brittle when dry, mostly irregularly plaited or crumpled and bladder-like. Chromosome number: 2n = 24 or 36.

D i s t r. This is a variable and widespread tropical Asian tree, native to the mixed forests from India and Burma, through Thailand and Malaya, to Java. It is very widely cultivated in almost all tropical countries of Asia and Africa for its commercially very valuable lumber and is cultivated as a curiosity in many countries of America, Europe, Australia, and Pacific Oceanica.

U s e s. Teak has been cultivated in plantations for its wood since 1844, when Connolly began the first plantation on the Malabar coast of India. A rather liquid black tar is distilled from the wood in small quantities in southern India and Burma for medicinal purposes in the manner of coal-tar. An oil may be extracted from the seeds, which is bland, fatty and odourless, and is said to be sometimes used medicinally in Burma. A plaster made from the powdered wood is used in treating bilious headaches in India and inflammatory swellings; taken internally it is said to be of use in treating dyspepsia and as a vermifuge. The charred wood soaked in poppy juice and made into a paste, is applied to swellings of the eyelids and is said by Dymock to be regarded by natives as strengthening sight. The bark is used as an astringent and the oil as a hair-tonic and to combat itchiness of the skin. In Amboina the bark is said to be used as a tonic and astringent and as a remedy for leucorrhoea. The wood tar is said to be effective, as a paste, to combat cutaneous inflammations from contact with members of the Anacardiaceae. In parts of India the tar is used to prevent maggot-breeding in the sores on cattle. The wood has long been used in construction, ship-building, bridge-making, and turnery, on wooden ships for the decks, masts, oars, and backing for armor-plating.

V e r n. Takku, Tekka, and Thekka (S); Tekku (T); Saigun (Hindi); Kyun (Burmese); Indian-oak, Teak, and Teak tree (E); over 125 other vernacular names are recorded from other parts of its present range.

N o t e s. There are several morphologic forms distinguished principally by leaf-characters. The typical—and, in Ceylon, commonest—form has the underside of the leaves glabrous and shiny, often quite silvery. Other forms differ in having them noticeably black-punctate (f. *punctata*), very densely canescent-farinaceous-puberulent (f. *canescens*), distinctly short-pilosulous on the larger venation (f. *pilosula*), or very densely yellowish-tomentellous (f. *tomentella*); a curious almost teratologic form has the blades irregularly lobed (f. *abludens*). The last four of these forms are not known from Ceylon. The leaves are sometimes attacked by the parasitic fungus, *Uncinula tectonae* Salmon.

S p e c i m e n s E x a m i n e d. KURUNEGALA DISTRICT: Dodanga-slande, 26 June 1965, large tree, flowers (petals) dull-white, wood used in furniture making, "teak", *Amaratunga 897* (PDA). PUTTALAM DISTRICT: cultivated in extensive plantation, Wanniyagama, low altitude, 25 Jan. 1974, trees 45 ft tall, in flower, *H.N. & A.L. Moldenke & Jayasuriya 28250* [in part] (AAU, ARIZ, CAI, KARACHI, LL, PDA, US). COLOMBO DISTRICT: common tree in Colombo District, often planted to demarcate boundaries in coconut plantations, Kotadeniyawa, 8 Dec. 1970, a tall tree, flowers white, wood of economic importance in furniture making, *Amaratunga 2150* (PDA); a line of trees cultivated as fencerow along roadway, perhaps the original introduction in Ceylon, Welisara, low altitude, 15 Jan. 1974, trees 50–75 ft tall, *H.N. & A.L. Moldenke & Jayasuriya 28118* (PDA, US); sprouts from stumps of a line of trees along roadside fencerow, Katana, 4 miles east of Kochchi-kade, 16 Jan. 1974, vigorous sprouts 15 ft tall, *H.N. & A.L. Moldenke, Jayasuriya, & Sumithraarachchi 28121* (US). KANDY DISTRICT: culti-vated, Royal Botanic Garden, Peradeniya, tree 80–150 ft tall, with white flowers and producing the well-known teak wood, *C.F. Baker 126* (AC, C, COLO, CU, DS, E, K, L, NY, NY, P, POM, U, UC, WTU); cultivated, Royal Botanical Garden, Peradeniya, 30 June 1904, *Hallier C. 34c* (HBG); Ginigathena, 2 June, 1939, "teak", *Worthington 388* (PDA); planted in Arbo-retum, northeast aspect, hillcrest, Kandy, 2120 ft alt. Nov. 1965, rainfall 80 inches, *Worthington 7117* (PDA); Royal Botanic Garden, 24 Sept. 1903, *s. coll.* 125/40 (PDA). MATALE DISTRICT: persistent after cultivation along fencerow, numerous, Nalanda, 500 ft alt. 23 Jan. 1974, *H.N. & A.L. Moldenke & Jayasuriya 28211* (KARACHI, PDA, US). NUWARA ELIYA DISTRICT: planted on estate, Pussellawa, 2000 ft alt. 20 June 1953, rainfall 100 (?) inches, *Worthington 6329* (PDA). TRINCOMALEE DISTRICT: planted on tank bund, Kantalai, 150 ft alt. 19 May, 1947, *Worthington 2789* (PDA). BATTI-CALOA DISTRICT: on government plantation, Punani, 60 ft alt., 14 June 1953, rainfall 65 inches, *Worthington 6292* (PDA).

f. **punctata** Moldenke, Phytologia 31: 28. 1975. Type: *E.L. Little Jr. 13522*, cultivated in Puerto Rico (NY).

This form differs from the typical form of the species in having the inter-stices of the veinlet reticulation on the lower leaf-surfaces conspicuously black-punctate. The punctae are elevated and greatly resemble a parasitic fungus, but have been examined microscopically by Dr. Rogerson, mycologist at the New York Botanical Garden, and declared non-fungal in nature. Punctations are frequently mentioned in the literature of this species and there is evidence that they may exist among and under the pubescence on some of the pubescent forms of the species. There also seems to be evidence that they do not occur on all the leaves of a given tree; more field study is obvi-ously required. The form has thus far been observed in cultivation in Florida, Cuba, Puerto Rico, Panama, Ecuador, Brazil, and the Philippines and in the wild state in Manipur, Burma, Luzon, Borneo, Java, and Sumatra.

Specimens Examined. PUTTALAM DISTRICT: cultivated in extensive plantation, Wanniyagama, low altitude, 25 Jan. 1974, trees 45 ft tall, in flower, *H.N. & A.L. Moldenke & Jayasuriya 28250* [in part] (US); in plantation cultivation and along apparently originally planted hedgerow, Panirendawa Forest Reserve, low altitude, 25 Jan. 1974, trees 45 ft tall, *H.N. & A.L. Moldenke & Jayasuriya 28251* (AAU, CAI, PDA, US). ANURADHA-PURA DISTRICT: abundant trees in plantations and along fencerow, culti-vated and persistent, Moragahawewa, low altitude, 25 Jan. 1974, *H.N. & A.L. Moldenke & Jayasuriya 28235* (LL, PDA, US). KANDY DISTRICT: in out door cultivation in Section E, Royal Botanic Garden, Peradeniya, 1550 ft alt., trees about 50 ft tall, *H.N. & A.L. Moldenke & Jayasuriya 28176* (PDA, US).

14. PREMNA

L., Mant. 2: 154 & 221. 1771 [nom. cons.]. Type species: *Premna serratifolia* L.

Cornutioides L., Fl. Zeyl., imp. 1, 195. 1747.
Appella Adans., Fam. Pl. 2: 84 & 519. 1763.
Midi Hermann ex Adans., Fam. Pl. 2: 199, in syn. 1763.
Sambucus Burm. ex Adans., Fam. Pl. 2: 199, in syn. 1763 [not *Sambucus* Tourn. ex L., 1753].
Cornutia Burm. f., Fl. Ind. 132, pl. 41, fig. 1. 1768 [not *Cornutia* Plum. ex L., 1754].
Scrophularioides Forst. f., Prod. 91. 1786.
Baldingera Dennst., Schlüss. Hort. Mal. 31. 1818 [not *Baldingera* Gaertn., Mey., & Scherb., 1799].
Permna Dumort., Anal. Fam. Pl. 22. 1829.—*Premnus* L. apud Hassk., Cat. Pl. Hort. Bogor. Cult. Alt. 134. 1844.—*Prenna* Bocq., Rév. Verbenac. 142, sphalm. 1863.—*Prenma* L. ex A. Chev., Cat. Pl. Jard. Bot. Saigon 36, sphalm. 1919.—*Premma* Angely, Liv. Gen. Bot. Bras. 52, sphalm. 1960.—*Premns* Fletcher ex Moldenke Résumé Suppl. 3: 34, in syn. 1962.—*Premna* Pieper ex C.A. Smith, Common Names S. Afr. Pl. 601. 1966.—*Prema* Fosberg, Pacific Sci. Assoc. Stand. Comm. Pacific Bot. Sympos. Plan. Util. Lowl. Trop. For. 168, sphalm. 1973.
Holochiloma Hochst., Flora 24: 371. 1841.
Gumira Rumpf, Herb. Amboin. 3: 209, pl. 134. 1741; Hassk., Cat. Pl. Hort. Bogor, Cult. Alt. 1844.—*Gumira* Hassk. apud Schau. in A. DC., Prod. 11: 630, in syn. 1847.
Phaenicanthus Thw., Enum. Pl. Zeyl. 242, in syn. 1861.—*Phoenicanthus* Thw. ex Post & Kuntze, Lexicon 433, in syn. 1904 [not *Phoenicanthus* Alston, 1931].—*Phoenicanthus* Post & Kuntze apud Airy Shaw in Willis, Dict. ed. 7, 858, in syn. 1966.
Tinus "L., 1754" apud Airy Shaw in Willis, Dict. ed. 7, 1126, in syn. 1966 [not *Tinus* Burm., 1906, nor L., 1754, nor L., 1759, nor Mill., 1754, nor Tourn., 1971, nor [Tourn.] L., 1735].

Subshrubs, shrubs, or trees, sometimes straggling or scandent; branches and branchlets glabrous, pubescent, or somewhat tomentose; leaves decussate-opposite, ternate or whorled in 4's, simple, exstipulate, deciduous, entire or variously dentate, sometimes sinuate, often dotted with resinous glands, mostly more or less petiolate, sometimes fetid, rarely minty; inflorescence cymose or corymbose, determinate, centrifugal, usually many-flowered and ample, mostly rather loose, the cymes often forming a corymbose or trichotomous panicle at the ends of the branchlets or crowded along the rachis of a terminal racemiform thyrse, rarely cauliflorous or axillary, opposite, pedunculate or subsessile; flowers usually very abundant and small or even minute, perfect or often polygamous by abortion, varying from greenish to whitish or bluish, rarely yellow or purple, often brunnescent in age, hypogynous; calyx minute, gamosepalous, campanulate or cupuliform, mostly actinomorphic, sometimes bilabiate, its rim truncate to sinuately 3–5-dentate or shortly 2–5-lobed, persistent and somewhat accrescent; corolla gamopetalous, mostly very small, usually somewhat hypocrateriform, its tube short, usually not exserted, narrowly infundibular or subcylindric, the throat often villous or marked by a ring of hairs inside, the limb usually 4-parted, the lobes mostly rounded, spreading, equal or subequal, the posterior one outside, sometimes larger and emarginate or even making a sub-bilabiate corolla, the anterior one inside and sometimes extruding or concave; stamens 4, usually inserted high up in the corolla-tube or at its mouth, didynamous or subdidynamous, shorter than the corolla or rarely more or less exserted; filaments usually very short, filiform; anthers ovoid or subglobose, usually barely exserted from the corolla-tube, the thecae parallel or divergent; pistil one, compound, consisting of two 2-celled carpels; style filiform or subulate; stigma shortly bifid, the lobes acute or rather obtuse; ovary 2-celled and each cell 2-ovulate or else by means of false partitions spuriously 4-celled; ovules 4, solitary in each cell or 2 in each cell if the ovary is only 2-celled, attached laterally at the middle or above the middle; fruiting-calyx usually patelliform; fruit drupaceous, small, globose or obovoid, the exocarp fleshy and juicy, often thin, the endocarp bony, undivided, 4-celled or by abortion 2- or 3-celled, with a central lumen; seeds oblong, exalbuminous, distributed endozoically.

A complex and very difficult genus of about 226 species and subspecific taxa, mostly native to the tropical and subtropical portions of Asia, Africa, Australia, and Pacific Oceanica, with a few extending north into China and Japan and into both northern and southern Africa. A few species are cultivated and one or two have become naturalized in parts of tropical or subtropical America. The taxa are in general separated by rather small and often obscure characters making accurate identification difficult. Great variability and probable hybridity further complicate the matter. The closely related herbaceous genus, *Pygmaeopremna* Merr., is often included here, but *Scobia* Nor. and *Solia* Nor., sometimes included in the synonymy of *Premna* actually are synonyms of *Lagerstroemia* L. in the Lythraceae.

The *Premna cordifolia* of Thwaites listed for Ceylon and based on his *C.P. 193* is actually *P. alstoni* Mold. and Thwaites' *P. micrantha* and *P. mucronata*, based on *C.P. 2541*, actually are *P. thwaitesii* Clarke. Similarly, *P. mucronata* Roxb., *P. bengalensis* Clarke, and *P. fulva* Craib, listed as occurring in Ceylon, are records based on misidentifications. The *P. cordifolia* of Mound & Halsey, Whitefly World 54 (1978), listed for Ceylon, is probably the same as that of Thwaites.

KEY TO THE TAXA

1 Corolla purple; calyx in anthesis truncate and subentire; a tall-climbing vine..........
....**6. P. purpurascens**
1 Corolla usually whitish, yellowish, or greenish; calyx 2-lipped or 5-toothed; mostly erect, scrambling, or procumbent, rarely scandent
  2 Calyx in anthesis bilabiate
    3 Calyx during anthesis with the lips mostly entire and rounded; leaf-blades small, narrowly lanceolate or deltoid
      4 Leaf-blades glabrous (or practically so) on both surfaces, marginally entire........
....**1. P. alstoni** var. **alstoni**
      4 Leaf-blades conspicuously pubescent beneath
        5 Leaf-blades marginally entire, the pubescence not especially dense beneath........
....**P. alstoni** var. **mollis**
        5 Leaf-blades apically subcrenate, very densely pubescent beneath.................
....**P. alstoni** var. **subcrenata**
    3 Calyx during anthesis with the abaxial lip conspicuously 2-lobed; leaf-blades not lanceolate
      6 Leaf-blades marginally entire or practically so, large
        7 Leaf-blades glabrous beneath or pilose only in the larger vein-axils; twigs, inflorescences, and petioles only lightly puberulent or glabrate.....................
....**9. P. obtusifolia** var. **obtusifolia**
        7 Leaf-blades conspicuously and rather densely pubescent beneath; twigs, inflorescences, and petioles densely pubescent or tomentose..........................
....**P. obtusifolia** var. **pubescens**
      6 Leaf-blades smaller, usually marginally more or less regularly serrate toward the apex; plants often prostrate, creeping, or sprawling
        8 Leaves small, usually 1.5–4 cm long and 1–2 cm wide, sometimes entire, apically obtuse or rounded.....................................**P. obtusifolia** var. **minor**
        8 Leaves larger, to 9 cm long and 6 cm wide, apically short-acuminate............
....**P. obtusifolia** f. **serratifolia**
    3 Calyx during anthesis only slightly bilabiate, sometimes nearly truncate and minutely 2-toothed or with the adaxial lip entire or shortly 3-toothed and the abaxial one 2-toothed...**2. P. divaricata**
  2 Calyx during anthesis almost equally 5-toothed or 5-lobed, not 2-lipped
    9 Mature leaf-blades marginally undulate, crenate, dentate, or serrate
      10 Leaf-blades marginally undulate and usually more or less coarsely and irregularly dentate; plants usually scandent, straggling, or procumbent; inflorescence small and corymbiform, to 4 cm long and 3 cm wide....................**5. P. procumbens**
      10 Leaf-blades marginally more or less regularly serrate, crenate-serrate, or serrulate; shrub or small tree; inflorescence usually large and paniculate, to 6 cm long and 4 cm wide..**P. thwaitesii** f. **glabrescens**
    9 Mature leaf-blades marginally entire or nearly so
      11 Mature leaf-blades glabrous or subglabrous beneath
        12 Leaves drying black or bluish-black on both surfaces or lighter beneath, basally rhomboid or cuneate
          13 Inflorescences usually abbreviated, small and compact, usually only 2–4 cm wide...**4. P. latifolia** var. **cuneata**
          13 Inflorescences usually more open and to 10 cm wide......**P. latifolia** var. **major**
        12 Leaves drying greenish, not conspicuously nigrescent, the surfaces concolorous, the blades to 15 cm long and 8 cm wide, basally acute..**P. latifolia** var. **viburnoides**

11 Mature leaf-blades distinctly pubescent or tomentose beneath
  14 Hairs branched or stellate
    15 Leaf-blades densely tomentose with branched hairs beneath.....................
    ....**8. P. tomentosa** f. **tomentosa**
    15 Leaf-blades more sparsely stellate beneath..................**P. tomentosa** f. **jejuna**
  14 Hairs simple
    16 Leaf-blades basally cordate..........................[**4. P. latifolia** var. **latifolia**]
    16 Leaf-blades basally not cordate
      17 Leaf-blades basally rhomboid, pubescence dense.......**P. latifolia** var. **mollissima**
      17 Leaf-blades basally obtuse or truncate
        18 Leaf-blades small, to 7.5 cm long and 3.7 cm wide, elliptic, apically crenate-
        serrate; inflorescence-branches hirsutulous; mature fruit orange...............
        ....**7. P. thwaitesii** f. **thwaitesii**
        18 Leaf-blades larger, to 20 cm long and 12.5 cm wide, broadly oval or ovate,
        marginally entire or apically crenate-serrate; inflorescence-branches more or
        less appressed-puberulent; mature fruit black............. ....**3. P. foetida**

1. Premna alstoni Moldenke, Phytologia 28: 101. 1974. var. **alstoni**. Trimen,
Handb. Fl. Ceylon 3: 351–352. 1895. Type: *Alston 1671* from Veragamtota,
Ceylon (PDA).

Premna "corymbosa Rottl." ex Trimen, Handb. Fl. Ceylon 3: 351–352. 1895
[not *P. corymbosa* (Burm. f.) Miq., 1856, nor (Burm. f.) Rottl. & Willd.,
1803, nor (Burm. f.) Roth & Willd., 1974, nor Miq., 1894, nor Rottl., 1803,
nor Rottl. & Willd., 1905, nor Willd., 1803].
Premna cordifolia Thw. ex Trimen, Handb. Fl. Ceylon 3: 351, in syn. 1895
[not *P. cordifolia* Beddome, 1885, nor Brand., 1829, nor Dalz., 1894, nor
Dalz. & Gibs., 1894, nor J. Grah., 1829, nor Roxb., 1814, nor Wall., 1830,
nor Wight, 1829].

    Slender depressed or scrambling shrub, often vine-like, to 3 m tall;
branches numerous, slender, virgate, pubescent; leaves small, decussate-
opposite, with a faintly smoky-aromatic scent when bruised, usually drying
olive-brownish; petioles very slender, 1.2-2.5 cm long; leaf-blades thinly
membranous, rarely firm in age, narrowly lanceolate-ovate or subdeltoid, 4–9
cm long, 2–4 cm wide, apically mostly regularly acuminate, marginally entire,
basally rounded or cordate to truncate, glabrous on both surfaces or practically so, very finely reticulate-venose; cymes several, usually very small and
abbreviated, terminal, mostly very few- (or to about 25-) flowered, sometimes
two opposite ones together forming a single flat-topped terminal inflorescence,
usually only 1.5–3 cm long and wide; bractlets very small, filiform; calyx
oblong-ovoid, glabrous, distinctly 2-lipped, the lips rounded and entire apically or the lower one very faintly 3-lobed, accrescent in fruit; corolla very
small, hypocrateriform, dull greenish or pale dingy yellowish-purple to dark-
yellow, white, brownish-orange, or brown (in age), closed by many hairs at
the mouth of the tube, the upper lip hooded and entire, the lower lip 3-lobed,
the lobes rounded, concave, the 2 lateral ones reflexed and the middle one

cupped and projecting much beyond the others; drupes irregularly globose, more than 6 mm long and wide when mature, at first green, later purple-black or black, shiny, the pyrenes thin, 1–4-celled, 1–4-seeded.

D i s t r. An apparently quite variable species or else perhaps prone to hybridization found in the dry and intermediate regions of Ceylon and there endemic. Trimen reports it (as *P. corymbosa*) from Bintenna, Galagama, Haragama, Kurunegala, Tissamaharama, and Trincomalee.

E c o l. Flowering from October to February.

V e r n. Gal-kera (S).

N o t e s. It can really only be confused with *P. thwaitesii* f. *glabrescens*, but in the latter the leaf-blades are more or less rounded, the apex acute, the inflorescence many- (up to 100 or even more) flowered, and the calyx is pubescent and regularly dentate. In *P. alstoni* the leaf-blades are typically deltoid-lanceolate, the apex plainly and regularly acuminate, the inflorescence very small and only few- (up to about 25) flowered, and the calyx is glabrous and distinctly bilabiate.

S p e c i m e n s   E x a m i n e d. JAFFNA DISTRICT: occasional in thick scrubby forest 2 miles west of Chunnavil toward Veravil, 10 Dec. 1970, elongate, vine-like, slender shrub, flowers brownish, *Fosberg & Balakrishnan 53578* (MOLDENKE). MANNAR DISTRICT: rather frequent in dry spiny woods about 12 km south of Pooneryn on the road to Mannar, 12 Oct. 1975, small scandent shrub, branches slender, fuscous, leaves ovate-subcordate, flowers dark yellow, *Bernardi 15343* (PDA, US). PUTTALAM DISTRICT: at edge of disturbed forest, Wanniyagama, low altitude, 25 Jan. 1974, reclining shrub, *H.N. & A.L. Moldenke & Jayasuriya 28239* (AAU, ARIZ, CAI, KARACHI, LL, MO, PDA, US). ANURADHAPURA DISTRICT: 5 to 6 miles northeast of Anuradhapura, 9 Dec. 1970, shrub 1.5 m tall, ripe fruit black, *Fosberg & Balakrishnan 53441* (MOLDENKE); occasional in scrub in mosaic or short grass with patches of spiny scrub, Plot W.14, Wilpattu National Park, near Eerige Ara confluence with Madegagama Ara, 29 Dec. 1968, slender shrub 2 m tall, flowers dull-yellowish, *Fosberg, Mueller-Dombois, Wirawan, Cooray, & Balakrishnan 50760* (LL); southern margin of Weweltenna, Ritigala Strict Natural Reserve, 1920 ft alt., 9 Aug. 1975, slender shrub 2.5 m tall, corolla brownish-orange, *Jayasuriya 1322* (MOLDENKE, PDA, US); jungle at Ritigala hill base, 6 April 1974, determined as *P. latifolia, Sumithraarachchi & Jayasuriya DBS. 219* (MOLDENKE, PDA, US); in dry evergreen primary forest, Ritigala, 11 Jan. 1974, shrub 2.5 m tall, *Waas 337* (NY, PDA, US); in secondary dry forest, Galapitagala-wewe, 13 Jan. 1974, *Waas 356* (LL, PDA, US). KANDY DISTRICT: in herb garden, probably cultivated, 7 July 1917, determined as *P. cordifolia, s. coll. 125/42* (PDA). MATALE DISTRICT: Dambulla, 20 March 1927, fruits black, *Alston 1325* (PDA). BADULLA DISTRICT: Veragamtota, 14 Feb.

1928, climber, flowers white, "gal-kera" in Sinhala, *Alston 1671* (PDA—type). AMPARAI DISTRICT: occasional on large rounded granite outcrop, Padagoda, south of Inginiyagala, 27 Nov. 1970, shrub 1–1.5 m tall, flowers dull-greenish, fruit green, *Fosberg & Sachet 53092* (MOLDENKE); in scrub over rock outcrop, Panama, low altitude, 3 May 1975, *Jayasuriya 2026* (LL, PDA, US). BATTICALOA DISTRICT: frequent in shade and in thickets, Kathiravel Bay westward to Manickakulam, 30 m alt., 4 Nov. 1975, robust twiggy shrub, almost climbing, leaves membranous, smooth, flowers dark, *Bernardi 15652* (PDA); in open scrub on extensive sand flat near Thulanku-dah, 4 Jan. 1969, rather depressed to scrambling shrub, flowers greenish-brown, *Fosberg, Mueller-Dombois, Wirawan, Cooray, & Balakrishnan 50995* (MOLDENKE). HAMBANTOTA DISTRICT: Block I, Ruhuna National Park, on the north to south boundary road, 15 Jan. 1969, *Cordia*-like straggl-ing shrub, "same as 69011401R", determined as *P. corymbosa* by Wirawan, *Cooray 69011504R* (MICH, PDA, US); not common, Block I, Ruhuna National Park, 17 Nov. 1969, straggling shrub, flowers brown, determined as *Cordia oblongifolia* Thw., *Cooray 69111721R* (PDA). LOCALITY UN-KNOWN: leaves glabrous beneath, *s. coll. C.P. 193* in part (PDA).

var. **mollis** Moldenke, Phytologia 41: 346. 1979. Type: *s. coll. s.n.* from Tis-samaharama, Ceylon, collected in December 1882 (PDA).

This variety differs from the typical form of the species only in having its leaf-blades more or less distinctly pubescent beneath and the ripe fruit is said to be orange in colour.

This taxon seems to be almost as widespread as the typical form, but does not seem to be merely a juvenile form of it because the pubescence character persists to the flowering and fruiting stages.

V e r n. Mulla (S).

S p e c i m e n s   E x a m i n e d. KURUNEGALA DISTRICT: Galaga-ma, *Gardner s.n.* [*C.P. 193* in part] (PDA); on the Kelimunai to Kurunegala road, 24 Oct. 1970, *Kundu & Balakrishnan 352* (PDA, US). PUTTALAM DISTRICT: rather frequent in dry shady woods, Wilpattu National Park, 10 to 15 m alt., 15 Oct. 1975, slender, scandent, branches dark-fuscous, leaves membranous, ovate, flowers fuscous, compare with no. 15343, deter-mined as *P. obtusifolia, Bernardi 15363* (US). ANURADHAPURA DIST-RICT: uncommon in patch of woods on sandy soil 1/4 mile south-southeast of Maradan-Maduwa, 28 Dec. 1968, straggling shrub to 1.5 m tall, aromatic when broken, *Fosberg, Mueller-Dombois, Wirawan, Cooray, & Balakrishnan 50752* (LL). KANDY DISTRICT: Haragama, 1833, *s. coll. C.P. 193* in part (PDA); Galagama, *s. coll. C.P. 193* in part (PDA). HAMBANTOTA DIS-TRICT: Tissamaharama, Dec. 1882, leaves pubescent on both surfaces, *s. coll. s.n.* (PDA—holotype); in forest patch in forest scrub, Plot E. 10, loamy soil, 10 to 20 m alt., 22 Jan. 1968, tree or straggling shrub, "mulla" in Sinhala, *Comanor 814* in part (MOLDENKE); in primarily deciduous scrub on reddish-brown earth, Plot 4, Block I, on the north to south boundary road, Situlpahuwa, 14 Jan. 1969, straggling shrub, opposite pubescent leaves, flowers purple-brown, fruit orange when ripe, not common, determined as *P. corymbosa*, *Cooray 69011401R* (MOLDENKE, PDA, US), same locality, 20 Oct. 1968, new shrub, velvet ovate leaves, terminal green-brown flower-clusters, straggling 2 m tall, determined as *P. corymbosa* by Wirawan, *Mueller-Dombois 68102007* (MOLDENKE, NY, PDA, US).

var. **subcrenata** Moldenke, Phytologia 41: 346. 1979. Type: *Jayasuriya & Balasubramaniam 448* from Haragama, Ceylon (PDA).

This variety differs from the typical form of the species in having its leaf-blades broadly elliptic or elliptic-ovate, more or less cordate basally, and very densely pubescent beneath, the margins subcrenate apically.

A puzzling taxon, possibly the result of natural hybridization with *P. latifolia* var. *mollissima*, known thus far only from two collections.

Ve r n. None reported.

Specimens Examined. KURUNEGALA DISTRICT: Kurune-gala, 1833, *Gardner s.n.* [*C.P. 193* in part] (PDA). KANDY DISTRICT: among shrubbery bordering rock outcrop in semi-sun, Haragama, 80°43′N., 7°16′ E., 500 m alt., 14 Dec. 1971, large shrub, *Jayasuriya & Balasubramaniam 448* (MOLDENKE—isotype, PDA—holotype, US—isotype).

2. **Premna divaricata** Wall., Num. List [48], no. 1781, hyponym. 1829; Schau. in A. DC., Prod. 11: 631–632. 1847; Clarke in Hook. f., Fl. Br. Ind. 4: 575. 1885; Brandis, Indian Trees 510. 1906; King & Gamble, J. Asiat. Soc. Bengal 74: 815. 1909; H.J. Lam, Verbenac. Malay. Arch. 121–122. 1919. Type: *Wallich 1781* from Cape Rochado, Malaya, on the Malacca Strait, collected 25 November 1822 (K).

Premna integrifolia Willd., Ges. Naturf. Freunde Berlin neue Schriften ser. 2, 4: 187. 1803; Roxb., Fl. Ind. 3: 81. 1803 [not *P. integrifolia* Auct., 1840, nor Blanco, 1837, nor Blume, 1959, nor Forbes & Hemsl., 1942, nor L., 1771, nor L. f., 1967, nor H.J. Lam, 1931, nor Roxb., 1959, nor "sensu Dunn & Fletcher", 1967, nor "sensu Forbes & Hemsl., 1963].

Premna lucidula Kurz apud Clarke in Hook. f., Fl. Br. Ind. 4: 575. in syn. 1885 [not *P. lucidula* Miq., 1856].

Premna no. 33 Hook. f. & Thoms. ex Clarke in Hook. f., Fl. Br. Ind. 4: 575, in syn. 1885.

Gumira divaricata (Wall.) Kuntze, Rev. Gen. Pl. 2 (2): 507. 1891.—*G. divaricata* Kuntze apud Durand & Jacks., Ind. Kew. Suppl. 1, imp. 1, 190, in syn. 1902.

Shrub, erect (in the open) or climbing (in the forest), with the odour of *Sambucus*; branchlets and inflorescences subglabrous or slightly pubescent; petioles slender, 1–4 cm long, practically glabrous; leaf-blades at first membranous, later often rigidly chartaceous, ovate or elliptic to elliptic-oblong, 6–15 cm long, 3–9 cm wide, rather shiny above, paler beneath, not nigrescent in drying, apically shortly acute or rather bluntly acuminate, marginally entire, basally rounded or subcordate (or sometimes attenuate), glabrous on both surfaces except somewhat pubescent on the venation, obscurely glandular-dotted and sometimes barbellate in the secondary vein-axils beneath; secondaries 5 or 6 per side; inflorescences terminal or axillary in the topmost leaf-axils, divaricate-cymose or paniculate; peduncles very slender, 1.5–5 cm long, subglabrous or minutely puberulous; corymbs many-flowered, dense or rather loose, 7.5–12.5 cm wide, the branches divaricate; flowers subsessile; calyx small, cupuliform, 1–1.5 mm long, slightly bilabiate, sometimes nearly truncate, usually minutely 2-toothed or the upper lip entire or shortly 3-toothed and the lower one 2-toothed, the teeth about 0.7 mm long, apically acute or rounded; corolla subinfundibular-hypocrateriform, 2.5–3 mm long, subbilabiate, externally puberulent, the tube cylindric, twice as long as the calyx, the limb subequally 4-lobed, the lobes eventually reflexed, ovate, apically obtuse or the upper retuse, the lower slightly larger; stamens inserted in the densely villous corolla-throat, exserted; style as long as the stamens; stigma very shortly bifid; drupes globose, 5–6 mm long and wide, 3- or 4-seeded.

Distr. This poorly understood species appears to be native to the Andaman Islands, Mergui Archipelago, Ceylon, Assam, Malaya, and Indonesia; erroneously reported from the Mascarene Islands and Madagascar; sometimes cultivated. It appears to be rare in Ceylon.

Vern. None recorded.

Specimens Examined. KANDY DISTRICT: Botanic Garden, Peradeniya, May 1887, *s. coll. 197* [125/42] (PDA); near the top of Ganoruwa hill, Peradeniya, 6 Oct. 1968, treelet 3 m tall, leaves to 12 cm long and 5.5 cm wide, acuminate, glabrous on both surfaces or sparsely pilosulous on the midrib beneath, collected as voucher for ecological observations, *Mueller-Dombois & Wirawan 630* (MOLDENKE, NY, PDA, US).

3. **Premna foetida** Reinw. ex Blume, Bijdr. 14: 816. 1826 [not *P. foetida* F.-Vill., 1877, nor Riv., 1924]; Hassk., Cat. Lands Pl. Buitenzorg 2: 135. 1844; Schau. in A. DC., Prod. 11: 630. 1847; Miq., Fl. Ind. Bat. 2: 891 (1856), Suppl. 1: 243. 1860; King & Gamble, J. Asiat. Soc. Bengal 74: 814. 1909; Elbert, Meded. Rijks-herb. 12: 16. 1912; H.J. Lam, Verbenac. Malay. Arch. 140–141. 1919. Type: A Reinwardt collection probably from Java (BO).

Gumira domestica Rumpf, Herb. Amboin. 3: 208, pl. 133. 1743.

Gumira mas Rumpf, Herb. Amboin. 3: 208. 1743.

Gumira femina Rumpf, Herb. Amboin. 3: 208. 1743.

Gumira domestica mas et femina Rumpf apud Schau. in A. DC., Prod. 11: 630, in syn. 1847.

Gumira foetida (Reinw.) Hassk., Flora 25: Beibl. 26. 1842; Kuntze, Rev. Gen. Pl. 2 (2): 507. 1891.—*G. fetida* Hassk., Cat. Pl. Hort. Bogor. Cult. Alt. 135. 1844.

Gumira fetida B integra Hassk., Cat. Pl. Hort. Bogor. Cult. Alt. 135. 1844.

Premna latifolia Thw. ex. Clarke in Hook. f., Fl. Br. Ind. 4: 576, in syn. 1885 [not *P. latifolia* Dalz. & Gibs., 1962, nor Roxb., 1814, nor Wall., 1940, nor Wight, 1885].

Premna tomentosa var. *detergibilis* Clarke in Hook. f., Fl. Br. Ind. 4: 576. 1885.

Premna integrifolia f. *foetida* H.J. Lam in H.J. Lam & Bakh., Bull. Jard. Bot. Buitenzorg, ser. 3, 3: 43. 1921.—*P. integrifolia* f. *foetida* Reinw. ex Moldenke, Résumé Suppl. 3: 34, in syn. 1962.—*P. integrifolia* typ. *foetida* H.J. Lam ex Moldenke, Résumé Suppl. 3: 34, in syn. 1962.

Shrub or tree, to 8 m tall, the branchlets more or less appressed-puberulent, glabrescent in age, drying yellowish or greenish-brown; leaves decussate-opposite, malodorous, usually brunnescent or nigrescent in drying; petioles to c. 15 cm long (or to only 1 cm in var. *parvifolia* Moldenke), puberulent or short-pubescent; leaf-blades membranous, elliptic to ovate or broadly oval, 7–20 cm long and 3–12.5 cm wide (or only 2–4 cm long and 1.5–2 cm wide in var. *parvifolia*), apically coarctate-acuminate, sometimes narrowed, basally obtuse or rounded to subtruncate, marginally entire or apically repand-serrate, glabrous above, more or less pubescent with simple often curvate hairs beneath especially along the rather conspicuous venation or glabrescent in age, often very fragile in drying; panicles terminal, divaricate-corymbose, many-flowered, 5–9 cm long, the peduncles, inflorescence-branches, and very short pedicels densely puberulent or short-pubescent; flowers fragrant; calyx cyathiform, membranous, exiguous, scarcely 1 mm long, externally densely appressed-puberulent or short-pubescent, subbilabiate, the rim obsoletely 4-denticulate; corolla infundibular, white, the tube almost twice the length of the calyx, the limb subequally 4-fid, hairy in the throat, the lobes reflexed; stamens and pistil long-exserted.

Distr. A widespread species native from Assam to Thailand, Indo-China, and Malaya, north to Hainan and Taiwan, eastward to the Philippines, Indonesia, New Guinea, New Britain, New Caledonia, and northern Australia; sometimes cultivated.

Vern. None recorded from Ceylon, but among the many from elsewhere are: Goemira, Indjaro, Inrelo, Ki pahang, Ki seungit, Singkil and Singkil alas.

Notes. It is obviously closely related to and is often confused with *P. obtusifolia* R. Br. Clarke's *P. tomentosa* var. *detergibilis* was based by him on *C.P. 2893* from probably cultivated Ceylon material and although he says that it differs from typical *P. tomentosa* only in having the "mature leaves with most of the wool rubbed off", examination of the type collection shows the hairs on the lower leaf-surface to be simple and not at all stellate-branched as in typical *P. tomentosa*. It appears that the presumed variety instead actually represents *P. foetida*, a species which seems to occur in Ceylon only in cultivation or as a persistent after former cultivation. *Premna sumatrana* Ridl., sometimes united with *P. foetida*, is probably distinct.

Specimens Examined. KALUTARA DISTRICT: in old botanical garden, Kalutara, perhaps cultivated, Sept. 1856, hairs not stellate, determined as *P. tomentosa* var. *detergibilis* and *P. latifolia*, s. coll. *C.P. 2893* in part (PDA). KANDY DISTRICT: Royal Botanic Garden, Peradeniya, perhaps cultivated, July 1889, determined as *P. latifolia* and *P. viburnoides*, s. coll. *s.n.* (PDA).

4. Premna latifolia Roxb., Hort. Beng. 46, nom. nud. 1814; Roxb., Fl. Ind. 3: 76. 1832 [not *P. latifolia* Dalz. & Gibs., 1894, nor Thw., 1885, nor Wall., 1940, nor Wight, 1885]; Schau. in A. DC., Prod. 11: 635. 1847; Dalz. & Gibs., Bombay Fl. 200 & 203. 1861; Thw., Enum. Pl. Zeyl. 2: 242. 1861; Beddome, Fl. Sylv. S. Ind. 172. 1872; Roxb., Fl. Ind., ed. 3, 483. 1874; Brandis, Forest Fl. 366. 1874; Kurz, Forest Fl. Burma 2: 261. 1877; Clarke in Hook. f., Fl. Br. Ind. 4: 577–578. 1885; Trimen, Cat. 68. 1885; Kuntze, Rev. Gen. Pl. 2 (2): 508. 1891; Watt, Dict. Econ. Prod. India 6 (1): 337. 1892; Gamble, Man. Indian Timb., ed. 2, 536–537. 1902; Brandis, Indian Trees 511. 1906; Willis, Cat. 69. 1911; H.J. Lam, Verbenac. Malay. Arch. 150–152. 1919; Haines, Bot. Bihar Orissa 4: 714 & 717–718. 1922; Gamble, Fl. Pres. Madras 6: 1094 & 1096. 1924; Parker, Forest Fl. Punjab, ed. 3, 586. 1956; Cooke, Fl. Pres. Bombay, ed. 2, 2: 507. 1958; Abeywick., Ceylon J. Sci., Biol. Sci. 2: 217. 1959; Prain, Bengal Pl., ed. 2, 2: 620. 1963; Gunawardena, Gen. Sp. Pl. Zeyl. 147. 1968; Fonseka & Vinasithamby, Prov. List Local Names Fl. Pl. Ceylon 53 & 67. 1971; Vivekanandan, Sri Lanka Forester, ser. 2, 11: 109 & 134. 1974. Type: *Roxburgh s.n.* from the Coromandel coast, Tamil Nadu, India (K).

Premna latifolia var. *typica* H.J. Lam, Verbenac. Malay. Arch. 151. 1919.
Premna leucophloea Roxb. ex Moldenke, Prelim. Alph. List Invalid Names 37, in syn. 1940.
Premna latifolia var. *latifolia* [Roxb.] apud Haines, Bot. Bihar Orissa 6: 717. 1924.—*P. latifolia* var. *latifolia* Haines ex Moldenke, Résumé Suppl. 15: 22, in syn. 1967.

Erect and sturdy shrub or small tree, 4–5 m tall, deciduous, or slender, straggly, and elongate vine-like; older stems sometimes with paired spine-like woody spurs; wood grey, with yellow, green, and purple streaks, softer than that of *P. tomentosa*, weight 38–43 lb/cubic foot; branchlets and twigs slender, more or less subtetragonal, grey, sparsely lenticellate, the youngest parts usually densely short- and rusty-pubescent, the older parts glabrous; nodes often annulate; principal internodes 0.5–3.3 cm long; leaves decussate-opposite or ternate, mostly more or less clustered on the very short twigs, strongly odorous; petioles very slender, 0.3–2.6 cm long, canaliculate above, densely short- and rusty-pubescent, not noticeably ampliate basally; leaf-blades thin-chartaceous, rather uniformly dark green on both surfaces or lighter beneath, usually very conspicuously nigrescent in drying (especially above) or bluish-black beneath [or drying green, both surfaces concolorous, in var. *viburnoides* (Wall.) Clarke], broadly elliptic or ovate to oblong-elliptic or lanceolate, 8–15 cm long, 6–12.5 cm wide (in var. *latifolia*) or much smaller (in vars.), apically abruptly acute or short-acuminate, marginally entire (rarely somewhat dentate apically), basally broadly rounded to subtruncate or cordate (in var. *latifolia*), varying to cuneate or rhomboid [in vars. *cuneata* Clarke, *mollissima* (Roth) Clarke, and *viburnoides* (Wall.) Clarke], or attenuate-acuminate at both ends [in var. *mucronata* (Roxb.) Clarke], varying from densely pubescent on both surfaces (var. *mollissima*) or densely puberulent to subglabrous (var. *viburnoides*) on both surfaces, or minutely pubescent on only the midrib beneath (var. *mucronata*), or glabrous and glanduliferous especially on the venation above (var. *glandulosa* Dop); midrib very slender, flat or subprominulent above, prominulent almost to the apex beneath; vein and veinlet reticulation rather abundant, mostly obscure or indiscernible above, flat beneath; inflorescence axillary and terminal, mostly terminal on abbreviated spur-like twigs, comparatively small and only 1–4 cm wide (or larger in vars. *latifolia* and *mucronata*), rather many-flowered, many times bifurcate, mostly rather densely appressed-puberulent throughout, often with a curry-like odour; bractlets linear, 1.5–3 mm long, puberulent; prophylla minute, setaceous, puberulent; flowers odorous; calyx 2-lipped, usually strigose (var. *cuneata*) or subpatently pubescent (var. *mucronata*), smaller in var. *mollissima* than in var. *cuneata*; corolla white or creamy-white to brownish (in age), pubescent in the throat, smaller in var. *mollissima* than in var. *cuneata*, the upper lip larger and whiter; fruiting-calyx campanulate, to 2.5 mm long and 6 mm wide, externally appressed-puberulent, the rim rather irregularly 4-lobed, the lobes broadly triangular, apically acute; drupes subglobose, 4–5 mm long and wide, fleshy, nigrescent in drying, decidedly verrucose (in var. *mucronata*) or hardly verrucose (var. *latifolia*). Chromosome number: n=19.

D i s t r. This is a very poorly defined and variously treated taxon, either extremely variable or else consisting of several closely related and probably hybridizing species; var. *mucronata* is widely regarded as a distinct species and var. *viburnoides* is also suggested by some authorities as worthy of specific rank. *Premna latifolia* has been circumscribed very differently by various authors in the past and their published descriptions disagree with each other in many points. Roxburgh's original type has broadly ovate, large, basally distinctly cordate (and not at all cuneate into the petiole) leaves and he emphasizes this character. Clarke (1885) asserts that the typical form apparently exists only in the Coromandel hills of the former Madras Presidency in southern peninsular India. I personally doubt that it occurs in Ceylon.

Clarke's var. *mucronata*, with the leaf-blades plainly attenuate-cuneate at both ends, is primarily from northern India, Nepal, and Sikkim, and is regarded as a distinct species by most authorities in that region. His var. *mollissima* was described by him from Madras and var. *viburnoides* also from southern India; var. *cuneata* was described from Burma, while Dop's var. *glandulosa* is native to Laos. Clarke's very brief description of the varieties accepted by him leave much to be desired by way of clarity and do not seem to be very plainly mutually exclusive. Kuntze (1891) complicates matters by accepting *P. mollissima* Roth (1821) as the valid name (being the oldest validly published) for the species and reducing *P. latifolia* Roxb. (1932) to synonymy under it.

U s e s. What has been called *P. latifolia* is said to be used medicinally in Ceylon. The leaves are eaten in curries, especially in southern India, and are also sometimes fed to cattle as fodder. In Sikkim the wood is used for construction and to obtain fire by friction. In Bangladesh the wood is used for fuel and to make charcoal.

N o t e. The species is said to be parasitized by the mistletoe, *Dendrophthoë falcata* (L. f.) Ettingsh.

var. **cuneata** Clarke in Hook. f., Fl. Br. Ind. 4: 578. 1885. Type: *Kurz s.n.* from Pegu in Upper Burma (K).

Premna viburnoides Kurz apud Clarke in Hook. f., Fl. Br. Ind. 4: 578, in syn. 1885 [not *P. viburnoides* Wall., 1831].

This variety differs chiefly in its much smaller leaves with the base of the blades more or less plainly rhomboid or cuneate into the petiole apex and the calyx plainly strigose-pubescent externally. It is a shrub or small tree, 3–4 m tall, "of the same dusky sombre colour of *P. latifolia* Roxb. type" (according to Clarke) and with a broad open crown, the trunk to 20 cm in diameter at breast height, the bark greyish, the branches very twisted; leaves small; petioles very slender, 0.6–3 cm long, minutely puberulent; leaf-blades thin-membranous and fragile, especially when young, plainly bicoloured, ovate, 2–7 cm long, 1.5–4 cm wide, mostly conspicuously nigrescent in drying ("the leaves drying blue-black above, ashy beneath"), apically acute or abruptly short-acuminate, marginally entire or with a few very shallow indistinct teeth on the upper half or third, basally acute to rhomboid or short-cuneate into the petiole apex, glabrous on both surfaces or obscurely puberulent on the midrib beneath ("often very pubescent when young" according to Clarke); calyx densely strigose-pubescent externally, the rim apparently regularly 4-dentate; corolla zygomorphic, white or pale greenish-white; fruit at first green, turning black at maturity.

D i s t r. This variety apparently is found from India and Ceylon, through Burma and Thailand, to Indo-China. Clarke cites also *Griffith 6035* from Burma, but I am regarding his first-mentioned citation, *Kurz s.n.* from Pegu, as the nomenclatural type.

V e r n. The only ones recorded are: Dangra seya and Maha-midi.

S p e c i m e n s E x a m i n e d. PUTTALAM DISTRICT: occasional in open thorn scrub with *Borassus* 1.5 miles beyond Kalpitya, 14 Nov. 1970, shrub 3 m tall, somewhat aromatic, branching decussate with 2 ranks predominating, *Fosberg & Jayasuriya 52746* (LL); Puttalam, 1881, interesting form with same fetid smell as *Clerodendrum inerme*, determined as *P. latifolia* and *P. integrifolia, Nevill s.n.* (PDA). ANURADHAPURA DISTRICT: in open forest scrub, Occapuvillu, in Plot W. 32, Wilpattu National Park, 11 July 1969, shrub 3 m tall, fruit green, determined as *P. latifolia* by Wirawan, voucher collected for ecological observations, *Wirawan, Cooray, & Balakrishnan 1085* (AAU, NY, PDA, US). POLONNARUWA DISTRICT: along forested margin of rock outcrop about 3 miles southwest of Elahera, near milepost 12/5, 400–500 ft alt., 10 Oct. 1974, small tree, about 4 metres tall, trunk 20 cm in diameter at breast height, flowers pale greenish-white, zygomorphic, fruit green, *Davidse 7331* (LL, PDA, US), same locality, shrub 3 m tall, fruit green, turning black at maturity, *Davidse 7344* (LL, PDA, US). MATALE DISTRICT: Dambulla rock, 12 Oct. 1966, flowers white or creamy white, "maha-midi", *Amaratunga 1155* (PDA); rather frequent on wooded hill near temple, Dambulla, 7 Oct. 1975, densely branching shrub, leaves simple, ovate, shiny, membranous, glabrous, flowers in dense-flowered cymes, whitish, determined as *P. latifolia, Bernardi 15246* (PDA, US); Eluwana Kande, Lagalla, Sept. 1893, leaves hairy on the venation, *s. coll. s.n.* (PDA); near Sigiriya Rock, Sept. 1885, leaves quite glabrous, flowers white, corolla woolly in the throat, *s. coll. s.n.* (PDA); in scrub jungle on the flat, Ratmalgaha Ela, Dambulla, 4 miles southeast, 700 ft alt., 9 Oct. 1947, *Worthington 3125* (K). HAMBANTOTA DISTRICT: rather frequent in shrubbery, Yala National Park, 10–20 m alt., 29 Oct. 1975, small tree, 3–4 m tall, crown open, bark greyish, branches very twisted, young leaves thin, bicoloured, ovate, cymes small, flowers white, *Bernardi 15547* (NY, PDA); in forest-scrub vegetation on the marine sand of sand dunes, Plot II, Block II, past Uda patana, Ruhuna National Park, 3 m alt., 29 Aug. 1967, tree, collected as voucher for ecological observations,*Comanor 01290867* (PDA, US); common at Rakinawala, Plot R.

33, Block I, Ruhuna National Park, 22, Oct. 1968, tree 3 m tall, opposite light green leaves, small white flowers in clusters, older branches have woody thorns, collected as voucher for ecological observations, *Cooray 68102201R* (MICH, MOLDENKE, NY, PDA, US); in sparse forest on rock knob plain off milepost 12/4 on the Naula to Elahera Road, 160 m alt., 10 June 1971, sturdy shrub 5 m tall, stem with paired spines, *Jayasuriya 317* (PDA, US); in closed scrub with scattered trees on reddish-brown loamy sand, Plot R. 20, Block I, at north to south boundary northeast of Katagamuwa tank, Ruhuna National Park, 20 m alt., 30 Sept. 1967, 3 m tall member of the scrub, leaves very small, *Mueller-Dombois, Comanor, & Cooray 67093034* (PDA, US); in deciduous scrub with scattered emergents in reddish-brown earth, Plot 1, Block I, north of Rakinawala at the Yala Road, Ruhuna National Park, 18 Oct. 1968, 5 m tall, broad crown, *Mueller-Dombois 68101818* (LL, PDA, US).

var. **major** Moldenke, Phytologia 41: 346. 1979. Type: *Sohmer 8986* from Buthawa bungalow, Ceylon (PDA).

This variety differs in having its inflorescences during full anthesis much larger, much more abundantly flowered, to 10 cm wide, its branches loosely and divaricately wide-spreading.

Specimens Examined. HAMBANTOTA DISTRICT: in scrub, Ruhuna National Park, between Andunorowawela and Talgasmankada, below 5 m alt., 14 Nov. 1977, white-flowered tree, 4 m tall, *Huber 622* (PDA, US); Buthawa bungalow, near the sea, Block I, Yala National Park, 4 Dec. 1973, flowers white, *Sohmer 8986* (LACROSSE isotype, NY isotype, PDA holotype, US isotype).

var. **mollissima** (Roth) Clarke in Hook. f., Fl. Br. Ind. 4: 578. 1885; Wall., Num. List 82, no. 2646a. 1831; Schau. in A. DC., Prod. 11: 635 & 638. 1847; Clarke in Hook. f., Fl. Br. Ind. 4: 578. 1885; Gamble, Fl. Pres. Madras 6: 1096. 1924.

Premna mollissima Roth, Nov. Sp. 286–287. 1821.
Gumira mollissima (Roth) Kuntze, Rev. Gen. Pl. 2 (2): 508. 1891.—*G. mollissima* Kuntze apud Durand & Jacks., Ind. Kew. Suppl. 1, imp. 1, 190, in syn. 1902.

This variety differs chiefly in its small, basally obtuse or rhomboid leaf-blades which are apparently permanently puberulent or short-pubescent on both surfaces or at least beneath, the terminal cymes only to 4 cm wide, and the very small calyx and corolla. It is described as a straggling climber, shrub, or tree to 20 m tall, the trunk often to 100 cm in girth; branches and branchlets slender, light-grey, often compressed at the nodes, the youngest parts rufescent-pubescent or -puberulent, glabrous in age, the old wood often with opposite blunt spines, the bark defoliating in flakes; leaves strongly odorous; petioles much shorter than the length of the blade; leaf-blades ovate or elliptic-ovate, dark green when fresh, conspicuously nigrescent and fragile in drying, 3–6 cm long, 2–6 cm wide, apically short-acuminate with an obtuse acumen, marginally entire, basally acute to obtuse or subcordate, centrally very often prolonged in cuneate fashion into the petiole apex, venose, more or less permanently, densely, and softly short-pubescent or puberulent on both surfaces or, at least, beneath; cymes terminal, dense, only to 4 cm wide, repeatedly dichotomous, ferruginous-puberulent throughout; bractlets linear-oblong, about 2 mm long, spreading, apically obtuse; calyx very small, smaller than in var. *cuneata*, externally pubescent, the rim truncate (ex Roth) or distinctly 4-dentate; corolla very small, smaller than in var. *cuneata*, whitish or yellow-green, externally tomentose, the limb 4-fid; fruiting-calyx campanulate, shallow, about 2 mm long, 4–5 mm wide, externally puberulent, the rim distinctly lobed or subtruncate; drupes black, subglobose, 3–5 mm long and wide, smooth, shiny, somewhat fleshy, 2-celled, each cell 2-seeded.

D i s t r. This taxon appears to be native from northwestern Pakistan, through India, Ceylon, Burma, and Thailand, to Indo-China, but it is not certain that the Ceylon material actually represents this variety. Clarke asserts that the leaves of *P. latifolia* var. *cuneata* are also densely pubescent when young, but the Ceylon material so determined does not seem to bear this out and the Ceylon material here determined as var. *mollissima* includes many specimens in full anthesis, in full fruit, or even past fruiting, with the leaves all equally densely puberulent or pubescent. The flowering calyx-rim characters do not agree with those stated by Roth for the type collection. It would appear that in Ceylon there are plants with both young and mature leaves glabrous and also other plants with both young and mature leaves pubescent. They are here assigned to *P. latifolia* var. *cuneata* and var. *mollissima*, respectively, only tentatively until the types can be studied and/or more intensive field work throughout the range can be completed.

V e r n. None reported.

S p e c i m e n s E x a m i n e d. BADULLA DISTRICT: Ooma-oya, 1880, leaves finely pubescent on both surfaces, flowers white, *Ferguson s.n.* (PDA). HAMBANTOTA DISTRICT: in discontinuous scrub with scattered emergent trees, soil coarse sand with pebbles, Block I, Komawa-wewa, Ruhuna National Park, 4–8 m altitude, shrub 3 m tall, bark dirty-white, opposite blunt spines on old wood, petals yellow-green, determined as "close to *P. serratifolia* L.", *Comanor 405* (LL, NY, PDA, US); in discontinuous scrub, soil brown loamy sand, on the road to Patanagala beach, Ruhuna National Park, 3 m alt., 30 Nov. 1967, spreading tree, 4 m tall, fruit black, edible, *Comanor 612* (AAU, NY, PDA, US); common growing near camp, Block I, Patanagala, Ruhuna National Park, 14 Nov., tree 3 m tall, fruits green when young, black when ripe, collected as voucher for ecological observations, *Cooray 69111403R* (MOLDENKE, NY, PDA, US); in sandy soil in scrub at junction of Yala and the road to Patanagala beach, Ruhuna National Park, 2 m alt., 31 Aug. 1967, tree 4 m tall, light dull green ovate leaves in clusters of 3 and umbellate inflorescences, leaves very small, with curry smell, *Mueller-Dombois 67083101* (PDA, US); common in open scrub in front of Smithsonian camp, Block I, Patanagala, Ruhuna National Park, 28 Oct. 1968, shrub 3 m tall, fruit green, collected as voucher for ecological observations, *Wirawan 682b* (LL, PDA, US).

var. **viburnoides** (Wall.) Clarke in Hook. f., Fl. Br. Ind. 4: 578. 1885; Schau. in A. DC., Prod. 11: 635. 1847; Thw., Enum. Pl. Zeyl. 242. 1861; Clarke in Hook. f., Fl. Br. Ind. 4: 578. 1885; Brandis, Indian Trees 511. 1906; Gamble, Fl. Pres. Madras 6: 1096. 1924; Petelot, Pl. Méd. Cambod. Laos Vietnam 2: 247 (1954) and 4: 151. 1954; Naithani, Bull. Bot. Surv. India 8: 259. 1966. Type: *Herb. Wight s.n.* from the Ginghee hills, India (K).

Premna viburnoides Wall., Num. List 82, no. 2646b. 1831.
Premna latifolia Wight apud Clarke in Hook. f., Fl. Br. Ind. 4: 578, in Syn. 1885 [not *P. latifolia* Dalz. & Gibs., 1894, nor Roxb., 1814, nor Thw., 1885, nor Wall., 1940].
Gumira viburnodes (Rich.) Kuntze, Rev. Gen. Pl. 2 (2): 508. 1891.—*G. viburnodes* Kuntze apud Durand & Jacks., Ind. Kew. Suppl. 1, imp. 1, 190, in syn. 1902.
Premna latifolia var. *gamblei* Haines, Bot. Bihar Orissa 4: 717. 1922.
Premna integrifolia Gamble apud Haines, Fl. Bihar Orissa 4: 717, in syn. 1922 [not *P. integrifolia* Auct., 1940, nor Blanco, 1942, nor Blume, 1907, nor Forbes & Hemsl., 1942, nor H.J. Lam, 1931, nor L., 1771, nor L. f., 1942, nor Roxb., 1845, nor Willd., 1803, nor "sensu Dunn & Fletcher", 1967, nor "sensu Forbes & Hemsl.", 1963].

This variety is said to differ from the typical and all other varieties in having its leaf-blades ovate and broad, not cordate, basally rhomboid, drying green, the surfaces concolorous, nearly glabrous even when young. Clarke asserts that "the green colour easily separates it from all [other]...forms of *P. latifolia*" and in his opinion Wallich may have been fully justified in regarding it as a distinct species.

Recent workers and collectors describe this plant as a large shrub, 4–8 m tall, with corky light-yellow bark; the young green branches and the leaves drying olive-green; leaves pleasantly and notably scented when crushed, decussate-opposite; petioles 1.5–3.5 cm long; leaf-blades thin, generally ovate to ovate-lanceolate or ovate-oblong, 5–9 cm long, 3.3–6 cm wide, apically acute-apiculate or rarely somewhat obtuse, marginally serrate or less often (notably on fruiting branchlets) entire, basally variable, generally cuneate or rounded, glabrous on both surfaces; inflorescence a corymbose panicle, terminal on the branchlets; peduncles ferruginous-tomentose and scale-covered; flowers hermaphroditic, often polygamous, arranged in dichasial cymes; bracts and bractlets present; pedicels to 1.6 mm long, pubescent and squamuliferous, ferruginous; calyx about 1.8 mm long and wide, externally glabrous but squamuliferous, 2-lipped, one lip 2-lobed, the other indistinctly 3-lobed, the lobes ovate, 0.75 mm long, apically obtuse; corolla 5 mm long, 2-lipped, densely bearded within, externally glabrous, the lobes 2 on one lip, 3 on the other; stamens 4, didynamous, epipetalous; ovary hypogynous, depressed-globose, 1 mm long and wide, glabrous; style terminal, 2.5 mm long, bifid; fruiting-calyx accrescent, about 4 mm wide; fruits few, drupaceous, 5 mm wide, light-green at maturity, drying black, the pericarp leathery, the endocarp stony, verrucose, 4-celled.

D i s t r. This variety is found mostly along the seacoast from Bombay (Maharashtra) south to Goa, Mysore, and possibly Kerala, mostly in the southern Deccan peninsula, being especially common in the Cochin and Gingee hills; possibly also in Ceylon.

U s e s. In India the tender leaves are ground with rice, etc., and fermented into a much sought-after sweet called "dosa". The roots are said to be used as one of the ten constituents of a time-honoured Ayurvedic medicine called "dasamula". It is not at all certain that the Ceylon material cited below really represents this taxon.

V e r n. Maha-midi, Nulla, Gel-kara (S); Naroli, Narval (T).

S p e c i m e n s E x a m i n e d. JAFFNA DISTRICT: Vaddukoddai, 24 Aug. 1955, shrub, stamens 4, exserted, anthers black, filaments white, flowers greenish-white, with white hairs in the throat of the corolla, *Silva s.n.* (PDA). ANURADHAPURA DISTRICT: at edge of jungle, Palukolawala, low altitude, 24 Jan. 1974, low trees, *H.N. & A.L. Moldenke & Jayasuriya 28230* (AAU, ARIZ, CAI, KARACHI, LL, MO, PDA, US). KURUNEGALA DISTRICT: Dodangaslanda, on the Dombawela to Ibbagamuwa road, 15 Oct. 1967, shrub, leaves aromatic when bruised, flowers brownish-white, *Amaratunga 1436* (PDA); Maspotha, 14 Nov. 1967, shrub, flowers brownish, determined as *P. corymbosa, Amaratunga 1474* (PDA). POLONNARUWA DISTRICT: in roadside forest edge 4 miles east of Habarana, along the road to Polonnaruwa, 450 ft alt., 12 Oct. 1974, slender shrub to 3 m tall, *Davidse 7463* (LL, PDA). MATALE DISTRICT: Lenadore, Oct. 1890, leaves glabrous, *Alexander s.n.* (PDA); Wahacotte, 7 Oct. 1969, a spreading tree, "maha-midi" in Sinhalese, determined as *P. latifolia, Amaratunga 1862* (PDA); at edge of jungle in limestone area at milepost 36 on the Kandy to Dambulla road, 400 ft alt., 23 Jan. 1974, small tree, branched to the base, *H.N.& A.L. Moldenke & Jayasuriya 28216* (AAU, CAI, KARACHI, LL, PDA, US); common low tree in jungle at temple, Dambulla rock, 800 ft alt., 23

Jan. 1974, *H.N. & A.L. Moldenke & Jayasuriya 28222* (AAU, CAI, LL, PDA, US). TRINCOMALEE DISTRICT: Sober Island, Trincomalee Bay, March 1872, very fetid, leaves glabrous, *Nevill s.n.* (PDA). DISTRICT UNKNOWN: Panguragama, young leaves with simple villous hairs, afterwards quite glabrous, *Gardner s.n.* [C.P. 2893 in part] (PDA); *s. coll. C.P. 1953* (BO).

5. Premna procumbens Moon, Cat. 1: 45. 1824; Wall., Num. List [48], no. 1780. 1829; Voigt, Hort. Suburb. Calc. 468. 1845; Schau. in A. DC., Prod. 11: 636. 1847; Thw., Enum. Pl. Zeyl. 243. 1861; Trimen, J. Ceylon Branch Roy. Asiat. Soc. 9: 69. 1885; Trimen, Handb. Fl. Ceylon 3: 354. 1895; Willis, Cat. 69. 1911; Gamble, Fl. Pres. Madras 6: 1094 & 1096. 1924; Alston in Trimen, Handb. Fl. Ceylon 6: 232. 1931; Razi, Half-yearly J. Mysore Univ. 7 (4): 64. 1946; Abeywick., Ceylon J. Sci., Biol. Sci. 2: 217. 1959; Gunawardena, Gen. Sp. Pl. Zeyl. 147. 1968; Fonseka & Vinasithamby, Prov. List Local Names Fl. Pl. Ceylon 50 & 60. 1971. Type: *Moon s.n.* from Uva, Ceylon, distributed as *Wallich 1780* (K).

Premna procumbens Wall. ex Schau. in A. DC., Prod. 11: 636. 1847.
Gumira procumbens (Moon) Kuntze, Rev. Gen. Pl. 2 (2): 508. 1891.—*G. procumbens* Kuntze apud Durand & Jacks., Ind. Kew. Suppl. 1, imp. 1, 190, in syn. 1902.

A small shrub or undershrub, sometimes straggling, sometimes arborescent, or a woody vine with "haustorial" connections to the host, to 2 m long; branches and branchlets very slender, obtusely tetragonal or subterete, the young parts finely short-pubescent, the nodes thickened and slightly annulate; principal internodes abbreviated, mostly 3–4.5 cm long; leaf-scars relatively large and prominent, corky; bark yellowish-white, smooth; leaves decussate-opposite, articulated, readily detached; petioles very slender, 5–40 mm long, more or less strigillose-pubescent, usually flattened above; leaf-blades coriaceous or chartaceous, dark green above, lighter beneath, oblong or ovate-oblong, 4.5–11.5 cm long, 1.7–4.3 cm wide, apically acute or subacute to subacuminate or obtusely mucronate, marginally undulate and usually very coarsely serrate or repand-dentate except at the very apex, basally obtuse or rounded to cordate or truncate, shiny above, glabrous or subglabrate on both surfaces except for the pilose midrib above, sometimes puberulent-punctate beneath or (when young) pubescent on the venation or even sparsely pubescent on both surfaces; midrib very slender, flat above, prominulent beneath; secondaries 4–8 per side, distant and irregular, flat or subimpressed above, prominulent beneath, arcuate-ascending, irregularly angulate-joined near the margins beneath; vein and veinlet reticulation fine, the larger parts often very slightly prominulent on both surfaces; leaf-scars prominent and lunate after leaf-shedding; cymes terminal, small, 2–3 cm long and wide, subsessile, dense, rounded-globose, much-branched, many-flowered, in fruit paniculate and pyramidal or subthyrsoid; pedicles and sympodia very short, densely short-pubescent or strigillose-pubescent; peduncles slender, mostly obsolete or nearly so; calyx campanulate, about 2 mm long, enlarged in fruit, purple, minutely pubescent or scabrid to nearly glabrous, the 5 segments unequal, short, very shallow and obtuse to rounded or subtruncate; corolla green, white, or greenish-white with a patch of yellow, about 3 mm long, the tube equalling the calyx, the lobes oblong, subequal or the upper shorter and sub-retuse and the lower slightly longer, the lateral ones narrower and reflexed, with a few hairs in the throat; stamens exserted, subequal; drupes obovate-ovoid or obovoid, about 5 mm long, tuberculate, the pyrenes thin, 4-seeded.

D i s t r. A possibly endemic species, doubtfully listed as also from southern India (Mysore) and Bangladesh, apparently rare in the wild; known mostly from cultivated specimens. Trimen says that it occurs in the low country of the dry region and is "rare in the wild state". It is frequently cultivated in native gardens, especially in the dry region, as a curry plant. He notes that "I have never seen it flowering nor met with it in the wild, yet it seems to be known only from Ceylon". Thwaites avers that it is "Not uncommon in the hotter parts of the island". Clarke saw only specimens cultivated in the Calcutta Botanical Garden. Moon's original (1824) description consists only of the one word, "procumbent", but this is sufficient under the present Code since it is descriptive of what seemed to him to be the distinctive characteristic of the species.

V e r n. Lekolapala (S); Mulla, Mullai (T).

N o t e. It is very possible that some, or all, of the more recently collected material cited below may not truly represent this taxon. Sohmer's description of his specimen is especially disquieting.

S p e c i m e n s   E x a m i n e d. JAFFNA DISTRICT: Kayts, Eluvativu island, 22 Sept. 1897, *s. coll. s.n.* (PDA). POLONNARUWA DISTRICT: in lowland dry forest about 3 miles west of Giritale, on the Giritale to Naula road, 7 Oct. 1973, woody vine with haustorial connections to the tree upon which it is growing, *Sohmer 8240* (PDA). MATALE DISTRICT: Dambulla hill, perhaps cultivated, July 1887, *s. coll. s.n.* (PDA). RATNAPURA DISTRICT: straggling on a tree near stream at milepost 66/11 on the Ratnapura to Pelmadulla road, 27 Aug. 1963, flowers small, greenish-white with a patch of yellow, *Amaratunga 706* (PDA); Pelmadulla, Feb. 1826, *Gardner s.n. [C.P. 325* in part] (PDA); Balangoda, Sept. 1857, *s. coll. C.P. 325* in part (MOLDENKE, PDA). BADULLA DISTRICT: Uva, *Moon s.n. [Wallich 1780]* (W isotype). AMPARAI DISTRICT: sandy dunes near Kalmunai, east coast, low altitude, 1 June 1971, shrub 2 m tall, flowers green, *Kostermans 24344* (US). TRINCOMALEE DISTRICT: Trincomalee, used as an herb in curries, *s. coll. s.n.* (PDA); Sober Island, Trincomalee, March 1892, tree, determined as *Cordia* sp. *Nevill s.n.* (PDA). HAMBANTOTA DISTRICT:

Middeniya, 30 March 1927, flowers white, *Alston 994* (PDA); forest patch in forest-scrub, Plot R. 10, Block I, Ruhuna National Park, 10–20 m alt., 22 Jan. 1968, straggling shrub, common in the park, *Comanor 809* (MOLDENKE); forest patch in forest-scrub, Plot R. 10, Block I, loamy soil, Ruhuna National Park, 10–20 m alt., 22 Jan. 1968, tree or straggling shrub, *Comanor 814* in part (PDA); in forest on sand, Patanagala rock outcrop area, Plot R. 10, Block I, Ruhuna National Park, 8 Dec. 1967, juvenile, leaves small, deeply dentate like *Gmelina asiatica*, voucher collected for ecological observations, determined by Wirawan as "sapling of *P. latifolia* Roxb.", *Mueller-Dombois 67120805* (PDA, US).

6. Premna purpurascens Thw., Enum. Pl. Zeyl. 242. 1861; Moon, Cat. 1: 45. 1824; Thw., Enum. Pl. Zeyl., imp. 1, 242. 1861; Clarke in Hook. f., Fl. Br. Ind. 4: 574. 1885; Trimen, J. Ceylon Branch Roy. Asiat. Soc. 9: 68. 1885; Trimen, Handb. Fl. Ceylon 3: 351 (1895) and pl. 72. 1893; Willis, Cat. 69. 1911; Abeywick., Ceylon J. Sci., Biol. Sci. 2: 217. 1959; Gunawardena, Gen. Sp. Pl. Zeyl. 147. 1968. Type: *C.P. 2698* from Ambagamuwa, Ceylon (PDA).

Phaenicanthus zeylanicus Thw., Enum. Pl. Zeyl., imp. 1, 242, in syn. 1861.
Gumira purpurascens (Thw.) Kuntze, Rev. Gen. Pl. 2 (2): 508. 1891.—*G. purpurascens* Kuntze apud Durand & Jacks., Ind. Kew. Suppl. 1, imp. 1, 190, in syn. 1902.

A beautiful, large, woody climber in tall trees; bark grey, smooth; branchlets terete, striate; petioles 1.5–5 cm long, purplish; leaf-blades broadly oblong to oval-oblong, 7.5–15 cm long, 3.5–7.5 cm wide, shiny-green, usually glabrous on both surfaces or fulvous-puberulent on the venation beneath, marginally entire, apically shortly and obtusely acuminate, basally obtuse or rounded to subcordate, very finely reticulate-venose beneath, the reticulation purplish on young leaves; secondaries about 8 pairs, purplish; inflorescence terminal and axillary, paniculate, about 15 cm long, corymbose, rather densely many-flowered or lax, much shorter than the subtending leaves, closely pubescent or puberulent to tomentellous, the cyme-branches numerous and divaricate, the bracts very small, purplish, caducous; peduncles and flower-buds purplish; pedicels very short, purplish; flowers minute, sweet-smelling, calyx small, less than 1 mm long, cinereous-pubescent externally, obscurely 2-lipped, the rim truncate and subentire; corolla pale-purple or dull brownish-purple, about 2 mm long, with a dense tuft of white woolly hair in the throat, the limb subequally 4-lobed, the lobes rounded, reflexed; stamens exserted, equal, inserted in the corolla throat; anthers pale-purple.

D i s t r. This appears to be a very rare endemic, according to Thawites inhabiting the low country below 1500 ft. alt., but more recently it has been collected at 2000 and 3600 ft.

V e r n. None reported.

N o t e. The *Premna purpurascens* var. *paucinervis* Clarke, of India, is now known as *P. paucinervis* (Clarke) Gamble.

S p e c i m e n s E x a m i n e d. KURUNEGALA DISTRICT: summit of Doluwa-kanda, 2000 feet altitude, 9 March 1911, *s. coll. s.n.* (PDA). KANDY DISTRICT: Ambagamuwa, at low elevation, *s. coll. C.P. 2698* (BO isotype, BR isotype, MOLDENKE isotype, NY isotype, PDA holotype, PDA isotype); Warriagala Estate on the Hantana to Nilambe road, 3600 ft alt., 9 Sept. 1947, *Worthington 3056* (K). GALLE DISTRICT: between Hiniduma and Mawanana, 10 March 1881, a beautiful plant, climbs on large trees, *s. coll. s.n.* (PDA).

7. Premna thwaitesii Clarke in Hook. f., Fl. Br. Ind. 4: 579. 1885. f. **thwaitesii.** Thw., Enum. Pl. Zeyl., imp. 1, 242. 1861; Clarke in Hook. f., Fl. Br. Ind. 4: 579. 1885; Trimen, Handb. Fl. Ceylon 3: 353. 1895; Pearson, J. Linn. Soc. Bot. 34: 352. 1899; Willis, Cat. 69. 1911; Abeywick., Ceylon J. Sci., Biol. Sci. 2: 217. 1959; Gunawardena, Gen. Sp. Pl. Zeyl. 147. 1968. Type: *C.P. 2541* from Maturata and Hanguranketa, Ceylon (PDA).

Premna micrantha Thw. ex Clarke in Hook. f., Fl. Br. Ind. 4: 579, in syn. 1885 [not *P. micrantha* Schau., 1847].
Gumira thwaitesii (Clarke) Kuntze, Rev. Gen. Pl. 2 (2): 508. 1891.—*G. thwaitesii* Kuntze apud Durand & Jacks., Ind. Kew. Suppl. 1, imp. 1, 190, in syn. 1902.

A straggling or scrambling shrub, 1–2 m tall, or a small tree to 6.5 m tall, aromatic when bruised, the young parts densely pubescent; leaves decussate-opposite, strongly scented; petioles 0.6–1.8 cm long, pubescent; leaf-blades oval or ovate, 5–7.5 cm long, 3.5–3.7 cm wide, thin-membranous, apically acute or subacuminate, marginally entire (or rarely remotely crenate or serrate-dentate on the upper part), basally cuneately subacute or rounded, finely puberulent above, densely soft-pubescent or velvety with violet-pink hairs beneath; secondaries about 5 pairs; inflorescence terminal, subthyrsoid-paniculate, the cymes small, about 3.5 cm long and 2.5 cm wide, rounded, much-branched, rather dense, short-pubescent throughout; bractlets small, linear, about 4 mm long, pubescent, persistent; pedicels short, pubescent; calyx campanulate, 1.5–2 mm long, externally minutely appressed-pubescent, its rim regularly and rather deeply 5-lobed, the lobes lanceolate, subequal, apically acute; corolla pale greenish-yellow or yellowish to dull greenish, darker within, becoming purple-brown in age, 3–4 mm long, hairy in the throat, the lobes apically truncate; fruit drupaceous, at first green, later orange, globose or subglobose, 4–8 mm long and wide, smooth.

D i s t r. This is apparently an endemic species of the moist and intermediate regions to 4000 ft alt. in Ceylon, the typical form quite rare.

V e r n. Mulla (S).

S p e c i m e n s E x a m i n e d. NUWARA ELIYA DISTRICT: Maturata, Aug. 1853, determined as *P. micrantha, s. coll. C.P. 2541* in part (MOL-DENKE cotype, PDA cotype); near Hanguranketa, Sept. 1857, determined as *P. micrantha, s. coll. C.P. 2541* in part (PDA cotype). BADULLA DIS-TRICT: Wilson's Bungalow, Sept. 1890, leaves pubescent beneath, strongly scented, *s. coll. s.n.* (PDA).

f. **glabrescens** Moldenke, Phytologia 28: 102. 1974. Type: *s. coll. s.n.* from Eluwana Kande, Lagalla, Ceylon (PDA).

This form differs from the typical form of the species chiefly in having its mature leaf-blades glabrescent to completely glabrous on both surfaces. It may be distinguished from the similar *P. latifolia* var. *cuneata* by its definitely paniculate many-flowered inflorescences and its marginally serrate leaf-blades. The form apparently inhabits woodlands and appears to be endemic and rare.

V e r n. None reported.

S p e c i m e n s E x a m i n e d. KANDY DISTRICT: occasional in wood-land 4 miles east of Madugoda, 2500 ft alt., 19 Jan. 1974, trees 20 ft tall, only in leaf now, *H.N. & A.L. Moldenke, Jayasuriya, & Sumithraarachchi 28190* (MOLDENKE, PDA, US). MATALE DISTRICT: Eluwana Kande, Lagalla, Sept. 1893, flowers greenish-yellow, leaves glabrous on both sides, determin-ed as *P. integrifolia, s. coll. s.n.* (PDA holotype); shrub, Moragalla, off the Naula to Elahera road, 250 m alt., 5 Oct. 1971, determined as *P. serratifolia, Jayasuriya 301* (PDA, US).

8. **Premna tomentosa** Willd. in L., Sp. pl., ed. 4, 3: 314. 1800 [not *P. tomentosa* Blanco, 1918, nor F.-Vill., 1883, nor Kurz, 1906, nor Miq., 1885, nor Rottl., 1803] f. **tomentosa.** Moon, Cat. 1: 45. 1824; Schau. in A. DC., Prod. 11: 634–635. 1847; Thw., Enum. Pl. Zeyl., imp. 1, 243. 1861; Clarke in Hook. f., Fl. Br. Ind. 4: 576. 1885; Trimen, Cat. 68. 1885; Watt, Dict. Econ. Prod. India 4 (1): 338. 1892; Trimen, Handb. Fl. Ceylon 3: 352. 1895; Gamble, Man. Indian Timb., ed. 2, 536. 1902; Brandis, Indian Trees 510. 1906; Willis, Cat. 69. 1911; Heyne, Nutt. Pl. Ned. Ind., ed. 1, 4: 111. 1917; H.J. Lam, Verbenac. Malay. Arch. 156–157. 1919; Abeywick., Ceylon J. Sci., Biol. Sci. 2: 217. 1959; Petelot, Pl. Méd. Cambod. Laos Vietnam 2: 248. 1963; Vivekanan-dan, Ceyl. Forester, ser. 2, 7: 108. 1966; Burkill, Dict. Econ. Prod. Malay Penins. 2: 1837 & 1839. 1966; Gunawardena, Gen. Sp. Pl. Zeyl. 147. 1968; Fonseka & Vinasithamby, Prov. List Local Names Fl. Pl. Ceylon 10 & 45. 1971; Vivekanandan, Ceylon Forester, ser. 2, 11: 109, 133, 144, & 148. 1974. Type: *Sonnerat s.n.* from India (B).

Cornutia corymbosa Lam., Enc. 1: 54–55. 1783 [not *C. corymbosa* Burm. f., 1768].

Premna flavescens A.L. Juss., Ann. Mus. Natl. Hist. Nat. 7: 77. 1806 [not
   P. flavescens Buch., 1845, nor Buch.-Ham., 1894, nor Hamlit., 1831].
Premna lanata Steud., Nom. Bot., ed. 1, 137. 1821.
Premna villosa Moon, Cat. 1: 45. 1824 [not *P. villosa*. Clarke, 1885].
Callicarpa lanata Lam. ex Steud., Nom. Bot., ed. 2, 1: 257. 1840 [not *C.
   lanata* Gamble, 1889, nor W. Griff., 1885, nor Hosseus, 1912, nor L.,
   1769, nor H.J. Lam, 1940, nor "L. sensu Gamble", 1971, nor Ridl., 1966,
   nor Roxb., 1839, nor Schau., 1870, nor Vahl, 1847, nor Wall., 1856, nor
   Walp., 1921, nor Willd., 1826, nor Zipp., 1841].
Premnus tomentosus Willd. apud Hassk., Cat. Pl. Hort. Bot. Bogor. Cult. Alt.
   134. 1844.
Premna flavida Miq., Fl. Bat. Suppl. 1: 243 & 570. 1860.

   Shrub to small or moderately sized tree, 4–16 m tall, often with many 1-
metre boles; trunk often crooked, basally fluted, often 25–40 cm in diameter
at breast height, often to 60 cm in girth, convoluted; crown broad; bark grey
or yellowish to light-brown or pale-rusty, much like that of teak, longitudinally fissured or striate and shaggy, shredding off in longitudinal flakes, fibrous;
wood smooth, moderately hard, close- and even-grained, seasoning and polishing well; branches and branchlets slender, obtusely tetragonal, greyish,
more or less densely brownish-puberulent, less so or even obscurely so in age,
the upper (or sometimes nearly all) branches often alternate, the youngest portions and the slender, tetragonal twigs very densely tomentose with yellowish
or fulvous branched hairs; nodes somewhat ampliate, usually not annulate;
principal internodes 0.5–3 cm long or even more abbreviated; leaves decussate-opposite or approximate, aromatic, deciduous, usually not blackening in
drying; petioles rather slender, 0.5–12 cm long, deeply canaliculate above,
densely tomentose with yellowish or fulvous hairs, becoming dark-brown in
age, not basally ampliate; leaf-blades firmly chartaceous to subcoriaceous [or
membranous in var. *pierreana* Dop], rather bright- or yellow-green on both
surfaces, usually rather shiny above, ovate or ovate-orbicular to ovate-oblong,
2.7–35 cm long, 2.6–22 cm wide, apically acute to attenuate or acuminate-
caudate, marginally entire (or serrate on young plants), basally acute or obtuse to rounded and cordate to subtruncate, very densely stellate-tomentose
on both surfaces when young, somewhat rugose and less tomentose or even
merely strigillose or even subglabrate on the lamina above and more or less
stellate-tomentose on the midrib and larger venation above when mature,
persistently very densely stellate-tomentose beneath with yellowish or fulvous
hairs; midrib slender or comparatively stout, flattened or subprominulous
above and usually densely tomentose, rounded-prominent beneath; secondaries slender, 5–7 per side, ascending, mostly rather straight, not much arcuate
except at the margins, subprominulent to more usually subimpressed above,
often more or less tomentose (especially toward the midrib), joined in loops

marginally; tertiaries numerous, rather straight and parallel, issuing at right angles to the secondaries and connecting them; inflorescence mostly terminal, often a pair also in the uppermost leaf-axils; cymes ovate, corymbose, 3–38 cm long, 2–6.5 cm wide, abundantly brachiate, many-flowered, dense, subsessile to long-pedunculate, the ultimate branches short, densely stellate-tomentose; peduncles slender, tetragonal, flattened, 1.5–11 cm long, often much abbreviated, densely stellate-tomentose; cyme-branches, bracts, bractlets, prophylla, and pedicels densely tomentose, the bracts and bractlets, when present, elliptic, subfoliaceous, of various sizes, stipitate, the prophylla rather numerous, linear or setaceous, about 1 mm long, the pedicels 0.5–1 mm long; flowers nearly 12 mm wide in full anthesis, fragrant, produced with the young leaves; calyx campanulate, 2.5–4 mm long, often subsessile, externally stellate-tomentose, the rim obtusely 5-dentate or 5-lobed, the lobes subequal; corolla white or greenish to greenish-yellow or yellow, slightly bilabiate, the tube 3–4 mm long, hairy in the throat, stellate-hairy and glandular-punctate externally, the central lower lobe largest, about 3 mm long, apically acute, with a yellow line, villous, the lateral lobes obtuse, the upper lobe retuse; stamens 1.5–2 mm long, slightly exserted; style-branches minute, 0.25–0.5 mm long; ovary apically densely short-hairy and glandulose; fruiting-calyx shallowly cupuliform or subpatelliform, 4–6 mm wide, externally more or less stellate-tomentose, the rim irregularly scalloped or lobed; fruit drupaceous, subglobose or broadly ovoid, 3–6 mm long and wide, deciduously stellate-hairy to slightly pulverulent or glabrate, at first green, eventually purple or blackish-violet to black; pyrenes osseous, rugose and strongly tuberculate, 4-celled and 4-seeded or, by abortion, 1–3 seeded.

D i s t r. A widespread species found from Nepal, India, and Ceylon, through Burma, Thailand, Indo-China, and Malaya, to the Philippines and Indonesia; sometimes cultivated.

E c o l. In Ceylon Thwaites reports it common to 3000 ft alt., while Trimen says that it is common in the low country and up to 4000 ft altitude.

U s e s. The wood is said to be useful for carving, turnery, fancy-work, furniture, weavers' shuttles, house-building, and fuel. The leaves contain limonene, caryophyllene, diterpene, and sesquiterpene, as well as a sesquiterpene alcohol. Medicinally they are reputed to have diuretic properties if the juice is taken internally, while externally it is applied in the treatment of dropsy. The aromatic leaves are also used as dinner plates in India, where the wood is employed to make native combs. The trees are often lopped to furnish a rather poor grade fodder for cattle. In Malaya root and leaf decoctions are employed immediately after childbirth and as a medicinal bath; the root decoction is also used to treat stomach-ache. In Indonesia an extract of the inner bark is used to cure diarrhoea and the powdered dry leaves are placed on animal wounds to aid their healing.

V e r n. Boo-sairou, Boo-sairoo-gass, Boo seru, Bu-séru (S); Kolkutti, Kollay-cottaynellay, Koluk-kutti, Loluto kutti, Mulla-mullai, Munnai, Podanganari (T); more than 35 other names are listed from other parts of its range.

N o t e s. The pollen is described by Nair & Rehman in Bull. Bot. Gard. Lucknow 76: 20 (1962) and the wood anatomy by Gamble (1902) and Janssonius (Mikrogr. Holz. Java 4: 754–802. 1926; Key Javan Woods 54 & 213. 1952).

Premna tomentosa is often host to *Loranthus tomentosus*, a mistletoe, and to the fungus, *Meliola callicarpae* Sydow.

Premna tomentosa is very closely related to the very similar *P. odorata* Blume which differs chiefly in its truncate, finely pubescent, not tomentose, calyx. Clark's *P. tomentosa* var. *detergibilis*, with simple (not stellate) hairs, is a synonym of *P. foetida* Reinw., while *P. tomentosa* f. *crenulata* Koord. & Val. is now known as *P. odorata* f. *crenulata* (Koord. & Val.) Moldenke. *Premna odorata*, sometimes listed as occurring in Ceylon, does not occur there.

S p e c i m e n s E x a m i n e d. MANNAR DISTRICT: common in dry scrub, Madhu, on the road to Mannar, low altitude, 28 May 1973, tree 5 m tall with many boles, bark fissured, pale-rusty, resembling that of teak, flowers white, fruit green, *Kostermans 24870* (AAU, US). KURUNEGALA DISTRICT: scattered at edge of jungle forest, Panirendawa, low altitude, 25 Jan. 1974, trees about 25 ft tall, *H.N. & A.L. Moldenke & Jayasuriya 28255* (US). PUTTALAM DISTRICT: scattered at edge of jungle forest, Wanniyagama, low altitude, 25 January 1974, trees about 25 ft tall, *H.N. & A.L. Moldenke & Jayasuriya 28241* (AAU, CAI, LL, PDA, US). ANU-RADHAPURA DISTRICT: common in open along wadies, Wilpattu, 200 ft alt., rainfall 60 inches, monkeys come for the striped bark, "mulla mullai", determined as *P. procumbens, Hoffman & Worthington 7148* (K); occasional in jungle forest, Kali Willu, Wilpattu National Park, low altitude, 24 Jan. 1974, trees about 20 ft tall, *H.N. & A.L. Moldenke & Jayasuriya 28231* (AAU, ARIZ, CAI, KARACHI, LL, PDA, US); in open forest scrub on sand in Plot W. 10 at Kali Willu, Wilpattu National Park, 11 Sept. 1968, trees 6–8 m tall, now in flower, collected as voucher for ecological observations, *Mueller-Dombois & Balakrishnan 68091109* (LL, PDA, US); in dry zone, Natchaduwa spill, 340 ft alt., 1 Aug. 1951, *Worthington 5383* (PDA). PO-LONNARUWA DISTRICT: Polannaruwa Sacred Area, 61 m alt. 26 Aug. 1969, *Dittus WD. 69082602* (US); in dry zone forest near irrigation tank, 60 m alt., Polonnaruwa Sacred Area, 9 Aug. 1969, a small tree, bark fibrous, yellowish, *Hladik 917* (PDA, US), *929* (US); common tree, Section 4A, Polonnaruwa Sacred Area, 61 m alt., 26 May 1969, in flower, *Ripley 133* (PDA, US), common small tree in open unshaded habitat, sandy soil, 22 Oct. 1968, *240* (PDA, US), same locality, 31 Jan. 1969, short tree, sterile, collected as voucher for primate studies, *260* (PDA, US). KANDY DISTRICT: Hantana, Peradeniya, drupe-stone 4-celled, 4-seeded, *Gardner s.n.* [*C.P. 747* in part] (BO, BR, PDA, US); low trees at edge of woods 4 miles east of Hunnasgiriya at milepost 24/14, 1700 ft alt., 19 Jan. 1974, only in leaf, *H.N. & A.L. Moldenke, Jayasuriya, & Sumithraarachchi 28186* (AAU, ARIZ, CAI, KARACHI, LL, MO, PDA, US); scattered at edge of forest 39 miles east of Kandy on the Mahiyangana road, 1000 ft alt., 19 Jan. 1974, trees about 20 ft tall, *H.N. & A.L. Moldenke, Jayasuriya & Sumithraarachchi 28193* (AAU, ARIZ, CAI, KARACHI, LL, MO, PDA, US); Kahawandala, Kadugannawa, 1000 ft alt., 12 April 1941, "boo seru", "loluto kutti", *Worthington 1106* (K). MATALE DISTRICT: on forested hills about 8 miles directly east-southeast of Dambulla, hills above the Mahaweli anicut, 900 ft alt., 11 Oct. 1974, small tree about 8 m tall, 20 cm in diameter at breast height, trunk convoluted, corolla white, slightly zygomorphic, lower petal with a yellow line, *Davidse 7412* (LL, US); near Dambulla, low altitude, 29 May 1971, tree 6 m tall, bark fissured, strips 5 mm wide, 3 mm thick, grey, living bark 2 mm thick, straw-colour, flowers white, *Kostermans 24290* (PDA,US); scattered at edge of forest, Madawela, 600 ft alt., 23 Jan. 1974, trees about 20 ft tall, in leaf only, *H.N. & A.L. Moldenke & Jayasuriya 28209* (LL, PDA, US); scattered trees on ascent to temple in broken forest, Dambulla rock, 800 ft alt., 23 Jan. 1974, trees about 30 ft tall, *H.N. & A.L. Moldenke & Jayasuriya 28221* (AAU, ARIZ, CAI, KARACHI, LL, MO, PDA, US); in dry disturbed site at edge of thicket, some limestone outcrops, at milepost 34/4 on the road from Naula to Dambulla, 14 July 1973, tree-shrub about 4–5 m tall, stems up to 8 cm in diameter at breast height, bark grey, slightly striate, fruit purple, *Nowicke, Fosberg, & Jayasuriya 324* (NY, PDA, US); one tree in more or less cultivated field at base of hill, dry forest, good understory, lots of granitic boulders, east slope of Lenadora hill on the road from Dambulla to Nalanda, at milepost 38/9, 15 July 1973, tree 4 m tall, immature fruit green, *Nowicke & Jayasuriya 380* (NY, PDA, US); jungle near Dambulla, 16 May 1931, flowers nearly 1/2 inch wide, *Simpson 8110* (PDA); Deltota, July 1837, *s. coll. C.P. 747* in part (PDA, US); Matale, *s. coll. C.P. 747* in part (PDA). KEGALLE DISTRICT: Ambepussa Farm, 14 Dec. 1926, small tree, leaves aromatic, fruit black, *Alston 1326* (PDA). BADULLA DISTRICT: scrubby jungle with fallen leaves, dry zone, Ella, 2200 ft alt., 1 Aug. 1947, "bu seru", *Worthington 2939* (K). MONERAGALA DISTRICT: Bibile, 24 Oct. 1925, leaves thin, *J.M. Silva s.n.* (PDA); roadside in secondary forest at milepost 145 on the Wellawaya to Monaragala road, 4 Oct. 1973, tree 7 m tall, *Waas 71* (NY, US). AMPARAI DISTRICT: rare in undergrowth at edge of scrubby forest, 8 miles west of Pottuvil, 26 Nov. 1970, large shrub, aromatic, flowers greenish, *Fosberg & Sachet 52995* (LL); member of alluvial jungle, Lahugala, one mile west of village at highway, 25 July 1967, tree 4 m tall, broad crown, collected as voucher for ecological observations, *Mueller-Dombois & Coma-*

nor 67072559 (PDA, US). BATTICALOA DISTRICT: on undulating sandy-gravelly terrain along the road from Tumpalachola to Unichchai, Batticaloa area, 27 July 1967, tree 5 m tall, with broad crown, very common, may be one of the important deciduous species, foliage yellow-green, *Mueller-Dombois & Comanor 67072701* (PDA, US). TRINCOMALEE DISTRICT: common trees, Soodaikuddai to Foul Point, 7 April 1974, bark brown, flowers white, *Sumithraarachchi & Jayasuriya DBS. 229* (LACROSSE, US); in dry zone, rainfall 65 inches, Trincomalee, Southampton hill, 50 ft alt., 26 June 1940, "bu-seru", *Worthington 1001* (K); in dry zone, Trincomalee, 50 ft alt., 30 March 1951, *Worthington 5184* (K). HAMBANTOTA DISTRICT: frequent in forest scrub, sandy soil, Plot R. 16, near Kumbukkan Oya, 8 m alt., 24 Jan. 1968, tree 8 m tall, bark brown, shaggy, leaves conspicuous, determined as *Clerodendrum* sp., *Comanor 1030* (AAU, NY, PDA, US); in upper alluvial habitat, Plot R. 19, Block I, at north to south boundary, Ruhuna National Park, 20 Oct. 1968, tree 7 m tall, not common here, light brown bark, leaves very pubescent, *Cooray 68102004R* (LL); in forest, Talgasmankada, Ruhuna National Park, below 5 m alt., 14 Nov. 1977, tree 8 m tall with white flowers, *Huber 623* (US).

f. **jejuna** Moldenke, Phytologia 41: 105. 1978. Type: *Comanor 722* from Matale District, Ceylon (NY).

This form differs from the typical form of the species in having the lower surface of the mature leaves merely sparsely stellate-tomentellous, rather than very densely so. It has hitherto been regarded as representing Clarke's var. *detergibilis*, which he described merely as 'Mature leaves with most of the wool rubbed off". But examination of the type collection of his variety shows plainly that the hairs on the under surface of the leaf-blades are simple rather than stellate-branched. His name falls into the synonymy of *P. foetida* Reinw.

V e r n. None reported.

S p e c i m e n s E x a m i n e d. MATALE DISTRICT: at edge of patch of roadside forest on the Matale to Dambulla road before milepost 44/A9, 215 m alt., 12 Jan. 1968, tree 6 m tall, *Comanor 722* (NY holotype, PDA isotype, US isotype). HAMBANTOTA DISTRICT: in forest scrub on sandy loam near Katagamuwa Tank road, Block I, at north to south boundary. Ruhuna National Park, 26 Feb. 1968, very tall tree, suckers at base eaten by deer, voucher collected for ecological observations, *Mueller-Dombois & Cooray 68022605* (PDA, US); at end of jeep trail parking spot, alluvial bottomland habitat, Rugamtota, Block I, Ruhuna National Park, 6 Dec. 1967, tree 8 m tall, crown reaching down to 1 m, voucher collected for ecological observations, *Muller-Dombois & Cooray 67120611* (PDA, US).

9. Premna obtusifolia R. Br., Prod. Fl. Nov. Holl. 1: 512. 1810; Hermann,

Mus. Zeyl., ed. 1, 14. 1717; Burm., Thes. Zeyl. 209. 1737; L., Fl. Zeyl., imp.
1, 195. 1747; Thw., Enum. Pl. Zeyl. 242. 1839; Schau. in A. DC., Prod. 11:
632. 1847; Trimen, Cat. 68. 1885; Clarke in Hook. f., Fl. Br. Ind. 4: 574. 1885;
Trimen, Handb. Fl. Ceylon 3: 352. 1895; Brandis, Indian Trees 510. 1906;
Willis, Cat. 69. 1911; Merr., Ind. Rumph. Herb. Amboin. 450–451. 1917; H.
J. Lam, Verbenac. Malay. Arch. 140–147. 1919; Fosberg, Taxon 2: 88–89.
1953; Petelot, Pl. Méd. Cambod. Laos Vietnam 2: 247 (1954) and 4: 27 & seq.
1954; Cooke, Fl. Pres. Bombay, ed. 2, 1: 506–507. 1958; Abeywick., Ceylon J.
Sci., Biol. Sci. 2: 217. 1959; Prain, Bengal Pl. 2: 620. 1963; Burkill, Dict. Econ.
Prod. Malay Penins. 2: 1838. 1966; Gunawardena, Gen. Sp. Pl. Zeyl. 147.
1968; Fonseka & Vinasithamby, Prov. List Local Names Fl. Pl. Ceylon 21, 57,
84 & 99. 1971; Gamble, Man. Indian Timb., ed. 2, 535. 1972. Type: Specimen
from "littora Novae Hollandiae intra tropicum tam orientalia quam septen-
trionalia", probably collected by Robert Brown (BM).

Sambucus zeylanica odorata aromatica Burm., Thes. Zeyl. 209. 1737.
Gumira litorea Rumpf, Herb. Amboin. 3: 209, pl. 134. 1743.—*G. littorea*
Rumpf apud Hassk., Cat. Pl. Hort. Bot. Bogor. Cult. Alt. 135. 1844.
Gumira silvestris Rumpf, Herb. Amboin. 3: 209, pl. 134. 1743.
Cornutioides L., Fl. Zeyl., imp. 1, 195. 1747.
Cornutia corymbosa Burm. f., Fl. Ind. 132, pl. 41, fig. 1. 1768 [not *C. corym-
bosa* Lam., 1791].—*C. corymbosa* Burm. apud Schau. in A. DC., Prod. 11:
682, in syn. 1847.
Premna integrifolia L., Mant. imp. 1, 2: 252–253 [nom. superfl.]. 1771 [not
P. integrifolia Blanco, 1942, nor Gamble, 1922, nor H.J. Lam, 1931, nor
Willd., 1803].—*P. integrifolia* Roxb. ex Voigt, Hort. Suburb. Calc. 465, in
syn. 1845.—*P. integrifolia* Blume apud Valet., Bull. Dep. Agric. Indes
Néerl. 10: 51. 1907.—*P. integrifolia* Auct. ex E.D. Merr., Interpret. Rum-
ph. Herb. Amboin. 450, in syn. 1917.—*Prenma integrifolia* L. ex A. Chev.,
Cat. Pl. Jard. Bot. Saigon 36, sphalm. 1919.—*Premna integrifolia* Forbes
& Hemsl. ex Moldenke, Prelim. Alph. List Invalid Names 37, in syn. 1942.
—*Premna integrifolia* sensu Forbes & Hemsl. ex Li, Woody Fl. Taiwan 830,
in syn. 1963.—*Premna integrifolia* sensu Dunn & Fletcher ex Moldenke,
Résumé Suppl. 15: 22, in syn. 1967.—*Premna integrifolia* L. f. ex Mold-
enke, Résumé Suppl. 15: 22, in syn. 1967.—*Premna intergifolia* L. ex Misra,
Tewari, & Misra, Biol. Abstr. 49: 230, sphalm. 1968.—*Premnia integrifolia*
L. ex Uphof, Dict. Econ. Pl., ed. 2, 263, sphalm. 1968.—*Premna integre-
folia* L. ex Inamdar & Patel, Indian Forester 97: 328, sphalm. 1968.—
Primna integrifolia L. ex Moldenke, Fifth Summ. 2: 612, in syn. 1971.
Premna corymbosa (Burm. f.) Rottl. & Willd., Ges. Naturf. Freunde Berlin
neue Schriften ser. 2, 4: 187 & 188. 1803.—*P. corymbosa* Rottl. & Willd.
apud Schau. in A. DC., Prod. 11: 632, in syn. 1847.—*P. corymbosa* (Burm.
f.) Miq., Fl. Ind. Bat. 2: 895. 1856.—*P. corymbosa* Roth & Wendl. ex Kun-

tze, Rev. Gen. Pl. 2 (2): 507, in syn. 1891.—*P. corymbosa* Rottl. ex Willis, Cat. 69. 1911.— *P. corymbosa* Miq. ex Hall. f., Meded. Rijks-herb. 37: 36, in syn. 1918.—*P. corymbosa* (Burm. f.) Roth & Willd. ex Kanjilal *et al.*, Fl. Assam 473. 1939.—*P. corymbosa* Willd. ex Moldenke, Alph. List Invalid Names suppl. 1: 19, in syn. 1947.—*P. corymbosa* (Burm. f.) Rottb. & Willd. ex Gillett, Numb. Check-list Trees Kenya 47, sphalm. 1970.

Premna serratifolia Willd., Ges. Naturf. Freunde Berlin Neue Schriften ser. 2, 4: 188. 1803 [not *P. serratifolia* Blanco, 1843, nor L., 1771, nor Wall., 1847].
—*P. serratifolia* Beddome apud Talbot, Syst. List Trees Shrubs Bombay 160, in syn. 1894.—*P. serratifolia* Lam. ex Moldenke, Résumé 339, in syn. 1959.

Premna media R. Br., Prod. Fl. Nov. Holl. 1: 512. 1810.

Premna ovata R. Br., Prod. Fl. Nov. Holl. 1: 512. 1810.

Citharexylum paniculatum Poir. in Lam., Tabl. Enc. 3: 95. 1823 [not *C. paniculatum* Gaertn., 1810, nor Poepp., 1940].

Premna ovalifolia Wall., Num. List [48], no. 1782, hynonym. 1829.

Premna cordifolia Beddome ex Clarke in Hook. f., Fl. Br. Ind. 4: 572, in syn. 1885; Moldenke, Fifth Summ. 2: 606, in syn. 1971 [not *P. cordifolia* Brand, 1829, nor J. Grah., 1829, nor Roxb., 1814, nor Thw., 1895, nor wall., 1830].
—*P. cordifolia* Wight ex Clarke in Hook. f., Fl. Br. Ind. 4: 572, in syn. 1885; Gamble, Fl. Pres. Madras 6: 1095, in syn. 1924.—*P. cordifolia* Dalz. & Gibs. ex Talbot, Syst. List Trees Shrubs Bombay 166, in syn. 1894.— *P. cordifolia* L. ex Jacks., Index Linn. Herb. 121. 1912.—*P. cordifolia* Dalz., in herb.

Premna densiflora Wall., Num. List [48], no. 1773, hyponym. 1829.

Premna sambucina Wall., Num. List [48], no. 1775, hyponym. 1829.

Premna doniana Hamilton ex Wall., Num. List 82, in syn. 1831.

Premna scandens Bojer, Hort. Maurit., imp. 1, 257. 1837 [not *P. scandens* Roxb., 1814].

Viburnum chinense Hook. & Arn., Bot. Beech. Voy. 190. 1841 [not *V. chinense* Zeyh., 1821].

Gumira integrifolia Hassk., Cat. Pl. Hort. Bot. Bogor. Cult. Alt. 135. 1844.
—*G. integrifolia* (L.) Hassk. apud Kuntze, Rev. Gen. Pl. 2 (2): 507. 1891.

Premna hircina Buch. ex Voigt, Hort. Suburb. Calc. 465. 1845.—*P. hircina* Wall. ex Moldenke, Fifth Summ. 2: 607, in syn. 1971.

Premna abbreviata Miq., Fl. Ind. Bat. 2: 892. 1856.

Premna laevigata Miq., Fl. Ind. Bat. 2: 895. 1856.

Premna opulifolia Miq., Fl. Ind. Bat. 2: 898. 1856.

Premna glycycocca F. Muell., Fragm. 3: 36. 1862.

Premna subcordata Turcz., Bull. Soc. Imp. Naturalistes Moscou 36 (2): 216. 1863 [not *P. subcordata* Nakai, 1926].

Premna truncata Turcz., Bull. Soc. Imp. Naturalistes Moscou 36 (2): 215. 1863.

Gumira corymbosa (Roth & Wendl.) Kuntze, Rev. Gen. Pl. 2 (2): 507. 1891.
—*G. corymbosa* Kuntze apud Durand & Jacks., Ind. Kew. Suppl. 1, imp.
1, 190, in syn. 1902.
Gumira truncata (Turcz.) Kuntze, Rev. Gen. Pl. 2 (2): 507. 1891.—*G. trun-
cata* Kuntze apud Durand & Jacks., Ind. Kew. Suppl. 1, imp. 1, 190, in syn.
1902.
Premna latifolia Dalz. & Gibs. ex Talbot, Syst. List Trees Shrubs Bombay
160, in syn. 1894 [not *P. latifolia* Roxb., 1814, nor Thw., 1885, nor Wall.,
1940, nor Wight, 1885].
Premna obtusifolia Guppy ex Schum. & Lauterb., Fl. Deutsch. Schutzgeb.
Südsee 523, in syn. 1900.—*P. obtusifolia* Sasaki apud Masam., Sci. Rep.
Kanazawa Univ. Biol. 4: 47, in syn. 1955.—*Prema obtusifolia* Fosberg,
Pac. Sci. Assoc. Stand. Comm. Pac. Bot. Sympos. Plan. Util. Lowl. Trop.
For. 168, sphalm. 1973.
Premna integrifolia subsp. *truncatolabium* H.J. Lam, Verbenac. Malay. Arch.
142. 1919.
Premna lasioneura Zipp. ex H.J. Lam, Verbenac. Malay. Arch. 145, in syn.
1919.
Premna integrifolia f. *sambucina* H.J. Lam in H.J. Lam & Bakh., Bull. Jard.
Bot. Buitenzorg, ser. 3, 3: 43. 1921.
Premna foetida Riv. ex H.J. Lam in Diels, Bot. Jahrb. Syst. 59: 26, in syn.
1924 [not *P. foetida* Reinw., 1826].
Premna integrifolia var. *obtusifolia* (R. Br.) P'ei, Mem. Sci. Soc. China 1 (3):
75. 1932.—*P. integrifolia* var. *obtusifolia* P'ei apud Tingle, Check List
Hong Kong Pl. 38. 1967.
Premna corymbosa var. *obtusifolia* (P'ei) Fletcher, Notes Roy. Bot. Gard.
Edinburgh 19: 178. 1936.—*P. corymbosa* var. *obtusifolia* (R. Br.) Fletcher,
Bull. Misc. Inform. 1938: 419. 1938.—*P. corymbosa* var. *obtusifolia* Flet-
cher apud Hatus., Mem. S. Industr. Sci. Inst. Kagashima Univ. 3: 31. 1962.
—*Premna corymbosa* var. *obtusifolia* (R. Br.) Kanjilal *et al.*, Fl. Assam
473. 1939.—*Premns corymbosa* var. *obtusifolia* (R. Br.) Fletcher ex Mold-
enke, Résumé Suppl. 3: 34, in syn. 1962.
Premna corymbosa var. *sambucina* (Wall.) Moldenke, Known Geogr. Distrib.
Verbenac., ed. 1, 68, 78, & 98. 1942.
Premna cordifolia var. *obtusifolia* (R. Br.) Fletcher ex Moldenke, Résumé 337,
in syn. 1959.
Sambucus madagascariensis Bojer, in herb.
Premna integrifolia var. *abbreviata* H.J. Lam, in herb.
Premna lucida Miq., in herb.

Shrub or tree, to 8 m tall, rarely scandent or a prostrate creeper (in var.
minor Ridl.); trunk to 10 cm in diameter at breast height; wood with very large
medullary rays; branches and branchlets medium-slender or slender, brown

or brownish, subterete or obtusely tetragonal, rather sparsely lenticellate, densely short-pubescent (in var. *pubescens* Moldenke) or obscurely appressed-puberulent, often glabrescent in age, medullose; twigs more slender, darker brown in drying, usually more densely appressed-puberulent; nodes annullate; principal internodes 1–6 cm long; leaf-scars usually prominent and corky; leaves decussate-opposite, deciduous; petioles slender or very slender, 4–14 mm long [or longer in var. *gaudichaudii* (Schau.) Moldenke], canaliculate above, varying from densely short-pubescent (in var. *pubescens*) or more or less appressed-puberulent to glabrate, slightly ampliate at the base; leaf-blades dull (or shiny in var. *madagascariensis* Moldenke), usually chartaceous or varying to firmly membranous, rather uniformly dark green on both surfaces or somewhat lighter beneath, varying from elliptic [elliptic and narrowed at both ends in var. *angustior* (Clarke) Moldenke] or oblong-elliptic to oblong or even subobovate, rarely subrotund (or broadly ovate in var. *gaudichaudii*), 2.5–8.5 cm long (to 12 cm or more long in var. *gaudichaudii*), 2–7.2 cm wide, varying from obtuse to short-acuminate or shortly mucronate apically, sometimes abruptly acute (or tapering in var. *angustior*), usually entire marginally, sometimes crenate or subserrate to coarsely serrate above the middle [in f. *serratifolia* (L.) Moldenke], often slightly revolute throughout in drying, varying from acute (or tapering-subacuminate in var. *angustior*) to obtuse, rounded, or even subcordate basally (cordate in var. *gaudichaudii*), more or less obscurely pulverulent or glabrate above except along the appressed-pilose midrib and larger veins (or softly velutinous throughout in var. *velutina* Benth.), usually glabrate or more or less obscurely pulverulent beneath, sometimes more or less densely pubescent along the midrib and larger veins and at their base or barbellate in the axils (softly velutinous throughout in var. *velutina*); midrib slender, flat or slightly prominulous above, prominent to the apex beneath but diminishing in size as the apex is approached; secondaries very slender, 3–5 per side, irregular, distant, usually not much arcuate except marginally, flat or subprominulous above, prominulous beneath, rather indistinctly joined in many loops marginally; vein and veinlet reticulation abundant, fine, only the larger portions subprominulous above, the remainder obscure or indiscernible, flat beneath or occasionally the tertiaries subprominulous (or vein and veinlets conspicuous and mostly prominulous on both surfaces in var. *madagascariensis*); inflorescence terminal, paniculate, 4–7 cm long, mostly 4–5 cm wide (or much smaller in var. *angustior*), many-branched with loosely spreading branches, many-flowered, rather densely appressed-puberulent (or pubescent in var. *pubescens*) throughout; peduncles slender, 2–2.5 cm long, mostly puberulent (or pubescent in var. *pubescens*); bracts often present, foliaceous, few, a pair subtending the lowest pair of inflorescence-branches, to 1.5 cm long and 7 mm wide; bractlets and prophylla always present, subtending each branch of the panicle, linear or linear-subulate to setaceous, 1–3 mm long, appressed-puberulent or pubescent; flowers small, rather unpleasantly aromatic;

calyx campanulate, about 2.6 mm long and 2.8 mm wide, densely appressed-puberulent and verruculose, its rim usually 2-lipped, the axial lip about 0.7 mm long and 2.2 mm wide, very indistinctly 3-toothed apically or almost rounded, the abaxial lip conspicuously 2-lobed with each lobe triangular, apically acute, about 0.5 mm long and 0.6 mm wide basally; corolla hypocrateriform, zygomorphic, pale yellowish-white to pale greenish-white or greenish, externally glabrate, the tube broadly cylindric, straight, about 3.4 mm long on the abaxial and 4.1 mm long on the axial side, about 2.8 mm wide, densely tomentose among the stamens and bearded in the throat within, the axial lip 1-lobed, about 1.5 mm long and 1.4 mm wide, apically rounded or obscurely emarginate, the abaxial lip 3-lobed, the largest lobe slightly concave, about 1.5 mm long and 2 mm wide, the two adjacent lobes each about 1.3 mm long and 1.5 mm wide, not concave, all the lobes elliptic-lingulate and apically rounded; stamens 4, didynamous, slightly exserted from the corolla-limb, the upper pair inserted about 2 mm and the lower pair about 1.8 mm above the base of the corolla-tube; filaments filiform, ampliate and pilose basally, about 1.8 mm long; anthers ovate, about 0.6 mm long and 0.3 mm wide, dorsifixed at about the middle, 2-celled, the thecae slightly divergent; pistil slightly exserted; style capillary, about 4.8 mm long, glabrous; stigma 2-lobed, the lobes equal and blunt; ovary subglobose, about 1 mm long and wide, glabrous, obscurely 4-lobed and umbilicate apically, incompletely 4-celled, 4-ovulate; fruiting-calyx very shallowly cupuliform or (usually) patelliform, 3–3.5 mm wide, 1–2 mm long, externally obscurely pulverulent or subglabrate, the rim rather irregularly 4-lobed; fruit drupaceous, subglobose, about 4 mm long and wide, pulverulent or glabrate.

D i s t r. This species in its typical form (var. *obtusifolia*) is found from Bangladesh to Thailand and southern China, westward to the Seychelles, Mauritius, Madagascar, and the coasts of Mozambique and Tanzania, eastward to the Ryukyu Islands, Taiwan, the Philippines, and most of the islands of Pacific Oceanica, south to Australia. The species is extremely variable and polymorphic, and more varieties and forms should probably be separated, but they, like the presently recognized ones, would be inter-connecting and difficult to differentiate by any hard and fast characters.

U s e s. The species is used medicinally as a decoction in the treatment of rheumatism and neuralgia, and, as one of the ten ingredients of the "dasamula" of India, for various other diseases. The leaves are used as a bitter and carminative; a soup made of them is employed as a stomachic. The leaves rubbed up with pepper are used as a depurative and pectoral in the treatment of colds and fevers. The powdered roots are used as a bitter, cordial, and stomachic in the treatment of fevers, anasarca, and tambavy. The powdered roots rubbed into a paste with water are used with clarified butter in cases of urticaria and roseola. The crushed leaves in coconut oil are used as a hair-wash. The leaves are often cooked with fish of objectional flavor to mask the odour and taste; eating them is also supposed to increase the flow of milk. The stem bark has been found to contain premnine, ganiarine, and tannin, while the root bark has an antibiotic effect. The wood is used for building purposes, poles, stakes, paddles, and knife handles. In the Ryukyu Islands the species is used to make sea- and wind-breaks on coastlines.

V e r n. Maha-midi, Middee-gass, Midhi, Sihin-midi, Wal-wel-midi (S); Erumaimulla (T); Headache-tree (E); some 55 other names are listed from other parts of its range.

N o t e s. The pollen of *P. obtusifolia* is described by Huang in his Pollen Fl. Taiwan 244, pl. 163, figs. 4 & 5 (1972). The species serves as host to the whitefly, *Dialeurodes kirkaldyi* (Kotinsky) Quant. & Bak., and to the fungus, *Asteridiella callista* (Rehm.) Hansf.

In addition to the names listed in the synonymy above, many other names are included by various authors but are regarded by me as not belonging here. Among these the following are regarded by me as separate and valid species: *P. cyclophylla* Miq., *P. divaricata* Wall., *P. foetida* Reinw., *P. nitida* Schum., *P. odorata* Blanco, *P. subglabra* Merr., and *P. timoriana* Decaisne. The following are now recognized as subspecific taxa of *P. obtusifolia*: *P. gaudichaudii* Schau. is var. *gaudichaudii* (Schau.) Moldenke, *P. serratifolia* L. is f. *serratifolia* (L.) Moldenke, and *P. spinosa* Roxb. is var. *angustior* (Clarke) Moldenke. The following are now reduced to synonymy under other taxa. *Folium hircinum* Rumpf = *Premna nitida* Schum., *P. cordifolia* J. Grah. = *P. coriacea* Clarke, *P. formosana* Maxim. = *P. microphylla* Turcz., *P. integrifolia* subsp. *dentatolabium* H.J. Lam = *P. mariannarum* Schau., *P. integrifolia* f. *taitensis* Bakh. = *P. taitensis* Schau., *P. japonica* Miq. = *P. microphylla* Turcz., *P. timoriana* H. Hall. = *P. nauseosa* Blanco, and *P. viburnoides* Wall. = *P. latifolia* var. *viburnoides* (Wall.) Clarke.

var. **obtusifolia**

S p e c i m e n s E x a m i n e d. JAFFNA DISTRICT: near Pottuvil, 6 March 1928, flowers greenish-white [with 3 large unattached leaves of *P. foetida*], *Alston s.n.* (PDA); Jaffna, perhaps cultivated, leaves quite glabrous, determined as *P. latifolia* and *P. viburnoides, s. coll. s.n.* (PDA). MANNAR DISTRICT: Talaimannar, 16 July 1916, determined as *P. latifolia* and *P. viburnoides, J.M. Silva s.n.* (PDA). KURUNEGALA DISTRICT: Batalagoda, 12 Sept. 1927, flowers white, *Alston s.n.* (PDA); in moist grassy patch near swamp, Ridigama, 26 June 1965, flowers pale yellowish-white or pale greenish-white, "maha-midi", *Amaratunga 895* (PDA); waste places around paddy fields, Ibbagamuwa, 8 miles northeast of Kurunegala, 600 ft alt., 1 July 1948, determined as *P. latifolia, Worthington 4034* (K). PUTTALAM DISTRICT: in sand along path in fishing village west of Wilpattu National

Park at Pallugaturai, 1 m alt., 1 Nov. 1974, shrub, mature fruit purplish-black, *Davidse & Sumithraarachchi 8214* (LL). COLOMBO DISTRICT: Makevita, 15 Aug. 1969, shrub, flowers small, dull white, *Amaratunga 1778* (PDA); Manningtown, Colombo, in rocky soil, 18 Nov. 1927, tree, flowers small, dull white, not particularly fragrant, *Ramachandra Rao 1* (PDA); Negombo, July 1930, shrub 5 ft tall, flowers light green, *Silva s.n.* (PDA). KANDY DISTRICT: cultivated in Botany Department gardens, University of Ceylon, Peradeniya, 1600 ft alt., 12 Dec. 1973, *D.B. & D. Sumithraarachchi DBS. 79* (US). AMPARAI DISTRICT: rather frequent among rocks on shore of Indian Ocean, Panama, 5 to 10 m alt., 1 Nov. 1975, cespitose shrub, branches straight, dark red, shiny, leaves membranous, orbicular, concolorous, cymes terminal, greenish, *Bernardi 15587* (PDA, US). BATTI-CALOA DISTRICT: Batticaloa, 1858, *Gardner s.n.* [*C.P. 1953* in part] (PDA). TRINCOMALEE DISTRICT: common on low berm of coral sand and gravel back of low beach ridges covered by unevenly closed scrub forest, Foul Point, south side of Koddiyar Bay, across from Trincomalee, 23 Oct. 1976, loosely branched somewhat reclining shrub, flowers greenish-white, *Fosberg 56414* (NY, PDA, US); in coastal scrub back of beach on sand flat at fishing village 14 miles northwest of Trincomalee, 4 miles southeast of Kuchchaveli ferry, 1 Dec. 1977, shrub 3 m tall, flowers pale-green, somewhat unpleasantly aromatic, *Fosberg & Jayasinghe 57095* (US); Trincomalee, *Gardner s.n.* [*C.P. 1953* in part] (PDA).

var. **minor** (Ridl.) Moldenke, Phytologia 5: 88 & 89. 1954. Type: Ridley collection from Pekan, Pahang, Malaya (BM).

Premna integrifolia var. *minor* Ridl., Fl. Malay Penins. 2: 619. 1923.
Premna corymbosa var. *minor* (Ridl.) Fletcher, Notes Roy. Bot. Gard. Edinburgh 19: 178. 1936.

Described originally by Ridley as "a prostrate creeper of the sandhills, leaves 1 inch long", but if Ceylon material so regarded now is correctly placed here, the variety varies to a shrub, 3 m tall, or even a tree, 6 m tall, the leaf-blades are small, rounded to short-elliptic, short-oblong, or subovate to subobovate, usually 1.5–4 cm long and 1–2 cm wide, on very short petioles, apically rounded or obtuse and there shallowly crenate-serrate.

The variety, as here considered, seems to occur from southern India [Kerala] and Ceylon, through the Mergui Archipelago and lower Thailand, north to Hong Kong, and east to Indonesia. It is cited for Ceylon both by Ridley (1923) and by Fletcher (1936), but the Ceylon collectors do not describe it as a prostrate creeper, so there is some doubt whether only a single taxon is here represented under this designation.

Specimens Examined. JAFFNA DISTRICT: in scrubland, Karaveddi, 15 Jan. 1970, shrub 2 m tall, *Balakrishnan NBK. 637* (US); rare on sandy seashore near the Karativu ferry, 12 Oct. 1975, shrub or treelet, branches slender, dark, cymes terminal, greenish, flowers in bud, leaves ovate-elliptic, obtuse, *Bernardi 15333* (PDA, US); dominant in roadside thicket, 9.5 miles south of Pooneryn, 10 Dec. 1970, tall shrub, 3 m tall, flowers pale-green, *Fosberg & Balakrishnan 53577* (MOLDENKE); common in small thicket near water channel on low dunes back of beach on south shore of Mannar island directly southwest of Pesalai, 11 Dec. 1970, tangled slender shrub 3 m tall, flowers green, *Fosberg & Balakrishnan 53620* (MOLDENKE); in mangrove vegetation, Nagarkovil, 23 Oct. 1973, tree 6 m tall, *Waas 237* (NY, PDA, US); in dry area under shade of kitul trees, Champiyanpattu, 12 Sept. 1974, shrub 4 m tall, flowers white, determined as *P. latifolia*, *Waas & Tirvengadum 819* (LL, PDA, US). PUTTALAM DISTRICT: common in disturbed jungle beside road, Palavi, 20 May 1976, sealevel, *Cramer 4668* (US); Puttalam, 1881, fruit and flowers, interesting form with same fetid smell as *Clerodendrum inerme*, leaves glabrous both sides, determined as *P. latifolia*, *Nevill s.n.* (PDA); Kolankanatta beach, Wilpattu National Park, 3 July 1969, shrub 2 m tall, fruit green, collected as voucher for ecological observations, *Wirawan, Cooray, & Balakrishnan 947* (LL, PDA, US). TRINCOMALEE DISTRICT: common on low berm of coral sand and gravel back of low beach ridges covered by unevenly closed scrub forest, Foul Point, south side of Koddiyar Bay, across from Trincomalee, 23 Oct. 1976, shrub 3 m tall, fruit globose, turning black, fleshy, *Fosberg 56426* (PDA, US). LOCALITY UNKNOWN: *Burman 49* (MU).

var. **pubescens** Moldenke, Phytologia 5: 88. 1954. Type: *Herb. Hort. Bot. Bogor. XV. F. 2*, cultivated in Java (BO).

Premna integrifolia var. *foliis subtus tomentosis* Blume, Bijdr. 9: 815. 1825.

This variety has the young twigs, inflorescence-branches, pedicels, peduncles, petioles, and at least the larger leaf-venation beneath densely short-pubescent or tomentose. It is known thus far only from Java (both wild and cultivated) and Ceylon, but doubtless will be found elsewhere.

Specimens Examined. GALLE DISTRICT: in scrubland, 20 Nov. 1971, *Balakrishnan NBK. 976* in part (PDA).

f. **serratifolia** (L.) Moldenke, Phytologia 36: 438. 1977; L., Fl. Zeyl. 195. 1747; L., Mant. imp. 1, 2: 253. 1771; Rottl. & Willd., Ges. Naturf. Freunde Berlin Neue Schriften ser. 2, 4: 188. 1803; Moon, Cat. 1: 45. 1824; Blume, Bijdr. 9: 815. 1825; Sweet, Hort. Brit., ed. 3, 551. 1839; Thw., Enum. Pl. Zeyl., imp. 1, 242. 1861; Dymock, Veg. Mat. Med. W. India 502. 1884; Trimen, Cat. 68. 1885; Baker in Thiselt.-Dyer, Fl. Trop. Africa 5: 288 & 290. 1900; Willis, Cat. 69. 1911; Gamble, Fl. Pres. Madras 6: 1094 & 1096. 1924; F. B. Br., Bernice

P. Bishop Mus. Bull. 130: 249. 1935; Savage, Cat. Linn. Herb. Lond. 107 &
217. 1945; Abeywick., Ceylon J. Sci., Biol. Sci. 2: 217. 1959; Gupta & Mar-
lange, Trav. Sect. Scient. Inst. Franç. Pond. Hors 3 (1): 78, 121, 129, & 131.
1961; Raju, Excurs. Fl. Simhach. 5 & 20. 1966; Sebastine & Ellis, Bull. Bot.
Surv. India 9: 197. 1967; Gunawardena, Gen. Sp. Pl. Zeyl. 147. 1968; Hartwell,
Lloydia 34: 386. 1971; Fonseka & Vinasithamby, Prov. List Local Names Fl.
Pl. Ceylon 21, 57, 84 & 99. 1971; Rao, Bull. Bot. Surv. India 13: 196. 1971;
Vivekanandan, Sri Lanka Forester, Ser. 2, 11: 109, 135, 139 & 143. 1974.
Type: Specimen from "India orientalis" (LINN).

Premna serratifolia L., Mant., imp. 1, 2: 253. 1771 [not *P. serratifolia* Beddome, 1894, nor Blanco, 1843, nor Lam., 1959, nor Roxb., 1971, nor Willd.,
   1803].—*Premnus serratifolius* L. apud Hassk., Cat. Pl. Hort. Bot. Bogor.
   Cult. Alt. 134. 1844.—*Premna serratifolia* Wall. ex Schau. in A. DC., Prod.
   11: 632, in syn. 1847.—*Premna sevratifolia* L. ex Moldenke, fifth Summ. 2:
   610, in syn. 1971.
Premna obtusifolia var. *serratifolia* (L.) Moldenke, Phytologia 28: 403. 1974.

In this form the leaves are in general larger than in var. *minor*, usually elliptic or oblong-elliptic, to 9 cm long and 6 cm wide, apically short-acuminate,
marginally shallowly crenate-serrate toward the apex.

This form seems to range from southern India and Ceylon northeastward
to Hong Kong, although it is possible that the populations from India and
Hong Kong may represent var. *minor* and that f. *serratifolia* actually is endemic to Ceylon, where it is most certainly most commonly collected.

Some authors (e.g., Baker, Gupta, Marlange, Schauer) adopt *P. serratifolia* L. as the accepted name for the species here known as *P. obtusifolia*,
giving *P. integrifolia* L. as a synonym, while others adopt *P. integrifolia* and
reduce *P. serratifolia* to its synonymy. Still others (e.g., Brown) maintain
both as distinct species. Brown states that the leaf-blades are pubescent beneath, while Baker avers that they are glabrous on both surfaces. It is possible that Brown is referring to var. *pubescens* or even to *P. foetida* Reinw.
The entire complex needs more intensive field study. The *Cornutioides* L.,
cited as a synonym by Linnaeus (1771), actually belongs in the synonymy of
P. obtusifolia var. *obtusifolia*.

In western India *P. serratifolia* is said to have the same medicinal properties as *Viburnum foetidum* Wall. and is there employed in a similar manner;
its roots are one of the ingredients of the local "dasamula" medication and
the leaves are a popular remedy for exanthematous fevers. The plant is often
attacked by a globose pouch gall, *Eriophyes premnae* Nalepa.

Specimens Examined. JAFFNA DISTRICT: A dominant shrub
growing as a shrub-tangle almost vicarious to *Scaevola* which we did not see
here, at side of Pottuvil rest house, in loose dune sand, 26 July 1967, upper

branches barren, probably due to salt spray, many leaves cuneate-based, *Mueller-Dombois & Comanor 67072606* (PDA, US). KURUNEGALA DISTRICT: in secondary scrub by stream edge, Narammala, 11 Aug. 1974, small treelet to 2 m tall, weak-stemmed branches, flowers white, determined as *P. latifolia, Waas 750* (LL, PDA, US). COLOMBO DISTRICT: rare, cultivated in garden, Negombo, seaward side by Negombo lagoon, 31 Oct. 1970, shrub 2 m tall, flowers in corymbiform or flat-topped cymes, very pale green, *Fosberg 52691* (MOLDENKE); in mangrove scrub, Pitipana, low altitude, 10 Aug. 1974, shrub 1.5 m tall, weak branches, drooping, flowers yellowish or off-white, *Waas 712* (PDA, US). KANDY DISTRICT: in outdoor cultivation in Medicinal Garden, Royal Botanic Garden, Peradeniya, 1550 ft alt., 18 Jan. 1974, sprouts from badly pruned-down stump, leaves serrate toward apex, *H.N. & A.L. Moldenke & Jayasuriya 28149* (PDA, US); in outdoor cultivation in Students' Garden, Royal Botanic Garden, Peradeniya, 1550 ft alt., 18 Jan. 1974, sprouts from severely pruned-back stump, some leaves serrate, *H.N. & A.L. Moldenke & Jayasuriya 28160* (PDA, US). AMPARAI DISTRICT: rare on low dunes back of the beach, dunes just north of Arugam Bay, 26 Nov. 1970, prostrate shrub, stems dark, flowers greenish, *Fosberg & Sachet 53041* (MOLDENKE, US). TRINCOMALEE DISTRICT: in sandy mangrove-sedge area at milepost 79 on the Trincomalee to Batticaloa road directly across the bay from Trincomalee, 1 m alt., 14 Oct. 1974, shrub 3 m tall, petals white, *Davidse 7572* (MOLDENKE, US); common on low berm of coral sand and gravel back of low beach ridge covered by unevenly closed scrub forest, Foul Point, south side of Koddiyar Bay, across from Trincomalee, 23 Oct. 1976, loosely branched somewhat reclining shrub, flowers greenish-white, *Fosberg 56414* (US). GALLE DISTRICT: in scrubland, 20 Nov. 1971, determined as *P. corymbosa, Balakrishnan NBK. 976* (PDA, US); Buonavista, Galle, 31 Oct. 1970, shrub 2 m tall, flowers white, fruit green, *Kundu & Balakrishnan 499* (PDA); on sea-facing slopes south of Closenberg, 6 Jan. 1974, shrub, smells like mint, flowers greenish-white, *Wambeek & H. & H.E. Wanntorp 2602b* (US). LOCALITY UNKNOWN: *Fraser 112* (US).

15. PYGMAEOPREMNA

Merr., Philipp. J. Sci. 5: 225. 1910. Type species: *Pygmaeopremna humilis* Merr. [=*P. herbacea* (Roxb.) Moldenke].

Tatea F. Muell., Trans. & Proc. Roy. Soc. S. Australia 6: 33. 1883 [not *Tatea* Seem., 1866].

Dwarf subshrubs of hard dry soils or burned-over areas, with elongated subterranean rhizomes giving rise to short, erect, annual branches usually only 10–25 cm tall; leaves mostly in 2 or 3 decussate-opposite pairs or (on very much reduced branches) apparently verticillate; petioles 2–4 mm long or obsolete; leaf-blades mostly obovate, oblanceolate, or elliptic, chartaceous, entire or irregularly dentate; inflorescence terminal, cymose, trichotomous, short and dense; flowers small, somewhat zygomorphic, yellow to pale yellowish or greenish; calyx cupuliform, the rim subequally 5-toothed, pubescent; corolla small, hypocrateriform, the tube very short, pilose in the throat, the limb obscurely 2-lipped, 4- or 5-lobed, the lobes very short, unequal, imbricate; stamens 4, didynamous, included; filaments very short, filiform; anthers more or less cordate, with parallel thecae; ovary 2-celled, each cell 1-ovulate, or by abortion 1-celled and 1-ovulate; fruit drupaceous, globose, black, collared below by the slightly enlarged persistent calyx; seeds 1 or 2, very hard; embryo upwardly twisted.

A small genus of two or three species, apparently derived from *Premna* and by most authorities united with it as pyrogenously derived. The plants grow either in areas of bare, hard, very dry soil or in savannas burned each year. The stems elongate horizontally underground and each year send up very short branches which may produce leaves, flowers, and fruit but are then usually burned off. The genus is found from Nepal and Bhutan, through India and Indo-China east to the Philippines, Celebes, Soemba, and New Guinea, south to northern Australia and north to Hainan and Yünnan. In Ceylon it is known only from a single specimen.

Pygmaeopremna herbacea (Roxb.) Moldenke, Phytologia 2: 54. 1941; Schau. in A. DC., Prod. 11: 637. 1847; Clarke in Hook. f., Fl. Br. Ind. 4: 581. 1885; Dymock, Warden, & Hooper, Pharmacogn. Ind. 3: 68–70. 1893; Brandis, Indian Trees 511. 1906; M. Kurz, Anatom. Untersuch. Verb. 35. 1911; Parker, Forest Fl. Punjab, ed. 2, 399–400. 1924; Junell, Symb. Bot. Upsal. 4: 85. 1934; Metcalf & Chalk, Syst. Anat. Dicot. 1032, 1033, & 1041. 1950; Merr., J. Arnold Arbor. 32: 73–78. 1951; Puri, Indian Forest Ecol. 662–663. 1960; Airy Shaw in Willis, Dict., ed. 8, 968 & 1131. 1973. Type: William Carey collection from Dinagepore, Bengal, collected in 1801 and cultivated as "Bhoomi—jumbooka" in the Botanical Garden at Calcutta (K).

Premna herbacea Roxb., Hort. Beng. 46, hyponym. 1814; Roxb., Fl. Ind. 3: 80. 1832.

Clerodendron humile Hamilton ex Wall., Num. List 87. 1831 [not *C. humile* Chiov., 1922].

Premna acaulis Wall., Num. List 86. 1831.

Premna acaulis suffruticosa Hamilton ex Wall., Num. List 86. 1831.

Premna gandaria Hamilton ex Wall., Num. List 86. 1831.

Premna ? pygmaea Wall., Num. List 86. 1831.

Tatea subacaulis F. Muell., Trans. & Proc. Roy. Soc. S. Australia 6: 34. 1883.

Tatea acaulis F. Muell., Syst. Census Suppl. 1: 3. 1884.

Gumira herbacea (Roxb.) Kuntze, Rev. Gen. Pl. 2 (2): 507. 1891.—*G. herbacea* Kuntze apud Durand & Jacks., Ind. Kew. Suppl. 1: 190, in syn. 1902.

Pygmaeopremna humilis Merr., Philipp. J. Sci. 5: 225. 1910.

Premna sessilifolia H.J. Lam, Verbenac. Malay. Arch. 133. 1919.

Premna timoriana H.J. Lam apud Merr., Enum. Philipp. Pl. 3: 390. 1923 [not *P. timoriana* Decne., 1834, nor H. Hallier, 1942].

Tatea herbacea (Roxb.) Junell, Symb. Bot. Upsal. 4: 85. 1934.

Tatea humilis (Merr.) Junell, Symb. Bot. Upsal. 4: 85. 1934.

Pygmaeopremna subacaulis (F. Muell.) Moldenke, Phytologia 2: 54. 1941.

Pygmaeopremna sessilifolia (H.J. Lam) Moldenke, Known Geogr. Distrib. Verbenac., ed. 1, 78. 1942.

Premna obovata Merr., J. Arnold Arbor. 32: 77. 1951.

Premna humilis Merr. ex Moldenke, Résumé Suppl. 15: 22. 1967.

Pygnacopremna herbacea (Roxb.) Moldenke ex Saxena, Bull. Bot. Surv. India 12: 56. 1970.

Dwarf or very small subshrub or undershrub, often forming extensive colonies in open ground, with a long woody taproot; stems rhizomatous, subterranean, elongate, nodose, with subglobular woody knots; branches (often referred to as "stems") annual, aerial, 2–30 cm tall, glabrous or subglabrous; leaves few, decussate-opposite, bright green above, very pale beneath, 1–3 pairs (usually only 4) or crowded in a rosette-like whorl at the much abbreviated branch apex (the whorl either appressed flat to the ground or sometimes cup-like), sessile or subsessile, all subequal in size or the uppermost smaller, submembranous-chartaceous, obovate, 2.5–15 cm long, 1.5–7.7 cm wide, apically obtuse, basally cuneate, glabrous on both surfaces, microscopically dotted above, or puberulent on the venation above and pubescent or villous beneath with soon deciduous hairs, often nigrescent in drying, rather irregularly and remotely coarsely sinuate-serrate or serrate-dentate, ciliate, the sinuses between the teeth often broad and the teeth acute or subobtuse; secondaries 4–6 per side, slender, not prominent; inflorescence cymose, corymbiform, terminal or pseudoterminal in the uppermost leaf-axils, mostly solitary, trichotomous, 2–4 cm long, 1.5–4 cm wide, rather densely flowered, subpubescent or villous throughout; peduncles absent or 0.7–3.7 cm long; flowers small, purple in bud, fragrant; calyx cupuliform, pale green, somewhat 2-lipped, 1–2.5 mm long, 2 mm wide, sparsely and closely pubescent externally, the rim ciliate, subequally and obtusely 5-toothed or the upper lip 3-toothed, the lower lip 2-toothed, the teeth ovate; corolla hypocrateriform, varying from yellow or pale yellow to yellowish-purple, cream, white, greenish-white, or greenish, 2.5–4 mm across, the tube subinfundibular, 1.5–3 mm long, externally glabrous on the lower portion and pubescent above, barbate-pubescent in the throat, the limb obscurely or conspicuously 2-lipped, externally pubescent, the lower lip often white, yellow at the base, the lobes 4, of which 2 are about 1.5 mm long and the other 2 only 1 mm long; stamens 4, included, didynamous but reaching the same height; filaments very short, less than 1 mm long; anthers about 0.5 mm long; style short, 0.7–1 mm long, included; stigma very minutely bifid; ovary globose, 0.7–1 mm in diameter, glabrous, apically glandular-punctate; fruit drupaceous, globose, 5–10 mm in diameter, at first green, finally black, fleshy, glossy, seated on a slightly enlarged and persistent fruiting-calyx, 1–4-chambered, 1–4-seeded.

D i s t r. This controversial plant appears to be spread quite widely from northern Pakistan, Nepal, and Bhutan, through much of India, eastward through Burma, Thailand, and Indo-China to the Philippines, Indonesia, and New Guinea, north to southern China and south to Australia. It is said to be (or to have been) cultivated in India and Ceylon.

E c o l. Many authors and/or collectors refer to it as "occasional" or "rare", while others report finding very extensive colonies. Parker (1924) and others refer to it as a pyrogenous species, supposedly permanently dwarfed and forced to survive by subterranean stems by periodic jungle- or grassland-fires over long periods of time. Numerous collectors and writers refer to it as appearing only after fires. Puri (1960) has investigated this matter and finds that while it is a "characteristic" plant of burned areas in India it is not found at all in nearby non-burned areas. On the other hand, Jacobs, in a personal communication to me, asserts that in Celebes he has found evidence that, given "favourable conditions", it is able to grow somewhat larger. While most collectors report encountering it after fires, or in areas which probably are subject to frequent burning (although they do not specifically say so) like "hillsides", "open grassy slopes", "open savannas", and "secondary grass-land", a few have encountered it in "pine forests" and in "moist spots in sal forests" where fires are probably not a usual occurrence. Specimens from these areas are indistinguishable in size and other characters from those collected in burned-over areas. Some authorities claim that the species is often found in hard, stiff, dry soils in open barren places where, again, it is doubtful that there is enough vegetation to support periodic fires. Plants from these areas are indistinguishable from the others. The plant is said to flower at any time from February to June.

U s e s. This plant has been used in medicine in India since very ancient times and the part used is usually said to be the "root" but it may be that the rhizomatous stem is also involved; at the Madras Exhibition it was displayed as "gantu bhárang". In Ceylon it is said to be a popular medicinal plant also and is further said to exist there only in cultivation. The juice is described as "hot, bitter, pungent, and digestive" and has been used in the treatment of dropsy, cough, phlegm, asthma, fever, and rheumatism, as well as, in Bihar, for atrophy, emaciation, cachexia, and cholera. It also enters into the preparation of a confection used like treacle. The oil expressed from the "root" is also applied externally in the treatment of marasmus of children; in Assam the juice is rubbed on both head and body to reduce fevers. In northern India the ripe fruits are eaten. The root juice is mixed with juice of ginger and warm water in the treatment of asthma and it enters into the composition of several medicines used to treat lung ailments. It should be noted, however, that much of what now passes in Indian pharmacy as "bhárang" is not *Pygmaeopremna herbacea*, but is taken from *Clerodendrum serratum*.

V e r n. Siritekku (S); Shirutek (T). More than 25 names are used for it in India and in other parts of its range, including: Bhumi jambu, Kada met [= buffalo's eye], Kamraj, Néla nívedu and Huniyan.

S p e c i m e n s E x a m i n e d: LOCALITY UNKNOWN: cultivated, *Ferguson s.n.* (PDA).

16. VITEX

Tourn. ex L., Sp. Pl., ed. 1, 635. 1753; L., Gen. Pl., ed. 5, 285. 1754. Type species: *Vitex agnus-castus* L.

Mailelou Rheede ex Adans., Fam. Pl. 2: 12 & 200. 1763.—*Mailelou* Adans. ex Airy Shaw in Willis, Dict. ed. 7, 687. 1966.

Wilckea Scop., Introd. Hist. Nat. 170. 1777.—*Wilkea* Post & Kuntze apud Airy Shaw in Willis, Dict. ed. 7, 1194. 1966.

Limia Vand., Fl. Lusit. 42, Pl. 3, fig. 21. 1788.

Nephrandra Willd. in Cothen., Disp. Veg. 8. 1790.

Allasia Lour., Fl. Cochinch., ed. 1, 84. 1790.—*Allazia* Silva-Manso, Enum. 36. 1836.

Tripinna Lour., Fl. Cochinch., ed. 1, 476. 1790.—*Tripina* Lour. ex Angely, Cat. Estat. Gen. Bot. Fan. 17: 6. 1956.

Chrysomallum Thou., Gen. Nov. Madag. 8. 1806.

Tripinnaria Pers., Syn. Pl. 2: 173. 1806.

Pyrostoma G.F.W. Mey., Prim. Fl. Esseq. 219. 1818.

Vitex Willd. ex Moon, Cat. 1: 46. 1824.

Wallrothia Roth, Nov. Pl. Sp. 317. 1821 [not *Wallrothia* Spreng., 1815].— *Walrothia* Roth ex Bocq., Rev. Verbenac. 181. 1863.

Ephialis Banks & Soland. ex A. Cunn., Ann. Nat. Hist., ser. 1, 1: 461. 1838.— *Ephiêlis* Banks & Soland. ex Angely, Cat. Estat. Gen. Bot. Fan. 17: 6. 1956.—*Ephialum* Wittst. ex Airy Shaw in Willis, Dict. ed. 7, 409. 1966.

Psilogyne A. DC., Biblioth. Univers. Genèv. 17: 132. 1838.

Casarettoa Walp., Rep. 4: 91. 1844.

Macrostegia Nees in P. DC., Prod. 11: 218. 1847 [not *Macrostegia* Turcz., 1852].

Agnus-castus Carr., Rev. Hort. 42: 415. 1871.—*Agnus-castus* [Tourn.] Carr. ex Jacks. in Hook. f. & Jacks., Ind. Kew. 1: 59. 1893.

Varengevillea Baill., Hist. Pl. 11: 116 [in part, flowers only]. 1892.— *Varangevillea* Willis ex Airy Shaw in Willis, Dict. ed. 7, 1173. 1966.

Lagasca Née ex Moldenke, Alph. List Invalid Names Suppl. 1: 11. 1947 [not
Lagasca Cav., 1803].
Agnus Runner, Rep. Groff Coll. 362. 1961.

Trees or shrubs, rarely woody vines, glabrous, tomentose, or villous;
branches and branchlets mostly more or less tetragonal; leaves usually decussate-opposite or ternate, palmately 3–7-foliolate, rarely 1-foliolate, deciduous,
usually petiolate, the leaflets chartaceous or membranous, sometimes coriaceous, mostly petiolulate, entire or dentate, rarely incised or lobed, equal in
size or often the lowest ones smaller and more caducous; inflorescence
cymose, the cymes short and dense or loosely divaricate, sessile or pedunculate in the leaf-axils or aggregated in terminal racemiform, thyrsoid, or
laxly diffuse panicles, more rarely contracted into heads, occasionally few-
or 1-flowered, rarely cauliflorous; flowers perfect, more or less zygomorphic;
bractlets and prophylla usually very small, mostly linear, sometimes more
enlarged and longer than the calyx; flowers often showy; calyx campanulate,
cyathiform, or rarely tubular-infundibular, 5-dentate or 5-fid, rarely 3-fid or
6-lobed, the teeth mostly slightly unequal; corolla varying from white or
yellowish to various shades of blue or violet, long-tubular or cylindric to
hypocrateriform, zygomorphic, the tube short or rarely elongate, cylindric,
straight or slightly incurved, sometimes slightly ampliate above, the limb
oblique, spreading, more or less bilabiate, the upper lip often bifid, the lower
lip trifid, the 2 posterior lobes exterior and usually shorter, the lateral lobes
larger, the anterior lobe largest, entire or emarginate, the upper lip erect,
arched, or resupinate; stamens 4, didynamous, inserted in the corolla-tube,
often exserted; anthers 2-celled, the thecae distinct, parallel to divergent or
arcuate, attached near the apex, dehiscing by longitudinal slits; pistil single,
compound, bicarpellary; style terminal, filiform, shortly bifid apically, the
branches acute; ovary at first imperfectly 2-celled, during anthesis usually
4-celled, the cells 1-ovulate; ovules attached laterally at or above the middle
of the cell; fruit drupaceous, fleshy, the endocarp hard, often horny, sometimes incrassate in relation to the cells, 4-celled; seeds obovate or oblong,
erect, without endosperm; fruiting-calyx often accrescent, usually patelliform
or very shallowly cupuliform, rarely partly enclosing the fruit. Chromosomes:
x = 6 or 8.

A complex genus of about 380 specific and infraspecific entities, mostly of
the tropics and subtropics of both hemispheres, a few also found in temperate Europe or Asia. Many species are widely cultivated for ornament or as
hedges and some have become naturalized; a few fossil forms are known from
Europe and Africa. *Chrysomallum*, a Madagascar group of species, may be
worthy of generic segregation.

KEY TO THE SPECIES, VARIETIES, AND FORMS

1 Some or all the leaves 1-foliolate
  2 Leaves long-petiolate (petioles 2–5 cm long), 9.5–20 cm long, 5–9 cm wide; cultivated . .
    . . . . **1. V. cofassus**
  2 Leaves sessile, subsessile, or short-petiolate (petioles 2–4 mm long), 1.5–6 cm long, 0.8–3.5 cm wide
    3 Leaves mostly 1-foliolate, rarely a few 2- or 3-foliolate; native . . . .
    . . . . **V. trifolia** var. **simplicifolia**
    3 Leaves commonly only 1-, 2-, and 3-foliolate, or the leaflets more or less binary, interspersed; cultivated . . . . **V. trifolia** var. **subtrisecta**
    3 Leaves 3- or mostly 5-foliolate, the 3 central long-petiolulate, conspicuously bicoloured
    . . . . **V. trifolia** var. **bicolor**
1 All the leaves on mature individuals regularly 2–5-foliolate
  4 Inflorescence capitate; cultivated . . . . **2. V. capitata**
  4 Inflorescence cymose or paniculate, not capitate
    5 Inflorescence axillary
      6 Inflorescence cymose; native
        7 Leaflets to 14.5 cm long and 4 5 cm wide, attenuate-subacuminate apically, margins regularly entire . . . . **5. V. leucoxylon** f. **leucoxylon**
        7 Leaflets to 9 cm long and 3.5 cm wide, apically obtuse, margins often more or less dentate . . . . **V. leucoxylon** f. **zeylanica**
      6 Inflorescence paniculate; cultivated . . . . **6. V. peduncularis**
    5 Inflorescence terminal
      8 Inflorescence branches divaricate, wide-spreading, intricately many-furcate
        9 Leaflets not white-tomentellous beneath, to 22.5 cm long and 10.5 cm wide, very firmly chartaceous; panicle to 18 cm wide, very dense and crowded, conspicuously bracteate, the bractlets foliaceous, to 17 mm long and 7 mm wide; large tree to 25 m tall . . . . **4. V. pinnata**
        9 Leaflets densely white-tomentellous beneath, to 7 cm long and 4 cm wide, thinly membranous; panicle to 4 cm wide, usually open and loose, not conspicuously bracteate, the linear bractlets 1–3 mm long; shrub or small tree to 6.5 m tall
          10 Leaflets mostly 3, central one long-petiolulate . . . . **8. V. trifolia** var. **trifolia**
          10 Leaflets mostly 5, two central ones long-petiolulate . . . . **V. trifolia** var. **bicolor**
      8 Inflorescence branches ascending or erect, elongate, narrow, dense
        11 Leaflets sessile or only the central one short-petiolulate, 3–6.5 cm wide
          12 Leaflets distinctly short-pubescent beneath, mostly 3 . . . .
          . . . . **3. V. altissima** f. **altissima**
          12 Leaflets glabrous or subglabrous beneath, sometimes 5 . . . .
          . . . . **V. altissima** f. **subglabra**
        11 Leaflets all distinctly petiolulate, 1.5–4 cm wide . . . . **7. V. negundo**

1. Vitex cofassus Reinw. ex Blume, Bijdr. 813. 1826; Rumph., Herb. Amboin. 3: 28–30, pl. 14, fig. 8. 1743; Schau. in A. DC., Prod. 11L 687. 1847; Heyne, Nutt. Pl. Ned. Ind. 4: 112. 1917; H.J. Lam, Verbenac. Malay. Arch. 172–173. 1919; Moldenke, Phytologia 5: 275–279 (1955), 5: 356 (1956), 8: 32–34 (1961), & 15: 97–98 & 231–232. 1967. Type: Rumphius collection from Amboina.

Cofassus Rumph., Herb. Amboin. 3: 28–30, pl. 14. 1743.

Vitex punctata Schau. in A. DC., Prod. 11: 687. 1847.—*V. punctata* DC. ex
Ettingsh., Kaiserl. Akad. Wiss. Wien, Math.-Naturwiss. Kl., Denkschr. 28:
219. 1868.—*V. punctata* Vahl ex Moldenke, Phytologia 5: 274. 1955.
Vitex monophylla Schum. & Hollr., Fl. Kais. Wilhelmsl. 121. 1889.—*V.
monophylla* Schum. ex Durand & Jacks., Ind. Kew. Suppl. 1: 457. 1906.
Vitex cofassus var. *typica* H.J. Lam, Verbenac. Malay. Arch. 173. 1919.

Medium-sized or large tree, to 40 m tall, the trunk to 26 dm in circumference, deeply fluted, often buttressed; bark brown, rough, very fibrous or
scaly, slightly furrowed, peeling in long thin flakes; wood heavy; branches
numerous, branchlets and twigs stout, obtusely or acutely tetragonal, sometimes sulcate, very medullose, light-grey or (at the tips) brownish in drying,
lenticellate, sparsely and obscurely puberulent or glabrate; leaves stiff, 1-
foliolate (perhaps very rarely 3-foliolate), turning yellow when old; petioles
rather stoutish, 2–5 cm long, obscurely margined, sparsely puberulent or glabrate, jointed at the apex; petiolules similar to the petiole in all respects but
only 1–3 mm long, plainly margined; leaflet-blades chartaceous, mostly dark
green and shiny above, paler or glaucous beneath, elliptic, 9.5–20 cm long,
5–9 cm wide, usually acuminate apically, entire, acute basally and prolonged
into the petiolule, glabrous on both surfaces; inflorescence terminal and axillary in the uppermost leaf-axils, paniculate, 14–17 cm long, 3–14 cm wide,
loosely many-flowered, each panicle simple or branched and composed of
many, small, more or less irregularly placed, few-flowered, stalked cymes; peduncles (4–6 cm long) and rachis rather stout, sharply tetragonal, lenticellate,
purple-green when fresh, usually brownish in drying, sparsely puberulent; pedicels slender, to 1 mm long, or obsolete, in fruit incrassate, to 2 mm long,
and puberulent; foliaceous bracts often present; bractlets small, linear, puberulent; calyx cupuliform, 2–2.5 mm long, 2.5–3 mm wide, with 2 small linear
prophylla at its base, externally sparsely pubescent and glandular, glabrous
or slightly pilose within, the rim truncate or with 2–5 very small teeth; corolla hypocrateriform, varying from blue to lilac, lavender, or purple, sometimes
pale mauve with darker markings, 2-lipped, 5-lobed, the tube pubescent and
glandular (except the lowest part), 3–6 mm long, the throat villous, the 4
smaller lobes ovate, 1–1.5 mm long, papillose on the inner surface, pubescent
and glandular on the outer, the fifth lobe 2–2.5 mm long, villous on the inner face; stamens little exserted; filaments stout; anthers reniform, dark-
violet, the thecae divergent; style about 6 mm long; stigma shortly bifid;
ovary depressed, glabrous, sparsely glandular; fruiting-calyx enlarged, patelliform, about 5 mm wide, sparsely and obscurely strigillose, venose, its rim irregularly scarious or lobed; fruit succulent when ripe, obovate, dark violet to
purple-black or black, 5–8 mm long and slightly wider, densely appressed-
puberulent or glabrate, mucronulate.

D i s t r. This species is native to the eastern Malay Archipelago and western Polynesia, where it is usually found in the second story of coastal forests and into the higher rainforests.

U s e s. It is sometimes cultivated. Its exceptionally strong and durable wood is used in the Molucca and Solomon Islands for making the large wooden bowls and platters used during native feasts, in which food is pounded in a manner similar to a mortar, and is also employed for making drumlogs. The wood is resistant to salt-water and moist soil and therefore is used in boat- and ship-building; it does not warp after cutting. In New Guinea it is used for panelling and carving. As "vitex" or "New Guinea teak" it is imported into the United States and Great Britain for making floor planks, furniture, house posts, axe handles, telephone poles, door-sills, and railway ties.

V e r n. At least 75 names are recorded from various parts of its range, including: Alawa, Cofassus, and Gofassus.

S p e c i m e n s E x a m i n e d. KANDY DISTRICT: cultivated, seed from Jard. Bot. Buitenzorg 3.3.01, 9 May 1910, *s. coll. s.n.* (PDA); 21 April 1926, flowers purple, reddish round the leaf, *s. coll. 343* (PDA).

2. Vitex capitata Vahl, Eclog. Amer. 2: 50, pl. 18. 1798; H.B.K., Nov. Gen. & Sp., ed. folio, 2: 200, 1817; Schau. in A. DC., Prod. 11: 689. 1847; Moldenke, Phytologia 5: 261–264 (1955), 5: 356 (1956), 5: 466 (1957), 15: 93–94 (1967), & 16: 497, 1968. Type: *John Ryan s.n.* (Herb. Willdenow 11712), collected in Trinidad in 1796 (B).

Limia Vand., Fl. Lusit. 42–43, pl. 3, fig. 21. 1788.

Vitex bignonioides H.B.K., Nov. Gen. & Sp. ed. folio, 2: 200. 1817.—*V. bignonioides* Humb. & Bonpl. apud Steud., Nom. Bot., ed. 1, 888. 1821.—*V. bignonioides* Kunth ex Ettingsh., Kaiserl. Akad. Wiss. Wien, Math.-Naturl. Kl., Denkschr. 28: 219. 1868.

Vitex brasiliensis Steud., Nom. Bot., ed. 1, 888. 1821 [not *V. brasiliensis* Mart., 1847].

Petraea bignonioides H.B.K. apud Pittier, Supl. Pl. Usual. Venez. 55. 1939.

Vitex wittrockiana Moldenke, Geogr. Distrib. Avicenn. 20 & 27, nom. nud. 1939; Moldenke, Phytologia 2: 31–32. 1941.

Shrub or small erect or spreading tree, to 18 m tall, with a dense rounded crown; trunk short, cylindric, to 40 cm in diameter; wood hard, heavy, taking polish well; bark medium brown, deeply rimose; branches often contorted, glabrous; branchlets rather slender or stoutish, grey to stramineous or brownish, obtusely tetragonal or subterete, not very pithy, hirtellous to sparsely and minutely puberulent especially toward the apex, soon glabrescent and shiny; leaves decussate-opposite or subopposite, 3- or 5-foliolate; petioles very slender, 2–6.5 cm long, sparsely hirtellous or puberulent; leaflets subequal in size or the 2 lowermost (when there are 5) much smaller and often caducous, all subsessile or the central one obscurely short-petiolulate, the petiolule 1–4 mm long, slightly puberulent and margined; leaflet-blades thin-chartaceous or submembranous, dark green and somewhat shiny above, somewhat lighter beneath, the central one narrowly oblong or elliptic to lanceolate to oblanceolate, 3.5–14.5 cm long, 2–3.5 cm wide, long-acuminate or caudate apically, entire, basally acute or acuminate, glabrous and shiny on both surfaces or slightly and obscurely puberulent along the midrib and sometimes also the larger veins; inflorescence axillary, capitate or subcapitate, rarely subumbelliform, long-pedunculate, 5–12 cm long, 1–3.5 cm wide, usually densely many-flowered, sometimes with a very few short branches arranged in subumbelloid fashion; peduncles slender, compressed or terete, 4–9.5 cm long, sparsely strigillose-puberulent, less so in age; pedicels very slender, 1–2 mm long and puberulent, or obsolete, to 6 mm long in fruit; bractlets setaceous or linear, 1–3 mm long, densely puberulent, obscured by the flowers in the dense heads; calyx campanulate, 1–2 mm long and wide, externally strigillose-puberulent or appressed-pilose, the rim subtruncate, often repand-denticulate or obsoletely 5-dentate; corolla hypocrateriform, blue to lavender or violet, 10–12 mm long, externally densely puberulent, the tube cylindric, much longer than the calyx, the limb 2-lipped, the upper lip 2-lobed, the lower 3-lobed with the middle lobe largest, ovate, undulate-margined, hirsute at the base inside; stamens purple, exserted; anthers dark-purple, elliptic; pollen pale yellow; style glabrous; fruiting-calyx enlarged and incrassate, shallowly cupuliform or patelliform, to 3 mm long and 10 mm wide, very lax, stramineous, very sparsely puberulent, the rim entire or scarious; fruit drupaceous, fleshy, black, oblong, 12–14 mm long, 8–9 mm wide, soft.

D i s t r. This species is a native of Trinidad and Tobago to Venezuela and Amazonian Brazil; cultivated in Ceylon, Vietnam, and elsewhere.

U s e s. The flowers are highly nectariferous and the tree would be useful for beekeepers. In Trinidad it is an esteemed timber tree; growing as it does in poor soils, it would be useful in reforestation projects.

V e r n. Among its dozen names in various parts of its range are: Acietuno, Bois de lizan, Escobillo, and Five-leaf fiddlewood.

N o t e. It is subject to attack by the fungus, *Uredo viticis* Juel.

S p e c i m e n s   E x a m i n e d. KANDY DISTRICT: South Garden, 125/46, Royal Botanic Garden, Peradeniya, 22 May 1903, small tree with bright purple flowers, *s. coll. 15* (PDA); in outdoor cultivation, Section E. 30, Royal Botanic Garden, Peradeniya, 1550 ft alt., 18 Jan. 1974, tree about 20 ft tall, *H.N. & A.L. Moldenke & Jayasuriya 28144* (AAU, LL, PDA, US); South Garden, Royal Botanic Garden, Peradeniya, 14 May 1930, flowers bright purple, *Senaratna 193* (PDA).

3. **Vitex altissima** L. f., Suppl. Pl. 294. 1781. f. **altissima.** Moon, Cat. 46. 1824;

Schau. in A. DC., Prod. 11: 685. 1847; Drury, Useful Pl. India 442. 1858;
Thw., Enum. Pl. Zeyl. 244. 1861; Clarke in Hook. f., Fl. Br. Ind. 4: 584.
1885; Trimen, Cat. 69. 1885; Watt, Dict. Econ. Prod. India 6 (4): 243. 1893;
Trimen, Handb. Fl. Ceylon 3: 357–358. 1895; Gamble, Man. Indian Timb.,
ed. 2, 540. 1902; Brandis, Indian Trees 504. 1906; Willis, Cat. 69. 1911;
Alston in Trimen, Handb. Fl. Ceylon 6: 232. 1931; Alston, Kandy Fl. 64–65,
fig. 347. 1938; Worthington, Ceylon Trees 348. 1959; Abeywick., Ceylon J.
Sci., Biol. Sci. 2: 217. 1959; Gunawardena, Gen. Sp. Pl. Zeyl. 147. 1968; Moldenke, Phytologia 5: 197–200 (1955), 5: 354–355 (1956), 5: 465 (1957), 6: 13
(1957), 8: 28 & 62 (1961), 15: 87–88 & 226 (1967), and 16: 495–496. 1968.
Type: *König 77* (in part) from Ceylon, *Herb. Linnaeus 811/2* (LINN).

Vitex appendiculata Willd., Ges. Naturf. Freunde Berlin, neue Schriften ser.
2, 4: 203. 1803 [not *V. appendiculata* Rottl., 1885].
Vitex altissima Moon, Cat. 46. 1824.—*V. altissima* Roxb. ex Wall., Num.
List [48]. 1829.—*V. altissima* L. ex Roxb., Fl. Ind., ed. 2 [Carey], 3: 71.
1832.—*V. altissima* Heyne ex Moldenke, Phytologia 5: 197. 1955.
Vitex pubescens Heyne ex Wall., Num List [48]. 1829 [not *V. pubescens* Vahl,
1794].
Vitex latifolia Wight ex Steud., Nom. Bot., ed. 2, 2: 777. 1840 [not *V. latifolia*
Blanco, 1837, nor Lam., 1788, nor Mill., 1768].
Vitex trifolia Moon apud Trimen, Handb. Fl. Ceylon 3: 357. 1895 [not *V.
trifolia* Grah., 1966, nor Hemsl., 1949, nor L., 1753, nor L. f., 1895, nor
Sessé & Moc., 1940, nor Vahl, 1941, nor "sensu Matsumura & Hayata",
1963].

Juvenile Form

Vitex alata Willd., Ges. Naturf. Freunde Berlin, Neue Schriften ser. 2, 4:
203. 1803 [not *V. alata* Kurz, 1885, nor Roxb., 1803, nor Schau., 1885, nor
Wall., 1947].—*V. alata* Heyne ex Roth, Nov. Pl. Sp. 316. 1821.—*V. alata*
Royen ex Moldenke, Prelim. Alph. List Invalid Names 49. 1940.
Vitex appendiculata Rottl. ex Clarke in Hook. f., Fl. Br. Ind. 4: 584. 1885 [not
V. appendiculata Willd., 1803].
Vitex altissima var. *alata* (Heyne) Trimen, Handb. Fl. Ceylon 3: 358. 1895.—
V. altissima var. *alata* Trimen ex Willis, Cat. 69. 1911.—*V. altissima* var.
alata (Willd.) Moldenke, Revista Sudamer. Bot. 5: 2. 1937.—*Vitex altissima*
f. juv. *alata* (Willd.) Moldenke, Phytologia 28: 468. 1974.

Large tree, to 33 m tall, with a dense crown and somewhat drooping
branches; wood grey, with a tinge of olive-brown, hard, close-grained, heavy,
50–63 lbs per c. ft; branchlets medium or slender, tetragonal or subterete, decussately flattened, dark brown or purplish, rather densely short-pubescent
when young with brownish hairs, becoming sparsely strigillose in age; leaves
decussate-opposite, 3-foliolate; petioles rather slender, 4.5–10.5 cm long,

rather densely puberulent or shortly strigillose, more sparsely so in age, slightly margined for the whole length, usually somewhat more pronouncedly so at the apex and base, those on immature individuals and turions more or less broadly alate from apex to base [see f. *alata*, below]; leaflets subequal in size or the central one slightly larger, the central one subsessile or petiolulate with slightly margined petiolules 1–3 mm long, the lateral ones usually sub-sessile or with obscure margined petiolules to 1 mm long; leaflet-blades thin-chartaceous, usually rather firm, dark-green above, somewhat lighter beneath, the central one elliptic or subobovate-elliptic, 10–20 cm long, 3–6.7 cm wide, apically acuminate or caudate, entire or slightly repand-undulate, basally acute or subacuminate, rather densely puberulent above when young, glabrescent (except for the midrib) in age, mostly rather densely short-pubescent beneath or strigillose only on the larger venation; inflorescence axillary and terminal, paniculate, 15–23 cm long, 3–24 cm wide, erect or drooping, sometimes simple or few-branched, often massive with 3–5 pairs of mostly arcuate-ascending branches, the individual branches narrow and rather densely flowered; pe-duncles 1.5–4 cm long, it and the rachis similar to the young branchlets, de-cidedly tetragonal and flattened, puberulent or short-pubescent and more or less incanous, lowermost panicle-branches longest, each with a rather long naked stalk and then 2–10 rather distant pairs of subsessile densely flowered cymes; bractlets narrowly oblong, apically acute, sessile, 1–5 mm long, densely short-pubescent and incanous; calyx cupuliform, about 3 mm long, external-ly pubescent, the rim 5-toothed, the teeth short, triangular, obtuse, spreading; corolla hypocrateriform, light-pink or white and blue-tinged to bluish-purple, about 6 mm long, externally puberulent, the tube scarcely surpassing the ca-lyx, often maroon-tinged, 2-lipped, the upper lip with 2 short, triangular, acute lobes, the lower 3-lobed, usually blue or dark-violet, with a yellow stripe at the base, the middle lobe more than twice as large as the others, pubescent, ciliate; ovary apically fulvous-villous; fruiting-calyx enlarged; fruit drupaceous, prolate-spheroidal, at first green, later bluish-black or black, about 8 mm wide, often white-dotted, apically fulvous-villous.

D i s t r. This much misunderstood species is found from India, Bangla-desh, and Ceylon eastward through Indo-China to Java, Sumatra, and New Guinea. It is sparingly cultivated in parts of the United States, Europe, and tropical Asia.

U s e s. In India its wood is prized for timber, being smooth, tough, dur-able, and reasonably resistant to termite attack. It does not split or warp and it polishes well. It is much used for construction, cabinet-work, furniture, turnery, well linings, agricultural implements, yokes, combs, and carts, espe-cially their wheels. A yellow dye can be extracted from the wood. The juice of the bark is applied externally in the treatment of chest pains. According to Alston this species flowers from July to October in Ceylon. Thwaites asserts that it is one of the most valuable timber trees on the island for build-ing and other purposes.

V e r n. Kaha-milla, Milla, Mililla-gass, Meeyan-mililla-gass, Miyanmilla, Sapu-milla (S); Kaaddmanakku, Kadamanakku, Kadamananakku, Maila, Mayila (T) ["maila" is also applied to *Bauhinia racemosa* Lam.]. Some 25 additional names are used in India and elsewhere in the species' range.

N o t e s. It has been widely confused in literature with *V. pinnata* (see below). Philippine references to *V. altissima* apparently all refer, instead, to *V. parviflora* A.L. Juss.

Vitex altissima is subject to attack by the insect, *Saissetia oleae* Bernard, in Puerto Rico and perhaps elsewhere. It seems to thrive best in calcareous soils.

S p e c i m e n s   E x a m i n e d. JAFFNA DISTRICT: Jaffna, *Gardner s.n. [C.P. 1958]* (PDA); Mulliativu, Oct. 1890, trees taller and straighter than the ordinary "milla", *Lewis s.n.* (PDA). VAVUNIYA DISTRICT: common in forest at rock outcrop about 2 miles southwest of Nedun-keni along road to Puliyankulam near milepost 21/3, 95 m altitude, 5 Dec. 1974, tree 8 m tall, fruit black, *Davidse & Sumithraarachchi 9075* (LL). KURUNEGALA DISTRICT: Magazine Hill, Kurunegala, 11 May 1962, flowers pale-violet, *Amaratunga 175* (PDA); Ibbagala, 26 July 1962, flowers small, mauve-pink, *Amaratunga 268* (PDA); rather common in jungle forest, Panirendawa, low altitude, 25 Jan. 1974, trees about 45 ft tall, *H.N. & A.L. Moldenke & Jayasuriya 28256* (AAU, PDA, US). PUTTALAM DISTRICT: scattered trees in jungle forest, Kalaoya, low altitude, 25 Jan. 1974, trees about 40 ft tall, many leaves with narrow wings on petioles, *H.N. & A.L. Moldenke & Jayasuriya 28238* (PDA, US). ANURADHAPURA/PUTTA-LAM DISTRICT: Wilpattu National Park, 15 Sept. 1968, very young, *Wira-wan s.n.* (PDA). ANURADHAPURA DISTRICT: Rare in rocky woods near Ritigala, 60 m alt., 18 March 1973, tree 14 m tall, bark ochraceous, branchlets tetragonal, sulcate, dark-green, leaves 3-foliolate, papery, panicles terminal, cymose, scorpioid, flexuous, flowers few, lilac, fruit now green, *Ber-nardi 14304* (US); exposed windswept rock outcrop on southwestern slope, Ritigala Strict National Reserve, 1300 ft alt., 8 Aug. 1973, small tree, corolla bluish-purple, *Jayasuriya 1262* (AAU, LL). AMPARAI DISTRICT: grow-ing in forest on light brown-red clayey lateritic loamy soil near spillway, Gal Oya Reservoir, 270 m alt., 13 Nov. 1967, common tree 6 m tall, bark light tan, petals pale blue, *Comanor 567* (US); in light-coloured sandy-pebbly soil, Gal Oya Reservoir area on dirt road to Siyambalanduwa, 270 m alt., 14 Nov. 1967, isolated tree 9 m tall, bark tan, fruit prolate-spheroidal, blue-black, *Comanor 576* (PDA, US). POLONNARUWA DISTRICT: Polonnaruwa Sacred Area, 61 m alt., 23 Oct. 1969, *Dittus WD. 69102302* (US), 6 Sep. 1971, flowers, *Dittus WD. 71090606* (US); common in dry zone forest near irrigation tank, Sacred Area where the undergrowth is cut, Polonnaruwa, 60 m alt., 16 June 1969, tree 10 m tall, bark yellowish-grey, flowers blue, *Hladik*

855 (PDA, US); Polonnaruwa Sacred Area, 61 m alt., 3 Nov. 1968, common tree in fruit, voucher for primate ecology observations, *Ripley 78* (PDA, US), 26 May 1969, common tree, blue flowers, voucher for primate ecology observations, *Ripley 135* (PDA, US), in sandy soil, Dec. 1969, tree in fruit, *Ripley 189* (PDA, US), common tree in flush, 19 Jan. 1969, fruit and flower, voucher for primate ecology observations, *Ripley 247* (US); common tree on rocky outcroppings 1 mile west of Giritale on the Giritale to Minneriya road, 6 Oct. 1973, fruit black, *Sohmer 8210* (NY); about 3 miles west of Giritale on the Giritale to Naula road, 7 Oct. 1973, trees 50 ft tall, flowers "orange", *Sohmer 8237* (LL, US). KANDY DISTRICT: in forest on steep slope about 6 miles northeast of Hunnasgiriya near milepost 27/16 on the Kandy to Mahiyangane road, 720 m alt., 14 Nov. 1974, tree 16 m tall, trunk 38 cm in diameter, fruit green, corolla violet-blue with lower lip a darker shade, white around margin of throat, *Davidse & Jayasuriya 8393* (LL); cultivated Royal Botanic Garden, Peradeniya, 30 June 1904, *Hallier 241* (HBG); common in evergreen forest, Nilembe, Hantana Ridge near Kandy, 700 m alt., 25 April 1969, tree 7 m tall, trunk 15 cm in diameter at breast height, bark rough, greyish-white, 1 mm thick, living bark 10 mm thick, dark yellow, flowers pale blue, *Kostermans 23289* (AAU); scattered trees at milepost 67 on the road from Ginigathena to Kitulgala, 1200 ft alt., 12 Feb. 1974, trees 20 ft tall, *H.N. & A.L. Moldenke, Dassanayake, & Jayasuriya 28329* (CAI, LL, PDA, US); on trail to Nitre Cave area from St. Martin's Estate near base of Dumbanagala Spur, 14 Nov. 1975, fruit black and fleshy at maturity, *Sohmer & Jayasuriya 10673* (NY); mid-country, Andiatenna, Kadugannawa, 2200 ft alt., 25 Aug. 1943, *Worthington 1325* (PDA); Hillcrest, Kandy, 211 ft alt., Dec. 1950, regenerated anywhere around, *Worthington 5013* (PDA); Kandy, 2130 ft alt., 24 Oct. 1957, *Worthington s.n.* (PDA). MATALE DISTRICT: Dambulla, 8 Sep. 1965, a large tree, calyx pale rust or brown, flowers bluish-purple with middle lobe of lower lip deep purple, "mille" in Sinhala, *Amaratunga 1023* (PDA); on wooded hill by temple, Dambulla, 7 Oct. 1975, frequent tree, seen all over the island, bark light, inflorescence candelabra-form, flowers pale-violet, *Bernardi 15240* (NY); roadside in village, Sigiriya, 700 ft alt., 11 Oct. 1974, large tree with pendulous inflorescences, fruit black, pericarp fleshy, *Davidse 7446* (LL, US); secondary forest at base of mountain, Erewalaga Tank, just east of the Kandalama Tank and about 6 miles directly east of Dambulla, 240 m altitude, 30 Oct. 1974, tall tree, trunk 12 cm in diameter, fruit dark blue, juicy, *Davidse & Sumithraarachchi 8153* (LL); occasional in fencerow along weedy roadside 3 miles southwest of Inamaluwa, north of Dambulla, on the Trincomalee road, 22 Oct. 1976, somewhat depressed spreading somewhat woody herb, flowers orange, closed in afternoon, *Fosberg 56373* (US); tree in jungle, Sigiriya, 3 Oct. 1969, *Reitz 30027* (AAU, US); 9 miles southeast of Kandalama, Dambulla, 17 Sept. 1974, trees 20 ft tall, leaves tripalmate, inflorescence purplish-bluish in colour, *Sumithraarachchi*

DBS. 462 (US); common trees in jungle, northwest end of Kandalama tank bund, 19 Sep. 1974, flowers bluish-purple, young fruits green and mature fruits purplish, bark brown, *Sumithraarachchi DBS. 508* (US); Dambulla, 1000 ft alt., 17 Dec. 1951, in 56 plus inches rainfall area, *Worthington 5552* (PDA). NUWARA ELIYA DISTRICT: mid-country, Nawalapitiya, 1 June 1939, "milla" in Sinhala, *Worthington 383* (PDA). RATNAPURA DISTRICT: submontane dry zone border, Rajawakanda, 2100 ft alt., 16 March 1948, very small tree owing to clearing, *Worthington 3764* (PDA). MONERAGALA DISTRICT: intermediate forest, Bakinigahawele, between Madagama and Monaragala, low altitude, 2 May 1975, tree 12 m tall, trunk 30 cm in diameter at breast height, corolla purplish-blue, lower lip blue, *Jayasuriya 1990* (LL, US); common in deciduous forest, Wellawaya, low altitude, 12 May 1969, tree 20 m tall, trunk diameter 90 cm, bark pale orange-brown, fissured, strips 2–3 cm wide, flowers pale blue, *Kostermans 23478* (AAU, NY). AMPARAI DISTRICT: common in edge of forest around extensive low granite outcrop between 7 and 8 miles west of Pottuvil, 26 Nov. 1970, large shrubs to 5 m tall, flowers bluish, ripe fruit black, *Fosberg & Sachet 53010* (LL, NY), *53011* (ARIZ); southeast corner, 100 yards north of irrigation bungalow, at forest edge next to villu grassland, Lahugula Tank, 36 m alt., 25 July 1967, prominent upper canopy tree, *Mueller-Dombois & Comanor 67072507* (PDA); east side at large rock outcrop, Lahugula Tank, 36 m alt., 25 July 1967, tree 10 m tall, crown 10 m wide, inflorescence terminal, blue, *Mueller-Dombois & Comanor 67072528* (PDA). BATTICALOA DIST-RICT: in shallow sand between outcropping rocks, Batticaloa area near Unichchai at a junction and place called Ayittiyamalai, 14 Aug. 1967, tree 8 m tall at roadside, very common in this area, *Mueller-Dombois 67081404* (PDA); dry zone jungle on road from Bibile to Batticaloa at milepost 87/2, 50 ft alt., 20 Aug. 1950, *Worthington 4906* (PDA). TRINCOMALEE DIST-RICT: common in open dry country, Palaiottu, sealevel, 25 Oct. 1974, tree about 12 m tall, outer bark cracked, dull brown, corolla-limb white, lower lip bluish-purple, *Cramer 4366* (US); Trincomalee, *s. coll. C.P. 1598* (PDA); in secondary dry forest, Monkey Bridge, low altitude, 24 May 1975, tree 7 m tall, 1.2 m bole, creamish-yellow outer bark, compound leaves, purplish-blue flowers, *Waas 1267* (US). HAMBANTOTA DISTRICT: Yodakandiya road near Yodakandera Vihare, 17 Nov. 1969, common tree 2.5 m tall, flowers purple, *Cooray 69111730R* (AAU, PDA). LOCALITY UNKNOWN: in deep forest, *König 77* in part [Linn. Herb. 811.2] (LINN type, MOLDENKE photograph of type, NY photograph of type); *J.M. Silva 185* (BROMMA); *Worthington 4506* (PDA).

Juvenile Form

Roth, Nov. Pl. Sp. 316. 1821; J. Grah., Pl. Bombay 156. 1839; Schau. in A. DC., Prod. 11: 685. 1847; Dalz. & Gibs., Bombay Fl. 201. 1861; Thw., Enum.

Pl. Zeyl. 244. 1861; Kurz, For. Fl. Burma 2: 269, 272, & 612. 1877; Clarke in Hook. f., Fl. Br. Ind. 4: 584. 1885; Trimen, Handb. Fl. Ceylon 3: 358. 1895; Brandis, Indian Trees 504. 1906; Willis, Cat. 69. 1911; Menninger, 1947 Cat. Fl. Trees 25 (1946) and 1953 Cat. 16. 1953; Moldenke, Phytologia 5: 200–202 (1955) and 28: 468. 1974; Dale & Greenway, Kenya Trees 593. 1961; Puri, Indian Forest Ecol. 154. 1960; Agarwal, Wood-yielding Pl. India 67. 1970; Menninger, Color Sky 10. 1975.

Although long regarded as a separate species or as a distinct variety of *V. altissima* by numerous authors in the past, it seems from field observation that this taxon is merely a juvenile form of *V. altissima*, distinguished by its leaves having more or less broadly winged petioles, the wings being 8–16 mm wide, continuous, dilated, cordate and subamplexicaul at the base. Such leaves are also found on the turions or "watersprouts" often produced on the periphery of stumps of cutdown mature individuals. They may also be seen on seedlings. Some authors have also observed that the leaves on non-flowering branches of mature trees may have somewhat broader margins on their petioles than are seen on those of neighboring flowering branches. This was confirmed by us in Ceylon. In our experience, however, these nowhere approach the width of the wings seen on the juvenile plants and seedlings. On seedlings the lowermost leaves may even be unifoliolate.

Numerous writers describe the flowers and fruits of "*Vitex alata*", but it seems most likely that they are referring not to this form but to *V. limonifolia* Wall., *V. peduncularis* Wall., or *V. peduncularis* var. *roxburghiana* Clarke, which are the taxa regarded as "*V. alata*" by Kurz, Roxburgh, Schauer, and Wallich. Clarke avers that he has seen specimens of this form with 5-foliolate leaves.

V e r n. Baruna in India.

S p e c i m e n s E x a m i n e d. KURUNEGALA DISTRICT: top of Doluwakande, 7 March 1911, petioles alate, *s. coll. s.n.* (PDA). PUTTALAM DISTRICT: scattered in jungle forest, Panirendawa Forest Reserve, low altitude, 25 Jan. 1974, all leaves on saplings with broadly alate petioles, mature trees nearby with only very slight or no wings, *H.N. & A.L. Moldenke & Jayasuriya 28252* (ARIZ, MO, PDA, US). POLONNARUWA DISTRICT: rare in clumps of bushes on almost bare ledge slope of decomposing pegmatite just southeast of Giritalewewa, 7 miles northwest of Polonnaruwa, near Circuit Bungalow, 9 Jan. 1970, erect shrub 2 m tall, sterile juvenile foliage, *Fosberg & Ripley 51942* (PDA, US); common tree on sandy soil, Polonnaruwa Sacred Area 4 west, near road, sapling, leaves with alate petioles, *Ripley 246* (PDA). COLOMBO DISTRICT: occasional in woodland, Seeduwa, low altitude, 16 Jan. 1974, samplings 10 ft tall, with broadly alate petioles, *H.N. & A.L. Moldenke, Jayasuriya, & Sumithraarachchi 28112* (AAU, CAI, KARACHI, LL, PDA, US). KANDY DISTRICT: Haragama, 23 April 1926, young plant, leaves alate, *Alston 1328* (PDA); scattered in forest 39 miles east of Kandy on the Mahiyangane road, 1000 ft alt., 19 Jan. 1974, saplings about 6 ft tall, with broadly alate petioles, *H.N. & A.L. Moldenke, Jayasuriya & Sumithraarachchi 28192* (AAU, ARIZ, CAI, KARACHI, LL, PDA, US). MATALE DISTRICT: scattered in broken forest on ascent to temple, Dambulla Rock, 800 ft alt., 23 Jan. 1974, watersprouts about 7 ft tall, petioles more or less broadly winged, neighbouring mature trees without broad wings, *H.N. & A.L. Moldenke & Jayasuriya 28223* (AAU, ARIZ, CAI, KARACHI, LL, MO, PDA, US). AMPARAI DISTRICT: Gal Oya National Park, Inginiyagala, 26 June, 1970, tree bole 15 ft, crown 20 ft, girth 6 ft, bole fluted and twisted at base, inner bark orange-brown, sapwood ochre, hard, *Meijer & Balakrishnan 135* (PDA, US). GALLE DISTRICT: in wet zone, Naunikita Ela, 150 ft alt., 25 Sept. 1946, petioles alate, lowest leaves unifoliolate, "milla", *Worthington 2332* (PDA). DISTRICT UNKNOWN: in dense forests, *König 77* in part [Linn. Herb. 811.3] (LINN, MOLDENKE photo, NY photo).

f. **subglabra** Thw. ex Clarke in Hook. f., Fl. Br. Ind. 4: 584, in syn. 1885; Moldenke, Phytologia 15: 226. 1967; Turcz., Bull. Soc. Imp. Naturistes Moscou 36 (2): 223. 1863; Thw., Enum. Pl. Zeyl. 244. 1861; Clarke in Hook. f., Fl. Br. Ind. 4: 584. 1885; Trimen, Cat. 69. 1885; Trimen, Handb. Fl. Ceylon 3: 458. 1895; Willis, Cat. 69. 1911; Moldenke, Phytologia 5: 202–203 (1955), 15: 88–89 & 226–227 (1967), and 16: 496. 1968. Type: *Walker s.n.*, from Ceylon (PDA).

Vitex zeylanica Turcz., Bull. Soc. Imp. Naturistes Moscou 36 (2): 223. 1863 [not *V. zeylanica* Burm. f., 1768].
Vitex altissima var. *zeylanica* (Turcz.) Clarke in Hook. f., Fl. Br. Ind. 4: 584. 1885—*V. altissima* var. *zeylanica* Clarke ex Willis, Cat. 69. 1911.

This is a form of questionable validity. It is described as having its mature leaf-blades "quite glabrate beneath" and 5 in number. In several collections cited below they are, indeed, apparently completely glabrous on both surfaces, but in others the depressions in the reticulation beneath are microscopically puberulent much as might be seen if the hairs were all brushed off of the typical form. Most of the specimens seen by me have 3 leaflets. More field work is needed to ascertain if this form is worth maintaining.

It should be noted that Burman's *Vitex zeylanica* (1768) is actually a species of *Stereospermum* in the *Bignoniaceae*, but it effectively precludes the use of the epithet, "*zeylanica*" by Turczaninow (1863) and therefore by Clarke (1885).

V e r n. Milla (S).

S p e c i m e n s E x a m i n e d. PUTTALAM DISTRICT: at edge of jungle, Kalaoya, low altitude, 25 Jan. 1974, trees 40 ft tall, one leaf 5-foliolate,

H.N. & A.L. Moldenke & Jayasuriya 28328 (AAU, ARIZ, CAI, KARACHI, LL, PDA, US). ANURADHAPURA DISTRICT: rather abundant at edge of and in jungle forest, Palukolawala, low altitude, 24 Jan. 1974, trees 30–40 ft tall, many leaves with narrow wings on the petiole, *H.N. & A.L. Moldenke & Jayasuriya 28228* (AAU, ARIZ, CAI, KARACHI, LL, MO, PDA, US). KANDY DISTRICT: on road from Kitulgale to Maskeliya, 200 m altitude, 15 May 1971, tree 20 m tall, trunk 30 cm in diameter, bark cracked, soft, light pinkish-brown, 1 mm thick, live bark 3 mm thick, orange-brown, flowers pink, *Kostermans 24109* (AAU, US); rather abundant in woodland, 3 or 4 miles east of Madugoda, 2500 ft alt., 19 Jan. 1974, trees 45–50 ft tall, mostly in fruit, many petioles with very narrow wings, others wingless on the same branch, *H.N. & A.L. Moldenke, Jayasuriya, & Sumithraarachchi 28188* (AAU, ARIZ, CAI, KARACHI, LL, MO, PDA, US), *28189* (AAU, ARIZ, CAI, KARACHI, LL, MO, PDA, US); submontane forest on steep hillside north of milepost 38 on the Kandy to Mahiyangane road near culvert 16, 870 m alt., 10 Oct. 1973, *Sohmer, Jayasuriya, & Eliezer 8271* (LL, NY, US). MATALE DISTRICT: Aluvihare, 26 June 1967, a large tree, flowers pale violet, "milla", *Amaratunga 1343* (PDA); abundant trees in jungle on ascent to temple, Dambulla Rock, 800 ft alt., 23 Jan. 1974, trees about 40 ft tall, many petioles with narrow wings, *H.N. & A.L. Moldenke & Jayasuriya 28220* (AAU, ARIZ, CAI, KARACHI, LL, MOLDENKE, PDA, US). RATNAPURA DISTRICT: Gilimale Forest Reserve, Ratnapura, 20 July 1970, tree with girth 4 ft, bole 15 ft, crown 20 ft, steep buttresses, inner bark yellow when freshly cut, sapwood ochre, *Meijer 412* (PDA, US); forest confines in open, Sinharaja Forest, wet zone, 900 ft alt., 8 March 1948, leaf has very long drip-points, cf. with those from drier districts, *Worthington 3672* (PDA). MONERAGALA DISTRICT: in forest, Uda Walawa area, 17 Oct. 1971, tree 8 m tall, trunk 1 m in diameter, green immature fruit in bunches, glabrous leaves, *Balakrishnan & Jayasuriya NBK. 886* (US). GALLE DISTRICT: road near the arboretum, Kottawa, on the Galle to Udugama road, 2 Oct. 1973, *Waas & Peeris 540a* (US). HAMBANTOTA DISTRICT: rare on rocky wooded hill, Yala region, at milepost 9 on the road from Tissamaharama to Kataragama, 220 m alt., 9 March 1973, tree 4 m tall, bark ochraceous-rose-red, leaves 3-foliolate, flowers pale blue and lilac, mixed with green fruit in scorpioid cymes, *Bernardi 14183* (US); growing in low stature evergreen forest on reddish sand in Plot R. 8, Ruhuna National Park, Block I south of Situlpahuwa, 21 Oct. 1968, 4 m tall subcanopy tree, collected with fruit, dominated by *Mischodon zeylanica, Mueller-Dombois 68102114* (LL, PDA). MATARA DISTRICT: amongst cultivated land, Akuressa, 16 March 1947, *Worthington 2528* (PDA). LOCALITY UNKNOWN: *Fraser 178* (DS, US); *Gardner 674* (LE); *Walker s.n.* (PDA, type).

4. Vitex pinnata L., Sp. Pl., ed. 1, 638. 1753 [not *V. pinnata* Lour., 1847]; L.,

Fl., Zeyl., ed. 1, 195. 1747; Burm. f., Fl. Ind. 138, pl. 43 [fig. 2]. 1768; Vahl,
Symb. Bot. 3: 85. 1794; Moon, Cat. 1: 46. 1821; Schau. in A. DC., Prod. 11:
685–686. 1847; Thw., Enum. Pl. Zeyl. 244. 1861; Clarke in Hook. f., Fl. Br.
Ind. 4: 585. 1885; Trimen, Handb. Fl. Ceylon 358. 1895; Heyne, Nutt. Pl.
Ned. Ind. 4: 114. 1917; H. Hallier, Meded. Rijks-Herb. 37: 45. 1918; Alston
in Trimen, Handb. Fl. Ceylon 6: 232. 1931; Alston, Kandy Fl. 65, fig. 347.
1938; Moldenke, Phytologia 6: 61–64 & 70–79 (1957), 8: 73–75 (1961), 15:
323–325 (1967), and 17: 22–24, 1968; Abeywick., Ceylon J. Sci., Biol. Sci. 2:
217. 1959; Backer & Bakh., Fl. Java 2: 606. 1965; Gunawardena, Gen. Sp.
Pl. Zeyl. 147. 1968; Fonseka & Vinasithamby, Prov. List Local Names Fl.
Pl. Ceylon 35, 36, 54, & 58. 1971; Vivekanandan, Sri Lanka Forester, ser. 2,
11: 119, 125, 129, 135, 139, & 143. 1974. Type: *Herb. Hermann 1: 16* [lower
left] from Ceylon (BM).

Katoú-mail-eloú Rheede, Hort. Mal. 5: 3–4, pl. 2. 1685.
Pistacio-Vitex L., Fl. Zeyl., ed. 1, 195. 1747.—*Pistacia vitex* L. ex Watt, Dict.
  Econ. Prod. India 6 (4): 250. 1893.—*P. vitex* Steud. ex Zohary, Palestine
  J. Bot. Jerusalem Ser. 5: 227. 1952.
Anonyma Hermann ex L., Fl. Zeyl., ed. 1, 195. 1747.
Vitex latifolia Lam., Enc. 2: 613. 1788 [not *V. latifolia* Blanco, 1837, nor
  Mill., 1768, nor Wight, 1840].—*V. latifolia* Vahl ex Moldenke, Phytologia
  6: 62. 1957.—*V. latifolia* Auct. ex Backer & Bakh., Fl. Java 2: 606. 1965.
Vitex negundo Noronha, Verh. Batav. Genootsch. Kunsten 5, ed. 1, art. 4: 86.
  1790 [not *V. negundo* Curtis, 1832, nor L., 1753, nor L.f., 1966, nor Lour.,
  1934, nor Royle, 1919, nor Willd., 1918].
Vitex pubescens Vahl, Symb. Bot. 3: 85. 1794 [not *V. pubescens* Heyne, 1829].
Vitex arborea Roxb., Hort. Beng. 46. 1814; Roxb., Fl. Ind., 3: 73. 1832 [not *V.
  arborea* Bréon, 1955, nor Brown, 1806, nor Desf., 1847, nor Fischer, 1829].
Wallrothia articulata Roth, Nov. Pl. Sp. 317. 1821.
Vitex articulata Steud., Nom. Bot., ed. 2, 2: 777. 1840.
Vitex digitata Wight ex Steud., Nom. Bot., ed. 2, 2: 777. 1840.
Vitex bracteata Horsf. ex Miq., Fl. Ind. Bat. 2: 862. 1858.
Vitex heterophylla Blume ex Miq., Fl. Ind. Bat. 2: 862. 1858 [not *V. hetero-
  phylla* Roxb., 1814, nor Schau., 1919, nor Williams, 1905].
Vitex inaequifolia Turcz., Bull. Soc. Imp. Naturalistes Moscou 36 (3): 223.
  1863.
Vitex pubescens var. *lilacina* Kuntze, Rev. Gen. Pl. 2: 511. 1891.
Vitex pubescens var. *bicolor* Kuntze, Rev. Gen. Pl. 2: 511. 1891.
Vitex pubescens var. *ptilota* Dop, Bull. Soc. Hist. Nat. Toulouse 59: 198.
  1928.—*V. pubescens ptilota* Dop ex Worsdell, Ind. Lond. Suppl. 2: 500.
  1941.
Vitex pubescens var. *genuina* Hochr., Candollea 5: 191. 1934.
Tetrandra? paucidens Miq. ex Moldenke, Résumé Suppl. 4: 13. 1962.

Small or medium-sized tree, to 25 m tall; trunk to 70 cm in diameter, usually crooked; main branches erect or ascending, crookedly re-branched and wide-spreading toward the top; branchlets greenish when fresh, acutely or obtusely angular, densely short-puberulent, mostly slightly ampliate at the nodes; wood very coarse-grained and hard, brittle, 55 lbs/cu. ft; bark greyish or yellowish-grey to brown, smooth or minutely checked longitudinally, defoliating in thin pieces, yellow within; leaves decussate-opposite, normally 3- or 5-foliolate (1- or 2-foliolate on seedlings); petioles 4–10.5 cm long, flattened and submargined above, densely short-puberulent, not noticeably ampliate basally nor disciform apically, sometimes winged on seedlings or shoots; leaflets mostly unequal in size, the lower ones often much reduced, all stalked on rather slender, puberulent, deeply canaliculate and margined petiolules 1–6 mm long or the lowest sessile or subsessile; blades firmly chartaceous, rather thick and firm when mature, rather uniformly dark green on both surfaces or somewhat lighter beneath, sometimes somewhat incurved or infolded, the central one elliptic or ovate, 8–22.5 cm long, 3.5–10.5 cm wide, acuminate or subcaudate apically, entire (the lowest ones often serrate-dentate on seedlings), broadly cuneate or acute basally and somewhat attenuate, minutely and obscurely pulverulent-puberulent above along the midrib and sometimes also along the secondaries or even on the lamina, more densely puberulent or short-pubescent beneath, especially on the larger venation, on petiolules to 6 mm long, the 2 lateral ones similar but usually smaller and more acute apically, 5.5–15.5 cm long, 2.5–7 cm wide, and on petiolules only to 2 mm long, the 2 lowest (when present) 1.5–5.2 × 0.7–2.3 cm and sessile or subsessile; inflorescence terminal, erect (sometimes also axillary in the upper leaf-axils), thyrsoid-paniculate, 6.5–25 cm long, 3.5–18 cm wide, densely many-flowered, brachiate, conspicuously and abundantly bracteate, densely short-pubescent or puberulent throughout with flavescent or sordid-brownish hairs, the branches often chestnut-coloured, tinged with green and purple when fresh; peduncles stout, reddish-brown when fresh, rather acutely tetragonal, often sulcate, 1.8–4 cm long; sympodia and inflorescence-branches tetragonal and sulcate; pedicels obsolete or to 1 mm long and densely flavescent-pubescent; bracts, bractlets, and prophylla very numerous and conspicuous, foliaceous, simple (or rarely 3-foliolate), pale or yellowish-green, varying to chestnut and tinged with green and purple, elliptic, 5–17 mm long, 2–7 mm wide, sessile, densely short-pubescent on both surfaces; calyx campanulate, about 4 mm long and 7 mm wide, densely short-pubescent outwardly and on the teeth within, the teeth deltoid, about 2 mm long; corolla hypocrateriform, 2-lipped, in general aspect varying from purple, purplish or violet to bluish-white, white, or light yellow, the tube about 10 mm long, the lower portions glabrous on both surfaces, the upper portion pubescent and glandular on the outside, the throat glabrous except near the somewhat villous base of the middle lobe of the lower lip and near the insertion of the stamens, the larger lip about 1 cm long and 5 mm wide, the lobes pubescent on the outside except near the margins of the lip, glabrous within, the smaller ones about 5 mm long and 3.5 mm wide; stamens exserted, 11–13 mm long, inserted at about the middle of the corolla-tube; filaments white; anthers dull greyish-brown or nearly black before opening; style white, 1.5–1.8 cm long, usually equalling the stamens; stigma bifid; ovary greenish except for the purple apex, glabrous; fruiting-calyx not much enlarged; fruit drupaceous, globose or flattened-globose, 7–13 mm long and wide, glabrous, dark purple, purplish-black, or black when mature.

D i s t r. This species is widely distributed in peninsular India and eastward through Bangladesh, Burma, Thailand, Indo-China, Malaya, and Indonesia to the Sunda Islands. It has been introduced in Guyana, Madagascar, and elsewhere and is cultivated in various parts of tropical Asia, Hawaii, Réunion, and elsewhere. Clarke (1885) refers to it as "frequent" not only in the southern Deccan peninsula of India but also in Ceylon and Hallier (1918) also records it from "Zeylon", but Trimen (1895) asserts that he has never observed anything in Ceylon resembling Wight's illustration of *V. arborea* Roxb. or, by inference, Vahl's *V. pubescens*. He therefore regarded Linnaeus' *V. pinnata* as applying to the common Ceylon *V. altissima* L.f. However, an examination of the type of Linnaeus' name in the Banksian Herbarium shows it quite definitely to be Vahl's and Wight's plant. The inappropriate specific epithet chosen by Linnaeus appears to be based on the unfortunate fact that the detached leaflets of one leaf on the type specimen were mounted in pinnate fashion on the sheet. Most recently collected Ceylon material distributed as *V. pinnata* represents *V. altissima* or one of its several subspecific taxa. The Dalman specimen from India named *V. pinnata* by Linnaeus himself in his own herbarium is *V. trifolia* L.

It is important to note that Moon (1824) lists both *V. altissima* and *V. pinnata* as distinct species and also lists *V. pubescens* as native in Ceylon. It would thus appear that, even if he did not know exactly what *V. pinnata* was and included it only from previous literature, he did know that what was then called *V. pubescens* was in Ceylon in his day. *Vitex pinnata* apparently has been cultivated in the Botanic Garden at Peradeniya for a long time since it was collected there by Mrs. Walker before 1895, by Foreman in 1911, and by Parsons in 1926. It is listed (as *V. pubescens* Vahl) by Thwaites & Hooker in 1861.

U s e s. The very durable wood is used in construction in various parts of southern India; in Burma it is employed to make wooden bells.

V e r n. According to Vivekanandan (1974): Kaha-milla, Milla, Miyan-milla, Niyan-milla, Sapu-milla (S), Kata-manakku (T), but these names most probably apply, instead, to *V. altissima*. In India and elsewhere in its range, *V. pinnata* has amassed over 80 vernacular names, among which are: Alaban,

Goelimpapa, Laban hout, Molave, Nowli eragu, Pagil, and Trasek.

N o t e. The leaves are sometimes attacked by a gall-wasp, *Eriophyes cryptotrichus.*

S p e c i m e n s E x a m i n e d. KANDY DISTRICT: Royal Botanic Garden, Peradeniya, 7 July 1911, *Foreman s.n.* (PDA), 20 April 1926, *Parsons 344* (PDA), *Walker 1122 [Alston 344]* (K).

5. Vitex leucoxylon L. f., Suppl. Pl. 293. 1781. f. **leucoxylon.** Moon, Cat. 1: 46. 1821; Schau. in A. DC., Prod. 11: 692. 1847; Thw., Enum. Pl. Zeyl. 244. 1861; Watt, Econ. Prod. India 5: 294, 6: 191, & 7: 255. 1883; Clarke in Hook. f., Fl. Br. Ind. 4: 587–588. 1885; Trimen, Cat. 69. 1885; Trimen, Handb. Fl. Ceylon 3: 358–359. 1895; Gamble, Man. Indian Timb., ed. 2, 542. 1902; Prain, Bengal Pl., ed. 2, 832 & 833. 1903; Brandis, Indian Trees 504. 1906; Willis, Cat. 69. 1911; Alston in Trimen, Handb. Fl. Ceylon 6: 232. 1931; Moldenke, Phytologia 5: 436–439 (1956), 8: 42 (1961), 15: 253 (1967), and 17: 8–9. 1968; Abeywick., Ceylon J. Sci., Biol. Sci. 2: 217. 1959; Worthington, Ceylon Trees 346. 1959; Gunawardena, Gen. Sp. Pl. Zeyl. 148. 1968; Fonseka & Vinasithamby, Prov. List Local Names Fl. Pl. Ceylon 35, 63, & 65. 1971. Type: *König 77* from "in vastis sylvis", Ceylon (LINN).

Wallrothia leucoxylon (L. f.) Roth, Nov. Pl. Sp. 317. 1821.
Vitex leucoxylon L. apud Wall, Num. List [48]. 1829 [not *V. leucoxylon* Blanco, 1895, nor Naves, 1918, nor Roth, 1956, nor Roxb., 1814, nor Span., 1856, nor Schau., 1893].—*V. leucoxylon* Willd. ex Roxb., Fl. Ind., ed 2, 3: 74–75. 1832.—*V. leucoxylon* Wall. apud Schau. in A. DC., Prod. 11: 692. 1847.
Vitex rheedii Kostel., Allg. Med.-pharm. Fl. 3: 826. 1834.
Vitex leucoxylon var. *albiflora* Span. ex Hook., Comp. Bot. Mag. 1: 349. 1836.
Wallrothia tomentosa Wight ex Clarke in Hook. f., Fl. Br. Ind. 4: 588. 1885.
Vitex tomentosa Wight ex Moldenke, Phytologia 5: 436. 1956 [not *V. tomentosa* Pav., 1940, nor Sessé & Moc., 1940, nor Rich., 1941].

Moderate-sized or large tree, 4–20 m tall; trunk to 1.3 m in diameter (although usually much less), with wavy and twisted ridges, much fluted in cross-section, branching profusely to form a full, spreading, rather dense crown, the bole often 10–15 m long; bark white to light grey or pale brown, smooth, striated, sometimes roughish; wood dark grey or light greyish-brown to purple-brown or pinkish, fine-grained, moderately hard, durable, shiny, weighing 48 pounds per cubic foot; branches and branchlets slender, light grey or whitish, more or less obtusely tetragonal, glabrate; twigs usually brunnescent in drying, more or less minutely puberulent; leaves 3–5-foliolate; petioles slender, 2.5–6.5 cm long, varying from appressed yellow- or brown-pubescent to sparsely and very minutely puberulent or even glabrate; petiolules very slender, puberulent or glabrate, the central one conspicuously longer, 1.4–2.5 cm long, the lateral ones 1–2 cm long, the basal ones (if present) 1–9 mm long; leaflet-blades coriaceous or thin-chartaceous, usually rather uniformly bright-green on both surfaces or lighter and more yellowish beneath, oblong to oblong-elliptic or elliptic, sometimes uniformly narrow-elliptic and 3–4 times as long as wide [f. *saligna* (Roxb.) Moldenke], usually apically obtuse or acute, normally entire, minutely puberulent or pubescent along the larger venation (especially beneath) or glabrate, usually densely pubescent beneath when young, eglandular, the central one 3.5–14.5 cm long, 1–4.5 cm wide, apically and basally acute or more or less attenuate-subacuminate, the lateral ones 5.5–9.5 cm long, 3–4.5 cm wide, basally mostly inequilateral, the lowermost ones (if present) 2.5–5 cm long and 1.5–2.5 cm wide, mostly basally inequilateral; inflorescence axillary, cymose, 3–17 cm long and wide, developing after the leaves, lax, loosely many-flowered, abundantly dichotomous-furcate with divaricate branches, often up to 6 times di- or trichotomous, varying from appressed yellow- or brown-pubescent to minutely puberulent or glabrate throughout; peduncles very slender, 1.8–7.5 cm long; pedicels 0.5–2 mm long; calyx cupuliform, sparsely appressed-puberulent, its tube about 2 mm long, the rim 5-toothed, the teeth equal, deltoid, about 0.5 mm long; corolla very irregular, white or whitish, purple-pubescent in the throat and the lower lip with purplish-bluish hairs toward the base above, occasionally wholly white (var. *albiflora* Span.) or with a slight yellowish tinge, the tube about 4.5 mm long, densely villous inside from the insertion of the stamens to the mouth, the upper lip 2-lobed, the lobes about 2.5 mm long, the lower lip 3-lobed, the lateral lobes rounded, about 2.5 mm long, glabrous above, the middle lobe about 3.5 mm long, sinuate-margined, densely villous or bearded, usually marked with a large purplish spot; stamens inserted about 1 mm below the mouth of the corolla-tube, slightly exserted; filaments thickened and villous toward the base; anthers purple or dark-purple; style somewhat surpassing the stamens; stigma shortly bifid; ovary globose, glabrous or hairy; drupes obovoid or elliptic, 1.2–2 cm long, mostly 1-seeded, black or purple-black when mature, fleshy, the lower 2/3 usually covered by the fruiting-calyx.

D i s t r. This species is a rather important tree in the peninsular portion of India, occurring also in Lahore (Pakistan) and Ceylon eastward to upper Burma; it has been reported erroneously from Malaya. It is or has been cultivated in Java, England, and elsewhere.

E c o l. It inhabits chiefly wet evergreen forests or (as in Ceylon) the banks of streams, lakes, and reservoirs. Thwaites refers to it as "not uncommon" in the hotter parts of Ceylon.

U s e s. The wood is used for making cart-wheels and the fruit, extensively eaten by parrots, is employed as a fish poison. In India it is an important timber tree and a decoction from the leaves is used to bathe patients suffering from fever or anemia.

V e r n. Nebedda, Né-bedda, Nabada (S); Kaddunchchi, Kardu-nochi, Nir, Nir-nochchi, Nir-nochi (T). There are numerous other names applied in India and elsewhere.

N o t e. Clarke (1885) claims that the typical form of the species has its 5 entire-margined leaflets coriaceous, shiny, yellowish beneath, and with obscure venation, while in the form known as f. *saligna* (Roxb.) Moldenke the leaflets are more membranous in texture, uniformly narrow-elliptic, 3–4 times as long as wide, with the reticulate venation distinct on both surfaces. They are also narrower and apically more attenuate-acute. In *Wallrothia tomentosa* we find "a very handsome form with broader leaflets" pubescent on both sides of the midrib beneath and the venation prominent above. He admits, however, that "the extreme membranous narrow-leaved *V. saligna* (Roxburgh's specimen) shows similar hair on each side of the midrib beneath". It often acts as host to the mistletoe, *Dendrophthoë falcata* (L.f.) Ettingsh., and it is attacked by the fungus, *Meliola cookeana* Speg.

S p e c i m e n s E x a m i n e d. JAFFNA DISTRICT: Jaffna, *Gardner s.n. C.P. 1957* in part (PDA). KURUNEGALA DISTRICT: Kurunegala, Dec. 1853, *s. coll. C.P. 1957* in part (PDA); in swamp, Ridigama, 20 Oct. 1965, a small tree, flowers white with mauvish hairs, ripe fruit purple-black, "nébedda" Sinhala, *Amaratunga 1037* (PDA). PUTTALAM DISTRICT: on forested sandy riverbank, Wilpattu National Park at crossing of the Modaragam Aru below Marichchukaddi on the road to Mannar, 15 m alt., tree 10 m tall, mature fruit black, with mushy pericarp, *Davidse & Sumi-thraarachchi 8234* (LL). ANURADHAPURA DISTRICT: near tank, Anuradhapura, 17 March 1927, large tree, flowers white, *Alston 1050* (PDA); Wilpattu, in ring of vegetation around Podi-villu, about sealevel, 6 June 1969, small tree, 9 m tall, trunk 18 cm in diameter, flowers purplish, leaves almost glabrous, *Hladik 817* (PDA, US), *824* (US); at edge of small abandoned tank 3 miles north of Dambulla at milepost 51/5, low altitude, trees 40 ft tall, 23 Jan. 1974, *H.N. & A.L. Moldenke & Jayasuriya 28224* (AAU, ARIZ, CAI, KARACHI, LL, MOLDENKE, PDA, US); in forest near 65/4 milepost on the Anuradhapura to Trincomalee road, 5 Oct. 1973, tree about 40 ft tall, immature fruit green, *Sohmer 8144* (NY, US); area at the south end of Nachcha-duwa Tank, 30 Nov. 1973, flowers white with purplish honey-guides, fruit green, *Sohmer 8953* (LACROSSE, US); Wilpattu National Park, Maduru Odai on the Mannar to Puttalam road at the junction to Periya Naga Villu, 30 June 1969, flowers white, collected as voucher for ecologic studies, *Wira-wan, Cooray, & Balakrishnan 914A* (LL, PDA); by waterside in dry zone, Nachaduwa Tank bed, 333 ft alt., 15 July 1949, 3 leaflets, "nebudda", *Wor-thington 4237* (PDA). POLONNARUWA DISTRICT: in swampy area on

Polonnaruwa to Batticaloa road 1 mile from Mahaweli Ganga river, 25 June 1970, treelet 20 ft tall, bole 15 ft, girth 2 ft, flowers white, leaflets all 5, *Meijer & Balakrishnan 119* (PDA, US); at Sungawila jungle on the way to Somawathiye, 28 May 1974, tree bole 30 ft, forming a canopy, trunk diameter 2 ft, with wavy ridges which are also twisted, branching profusely at the top, leaves compound, usually 3 or 5 leaflets present, bark brownish and cracked, flowers white, the lower lip with purplish-bluish hairs inside, *Sumithraarachchi DBS. 352* (AAU, CAI, LACROSSE, LL); savanna along roadside between Polonnaruwa and Batticaloa at approximately milepost 60, 15 March 1973, scattered evergreen tree with dense rounded crown about 26 ft tall, flowers white, *Townsend 73/253* (US); in primary forest, Yakkure, west of Wasgomuwa Reserve, 7 June 1974, tree with bluish flowers, *Waas 606* (NY, US). KANDY DISTRICT: in Great Circle, Royal Botanic Garden, Peradeniya, leaves pubescent along midrib beneath, leaflets 3, flowers white with purple hairs at tip, *Alston 2478* (PDA); cultivated, *Gardner s.n.* (K); cultivated, Royal Botanic Garden, 16 May 1922, *Petch s.n.* (BH, NY). MATALE DISTRICT: Sigiriya, 800 feet altitude, 25 Nov. 1960, 3–5 leaflets, rainfall 70 inches, *Hancock 346 [Worthington 6964]* (PDA); Sigiriya, along roadside near Sigiriya Tank, 700 ft alt. 11 Oct. 1974, large tree, mature fruit black, 1-seeded, pericarp fleshy, being eaten by parrots, *Davidse 7439* (LL, US); by secondary stream in loose sandy loam, Galboda, off the Naula to Elahera road, low altitude, 5 Oct. 1971, tree 60 ft tall, girth 4 ft, leaves hairy, blades 10–12 cm long, *Jayasuriya 305* (PDA, US); at edge of granitic outcrop, Sigiriya Tank, 15 July 1974, tree 20 m tall, trunk about 1 m in diameter at breast height, bark pale brown, striate, flowers (2 only) white, with purple pubescence in throat, anthers dark-purple, fruits pear-shaped, green, turning purple, used as fish poison, *Nowicke, Fosberg, & Jayasuriya 364* (NY, PDA, US); at edge of water, Sigiriya Tank, 15 July 1973, tree about 20 m tall, trunk about 1.3 m in diameter at breast height, very fluted in cross-section, bark pale brown and striated, flowers white, purple-pubescent in the throat, anthers purple, *Nowicke, Fosberg, & Jayasuriya 365* (NY, PDA, US); Sigiriya, 30 Oct. 1969, tree, *Reitz 30021* (US); secondary forest at Kalugaloya stream edge at 5/10 milepost on the Naule to Elahera road, 6 June 1974, tree 12 m tall, flowers faintly blue, *Waas 573* (LL, US); Galewela, 650 ft altitude, in dry zone always by water, 28 July 1949, 3 leaflets, *Worthington 4257* (PDA). BADULLA DISTRICT: at milepost 54 between Mahiyangane and Padiyatalawa, low altitude, 7 May 1975, small tree 6 m tall, corolla whitish, *Jayasuriya 2118* (LL, US). MONERAGALA DISTRICT: in riparian forest, Bibile, low altitude, 1 May 1975, tree 10 m tall, trunk 45 cm in diameter breast height, corolla white with purple hairs above, anthers purple, *Jayasuriya 1937* (AAU, US); Galoya National Park, in riparian forest bordering savanna, low altitude, 1 May 1975, medium-sized tree, *Jayasuriya 1961* (LL, US). BATTICALOA DISTRICT: in swampy ground, "nir nochi", *Vincent 13* (PDA); Batticaloa,

Sept. 1885, "nir nochi", *Walker 180* (PDA); Talawa ravine, in dry zone savanna at 42/11 milepost on Bibile to Batticaloa road, 500 ft alt. 21 April 1950, sapling, 3 leaflets, *Worthington 4649* (PDA). TRINCOMALEE DISTRICT: Andankulam, 20 June 1970, scattered trees 1.25 m tall, outer bark smooth, white, leaves hairy, flowers white, scented, *Cramer 3006* (PDA, US); Kantalai Tank bed, 130 ft alt. 21 Aug. 1946, a water-lover, 3 or 4 leaflets, "nebedda" in Sinhala, "nir" or "kardu-noch" in Tamil, *Worthington 2046* (PDA). HAMBANTOTA DISTRICT: in sand around 1-acre waterhole on Plot R. 10, Ruhuna National Park, near Patanagala Beach, in large rock outcrop area south of beach, 31 Aug. 1967, important tree, 6 m tall, with full round crown, *Mueller-Dombois & Comanor 67083110* (US). LOCALITY UNKNOWN: in vast woods, *König 77* in part (LINN type, MOLDENKE photo of type, NY photo of type, S photo of type).

f. **zeylanica** (Moldenke) Moldenke, Phytologia 36: 164. 1977. Type: *Mueller-Dombois & Balakrishnan 68091211* from Wilpattu National Park, Ceylon (US).

Vitex leucoxylon var. *zeylanica* Moldenke, Phytologia 21: 419. 1971.

This form differs from the typical form of the species chiefly in its leaflets averaging smaller, 2.5–9 cm long and 1.3–3.5 cm wide, at least the larger ones more or less serrate with irregularly placed, often remote, appressed, antrorse teeth toward the apex or only undate-repand, mostly dull grey above in drying, the veinlet reticulation usually conspicuous and obtusely subprominulent above, apically often obtuse.

Three of the collections cited below are in fruit and the other is in flower, so the characters of the leaves cannot be dismissed as a seedling, juvenile, or sucker (watersprout) condition as was the case in the form of *V. altissima* L.f. with broadly winged petioles.

Specimens Examined. ANURADHAPURA DISTRICT: Wilpattu National Park, between Weerakuti Villu and Maduru Odai, a little north of Hindu temple in ruins, 100 m into the sedge wewa, associated with *Syzygium*, 12 Sept. 1968, tree 4 m tall, 3 leaflets, collected as voucher for ecologic studies, *Mueller-Dombois & Balakrishnan 68091211* (MOLDENKE isotype, PDA isotype, US type, US isotype); at south end of tank near Tirappana, Nachchaduwa tank, 30 Nov. 1973, flowers white with purplish honey-guides, fruit green, *Sohmer 8953* (S); in main tank edge, Hinukkiriyawa Wewa, 13 Jan. 1974, tree 12 m tall, *Waas 367* (NY, US); Wilpattu National Park, at Periya Naga Villu, in Plot W. 38 A, 30 June 1969, tree 8 m tall, trunk 30 cm in diameter, bark white, somewhat rough, flowers white, fruit green, collected as voucher for ecologic studies, *Wirawan, Cooray, & Balakrishnan 914* (LL, PDA, US). MATALE DISTRICT: in sparse forest on rock knob plain off the 12/4 milepost on the Naula to Elahera road, 160 m alt. 6 Oct. 1971, treelet 6 m tall, flowers white, fragrant, with purplish pubescence on the upper corolla-lobes, fruit green, hard-seeded, *Jayasuriya 316* (PDA, US). AMPARAI DISTRICT: Lahugala Sanctuary, Kitula, at south side of tank, on shallow cap over gneiss, 30 m alt. 14 Nov. 1967, isolated tree 9 m tall, spreading, bark grey-brown, fissured, leaves hairy, fruit olive-shaped, black, *Comanor 595* (MICH, NY, PDA). TRINCOMALEE DISTRICT: in grassy openings, Peryakulam, near Trincomalee, on the northern road westward along the seashore, 10 Oct. 1975, medium-height dense tree, olive-like, branches terete, robust, white-fuscous, leaves 5-foliolate, very coriaceous and bicoloured, cymes open, slender, rachis green, flowers white, fruit ovoid, 2 cm long, *Bernardi 15282* (M, NY); one tree in sandy soil of beach and dunes along the beach road to Gangai Ferry on the way to Muttur from Trincomalee, 11 July, 1973, tree about 6 m tall, bark grey-white, trunk about 15 cm in diameter at breast height, flowers white, the throat pubescent, *Nowicke & Jayasuriya 280* (NY, US); at margin of abandoned tank (reservoir), Nabadagas Wewa, Nabadagas Ara (watercourse), Block 2, 6 Jan. 1969, tree 10 m tall, trunk 50 cm in diameter at breast height, flowers white with mauve centre to lower lip, fragrant, *Fosberg, Mueller-Dombois, Wirawan, Cooray, & Balakrishnan 51081* (NY, PDA, US); 1 Sept. 1931, flowers white, "nirnochchi", *Simpson 8508* (NY); in dry area near village, Sept., a small tree with drooping branches, fruit pale green, unripe, bluish-black and soft when ripe, *Van Beusekom 1643* (US).

6. Vitex peduncularis Wall., Num. List [48], no. 1753, hyponym. 1829; Schau. in A. DC., Prod. 11: 687. 1847. f. **peduncularis.** Schau. in A. DC., Prod. 11: 687. 1847; Clarke in Hook. f., Fl. Br. Ind. 4: 584 & 587. 1885; Watt, Dict. Econ. Prod. India 6 (4): 250. 1893; Gamble, Man. Indian Timb., ed. 2, 541. 1902; Prain, Bengal Pl. 832. 1903; Basu, Indian Med. Pl. 3: 3, pl. 741. 1918; Vaughan, Indian Forester 47: pl. 9 & 10. 1921; Gamble, Fl. Pres. Madras 2: 1102 & 1103. 1924; Burkill, Dict. Econ. Prod. Malay Penins. 2: 2277. 1966; Uphof, Dict. Econ. Pl., ed. 2, 545. 1968; Moldenke, Phytologia 6: 49–51 (1957), 8: 72 (1961), 15: 319–320 (1967), and 17: 21–22. 1968; Agarwal, Wood-yielding Pl. India 67. 1970. Type: *Wallich 1753* from Palmyra, Silhet, Bangladesh, East India Company Herbarium (K).

Vitex morava Buch.-Ham. ex Wall., Num. List [48], no. 1752. 1829.

Vitex pentaphylla Lamb. ex Moldenke, Prelim. Alph. List Invalid Names 52. 1940 [not *V. pentaphylla* Merr., 1909, nor Pavon, 1940, nor Sessé & Moc., 1940].

Vitex alata Wall. ex Moldenke, Alph. List Invalid Names Suppl. 1: 28. 1947 [not *V. alata* Heyne, 1821, nor Roxb., 1829, nor Royen, 1940, nor Schau., 1885, nor Willd., 1803].

Vitex procumbens Hort. ex Moldenke, Phytologia 6: 49. 1957.

Vitex pedunculata Wall. ex Moldenke, Résumé Suppl. 3: 42. 1962.

Juvenile Form

Vitex alata Roxb. ex Willd. in Rottl., Ges. Naturf. Freunde Berlin Neue
Schriften 4: 203. 1803 [not *V. alata* Heyne, 1821, nor Schau., 1885, nor
Royen, 1940, nor Wall., 1947, nor Willd., 1803].
Vitex peduncularis var. *roxburghiana* Clarke in Hook. f., Fl. Br. Ind. 4: 587.
1885.
Vitex roxburghiana Kanjilal in Kanjilal *et al.*, Fl. Assam 3: 485 & 561. 1939.
Vitex peduncularis f. juv. *roxburghiana* (Clarke) Moldenke, Phytologia 37:
275. 1977.

Shrub, 1.5 m tall, or small tree, to 32 m tall; trunk to 30 cm in diameter
and 1.1 m in circumference; bark from whitish to dark brown or blackish;
wood reddish-grey to light brown, very heavy (27.4 kg/cu ft), hard, close-
grained, even textured, seasoning slowly, not very durable, polishing well,
susceptible to insect attack; branchlets and twigs very slender, obtusely
tetragonal or subterete, medullose, the younger parts often dark brown or
purplish in drying, minutely and very sparsely strigillose-puberulent or pulverulent, eventually glabrous and shiny; leaves 3- or 5-foliolate (mostly 3),
fully expanded during anthesis; petioles very slender, 3.5–7 cm long, conspicuously flattened and sometimes more or less margined, sparsely strigillose or
glabrous; leaflets subequal, all subsessile or on petiolules 1–10 mm long;
leaflet-blades subchartaceous, uniformly bright-green on both surfaces and
with oil glands showing as pellucid dots, the very immature ones brunnescent
in drying, the central one oblong, narrow-elliptic or lanceolate, 7–16 cm long,
1.8–4.9 cm wide, apically acuminate, entire, basally acuminate and attenuate
into the petiolule, minutely and sparsely pulverulent on both surfaces when
young, eventually glabrate above and very sparsely pulverulent or glabrate
beneath, rather densely covered with tiny resinous puncta beneath even in
age; secondary veins very numerous and close together, not distinctly joined
marginally; veinlet reticulation rather abundant, very fine, slightly subprominulous on both surfaces or obscure beneath; inflorescence axillary, paniculate, solitary or paired in the upper leaf-axils, 8–25 cm long, 3–6 cm wide,
long-pedunculate, composed of 7–11 pairs of opposite or subopposite, long-
stipitate, 1–3 times dichotomous, loosely few-flowered cymes; peduncles very
slender, 3–9.5 cm long, mostly slightly flattened, minutely pulverulent-puberulent; cyme-branches elongate, flattened, rather densely canescent-puberulent; bractlets linear, 1–3 mm long, puberulent; flowers often slightly
aromatic; calyx dotted with golden scale-like glands; corolla white or light-
pink, fading yellow or cream-colour, stiffly white-strigillose; fruit globose,
red, slightly bitter, with a 3- or 4-celled central stone.

D i s t r. This is a rather widespread species of the upper mixed, deciduous or tropical forests from northern Pakistan, Assam, and Sikkim through

much of India to Bangladesh, Burma, Thailand, Indo-China, Malaya, and the Mergui Archipelago; sometimes cultivated in India and elsewhere.

U s e s. *Vitex peduncularis* has numerous recorded economic uses. In Assam a decoction made from the leaves and bark is used as a febrifuge in the treatment of blackwater fever (for which it is so highly regarded that the seeds and seedlings have been widely exported to other parts of India) and malaria. In Pakistan the ripe fruits are eaten and the wood is used to make agricultural implements; the leaves are eaten as a vegetable in cases of ophthalmia. In Burma the wood is used in the construction of buildings, the manufacture of harrows, wells, sugarcane crushers, rice pounders, oilmill mortars and pestles, oars, and yokes, and for carving. In India the wood is used to make posts, beams, and yokes, and, medicinally, the juice is used for its supposed antihaemolytic activity in cases of cobra bites and to treat spleen complaints, muscular pains, stab wounds, dysentery, and bone fractures. The immature leaves contain a light yellow crystalline substance known as vitexin ($C_{15}H_{14}O_6$) also found in the related *V. parviflora* A.L. Juss. and unrelated *Saponaria officinalis* L.

V e r n. In India and elsewhere: Awal, Bhadu, Boruna, Kyetyo, Osai, Pazin-nyo, Popoul thmar, and Tin nok.

N o t e. The inflorescences are sometimes attacked by a species of *Cecidomya* gall-wasp.

The "Mail-elau" of Rheede (1685), often placed in the synonymy of *V. peduncularis*, belongs in that of *V. altissima* L.f. The illustration given by Basu (1918) probably applies to the following juvenile form.

Juvenile Form

Voigt, Hort. Suburb. Calc. 469. 1845; Gamble, Man. Indian Timb., ed. 1, 298 & 522. 1881; Watt, Econ. Prod. India 7: 254. 1883; Clarke in Hook. f., Fl. Br. Ind. 4: 587. 1885; Watt, Dict. Econ. Prod. India 6 (4): 250. 1893; Gamble, Man. Indian Timb., ed. 2, 541. 1902; Kanjilal *et al.*, Fl. Assam 3: 485 & 561. 1939; Prain, Bengal Pl. 832. 1963; Moldenke, Phytologia 6: 51–52 (1957), 15: 320 (1967), and 17: 22. 1968; Jain & Tarafder, Econ. Bot. 24: 266. 1970; Agarwal, Wood-yielding Pl. India 67. 1970. Type: Lectotype: *Edgeworth s.n.* from Parasnath, Bihar, India (K).

This form differs from the typical form of the species in having more or less uniformly winged petioles. It is also said to be "less grey-pubescent" and the "panicles more laxly few-flowered". This seems mostly to be a juvenile form represented by young plants or coppice-shoots, but Haines (1922) definitely states that the winged petioles "persist sometimes to maturity". Prain (1903) refers to it as "a considerable tree" and Watt (1893) calls it "a good timber tree". It is reported from Pakistan and India to Bangladesh and Burma. An extract is used in the treatment of chest pains, blackwater fever, and the bite of a rabid dog or jackal in India.

V e r n. In India reported names are: badu marak, boruna, goda, and krawru.

S p e c i m e n s   E x a m i n e d: KANDY DISTRICT: near stores, Royal Botanic Garden, Peradeniya, 21 March 1946, leaves from young plant, petioles alate, blades serrate, *de Silva 1002* (PDA).

7. Vitex negundo L., Sp. Pl., ed. 1, 638. 1753; Hermann, Mus. Zeyl., ed. 1, 47. 1717; L., Fl. Zeyl. 194. 1747; Moon, Cat. 1: 46. 1824; Schau. in A. DC., Prod. 11: 684–685. 1847; Thw., Enum. Pl. Zeyl. 244. 1861; Clarke in Hook. f., Fl. Br. Ind. 4: 583–584. 1885; Trimen, Cat. 69. 1885; Watt, Dict. Econ. Prod. India 6 (4): 248. 1893; Trimen, Handb. Fl. Ceylon 3: 357. 1895; Gamble, Man. Indian Timb., ed. 2, 539–540. 1902; Prain, Bengal Pl. 832 & 833. 1903; Brandis, Indian Trees 503–504. 1906; Willis, Cat. 69. 1911; Heyne, Nutt. Pl. Ned. Ind. 4: 115. 1917; Hallier, Meded. Rijks-Herb. 37: 43–44. 1918; Parker, Forest Fl. Punjab, ed. 2, 395. 1924; Pieper, Bot. Jahrb. Beibl. 141: 53 & 77. 1928; Alston in Trimen, Handb. Fl. Ceylon 6: 232. 1931; Benthall, Trees Calcutta 355–356. 1933; Moldenke, Phytologia 2: 120–121 (1944), 5: 486–498 (1957), 6: 14 (1957), 8: 64–66 (1961), 15: 267–268 & 304–308 (1967), and 17: 12–16. 1968; Cooke, Fl. Pres. Bombay, ed. 2, 2: 508. 1958; Abeywick., Ceylon J. Sci., Biol. Sci. 2: 217. 1959; Worthington, Ceylon Trees 347. 1959; Burkill, Dict. Econ. Prod. Malay Penins. 2: 2279–2280. 1966; Gunawardena, Gen. Sp. Pl. Zeyl. 147. 1968; Fonseka & Vinasithamby, Prov. List Local Names Fl. Pl. Ceylon 30, 64, 65, 86, & 96. 1971; Vivekanandan, Sri Lanka Forester, ser. 2, 11: 119, 128, 129, 139, & 149. 1974. Type: *Herb. Linnaeus 811/8* from somewhere in India.

Negundo foemina, acostae Delechamps, Hist. Gen. Pl. 1867. 1586.—*Negundo foemina* Acosta ex Rheede, Hort. Mal. 2: 15. 1679.

Negundo mas, Acostae Delechamps, Hist. Gen. Pl. 1586.—*Negundo mas* Acosta ex L., Fl. Zeyl. 195. 1748.

Negundo masle de Acosta Orta, Hist. Drogues, ed. 2, 115. 1619.

Negundo femelle de Acosta Orta, Hist. Drogues, ed. 2, 116. 1619.

Negundo arbor mas J. Bauhin, Hist. Pl. Univers. 2: 189. 1651.—*Negundo arbor mas* J. Bauhin ex L., Sp. Pl., ed. 1, 2: 638. 1753.

Negundo arbor femina J. Bauhin, Hist. Pl. Univers. 2: 189. 1651.—*Negundo arbor femina* J. Bauhin ex L., Fl. Zeyl. 194. 1747.—*Negundo femina* Acosta ex L., Fl. Zeyl. 194. 1747.

Bem-nosi Rheede, Hort. Mal. 2: 15, pl. 12. 1679.—*Bemnosi* Rheede ex L., Sp. Pl., ed. 1, 2: 638. 1753.

Vitex orientalis angustis foliis, semper tripartito divisis Plukenet, Alm. Bot. 390. 1696.

Vitex trifolia minor indica serrata Breyn. ex Plukenet, Alm. Bot. 390. 1696.—*Vitex trifolia minor indica serrata* Plukenet ex L., Sp. Pl., ed. 1, 2: 638, in

syn. 1753.—*V. trifolia indica minor serrata* Plukenet ex Burm. f., Fl. Ind.
138, in syn. 1768.

Vitex trifolia odorata silvestris indica Hermann, Mus. Zeyl., ed. 2, 47. 1726.
—*V. trifolia odorata sylvestris indica* Burm. ex L., Fl. Zeyl. 194. 1748.—*V.
trifolia sylvestris indica odorata* Burm. f., Fl. Ind. 138, in syn. 1768.

Vitex trifolia major Rauwolf ex Hermann, Mus. Zeyl., ed. 2, 47. 1726.

Walnika Hermann, Mus. Zeyl., ed. 2, 47. 1726.

Negundo prior, sive mas, Acostae Breyn, Prod. Fasc. Rar. Pl., ed. 2, 2: 106.
1739.

Lagondium litoreum Rumpf, Herb. Amboin. 4: 50, pl. 19. 1743.—*Lagondium
littoreum* Rumph. apud Schau. in A. DC., Prod. 11: 685, in syn. 1847.

Vitex foliis quinatis, ternatisque serratis, floribus racemoso-paniculatis L. ex
Burm. f., Fl. Ind. 138. 1768.

Vitex paniculata Lam., Enc. 2: 612. 1788.

Vitex trifolia β foliolis obtuse crenatis Lam., Enc. 2: 613. 1788.

Vitex spicata Lour., Fl. Cochinch. 2: 390–391. 1790.

Vitex gracilis Salisb., Prod. Stirp. Hort. Allert. 107. 1796.

Vitex negunda Willd. ex Roxb., Fl. Ind., ed. 2, 3: 70. 1832 [not *V. negunda*
Mill., 1768].—*V. negunda* L. ex Moldenke, Phytologia 8: 64. 1961.—*V.
negondo* L. apud Bojer, Hort. Maurit. 258. 1837.—*V. negundo* Willd. ex
Gandoger, Bull. Soc. Bot. France 65: 64. 1918 [not *V. negundo* Curtis, 1832,
nor Lour., 1934, nor Noronha, 1790].—*V. negundo* Royle ex H.J. Lam,
Verbenac. Malay. Arch. 369. 1919.—*V. nugunde* L. ex B. Singh, Bull. Lucknow Natl. Bot. Gard. 69: 57. 1962.—*V. negundo* L. f. apud Naithani,
Bull. Bot. Surv. India 8: 260. 1966.—*V. nigundo* L. ex Moldenke, Résumé
Suppl. 11: 8. 1964.—*V. negungo* Hyland, U.S. Dept. Agric. Pl. Invent. 173:
272. 1969.—*V. negundu* L. ex Vohora, Khan, & Afaq, Indian J. Pharm. 35:
100 & 101. 1973.—*V. negundo* Roxb. ex Moldenke, Phytologia 36: 48, in
syn. 1977.

Agnus castus negundo Carr., Rev. Hort. 1870: 416. 1871.—*Agnus-castus negundo* Carr. apud Jacks. in Hook. f. & Jacks., Ind. Kew. 1: 59. 1893.

Agnus castus robusta paniculata Carr., Rev. Hort. 1874: 499. 1874.

Vitex agnus-castus var. *negundo* (L.) Kuntze, Rev. Gen. Pl. 2: 510–511. 1891.

Vitex leucoxylon Blanco apud Jacks. in Hook. f. & Jacks., Ind. Kew. 2: 1214.
1895 [not *V. leucoxylon* L., 1829, nor L. f., 1781, nor Roth, 1956, nor
Roxb., 1814, nor Schau., 1893, nor Span., 1856, nor Wall., 1842, nor
Willd., 1832].

Vitex quinata Schumacher ex Moldenke, Prelim. Alph. List Invalid Names
52. 1940 [not *V. quinata* (Lour.) F.N. Will., 1905].

Vitex trifolia Graham ex Chavan & Oza, Bot. Mem. Maharaja Savajirao
Univ. Baroda Fac. Sci. 1: 187. 1966 [not *V. trifolia* Hemsl., 1949, nor L.,
1753, nor L. f., 1895, nor Moon, 1895, nor Sessé & Moc., 1940, nor Vahl,
1941, nor "sensu Matsumura & Hayata", 1963].

Vitex negundo var. *negundo* [L.] apud Encke & Buchheim in Zander, Handwörterb. Pfl.-Namen, ed. 10, 525. 1972.
Nika silvestris Hermann ex Moldenke, Phytologia 31: 403, in syn. 1975.

Large shrub or small, slender, aromatic, deciduous tree to 8 m tall, often
gregarious; trunk sometimes to 2 1/2 feet in girth; wood greyish-white, hard,
weighing 42–48 lb/cubic foot; bark pale, somewhat reddish-brown, slightly
rough, peeling off in thin papery strips; lowest branches often decumbent at
base, wide-spreading, sometimes rooting when in contact with the soil; branchlets and twigs slender, brownish or buff, medullose, not lenticellate, rather
densely white- or whitish-tomentellous or puberulent; nodes annulate; leaves
strongly aromatic, decussate-opposite; petioles slender, 2.5–6 cm long, rather
densely puberulent; leaflets regularly 3 [var. *trifoliolata* Moldenke] or 3–5
(rarely 1), narrowly oblong or elliptic to lanceolate or ovate-lanceolate, apically acutely attenuate or subacuminate, basally acute or short-acuminate,
mostly entire to sinuate or with a very few scattered and irregular teeth above
the middle, sometimes regularly sparsely dentate [f. *intermedia* (P'ei) Mold-
enke], sometimes regularly antrorsely serrate except at the base and apex
[var. *cannabifolia* (Sieb. & Zucc.) Hand.-Mazz.] or deeply and irregularly incised [var. *heterophylla* (Franch.) Rehd.] or deeply pinnatifid [var. *heterophylla* f. *multifida* (Carr.) Rehd.], 5–15 cm long [or only 1–4 cm long, mostly
5, and entire in var. *microphylla* Hand.-Mazz.], minutely puberulent or glabrous above [or white-mealy in f. *alba* P'ei], densely whitish- or greyish- [or
purple- in var. *purpurascens* Sivarajan & Moldenke] tomentellous or appressed-puberulent beneath, membranous or thin-chartaceous, subequal (if 3) or
the basal ones somewhat smaller (if 5), usually all 3 or only the central 3 (if
5) petiolulate, the petiolule longest (1–2.5 cm long) on the central one and
unequally shorter or almost absent on the lateral ones, sometimes all sessile
[var. *sessilis* Moldenke]; flowers 3–7.5 cm wide, subsessile or on pedicels to 1
mm long, borne in opposite or subverticillate cymes arranged in oblong,
pedunculate, terminal, tapering panicles which are mostly simple or sometimes branched at the base and thyrsoid [var. *densiflora* Haines], mostly 5–25
cm long, usually blooming and fruiting all year, sometimes widely branched
with loose-flowered branches to 20.5 cm long [f. *laxipaniculata* P'ei]; peduncles 4.5–7 cm long, with the rachis slender, acutely tetragonal or flattened,
densely short-pubescent or puberulent with canescent or sordid-grey hairs;
flowers fragrant; calyx obconic-cyathiform, 1.5–2 mm long and wide, densely
canescent-puberulent, 5-nerved, its rim sinuate or very shortly 5-dentate with
patulous acute teeth, occasionally subcuspidate, the upper ones ovate, the
lower ones lanceolate; corolla hypocrateriform, blue or pale-blue to lavender, pink, or sometimes white [f. *albiflora* Moldenke], the tube infundibular,
3–4 mm long, pulverulent-puberulent outside, the upper lip 2-lobed, the
lower 3-lobed with the middle lobe larger, obovate, undulate-margined, sub-

lanuginous basally, with white or yellow and purple patches, the other lobes shorter, subequal, obtuse; stamens and pistil shortly exserted, the pistil longer; fruiting-calyx campanulate, 2.5–3 mm long, 4–5 mm wide, densely puberulent, its rim shallowly sinuate-5-dentate; fruit globose or subglobose to subovoid, 3–5.5 mm long and wide, glabrous, purple or black, the exocarp succulent, the endocarp bony, 4- (or by abortion fewer) celled and seeded. Chromosome number: 24, 26, & 34.

Distr. This very polymorphic and variable species is native from Zanzibar, Mozambique, and Madagascar through Iran, Afghanistan, Pakistan, India and Ceylon to Burma, Indo-China, and Malaya, north into China, Formosa, Japan, Hainan, and Hong Kong, east to the Philippines, Sarawak, and Guam. It is very widely cultivated in Europe, Asia, North America, and the West Indies, with a distinct tendency to escape and become naturalized. It is extensively cultivated in temple gardens in Thailand.

Ecol. In Ceylon it is common on the banks of rivers and smaller streams up to altitudes of about 3000 ft, but most commonly in the low country and coastal areas, and is often planted as a hedge and for ornamental and medicinal use.

Uses. The leaves contain an essential oil and resin and are used in various parts of the species' range as an anodyne, bitter tonic, aromatic, febrifuge, discutient, and antiparasitic. The fruits contain various acids, resin, and a colouring agent and are employed as a nervine, emmenagogue, and cephalic, the dried fruits as a vermifuge and in treating enlargement of the spleen. The root is used as a tonic, expectorant, febrifuge, and diuretic. The leaves laid on grass are said to act as an insect repellent. Warmed leaves are applied as a remedy for inflammatory swellings of the joints as well as for painful rheumatic swellings. A pillow stuffed with the leaves is placed under the head to relieve headache and macerated ones are applied to the forehead as a cooling agent. A paste made from the leaves is applied to skin sores. In India the flowers are used in the treatment of diarrhoea, cholera, and liver disorders; an infusion of the roots and leaves is drunk or used as a poultice as a tonic and febrifuge. A decoction of the leaves or their expressed juice is employed in draughts for headaches, catarrh, etc. In fact, in various parts of India the plant serves in the treatment of headache, swelling of the head, eye inflammation, dropsy, anasarca, madness, rheumatism, hemiplegia, epilepsy, post-natal complaints, scabies, sores, syphilis, and rinderpest. The fruit is widely used medicinally in China and is even exported for use by Chinese elsewhere. The pliable twigs are used for wattle-work and rough basket-work. In the Philippines the species is highly regarded in the treatment of rheumatism, beri-beri, etc. In New Caledonia it is used as an insect repellent; the bark, leaves, and roots for toothache, fevers, rheumatism and eye ailments, as well as a tonic, carminative, and vermifuge; the dry leaves are smoked in cases of severe headache and migraine; the roots and fruits are used as an emmenagogue.

V e r n. Over 200 are listed. The recommended English name is, Chinese chaste-tree. Helarika, Nika, Nike, Nil-nika, Sooddoo-nikka-gass, Sudu-nika, Nirgundi (S); Nir-nochchi, Nochchi, Vallai-nochchi, Vennochchi (T). The last-mentioned also applied to *Capparis zeylanica* L.

N o t e s. Chemically the following substances have been isolated from *V. negundo*: vitamin C, carotene, vitexin, nishindine, an alkaloid, a diterpene in volatile oil, cineole, 1-sabinene, 1-a-pinene, camphene, a monohydric terpene alcohol, b-caryopyllene, a tricyclic sesquiterpene like copaene, another sesquiterpene, azulene, gluconitol, p-hydroxybenzoic, 5-hydroxyisophalic, and 3,4-dihydroxybenzoic acids, and a glucoside. The pollen of this species is described and illustrated in Huang, Pollen Fl. Taiwan 244, Pl. 163, fig. 12–14 (1972) and Mallick & Chaudhuri, Bull. Bot. Soc. Bengal 22: 107, pl. 1 (1968).

The species grows readily from cuttings—young leafy shoots, planted nearly horizontally during the rainy season, rooting better than older wood. It readily produces root-suckers and may be of value in reforestation work, but not in dry areas. It is not usually browsed. It may be attacked by the fungi *Asteridiella depokensis* Hansf., *Ostropa indica* Tilak & Kale, and *Irenopsis aciculosa* var. *viticis* (Rehm) Stev. Its roots may be parasitized by *Alectra parasitica* var. *chitrakutensis* Rau and its branches by *Cuscuta reflexa* Roxb.

S p e c i m e n s E x a m i n e d. JAFFNA DISTRICT: Jaffna, *Gardner s.n.* [*C.P. 1956* in part] (PDA). KURUNEGALA DISTRICT: Gokarella, 20 July 1967, a small tree, flowers bright lilac-blue, "nika", *Amaratunga 1362* (PDA). POLONNARUWA DISTRICT: Melsiripura, 17 Nov. 1966, small tree, flowers bright lilac-blue, *Amaratunga 1180* (PDA); 3 miles southwest of Elahera, near milepost 12/5 along forested margin of rock outcrop, especially in secondary shrubby area, 400–500 ft alt., 10 Oct. 1974, shrubs 3 m tall with widely spreading branches, corollas violet, top of lower lip white, *Davidse 7345* (LL, US). KANDY DISTRICT: in outdoor cultivation, Medicinal Garden, Royal Botanic Garden, Peradeniya, 1550 ft alt., 18 Jan. 1974, treelet 5 ft tall, leaflets all 3, *H.N. & A.L. Moldenke & Jayasuriya 28147* (PDA, US); in garden, Getambe, Kandy, 1550 ft alt., 27 Jan. 1974, solitary tree, cultivated for medicinal purposes, corollas purplish, sparse, not showy, leaflets all 3, *H.N. & A.L. Moldenke & Jayasuriya 28260* (PDA, US); Peradeniya, *s. coll. C.P. 1956* in part (PDA). MATALE DISTRICT: several trees in outdoor garden cultivation and along fencerows, Nalanda, 500 ft alt., 23 Jan. 1974, flower-buds pale-lavender, opening light-purple within, with a white spot on the lower lip, cultivated for medicinal purposes, leaflets mostly 3, some 5, only the 3 central ones petiolulate, *H.N. & A.L. Moldenke & Jayasuriya 28210* (AAU, ARIZ, CAI, KARACHI, LL, PDA, US); large colony apparently naturalized along roadside fencerow near bridge 1 mile north of

Nalanda, 500–600 ft alt., 23 Jan. 1974, treelets 15 ft tall, forming a considerable dense colony, leaflets all 3 and petiolulate, central one largest, 2 lateral ones unequally petiolulate, *H.N. & A.L. Moldenke & Jayasuriya 28212* (AAU, ARIZ, CAI, KARACHI, LL, PDA, US); planted in garden, Goomera bungalow, Madulkelle, 3300 ft alt., 24 July 1960, a narrow-leaved but handsome specimen, "nika", *Worthington 1976* (PDA); Nalanda Gorge, 900 ft alt., rainfall may be 90 inches, 19 Aug. 1953, *Worthington 6378* (PDA). NUWARA ELIYA DISTRICT: in outdoor garden cultivation, Rambode, 3240 ft alt., 28 Jan. 1974, single tree 30–40 ft tall, leaflets all 3, all petiolulate or the smaller ones with 2 basal ones sessile, *H.N. & A.L. Moldenke, Jayasuriya, & Sumithraarachchi 28266* (AAU, ARIZ, CAI, KARACHI, LL, MO, PDA, US). KEGALLE DISTRICT: in outdoor garden cultivation, Thaligama, 500 ft alt., 12 Feb. 1974, tree 8 ft tall, used in native medicine, leaflets all 3, central one petiolulate. *H.N. & A.L. Moldenke, Jayasuriya, & Dassanayake 28332* (LL, PDA, US); in native garden, Ratnapura, low altitude, 12 Feb. 1974, isolated (pruned) tree 15 ft tall, corolla lavender, used in native medicine, leaflets all 5, the central 3 petiolulate, *H.N. & A.L. Moldenke, Jayasuriya, & Dassanayake 28337* (CAI, PDA, US). TRINCOMALEE DISTRICT: Trincomalee, along roadsides and in waste places on main road A. 6 before town, 10–20 m alt., 14 Nov. 1968, common shrub 1–4 m tall, flowers lilac, the petals recurved, fruit globular, pollen collected, *Comanor 778* (AAU); in waste ground, Trincomalee, 23 Oct. 1976, large shrub, flowers blue-purple, *Fosberg 56392* (NY, US); China Bay, low altitude, 11 Sept. 1974, shrub 2 m tall, flowers purplish-blue, *Waas & Tirvengadum 810* (LL, US); Trincomalee, 10 ft alt., 5 May 1939, "nikka" in Sinhala, "ven-nochi" in Tamil, *Worthington 184* (PDA). LOCALITY UNKNOWN: 1849, *Fraser 196* (US); "nika", "nike", *Burman 60* (M).

8. Vitex trifolia L., Sp. Pl., ed. 1, 2: 638 [as "*trifoliis*"]. 1753 var. **trifolia.** Hermann, Mus. Zeyl. 48. 1717; Burm., Thes. Zeyl. 209–210 & 229, pl. 109. 1737; L., Fl. Zeyl. 413. 1747; Moon, Cat. 1: 46. 1824; Schau. in A. DC., Prod. 11: 683–684. 1847; Thw., Enum. Pl. Zeyl. 244. 1861; Clarke in Hook. f., Fl. Br. Ind. 4: 583. 1885; Trimen, Cat. 69. 1885; Trimen, Handb. Fl. Ceylon 3: 356. 1895; Brandis, Indian Trees 504. 1906; Willis, Cat. 69. 1911; Alston in Trimen, Handb. Fl. Ceylon 6: 232. 1931; Cooke, Fl. Pres. Bombay, ed. 2, 2: 508–509. 1958; Moldenke, Phytologia 6: 165–174 (1958), 8: 83–84 (1961), and 17: 47–51. 1968; Abeywick., Ceylon J. Sci., Biol. Sci. 2: 217. 1959; Worthington, Ceylon Trees 347. 1959; Burkill, Dict. Econ. Prod. Malay Penins. 2: 2279–2282. 1966; Gunawardena, Gen. Sp. Pl. Zeyl. 147. 1968; Fonseka & Vinasithamby, Prov. List Local Names Fl. Pl. Ceylon 64, 65, 86, & 95. 1971; Vivekanandan, Sri Lanka Forester, ser. 2, 11: 119 & 146. 1974. Type: *Herb. Linnaeus 811/7* from somewhere in India (LINN).

Piperi similis fructus striatus, femina C. Bauhin, Pinax. 412. 1671.—*Piper similis fructus striatus, femina* Banks ex Moldenke, Prelim. Alph. List Invalid Names 36, in syn. 1940.—*Piperi similis fructus striatus faemina* Baux. ex L., Fl. Zeyl. 194, in syn. 1747.

Vitex latiore folio C. Bauhin, Pinax 475. 1671.

Caranosi Rheede, Hort. Mal. 2: 13, Pl. 2. 1679.—*Cara-nosi* Rheede ex L., Fl. Zeyl. 194, in syn. 1747.

Vitex trifolia indica, odora, hortensis, floribus caeruleis racemosis Hermann apud Breyne, Prod. Fasc. Rar. Pl., ed. 2, 105–106. 1688.—*V. trifolia indica, odora, hortensis, floribus caeruleis racemosis* Burm., Thes. Zeyl. 229. 1737.— *V. trifolia indica odorata hortensis, floribus caeruleis racemosis* Burm. ex L., Fl. Zeyl. 194. 1747.

Vitex trifolia minor indica Breyne ex Plukenet, Alm. Bot. 390, Pl. 206, fig. 5. 1696.—*V. trifolia minor indica* Plukenet ex L., Sp. Pl., ed. 1, 2: 638, in syn. 1753.

Nika Hermann, Mus. Zeyl. 48. 1717.

Vitex trifolia floribus per ramos sparsis Burm., Thes. Zeyl. 229, pl. 109. 1737.—*V. trifolia, floribus per ramos sparsis* Burm. f., Fl. Ind. 137, in syn 1768.

Vitex triflora odorata, sylvestris Burm., Thes. Zeyl. 209–210, pl. 109. 1737.

Lagondium vulgare Rumph, Herb. Amboin. 4: 48, pl. 18. 1743.

Frutex indicus baccifer, fructu calyculato monopyreno Ray ex L., Fl. Zeyl. 194, in syn. 1747.

Vitex integerrimis Mill., Gard. Dict., ed. 8, *Vitex* no. 3. 1768.—*V. integerrima* Mill. apud Jacks. in Hook. f. & Jacks., Ind. Kew. 2: 1213. 1895.

Vitex indica Mill., Gard. Dict., ed. 8, in errat. 1768.

Vitex foliis ternatis quinatisve integerrimis, paniculis dichotomis L. ex Burm. f., Fl. Ind. 137. 1769.

Vitex variifolia Salisb., Prod. Stirp. Hort. Allert. 107. 1796.

Vitex trifolia α *trifoliata* Cham., Linnaea 7: 107. 1832.—*V. trifolia* var. *trifoliata* Cham. ex Moldenke, Phytologia 6: 165, in syn. 1958.

Vitex triphylla Royle, Ill. Bot. Himal. 299. 1839.—*V. triphylla* L. ex Moldenke, Alph. List Invalid Names Suppl. 1: 29. 1947.

Vitex trifolia α *trifoliolata* Schau. in A. DC., Prod. 11: 683. 1847.—*V. trifolia* var. *trifoliolata* Schau. ex Moldenke, Prelim. Alph. List Invalid Names 52. 1940.—*V. trifolia* var. *trifoliolata* H.J. Lam ex Moldenke, Phytologia 8: 83. 1961.—*V. trifolia trifoliolata* "Schau. ex Blanco" apud Stapf, Ind. Lond. 6: 479. 1931.

Vitex agnus castus var. *trifolia* (L.) Kurz, For. Fl. Burma 270. 1877.—*V. agnus-castus* β *trifolia* (L.) Kurz ex Kuntze, Rev. Gen. Pl. 2: 510 & 511. 1891.—*V. agnus castus* var. Kurz ex Watt, Dict. Econ. Prod. India 6 (4): 251. 1893.—*V. agnus-castus* var. *trifolia* (L.) Kurz ex Moldenke, Alph. List Invalid Names 52. 1942.

Vitex incisa Wall. apud Watt, Dict. Econ. Prod. India 6 (4): 251. 1893 [not *V. incisa* Bunge, 1927, nor Lam., 1788, nor Thunb., 1947].

Vitex trifolia L. f. ex Schum., Notizbl. Konigl. Bot. Gart. Berlin App. 1: 55. 1895 [not *V. trifolia* Graham, 1966, nor Hemsl., 1949, nor Moon, 1895, nor Sessé & Moc., 1940, nor Vahl, 1941, nor "sensu Matsumura & Hayata", 1963.—*Viiex trifolia* L. ex Hosokawa, J. Soc. Trop. Agric. 6: 206. 1934.

Vitex agnus-castus Kurz apud Jacks. in Hook. f. & Jacks., Ind. Kew. 2: 1213. 1895 [not *V. agnus-castus* L., 1753].

Vitex trifoliata L. ex Decne., Nouv. Ann. Mus. Hist. Nat. 3: 400. 1834 [not *V. trifoliata* Pav., 1940].—*V. trifoliata* L. f. ex Merr., Bur. Govt. Labs. Philipp. Bull. 6: 17–18. 1904.—*V. trifoliata* P. Henderson, Handb. Pl., ed 2, 482. 1910.—*V. trifoliata* Lam. ex Moldenke, Alph. List Invalid Names Suppl. 1: 29, in syn. 1947.—*Vitis trifoliata* L. f. ex Moldenke, Phytologia 6: 166. 1958 [not *V. trifoliata* Baker, 1871, nor Thunb., 1825].

Vitex langundi Ridl., J. Straits Branch Roy. Asiat. Soc. 45: 50. 1906.

Vitex trifoliolata L. apud J. Matsumura, Ind. Pl. Jap. 2 (2): 534–535. 1912.— *V. trifoliolata* Schau. apud P'ei, Verbenac. China 99. 1932.

V. trifoliolata var. *trifoliolata* Schau. apud J. Matsumura, Ind. Pl. Jap. 2 (2): 534–535. 1912.

Vitex negundo "(non L.) Matsum." apud Masamune, Sci. Rep. Kanazawa Univ., Biol. 4: 49. 1955 [not *V. negundo* Curtis, 1832, nor Hausskn., 1975, nor L., 1753, nor L. f., 1966, nor Lour., 1934, nor Noronha, 1790, nor Roxb., 1977, nor Royle, 1919, nor Willd., 1918].

A slender bush, shrub, or small tree to 6.5 m tall; stems to 15 cm in diameter, freely branched from near the base; wood soft, whitish or yellowish except for the murky-brown centre, moderately to very hard, often brittle, of fine to moderately fine texture, odourless and tasteless; bark smooth or (when old) finely checked, brown or light-brown; branches numerous, lax; branches and twigs slender, brownish, acutely or obtusely tetragonal or subterete, densely puberulent with sordid or cinereous hairs most conspicuous on the youngest parts; nodes annulate; leaves decussate-opposite, mostly horizontal, resinous-aromatic when crushed, normally 3-foliolate; petioles slender, 0.6–3.3 cm long, flattened and somewhat canaliculate above, densely appressed puberulent with sordid or whitish hairs; leaflets subequal in size or the 2 lateral ones much smaller, the central one usually petiolulate on petiolules 1–6 mm long, puberulent, and decidedly margined, the lateral ones usually sessile or subsessile; leaflet-blades thin-membranous, rich deep or dark green above, usually brunnescent or nigrescent in drying, greyish or white beneath, nearly flat and subnitid on the upper surface, the central one varying from oblong-elliptic to oblanceolate or obovate, 2.5–7 cm long, 1–4 cm wide, apically acute or short-acuminate (varying to obtuse, rounded, or emarginate), entire, basally acute or acuminate to cuneate-attenuate, pulverulent-puberulent and more or less resinous-dotted above (especially when young), becoming glabrescent, sometimes more densely puberulent above and white-tomentose on the margins, densely tomentulose-puberulent with white or greyish matted hairs beneath, the lateral ones similar but usually smaller and less attenuate basally; inflorescence terminal and axillary in the uppermost leaf-axils, paniculate, erect or suberect, 3–23 cm long, 2–4 cm wide, composed of many opposite stipitate and usually several times branched many-flowered cymes, cinereous- or sordid-puberulent throughout, often much abbreviated; peduncles (1–5 cm long) and rachis slender, usually acutely tetragonal, similar to the adjacent twigs in colour, texture, and puberulence; sympodia sometimes few and abbreviated, often numerous and 1–1.5 cm long; pedicles very slender, about 1 mm long or less, densely white-puberulent; foliaceous bracts often present in the larger panicles, simple or 2- or 3-foliolate, resembling the leaf-blades in texture, colour, and puberulence but much smaller, usually subtending only the lowest (or two lowest) pairs of cymes; bractlets linear, 1–3 mm long, densely white-puberulent; flowers odourless or with the fragrance of sage (*Salvia officinalis*), about 12 mm long; calyx cyathiform, 4–5 mm long, 2.5–3.5 mm wide, 5-veined, very densely white-tomentulose externally, its rim shortly and acutely repand-dentate (or sometimes the teeth blunt); corolla hypocrateriform, varying from blue, pale-blue, or bright-blue to lavender, purple, or violet, 2-lipped, pulverulent or puberulent externally, its tube infundibular, 10–13 mm long, the lower lip expanded into a villous tongue about 6 mm long, the remaining lobes smaller; stamens exserted; filaments hairy basally; pistil exserted; fruiting-calyx cupuliform, herbaceous, about 5 mm long and wide, densely cinereous-puberulent externally, its rim regularly 5-dentate; drupes at first green, then yellow or reddish, finally blue or black, globose or ovoid, 5–6 mm long, about 5 mm in diameter. Chromosome number reported as 26, 32, or 34.

D i s t r. This is a widespread species from Afghanistan to India, Bangladesh and eastward through Burma, Malaya, Indonesia, New Guinea, northern Australia, and New Caledonia, north into southern China, the Philippines, and Japan, and westward to Mauritius, Madagascar, and Natal.

E c o l. It is often found in tropical moist edaphic mangrove forests.

U s e s. It is employed medicinally rather extensively from India to the Fiji Islands. In India it is used as an anodyne and diuretic, in fomentations and baths for beri-beri and burning of feet. The leaves are there employed in the treatment of rheumatism, contusions, and swollen testicles, as a discutient in sprains, and as an alterative, tonic, febrifuge, and demulcent; from the roots is expressed a juice used as a tonic, febrifuge, expectorant, and local anodyne; the fruit furnishes a nervine, cephalic, and emmenagogue. In Malaya and Indonesia the boiled leaves and twigs are made into a paste for treating bruises and open wounds and, with the addition of the leaves of *Blumea bal-samineara* DC., for beri-beri. The juice of the leaves is also used in cases of dropsy. In New Caledonia the plant is used in the treatment of rheumatism, intermittent fevers, and tumours, the fruit and leaves as an emmenagogue and vermifuge. In Java the leafy branches are placed on ricefields to drive off pests. In China a potion is made for the treatment of glandular tumours, breast cancers, and old cancers in general. In Malaya the leaves are burned to drive off mosquitoes "and evil spirits" and as an insect repellent in clothes closets and rice bins. In that area of Asia poultices are made from this species for use in the treatment of almost all human complaints, sometimes with the ad-dition of lime, camphor, vinegar, pepper, *Nigella* seed, or rice, as well as in treating the swollen trunk of work elephants. The ground leaves, with the addition of garlic, turmeric, and pepper, are used to treat consumption, and the boiled roots, in infusion form, are regarded as diaphoretic and diuretic, widely drunk in cases of fever and after childbirth. In Indonesia the leaves are used in medicinal baths and a tincture or decoction of them for intestinal complaints. They contain an alkaloid, two methylated flavones, artematin, an involatile oil containing 1-d-pinene, camphene, cineol, terpinyl acetate, and diterpene alcohol.

The species is often used, especially in Malaya, for hedges, but it should be noted that many people have hayfever-like reactions when trimming or prun-ing these hedges, with asthma-like symptoms, respiratory irritation, dizziness, headache, and nausea.

V e r n. Over 80 vernacular names have been recorded from various parts of its range. In Ceylon it is usually called Nika or Sudu-nika (S) and Mochchi, Nochchi, or Vettai-nochi (T). In English it is known as Indian privet, Indian wild pepper, Hand of Mary, and Indian three-leaved vitex.

N o t e. The species is very variable and polymorphic. A uniformly purple-flowered form is var. *purpurea* Lord and one with variegated leaflets, often seen in hedges, is var. *variegata* Moldenke.

S p e c i m e n s   E x a m i n e d. JAFFNA DISTRICT: Kankesanturai, Feb. 1890, *s. coll. s.n.* (PDA). KANDY DISTRICT: South Garden, Royal Botanic Garden, Peradeniya, 1550 ft alt., 22 Oct. 1914, *s. coll. s.n.* (PDA). TRINCOMALEE DISTRICT: on beach just south of Elizabeth Point about opposite the 5 mile milepost on the Trincomalee to Nilaveli road, on beach among coconuts just back of the *Spinifex* zone, near sealevel, 13 Oct. 1974, shrub 0.5–1 m tall, corollas blue, *Davidse 7530* (US); Trincomalee, Sep. 1860, *Gardner s.n. [C.P. 1955]* (BR, PDA); Dead Man's Cove, Trincomalee, 5 ft alt., 25 April 1939, *Worthington 177* (PDA).

var. **simplicifolia** Cham., Linnaea 7: 107 [as "*β simplicifolia*"]. 1832; H.J. Lam, Verbenac. Malay. Arch. 182. 1919; L. f., Suppl. Pl. 294. 1781; R. Br., Prod. Fl. Nov. Holland. 1: 511. 1810: Voigt, Hort. Suburb. Calc. 473. 1845;

Schau. in A. DC., Prod. 11: 683. 1847; Hara, Enum. Sperm. Jap. 1: 190–191.
1948; Petelot, Fl. Méd. Camb. Laos & Viet-Nam 2: 251. 1953; Masamune,
Sci. Rep. Kanazawa Univ., Biol. 4: 48. 1955; Liu, Illust. Nat. & Introd. Lign.
Pl. Taiwan 2: 1231. 1962; Ohwi, Fl. Jap. 765. 1965; Moldenke, Phytologia 6:
183–192 & 197 (1958), 8: 86–88 (1961), and 17: 54–56 & 114–117. 1968;
Huang, Pollen Fl. Taiwan 244, Pl. 163, fig. 15–17. 1972; M.R. Henderson,
Malay. Wild Fls. Dicot. 1: 387. 1974. Type: From sandy shores near Cavite,
Luzon, Philippine Islands, the collector undesignated, probably (B).

Vitex rotundifolia L. f., Suppl. Pl. 294. 1781.—*V. rotundifolia* L. ex Sasaki,
   List Pl. Formos. 353 & 354. 1928.—*V. rotundifolius* Hara, Outline Phyto-
   geogr. Japan 56. 1959.
Vitex ovata Thunb., Fl. Jap. 257. 1784.— *V. ovata* Lam. ex Moldenke, Alph.
   List Invalid Names Suppl. 1: 29. 1947.
Vitex repens Blanco, Fl. Filip., ed. 1, 513. 1837.
Vitex trifolia β unifoliolata Schau. in A. DC., Prod. 11: 683. 1847.—*V. trifolia*
   var. *unifoliolata* Mann, Proc. Amer. Acad. Arts. 7: 194. 1867.—*V. trifolia*
   var. *unifoliata* Miq., Cat. Mus. Bot. Lugduno-Batavum 70. 1870.—*V.*
   trifolia var. *unifoliata* Hillebr., Fl. Hawaiian Islands. 342. 1888.—*V.*
   trifolia var. *unifoliata* Schau. ex Kawakami, List Pl. Formos. 85. 1910.—
   V. trifolia unifoliolata Schau. ex Stapf, Ind. Lond. 6: 457. 1931.—*V. trifolia*
   var. *unifoliolata* Hillebr. ex Moldenke, Suppl. List Invalid Names 11.
   1941.—*V. trifolia* var. *unifoliata* DC. ex Moldenke, Phytologia 6: 184.
   1958.—*V. trifolia* var. *unifoliolata* DC. ex Moldenke; Phytologia 6: 184.
   1958.—*V. trifolia* var. *unifolia* Judd ex Moldenke, Phytologia 17: 54.
   1968.—*V. trifolia β unifoliata* Schau. ex Moldenke, Phytologia 17: 54–55.
   1968.
Vitex trifolia α obovata Benth., Fl. Austral. 5: 67. 1870.—*V. trifolia* var.
   obovata Benth. ex F.M. Bailey, Compreh. Cat. Queensland Pl. 386. 1913.
Vitex agnus-castus η ovata Kuntze, Rev. Gen. Pl. 2: 510 & 511. 1891.—*V.*
   agnus-castus η ovata (Thunb.) Kuntze ex Hara, Enum. Sperm. Jap. 1: 190.
   1948.
Vitex trifolia var. *ovata* (Thunb.) Makino, Bot. Mag. (Tokyo) 17: 92. 1903.—
   V. trifolia var. *ovata* (Thunb.) Merr., Sp. Blanc. 332. 1918.—*V. trifolia* var.
   ovata Mak. apud Degener, Fl. Hawaii. 3: 315: Vitex: Trif: Ovat. 1932.—*V.*
   trifolia ovata Mak. ex Worsdell, Ind. Lond. Suppl. 2: 501. 1941.—*V. trifolia*
   var. *ovata* Thunb. ex Moldenke, Alph. List Invalid Names Suppl. 1: 29.
   1947.
Vitex trifolia var. *repens* Ridl., Fl. Malay Penins. 2: 631. 1923.
Vitex trifolia var. *simplicifolia* Cham. & Schlecht. ex Skottsb., Acta Horti
   Gotob. 15: 435. 1944.
Vitex simplicifolia Merr., Pl. Life Pacif. World 282. 1945 [not *V. simplicifolia*
   Clarke, 1885, nor Oliv., 1875].

Vitex trifolia Hemsl. apud Rehd., Bibliog. Cult. Trees 585. 1949 [not *V. tri-folia* Graham, 1966, nor L., 1753, nor L. f., 1895, nor Moon, 1895, nor Sessé & Moc., 1940, nor Vehl, 1941].—*V. trifolia* "sensu Matsum. & Hayata" apud Li, Wood. Fl. Taiwan 834. 1963.

Vitex trifolia ssp. *litoralis* Van Steenis, Blumea 8: 516. 1957.

Vitex rotundifolia var. *rotundifolia* Mizushima ex Moldenke, Phytologia 8: 86. 1961.

This variety differs from the typical form of the species in being usually a low bush or shrub of the seashores, with procumbent or creeping stems, rooting at the nodes, and erect branches, its leaves mostly 1-foliolate and sessile or subsessile, the blades often smaller, 1.5–4.5 cm long and 0.8–3.5 cm wide, mostly broadly oblong, subrotund, or obovate-spatulate, and rounded at both apex and base or very abruptly short-acuminate, usually remaining densely puberulent above and sometimes velutinous-tomentellous beneath, and the mostly terminal and greatly abbreviated inflorescences. The chromosome number is $x = 16$.

D i s t r. This is a widespread and variable variety found mostly on sandy seashores from China, Taiwan, and Japan, southward through the Ryukyu and Philippine Islands to Indo-China, Malaya, Thailand, the Andaman Islands, Ceylon, and India, west to Mauritius, and eastward almost throughout Indonesia and the Pacific Islands to New Guinea, Fiji, Australia, and Hawaii, introduced as a sand-binder in Brazil and elsewhere. In China (and perhaps elsewhere) it has been found growing far from the seashore and to at least 185 m altitude, but in general it is var. *trifolia* which occurs inland, while var. *simplicifolia* is confined to seashores and dunes. Ridley affirms that the coastal plant grown inland will develop into the typical form, but Backer and Corner, among others, dispute this. Modern taxonomists are divided among those who regard it as a true species (*V. rotundifolia*), a subspecies, or a variety.

U s e s. The plant is used as a drug in Honam Island and is regarded as medicinal in many other lands, including Thailand and Japan; the seeds are widely used in native medicine in Japan, while in Malaya the plant furnishes medicine used in treating consumption. In parts of China it is used to treat glandular tumours. In the Hawaiian Islands a tea is made from the leaves; the seeds and wood are used, and all parts of the plant used as a bath for treating backache, swollen feet, and rheumatism.

V e r n. Some 35 names are recorded from various parts of its range, among them being: Polinalina, Beach vitex, and Oval-leaved chaste-tree.

N o t e s. The fruit has been found to contain a flavone pigment, vitexicarpin. The pollen is described and illustrated by Huang (1972).

The plant is of considerable value as a sandbinder to prevent beach erosion. It is attacked by an *Alternaria* sp., a *Bacterium* sp., and *Cuscuta chinensis* Lam. A white-flowered form is f. *albiflora* (Y. Matsumura) Moldenke.

Specimens Examined. HAMBANTOTA DISTRICT: on sand dune foreshore, Bundala, 20 July 1972, small shrub with several almost single branches about 60 cm long arising from the rootstock, with glaucous rather fleshy leaves and green fruit, *Hepper & de Silva 4757* (US).

var. **subtrisecta** (Kuntze) Moldenke, Phytologia 8: 88. 1961; Hara, Enum. Sperm. Jap. 1: 191. 1948; Moldenke, Phytologia 6: 180–183 (1958), 8: 88–90 (1961), and 17: 117–118. 1968; Pope, Man. Wayside Pl. 195 & 196, Pl. 111. 1968; Backer, Atlas 220 Weeds [Handb. Cult. Sugarcane 7:] Pl. 521. 1973; Walker, Fl. Okin. & South. Ryuk. 893–894. 1976. Type: *Kuntze 5817* from the Willisgebirge in Java (NY).

Vitex agnus-castus δ subtrisecta Kuntze, Rev. Gen. Pl. 2: 510 & 511. 1891.—
    V. agnus-castus var. *subtrisecta* Kuntze apud Moldenke, Phytologia 6: 165. 1958.
Vitex rotundifolia var. *heterophylla* (Roxb.) Makino, Ill. Fl. Nipp. 186. 1940 [not *V. heterophylla* Roxb., 1814 & 1832].—*V. rotundifolia* var. *heterophylla* Makino ex Hara, Enum. Sperm. Jap. 1: 191. 1948.—*Vitex rotundifolia* var. *heterophylla* "[Roxb.?] Makino" apud Walker, Fl. Okin. & South. Ryuk. 894. 1976.
Vitex trifolia var. *heterophylla* (Mak.) Moldenke, Phytologia 3: 178. 1949.
Vitex trifolia var. *subincisa* Kuntze ex Moldenke, Phytologia 8: 88. 1961.
Vitex rotundifolia f. *heterophylla* (Mak.) Kitamura in Kitamura & Murata, Acta Phytotax. Geobot. 25: 34. 1972.

This variety differs from the typical form of the species in being a dwarf, erect or prostrate shrub with both 1-foliolate and 3-foliolate leaves regularly interspersed on the branchlets; often the single leaflets are deeply bi- or tri-sected or binary. A white-flowered form is f. *albiflora* Moldenke.

This is a very variable variety, apparently native from the littoral belt close to mangrove formations to riverbanks and inland hillsides as much as 4000 ft in altitude, from India, the Andaman Islands, Burma, Thailand, Malaya, and Indo-China north to southern China and Japan, west to the Mascarene Islands and Madagascar, east through the Ryukyu and Philippine Islands to Indonesia, the Lesser Sunda Islands, New Guinea, New Caledonia, Fiji, and Polynesia, and south to northern Australia. It is widely cultivated, especially as a hedge, and tends to persist or escape. It is regarded as medicinal on Hainan island, and the bark and roots provide a febrifuge in Thailand.

It is very possible that *Vitex trifolia* var. *acutifolia* Benth. in Benth. & F. Muell., Fl. Austr. 5: 67 (1870) may be the valid name for this variety, but an examination of the type at Kew is required to substantiate or disprove this suspicion.

V e r n. Ten names are recorded from various parts of its range, including: Lagondee and Salt-bush.

Specimens Examined. KANDY DISTRICT: in outdoor cultivation in the Medicinal Garden, Royal Botanic Garden, Peradeniya, 1550 ft alt., 18 Jan. 1974, bush about 4 ft tall, leaflets white beneath, *H.N. & A.L. Moldenke & Jayasuriya 28148* (US).

var. **bicolor** (Willd.) Moldenke, Known Geogr. Distrib. Verbenac., ed. 2, 79. 1942; Schau. in A. DC., Prod. 11: 683. 1847; Bakh. & H.J. Lam, Bull. Jard. Bot. Buitenzorg, ser. 3, 3: 56 (1921), 4 (2): 285 (1922), and 5 (2): 178. 1922; Merr., Enum. Philipp. Pl. 3: 394. 1923; H.J. Lam, Just's Bot. Jahresber. 59: 27 & 93. 1924; Moldenke, Phytologia 6: 174–180 (1958), 8: 84–86 (1961), and 17: 51–53. 1968. Type: a cultivated specimen from the Botanical Garden at Berlin (B); "Habitat in India orientali".

Vitex bicolor Willd., Enum. Hort. Berol. 2: 660. 1809.
Vitex negundo var. *bicolor* (Willd.) H.J. Lam, Verbenac. Malay. Arch. 191.
    1919.—*V. negundo* var. *bicolor* Lam. ex Moldenke, Phytologia 17: 51. 1968.
Vitex petiolaris Domin, Bibl. Bot. 22 (89-C): 1115. 1928.
Vitex iriomotensis Ohwi, Acta Phytotax. Geobot. 7: 29. 1938.
Vitex ternifolia Hort. ex Moldenke, Phytologia 6: 174. 1958.

This variety differs from the typical form of the species in having its leaves 3–5-, but mostly 5-foliolate, decidedly silvery and white-tomentose beneath, the upper surface always nigrescent in drying imparting to the leaves a decided black-and-white bicoloured appearance, all the leaflets distinctly petiolulate or the 3 central ones on petiolules to 2 cm long and the 2 basal ones sessile or subsessile.

Distr. Found mostly on or near the seacoasts from Tanzania, Madagascar, and the Comoro Islands eastward along the coasts of India, Ceylon, Malaya, and Indo-China, north to Hainan, east through Pacific Oceania from the Philippine Islands and Indonesia to New Guinea, Fiji, New Caledonia, Hawaii, Solomon Islands, and Samoa, and south to the coasts of Australia. It is sometimes cultivated as a hedge. Some taxonomists regard it as a natural hybrid between *V. negundo* L. and *V. trifolia* L., but this does not seem likely.

Uses. In the Solomon Islands the macerated bark and sap of *V. trifolia* var. *bicolor* are used in the treatment of toothache and headache. In the Fiji Islands the plant is used similarly for abscesses in the ear; also there the leaves are mashed, coconut oil is added, the mixture then is placed on a good fresh banana leaf and heated—broken bones are then rubbed hard with this concoction and tied tight. In the Philippine Islands the leaves are soaked and the water used for bathing patients that have suffered from malarial fevers for a long period of time. In Samoa the leaves are rubbed on the head and body as a febrifuge in cases of intermittent fevers, the sap of the stem is used in treating tuberculosis, the macerated leaves made into a poultice and placed on abrasions. Also in those islands the mashed leaves, with the addition of those of *Alphitonia zizyphoides*, are used in treating headaches, inflammation of the brain, and swellings.

V e r n. Almost 50 vernacular names are listed for this plant in various parts of its range, including: Agalonte, Dralawa, Gamulega, Lala taki, Namulega; Nieke, Nikki, Nochchi (S).

N o t e s. It is possible that *V. trifolia* var. *parviflora* Benth (Fl. Austr. 5: 67. 1870)—on which *V. benthamiana* Domin (Bibl. Bot. 22 (89–6): 1114 & 1117, fig. 182. 1928) is based—may be the same taxon here called *V. trifolia* var. *bicolor*, as seems very likely from a study of the description and figure. If so, then obviously Bentham's epithet would be the one that would have to be adopted for it. An examination of Bentham's type is necessary to decide this point. Likewise *V. agnus-castus* δ *negundodes* Kuntze (Rev. Gen. Pl. 2: 510 & 511. 1891) from Deccan, India, and *V. agnus-castus* ε *javanica* Kuntze (l.c.) from Java may also prove to belong in the synonymy of var. *bicolor*. Either of these would take priority over *bicolor* if one were to regard the Greek-letter subspecific designations of Kuntze as equivalent to "var." rather than to "ssp" or "f." and if Bentham's name were found to be not applicable. Kuntze's types have not yet been found by me in his herbarium at the New York Botanical Garden and were probably sent to some other herbarium in exchange.

The plant is sometimes attacked by the parasitic fungus, *Irenina vilis* (Sydow) Stevens.

A white-flowered form is f. *albiflora* (Kuntze) Moldenke.

S p e c i m e n s   E x a m i n e d. JAFFNA DISTRICT: at edge of lagoon, Mullaitivu, 19 March 1927, flowers mauve, *Alston 1327* (PDA). BATTICA-LOA DISTRICT: on beach 1/4 mile north of Kalkudah, 1 m alt., 4 Dec. 1974, shrub 1.5 ft tall, flowers blue, *Davidse & Sumithraarachchi 9025* (LL); on sandy beach of sheltered bay with *Spinifex* mixed in herb layer, Passikudah Bay, northeast of Kalkudah, 17 miles north of Batticaloa, 19 April 1968, shrub 3 m tall, pale-blue terminal flower clusters, leaves compound, 3–5 leaflets, several shrubs forming a single row, collected as voucher for ecological observations, *Mueller-Dombois 68041901* (AAU, PDA); in shore scrub, Passikudah, 9 June 1974, treelet, flowers bluish, *Waas 637* (US); on the coral quarries, Kalkudah, 4 ft altitude, 26 March 1951, "nikki" Sinhala, *Worthington 5142* (PDA). TRINCOMALEE DISTRICT: along brackish-water coast line, Kinniyai Ferry, 28 March 1963, shrub, flowers purple, *Amaratunga 569* (PDA); on beach just south of Elizabeth Point, about opposite the 5 mile marker on the Trincomalee to Nilaveli road, among coconuts just back of the *Spinifex* zone, near sealevel, 13 Oct. 1974, shrub 0.5–1 m tall, corollas blue, *Davidse 7530* (LL); common on low berm of coral sand and gravel rock of low beach ridge covered by unevenly closed scrub forest, Foul Point, south side of Koddiyar Bay, across from Trincomalee, 23 Oct. 1976, shrubs 4 m tall, flowers lavender, as *V. negundo, Fosberg 56425* (NY, US); in jungle near sea, Foul Point, 20 May 1932, maritime form, leaves broad, "nochchi", *Simpson 9688* (PDA); very common trees, Foul Point, 7 April 1974, height variable, 5–12 ft tall, flowers bluish-purple, *Sumithraarachchi & Jayasuriya DBS. 232* (LL, PDA, US); common tree, Kinniyai, near ferry, 25 June 1975, flowers blue, fruit black, *Sumithraarachchi & Sumithraarachchi DBS. 861* (US); locally abundant on beach along edge of sea below fort at Trincomalee, sealevel, 11 July 1968, small shrub, 1–2 ft tall, *Theobald & Grupe 2320* (PDA). LOCALITY UNKNOWN: *Herb. Schmiedel s.n.* (M); no date "nieke" Sinhala, *Oltmans 34* (L), *62* (L); *69* (L).

17. GMELINA

L., Sp. Pl., ed. 1, 2: 626. 1753; L., Gen. Pl., ed. 5, 274. 1754. Type species: *Gmelina asiatica* L.

Cumbulu Rheede, Hort. Mal. 1: 75, Pl. 41. 1678.—*Kumbulu* Adans., Fam. Pl. 2: 546. 1763.—*Cumbula* Adans. ex Steud., Nom. Bot., ed., 2, 1: 310 & 453. 1849.—*Cumbula* Steud apud Jacks. in Hook. f. & Jacks., Ind. Kew. 1: 666. 1893.—*Cumbalu* Adans. apud Jacks. in Hook. f. & Jacks., Ind. Kew. 1: 666 & 1458. 1893.—*Kumbalu* Adans. ex Moldenke, Alph. List Invalid Names Suppl. 1: 11. 1947.—*Cumbulu* Adans. (in part) apud Bakh. & Van Steenis, Taxon 5: 81. 1956.—*Cunibalu* B.D. Jacks. ex Airy Shaw in Willis, Dict. ed. 7, 309. 1966.

Bonvaro Bram. ex Adans., Fam. Pl. 2: 527 & 546. 1763.

Lycium Plukenet ex Adans., Fam. Pl. 2: 199. 1763 [not *Lycium* L., 1753].

Michelia Amman ex Adans., Fam. Pl. 2: 199. 1763.

Tittius Rumph. ex Adans., Fam. Pl. 2: 199, 546, & 611. 1763.

Gmelina Willd. ex Moon, Cat. 1: 45. 1824.—*Gmelinia* L. ex Spreng. in L., Gen. Pl., ed. 9, 2: 481. 1831.—*Gmebina* Roxb. ex Wight, Ic. Pl. Ind. Or. 4 (3): Pl. 1470. 1849.—*Gurelina* Wight, Ill. Ind. Bot. 2: Pl. 174. 1850.—*Gmelinia* Spreng. apud Jacks. in Hook. f. & Jacks., Ind. Kew. 1: 1040. 1893.—*Cmelina* Chadhuri, Bull. Bot. Soc. Bengal 23: 123. 1969.—*Gmelia* Joshi, Indian Forester 94: 152. 1969.

Trees or shrubs, erect or subscandent (especially when young), sometimes spinose, glabrous to more or less pubescent or tomentose, the youngest shoots usually more or less tomentose, the spines (when present) morphologically aborted branchlets, axillary, divaricate, stiff; leaves decussate-opposite, petiolate or sessile, thin-membranous to rather thick-coriaceous, deciduous, mostly entire, sometimes dentate or lobed on young plants or on turions, often with a few rather large sunken nectariferous glands near or at the base beneath; inflorescence racemiform or paniculate, terminal, bracteate or only bracteolate; bracts usually small and linear, deciduous, rarely large, foliaceous and brightly coloured; flowers usually large, often tomentose (at least when young), solitary in the leaf-axils or borne in small, simple or branched, dense or lax, opposite, sessile or pedunculate, mostly 1–5-flowered cymules, these sometimes combined into a terminal, erect, simple or branched panicle or into a nodding or drooping raceme; calyx gamosepalous, campanulate or obconic, coriaceous, persistent, often somewhat irregular or oblique, often with external glands on the anterior side, its rim shortly 4- or 5-toothed, sinuate-lobed, or subentire to truncate; corolla gamopetalous, zygomorphic, obliquely campanulate or infundibular, blue or purple-violet to yellow or brownish, more or less bilabiate, the tube basally slender, greatly ampliate apically and dilated into the usually campanulate limb, the limb oblique, spreading, 4- or 5-lobed or -fid, the upper lobe convex or arched and usually entire (or 2-lobulate), the 2 lateral lobes rounded, the lowest 3-fid, sometimes the 2 posterior lobes connate, the middle or anterior lobe largest; stamens 4, distinctly didynamous, inserted on the corolla-tube usually at the base of the ampliate portion, included or subexserted, shorter than the corolla-lobes; the 2 longer filaments glanduliferous, decurved; anthers oblong, 2-celled, medi-fixed or inserted in a basal incision, divaricate, the cells opening by parallel slits; pistil solitary; style filiform, apically decurved; stigma subulate or short-ly and unequally bifid, the posterior branch usually shorter; ovary 4-celled during anthesis, each cell 1-ovulate; ovules attached laterally at or above the middle, pendulous; fruit a more or less succulent drupe, borne on a scarcely enlarged fruiting-calyx, ovoid-ellipsoid to obovoid, the exocarp usually yellow and juicy, the endocarp hard and bony, undivided, 4- (or by abortion only 2- or 3-) celled, each cell 1-seeded; seeds oblong, without endosperm, the cotyledons thick; radicle inferior. Chromosome number 2n = 36, 38, or 40.

A genus of about 48 species and subspecific taxa, native to tropical and subtropical Asia from Pakistan, Bhutan, Nepal, and India to Thailand, Indo-China, and Malaya, north to southern China, eastward through the Philippine and Palau islands, Indonesia, Micronesia, and Melanesia and south to northern Australia. Several species are widely cultivated in tropical regions or as specimen plants elsewhere. In Ceylon there are only 2 native and one cultivated species.

KEY TO THE SPECIES AND VARIETIES

1 Bracts small, linear
  2 Tree; leaf-blades large, ovate-cordate, 10–25 cm long, usually cordate or subcordate basally; branches unarmed; inflorescence erect, paniculate; calyx mostly 5-toothed
    3 Leaf-blades densely fulvous-tomentose beneath...........**1. G. arborea** var. **arborea**
    3 Leaf-blades merely glabrous beneath...................**G. arborea** var. **glaucescens**

2 Mostly shrubby, often climbing; leaf-blades small, ovate or obovate, 1–9.5 cm long, usually acute or acuminate basally; branches often spiny; inflorescence pendulous; calyx mostly 4-toothed..**2. G. asiatica**
1 Bracts very large and foliaceous, persistent, usually bright red, red-purple, or yellow during anthesis; racemes elongate, 10–20 cm long, nutant or pendent. .**3. G. philippensis**

1. Gmelina arborea Roxb., Hort. Beng. 46, hyponym. 1814; Roxb., Pl. Corom. 3: 41–42, Pl. 246. 1819; Moon, Cat. 1: 45. 1824; Spach, Hist. Nat. Veg. Phan. 9: 232–233. 1840; Schau. in A. DC., Prod. 11: 638 & 680. 1847; Thw., Enum. Pl. Zeyl. 244. 1861; Clarke in Hook. f., Fl. Br. Ind. 4: 581. 1885; Trimen, Cat. 69. 1895; Trimen, Handb. Fl. Ceylon 3: 355. 1895; Gamble, Man. Indian Timb., ed. 2, 537–539. 1902; Brandis, Indian Trees 509. 1906; Willis, Cat. 69. 1911; Troup, Silvicult. Indian Trees 2: 769–776. 1921; Alston in Trimen, Handb. Fl. Ceylon 6: 232. 1931; Benthall, Trees Calcutta 353–354. 1933; Dop in Lecomte, Fl. Gén. Indo-Chine 4: 843. 1935; Alston, Kandy Fl. 64, fig. 345. 1938; Dastur, Med. Pl. India 126–127. 1952; Petelot, Pl. Méd. Cambod. Laos & Viet-Nam 2: 252 and 4: 59. 1954; Bakh. & Van Steenis, Taxon 5: 81. 1956; Cooke, Fl. Pres. Bombay, ed. 2, 504–505. 1958; Abeywick., Ceylon J. Sci., Biol. Sci. 2: 217. 1959; Worthington, Ceylon Trees 345. 1959; Burkill, Dict. Econ. Prod. Malay Penins. 1: 1105–1106. 1966; Gunawardena, Gen. & Sp. Pl. Zeyl. 147. 1968; Hughes & Esan, Trop. Sci. 11: 23–37. 1969; Fonseka & Vinasithamby, Prov. List Local Names Fl. Pl. Ceylon 21, 27, & 93. 1971. Type: *Roxburgh s.n.*, growing in the Calcutta Botanical Garden, probably in the East India Company herbarium (K), probably from the Coromandel coast.

Cumbulu Rheede, Hort. Mal. 1: 75. Pl. 41. 1678.
Premna arborea Roth, Nov. Sp. Pl. 287. 1825 [not *P. arborea* (Forst. f.) Farwell, 1919].
Gmelina arborea L. ex Spreng. in L., Syst. ed. 16, 5 (2): 765. 1827.—*Gmebina arborea* Roxb. apud Wight, Ic. Pl. Ind. Or. 4 (3): Pl. 1470. 1849.—*Gmelina arborea* Wight apud Thw., Enum. Pl. Zeyl. 244. 1861.—*Gmelina arborea* Smith apud Bakh. & Van Steenis, Taxon 5: 81. 1956.—*Gmelia arborea* Joshi, Indian Forester 95: 152. 1969.—*Cmelina arborea* Chadhuri, Bull. Bot. Soc. Bengal 23: 123. 1969.
Gmelina tomentosa Wall., Num. List 87. 1831 [not *G. tomentosa* Fletcher, 1938].
Gmelina rheedii Hook. in Curtis, Bot. Mag. 74 [ser. 3, 4]: Pl. 4395. 1848.
Premna tomentosa Miq. apud Clarke in Hook. f., Fl. Br. Ind. 4: 581. 1885 [not *P. tomentosa* Blanco, 1845, nor Blume, 1885, nor F.-Vill., 1883, nor Kurz, 1877, nor Rottl., 1803, nor Willd., 1800].—*P. tomentose* Miq. ex Petelot, Bull. Econ. Indochine 37: 1295. 1934.

Juvenile Form

Gmelina arborea f. *dentata* Moldenke, Phytologia 8: 14. 1961.

A medium-sized to large tree, to 20 m tall, unarmed, widespreading, rapidly growing, often branched to the base when young; trunk straight, to 2.4 m in girth, the bole clear to 10 m in old trees; bark smooth, pale-ashy-grey or greyish-yellow with blackish patches and conspicuous circular lenticels, rather corky, rapidly turning brown on exposure, exfoliating into thick woody plates or scurfy flakes, the blaze pale orange, freely mottled with darker orange; wood light, weight 28–35 lb/cubic foot, very durable, greyish to yellowish- or reddish-white when fresh, coarse-textured, close- and even-grained, soft, strong, seasoning well without warping or cracking, taking a good polish, resistant to termites and shipworms; branchlets and young parts yellowish-tomentose; branches few or numerous, spreading, forming a large shady crown; leaves deciduous, decussate-opposite, mostly rather soft and limp; petioles cylindric, 5–15 cm long, puberulent or glabrous; leaf-blades broadly ovate, 10–25 cm long, 7.5–18 cm wide, apically long-acuminate or caudate, entire on mature plants but strongly toothed or lobed on young plants and turions (f. juv. *dentata* Moldenke), usually cordate or truncate basally, usually with a short cuneate attenuation into the petiole, densely tomentose above when young, becoming glabrous above when mature, permanently densely fulvous-tomentellous with stellate hairs beneath, glanduli-ferous just above the petiole on the basal attenuation, the lateral secondaries 5–10 pairs, the lowest pair sub-basal; inflorescences terminal and axillary, fulvous-tomentose throughout, erect, 7.5–39 cm long; bracts linear or linear-lanceolate, about 1 cm long; flowers appearing before or with the young leaves, arranged in 1–3-flowered cymules on the panicle branches; calyx broadly campanulate, about 5 mm long, densely fulvous-tomentose externally, the rim with 5 small, triangular, acute teeth; corolla large, showy, somewhat like *Catalpa*, varying from yellow or brilliant orange to reddish- or brownish-yellow, dull yellow-brown, pinkish-brown, or orange-whitish, 2.5–4 cm long, tubular below, obliquely funnelform at the throat, the tube often madder-purple, densely pubescent externally, the limb 2-lipped, the upper lip often orange-pink, deeply divided into 2 oblong, obtuse back-wardly curled lobules, the lower lip often lemon-yellow, about as long or twice as long as the upper and 3-lobed, the ovate middle lobe much longer and broader than the obovate-rounded lateral ones, projecting forward, sub-obtuse, and with an irregularly crenulate margin; stamens 4, didynamous, exserted from the mouth of the corolla-tube, sometimes one pair sterile; anthers oblong, the cells separate, parallel; pistil exserted from the mouth of the corolla-tube; style slender; stigma shortly bifid; ovary 4-celled, each cell 1-ovulate; ovules attached near top of the cell; drupes ovate or obovoid-pyriform, 2–2.5 cm long, borne on the unenlarged fruiting-calyx, orange-yellow when mature, aromatic, bittersweet, the exocarp succulent, the endocarp bony, usually 2-celled and (by abortion) 1- or 2-seeded, sometimes 3-celled and 3-seeded. Chromosome number: $2n = 36, 38$, or 40.

D i s t r. Native from Pakistan, Bhutan, and India east through Bangladesh, Burma, and Thailand to Indo-China, Malaya, and Indonesia, north to southern China; introduced in many parts of tropical Africa, South America, and elsewhere; rather extensively cultivated as a source of paper-pulp, lumber, shade, and ornament.

U s e s. This species is of considerable economic importance. In Pakistan the roots, bark, fruit, and seeds are used medicinally. In India the tree is planted for shade along streets and avenues and in gardens and parks. Its wood resembles that of teak and is employed for similar purposes. It is, in fact, said by some writers to be superior to that of teak for naval construction. It is even-grained, easily worked, very durable, does not warp, shrink, or crack on drying, takes paint, polish, and varnish well, and is resistant to termite and shipworm attack. The tree reproduces well in coppices and is easily propagated by cuttings. It cannot, however, withstand severe frost.

The timber is widely employed in carriage-building and ornamental cabinet work, in the manufacture of palanquins, shafts, axles, yokes, agricultural instruments, grain measures, cattle-bells, toys, lacquered tea-boxes, sandals, dugouts, and even matches in India. It is valued for well and sluice construction, planking, and panelling, as well as in the making of furniture, boat-decks, artificial limbs, canoes, native stethoscopes, clogs, picture-frames, and musical instruments like drums, tom-toms, and sitars. In Burma it is used as mining timber, and in recent years the tree has been planted in large plantations in parts of Africa and South America as a fast-growing source of paper-pulp.

In parts of India the bitter roots are used as a tonic, stomachic, laxative, anthelmintic, and anodyne, widely employed in the treatment of fevers, indigestion, anasarca, abdominal pains, burning sensations, and even hallucination; taken with liquorice, honey, and sugar the decoction is said to increase lactation. The leaves are widely used as cattle fodder; the juice of the young leaves is used as a demulcent in the treatment of gonorrhoea and coughs, either alone or combined with other drugs, and as a lotion for wounds and ulcers. The flowers are used in the treatment of leprosy and blood diseases.

The fruit is edible and is widely eaten in parts of India. For this purpose it is thoroughly rubbed by hand, the rind removed, then dried in the sun, and finally boiled. From the fruit is also made a cooling decoction useful against fevers, bilious complaints, anemia, leprosy, ulcers, and consumption. It is also supposed to promote the growth of hair. The fruit and young shoots are favorite food of deer and antelope. The wood ashes and the fruit both yield a very persistent yellow dye. The tree is recommended for growing silkworms and, because of its pioneering tendencies in grassland, is used to crowd out noxious grasses which it kills off by its shade.

V e r n. At-demmata, At-demata, At-dembata, Eth-demata (S); Gumadi, Gumudu-takku, Kainadi, Kumil, Umi (T); Candahar-tree, Comb-tree, Kashmir-tree, Malay beechwood, Snapdragon tree, Tall beechberry (E). In addition some 85 other names are recorded from various parts of its range.

N o t e s. The pollen is described in detail by Nair & Rehman (Bull. Bot. Gard. Lucknow 76: 13 & 16–18. 1962). Details of the wood anatomy are given by Gamble (1902). Unfortunately, it is susceptible to attack by no less than 7 species of fungi, by *Tapinanthus* sp., by a mollusk, a myriapod, 5 kinds of mammals, and 44 species of insects according to Browne (Pests & Diseases of Forest Plantation Trees, 1968).

Besides the following variety there is also var. *canescens* Haines (in India) with the leaves merely grey-pubescent, not stellate-tomentose, on the lower surface.

S p e c i m e n s E x a m i n e d. KANDY DISTRICT: Ambagamuwa and Ramboda, *Gardner s.n.* [*C.P. 128*] (PDA); Royal Botanic Garden, Peradeniya, 28 April 1903, flowers and fruit, *Hallier C. 243* (HBG, L); wild at river edge, Royal Botanic Garden, Peradeniya, 27 April 1904, small tree, sterile, nectaries at leaf-base beneath, *Hallier C. 3514* (HBG); in outdoor cultivation, Section E, Royal Botanic Garden, Peradeniya, 1550 ft alt., 18 Jan. 1974, tree 12 ft tall, numbered 32, *H.N. & A.L. Moldenke & Jayasuriya 28141* (LL, PDA, US); in outdoor cultivation, Students' Garden, Royal Botanic Garden, Peradeniya, 1550 ft alt., 18 Jan. 1974, small tree, 10 ft tall, *H.N. & A.L. Moldenke & Jayasuriya 28177* (AAU, PDA, US); in outdoor cultivation in temple garden, Lagamuwa temple, Poilakanda, Kadugannawa, 1900 ft alt., 22 Jan. 1974, in leaf only, said never to have bloomed, actually growing from old stump of original tree cut down many years ago, original tree said to have been gift to temple, *H.N. & A.L. Moldenke & Sumithraarachchi 28200* (CAI, LL, MOLDENKE, PDA, US); in forest on steep disturbed mountainside at milepost 18/14 south of Kandy on the Nuwara Eliya road, 2000 ft alt., 30 Jan. 1974, scattered trees 18 ft tall, *H.N. & A.L. Moldenke, Jayasuriya, & Sumithraarachchi 28312* (AAU, ARIZ, CAI, KARACHI, LL, MO, PDA, US); Bible Rock, 2618 ft alt., 19 March 1974, leaves opposite, hairy on the lower side, flowers yellow, fruit green, *Sumithraarachchi & Fernando DBS. 161* (LL, US); in jungle but not heavy shade, Poilakanda, Kandugannawa, 1800 ft alt. 18 April 1940, "et demata" Sinhala, "kumil" Tamil, *Worthington 887* (PDA); Attabage, 2556 ft alt., 14 June 1947, *Worthington 2824* (PDA); Ampitiya patanas, 2400 ft alt., 7 April 1953, rainfall 87 inches, *Worthington 6266* (PDA); patana grassland, Kadugannawa, 1800 ft alt., 6 Oct. 1955, rainfall 95 inches, "et-demata" *Worthington 6777* (PDA). MATALE DISTRICT: in shade of forest at forest edge at 32 1/2 milepost, Nalanda, 1000 ft alt., 19 May 1947, old leaves fallen off, "et-dembata", *Worthington 2737* (PDA). MONERAGALA DISTRICT: rare in savanna on hill slope between Medagama and Dambagalla, low altitude, 2 May 1975, small tree, 6 m tall, branched at base, fruit bittersweet, cherished by antelopes, *Jayasuriya 1989* (AAU, LL).

var. **glaucescens** Clarke in Hook. f., Fl. Br. Ind. 4: 582. 1885. Type: *J.D. Hooker s.n.* from the Khasia Mountains, India, altitude "0–2000 feet" (K).

This variety differs from the typical variety mostly in its mature leaf-blades being glabrous and glaucous beneath and the triangular calyx-teeth somewhat larger. In many respects var. *canescens* Haines, not known from Ceylon, with the lower leaf-surface canescent-pubescent, is intermediate.

Variety *glaucescens* is known from northern Pakistan and Nepal, through northern India, to Burma. It is rather widely cultivated in tropical Asia, Java, Florida, Venezuela, Germany, and elsewhere, mostly for ornament.

V e r n. It is known in India as Gambar or Gumhar.

S p e c i m e n s E x a m i n e d. BADULLA DISTRICT: two blocks planted, no. 21 and no. 23, in a hollow, Erabedde Arboretum, 4000 ft alt., 26 June 1952, rainfall 60 inches, very poor specimens, *Worthington 5932* (PDA).

2. Gmelina asiatica L., Sp. Pl., ed. 1, 2: 626. 1753. Hermann, Mus. Zeyl. 3, 9, 12, & 21. 1717; Burm., Thes. Zeyl. 197. 1737; Moon, Cat. 1: 45. 1824; Roxb., Fl. Ind., ed. 2, 3: 87. 1832; Schau. in A. DC., Prod. 11: 638 & 679. 1847; Thw., Enum. Pl. Zeyl. 244. 1861; Clarke in Hook. f., Fl. Br. Ind. 4: 582. 1885; Trimen, Cat. 69. 1885; Trimen, Handb. Fl. Ceylon 355–356. 1895; Brandis, Indian Trees 509. 1906; Willis, Cat. 69. 1911; Gamble, Fl. Pres. Madras 6: 1097–1098. 1924; Cooke, Fl. Pres. Bombay, ed. 2, 2: 504 & 505. 1958; Abeywick., Ceylon J. Sci., Biol. Sci. 2: 217. 1959; Gunawardena, Gen. Sp. Pl. Zeyl. 147. 1968; Fonseka & Vinasithamby, Prov. List Local Names Fl. Pl. Ceylon 16, 27, 48, & 63. 1971. Type: *Herb. Linnaeus 780/2* (LINN).

Arbuscula bisnagarica aceris folio parvo aculeata, foliis e regione binis Plukenet, Almag. Bot. 1: Pl. 14, fig. 4. 1691.—*Arbuscula bismagarica* Plukenet apud H.J. Lam in Lam & Bakh., Bull. Jard. Bot. Buitenzorg, ser. 3, 3: 69. 1921.

Lycium maderaspatanum indici, alpino putati aemulum, foliis minoribus & majoribus bijugis, & grandioribus aculeis horridis Plukenet, Almag. Bot. 5: 234, Pl. 303, fig. 3, & Pl. 97, fig. 2. 1700.—*Lycium maderaspatanum* Plukenet apud H.J. Lam in Lam & Bakh., Bull. Jard. Bot. Buitenzorg, ser. 3, 3: 69. 1921.

Dematha zeylanensibus Hermann, Mus. Zeyl. 3, 9, 12, & 21. 1717.

Prunus indica sylvestris, fructu flavo, pyriformi Burm., Thes. Zeyl. 197. 1737.—

Premna indica et sylvestris Burm. apud Petelot, Pl. Méd. Camb. Laos &
Viet-Nam 2: 252. 1954.—*Premna indica* Burm. apud Petelot, Pl. Méd.
Camb. Laos & Viet-Nam 4: 151. 1954.—*Premna sylvestris* Burm. apud Pe-
telot, Pl. Méd. Camb. Laos & Viet-Nam 4: 151. 1954.—*Prunus indica syl-
vestris* Burm. ex Moldenke, Résumé 341. 1959.
Michelia spinosa, floribus luteis Amman, Acta Petrop. 8: 218, Pl. 18. 1739.—
M. spinosa Amman apud Schau. in A. DC., Prod. 11: 679. 1847.
Gmelina coromandelica Burm. f., Fl. Ind. 132. 1768.—*G. coromandeliana*
Burm. apud Schau. in A. DC., Prod. 11: 679. 1847.—*G. coromandeliana*
Burm. f. apud Clarke in Hook. f., Fl. Br. Ind. 4: 582. 1885.—*G. coromande-
lina* Burm. apud Jacks. in Hook. f. & Jacks., Ind. Kew. 1: 1039. 1893.
Gmelina parvifolia Roxb., Pl. Corom. 2: 32, Pl. 162. 1798.—*G. parviflora* Roxb.
ex Pers., Syn. Pl. 2: 142. 1807.—*G. parviflora* Pers. apud Jacks. in Hook. f.
& Jacks., Ind. Kew. 1: 1040. 1893.—*G. purvifolia* Roxb. ex Moldenke,
Alph. List Invalid Names Suppl. 1: 10. 1947.
Premna parvifolia Roth, Nov. Pl. Sp. 288–289. 1821.
Gmelina inermis Wight ex Wall., Num. List 87. 1831 [not *G. inermis* Naves,
1918].—*G. inermis* Blanco, F. Filip., ed. 1, 493. 1837.
Gurelina asiatica L. ex Wight, Ill. Ind. Bot. 2: Pl. 174. 1850.—*Gmelina asiatica*
var. *typica* Bakh. ex Lam & Bakh., Bull. Jard. Bot. Buitenzorg, ser. 3, 3: 69.
1921 [not *G. asiatica* Auct., 1917, nor Blanco, 1837, nor Burm., 1921, nor
Kurz, 1902, nor Lour., nor Schau., 1918, nor Wall., 1831].
Gmelina tomentosa Roxb. ex Moldenke, Alph. List Invalid Names Suppl. 1:
10. 1947 [not *G. tomentosa* Fletcher, 1938].

Juvenile Form

Gmelina asiatica f. *lobata* Moldenke, Phytologia 32: 47. 1975.

A large straggling or scrambling deciduous bush or shrub, rather hardy,
to about 3 m tall, or rarely a semi-evergreen tree to 8 m tall, sometimes prostrate, usually spiny, sometimes unarmed [f. *inermis* (Blanco) Moldenke],
much-branched, with basitonic branching, very variable in size and habit;
bark yellowish- or brownish-white, thin, smooth; wood hard, grey; branchlets
horizontal, rigid, often compressed, puberulous or even villosulous when
young; twigs frequently much abbreviated and apically spinose, these axillary
spines sometimes leaf-bearing; leaves small; petioles 0.5–3 cm long, slender;
leaf-blades membranous or chartaceous, varying from oval or ovate to elliptic, obovate, subrhomboid, or triangular in outline, very variable, mostly 1–
9.5 (rarely to 13) cm long, 1.5–6 cm wide, entire or 3–5 lobed when young
and on turions (f. *lobata* Moldenke), basally mostly acute to cuneate, sometimes rounded, apically acute or obtuse, glabrous on both surfaces when
mature, often more or less pubescent when young, dark and shiny above, pale
green, glaucescent, and minutely white-glanduliferous beneath, the glands
round; inflorescences axillary and terminal, nodding or pendulous, appressed-

tomentose; bracts usually rather small, linear or lanceolate, cuspidate, 2–3 times as long as the calyx, caducous; flowers large, borne in short cymules in mostly terminal fulvous-tomentose racemiform panicles 2.5–5 cm long, falling after dawn or as soon as picked in daylight hours; pedicels pubescent; calyx about 4 mm long, somewhat contracted apically, externally pubescent-tomentose, glanduliferous, the rim very shortly 4-toothed, the teeth acute, the glands many, large, bare, antrorse, flattened, discoid; corolla large, yellow or bright sulphur-yellow, 4–5 cm long, bilabiate, externally finely pubescent or reddish-tomentose, internally glabrous, the tube narrow and curvate below, apically ampliate into a broad ventricose throat, the limb 4-lobed, the lobes ovate, subacute, the lowest largest; fertile stamens 2; staminodes 2; drupes ovoid or obovoid-pyriform, yellow when ripe, with a watery or soapy exudate, 1.8–2.8 cm long, glabrous, 1- or 2-celled and -seeded. Chromosome number: 2n = 38 or 40.

D i s t r. A widely distributed and highly variable species found from India, Ceylon, and Bangladesh, through Burma and Thailand to Malaya and Indo-China, east to Indonesia, north to southern China, and west to Réunion and Mauritius; cultivated widely in various parts of North, Central, and South America, West Indies, Europe, Asia, and Africa, as well as some Pacific islands like Hawaii; in a few cases naturalized to a limited extent.

U s e s. *Gmelina asiatica* is widely used as a hedge plant in India and is there regarded medicinally as a demulcent and alterative. Its wood is used for fences and churning sticks and burned as fuel. The root is astringent, aromatic, mucilaginous and slightly bitter; it is employed as a blood purifier and in the treatment of rheumatism, incontinence, gonorrhoea and syphilis, as well as for catarrh of the bladder and to promote micturition. The bark is said to aid the fermentation of toddy. The leaves, placed in water, render the water mucilaginous and this is then employed medicinally since it is said to exhibit an antibiotic effect against *Escherichia coli* and *Staphylococcus aureus*. The macerated leaves and young shoots are used in treating blen-norrhoea and gleet. The fruit is edible, while elephants and monkeys feed on the leaves. The seeds yield 7.5 percent of a greenish-yellow semi-drying fatty oil. In Cambodia an infusion made from the plant is used against rheuma-tism, yaws, and nervous diseases, that made from the roots being used inter-nally and that from the leaves externally. The plant has been found to contain a glycosidic substance as well as palmitic, stearic, arachidic, oleic, and linoleic acids, but no saponin. The Portuguese formerly dug the roots (which they called "rais Madre de Deos") only on St. Mary's Day and only those roots which turned northward were used as an antidote for almost any known poison and as a remedy for almost any disease, especially as an emol-lient and alterative.

V e r n. Demata, Demette ette, Gatta-demmata (S); Gumadi, Kumil,

Nela-kumi, Nilacumal, Nila-kumi (T); Asiatic beechberry (E); some 25 other names are recorded from various parts of its range.

Note. The pollen of *G. asiatica* is described in detail by Nair & Rehman (Bull. Bot. Gard. Lucknow 76: 18. 1962) and the wood anatomy by Gamble (Man. Ind. Timb., ed. 2, 539. 1902).

Many authors include *Radix deiparae spuria* Rumph., *Jambosa sylvestris* Rumph., and *Gmelina lobata* Gaertn. in the synonymy of *G. asiatica*. The first of these, however, applies to the related permanently hairy-leaved *G. elliptica* Smith [*G. asiatica* var. *villosa* (Roxb.) Bakh.] and the other two to its juvenile form.

The plant is often parasitized by *Dendrophthoë falcata* (L.f.) Ettingsh.

Specimens Examined. JAFFNA DISTRICT: Jaffna, *s. coll. C.P. 1952* in part (PDA). MANNAR DISTRICT: hardly frequent in dry spiny thickets about 12 km from the centre of Pooneryn on the road to Mannar, 12 Oct. 1975, branched shrub, stems stout, grey, decussate, flowers conspicuous, yellow, *Bernardi 15339* (US). VAVUNIYA DISTRICT: occasional tree in dense scrub forest, 4 miles north of Mankulam, 10 December 1970, rigid shrub, fruit green, *Fosberg & Balakrishnan 53542* (ARIZ, US). KURUNE-GALA DISTRICT: on the Kurunegala to Nikaweratiya road, 4 Sept. 1962, a much-branched shrub, flowers bright sulphur-yellow, *Amaratunga 318* (PDA); occasional along border of scrub beside the Gonagama to Ganewatta road, Gonagama, 120 m alt., 4 April 1973, shrub with diffuse branches, flowers conspicuous, yellow, fruit obovoid, up to 2.8 × 2.4 cm, *Cramer 4096* (US); in scrub on west shore of Batalagoda tank, 5 Feb. 1973, weak straggl-ing shrub arching and flopping over adjoining shrubs, very strongly spiny, flowers jasmine-yellow, pendulous, with the lip directed upwards, falling im-mediately after picking, *Townsend 74/41* (US). ANURADHAPURA DIS-TRICT: common in edge of forest, Marai Villu, Wilpattu National Park, 31 Dec. 1968, tall shrub with a number of trunks crowded together, spreading crown, bright yellow corollas falling after dawn, greenish yellow fruit, *Fos-berg, Mueller-Dombois, Wirawan, Cooray, & Balakrishnan 50933* (US); rare in open belt next to forest margin dominated by low suffrutescent herbs, on sand, Kali Villu, plot W. 9. Wilpattu National Park, 31 Dec. 1968, prostrate shrub, sterile, odourless, *Fosberg, Mueller-Dombois, Wirawan, Cooray, & Balakrishnan 50967* (US); outskirts of forest, Smithsonian Camp, Wilpattu National Park, about sealevel, 6 June 1969, shrub, flowers yellow, fruit yel-low, *Hladik 821* (US); spiny shrubs at edge of jungle, Wilpattu National Park, low altitude, 24 Jan. 1974, corolla yellow, *H.N. & A.L. Moldenke & Jayasuriya 28226* (PDA, US); among hedges, growing with various euphorbs, Bulan-kulama, on the Anuradhapura to Puttalam road, low altitude, 29 Aug. 1974, shrub 4 m tall, flowers large, 2-lipped, upper one 3-lobed, stamens 2 fertile, 2 sterile, fruit pyriform, green, yellow when ripe and with watery or soapy exu-date, *Tirvengadum & Waas 419* (NY, US); scrub in dry zone, common around ends of tanks, etc., Naela, west of Ritigala, 460 m alt., 20 March 1951, yellow trumpet flower, stem good for axe handles, "demata", *Worthington 5172* (PDA). POLONNARUWA DISTRICT: near rock outcrops on exposed sandy soil in roadside jungle east and north of Rankot, 61 m alt. 1 Feb. 1971, sterile shrub, one variegated twig, monkeys feed on the leaves, voucher for primate studies, *Ripley 378* (PDA, US). KANDY DISTRICT: Kadugannawa, 1800 ft alt., Jan. 1959, rainfall 90 inches, "demata", *Banda & Worthington 6893* (PDA); spiny shrubs 6 ft tall, in outdoor cultivation, Students' Garden, and in Section E, Royal Botanic Garden, Peradeniya, 1550 ft alt., 18 Jan. 1974, trunks and branches very spiny, *H.N. & A.L. Moldenke & Jayasuriya 28175* (PDA, US). MATALE DISTRICT: Dambulla, 20 July 1967, a bush or shrub, flowers yellow, fruit yellow at maturity, "demata", *Amaratunga 1357* (PDA); rather frequent east of Dambulla, near Bakamuna Bay, in Wasgomuwa Strict Natural Reserve, 150 m alt., 21 March 1973, shrub, branches decussate and armed, flowers bright yellow, tubular, incurved, *Bernardi 14357* (US); in dry forest around margin of presently dry tank, Ereula tank, about 5 miles east-southeast of Dambulla, 650 ft alt., 11 Oct. 1974, shrubs 3–4 m tall, corolla yellow, fruit green, one-seeded, with juicy inner pericarp, *Davidse 7406* (LL, US). KEGALLE DISTRICT: Ambepussa, 23 Aug. 1968, a tall shrub, flowers bright sulphur-yellow, "demata", *Amaratunga 1627* (PDA). RATNAPURA DISTRICT: on the Bowatte to Balangoda road, 24 Jan. 1963, flowers yellow, *Amaratunga 455* (PDA). BADULLA DISTRICT: shrub beside bund of tank, Dambara Wewa, 81°01' N., 7°14' E., low altitude, 29 Oct. 1971, shrub 2 m tall, fruit green with whitish spots, *Jayasuriya 401* (PDA, US). MONERAGALA DISTRICT: common in open forest with tall grass on coarse gritty soil, the trees 15 m tall, 7 miles east of Bibile, 245 m alt., 28 Nov. 1970, tall shrub, flowers yellow, *Fosberg & Sachet 53158* (KARACHI). AMPARAI DISTRICT: very common near tree hut in shrub ecotone between forest and tank, light-coloured soil, Lahugala Sanctuary, Kitulana, 30 m alt., 14 Nov. 1967, shrub 2 m tall, flowers bright yellow, zygomorphic, pollen collected, *Comanor 592* (AAU, NY); in edge of thicket on soil pockets on gneissic granite outcrops, Lahugala tank, 27 Nov. 1970, shrubs 2–3 m tall, tangled, flowers bright yellow, *Fosberg & Sachet 53060* (LL, US); a member of thicket surrounding rock outcrops in forest on dry land, southeast corner of Lahugala tank, 36 m alt., 25 July, 1967, 2 m tall, very bushy partly deciduous thorn shrub, collected as voucher for ecological observations, *Mueller-Dombois & Cooray 67072545* (PDA); in dry zone scrub, Padiyatalawa, at 56/8 culvert on the Bibile to Batticaloa road, 350 m alt., 16 June 1951, flowers yellow, "demata" Sinhala, "kumil" Tamil, *Worthington 5325* (PDA). BATTICALOA DISTRICT: Vakarai, 10 m alt., 16 June 1951, rainfall 60 inches, "demata", *Worthington 6532* (PDA). TRINCOMALEE DISTRICT: on brushy coastal hills, 10–20 m alt., Kinniyai, 9 miles south of Trincomalee, 1 May 1970, spiny shrub to 10 ft tall, yellow flowers, *Gould & Cooray 13666*

(US); Foul Point, 7 April 1974, shrub 8 ft tall, thorns present, fruit green, *Sumithraarachchi & Jayasuriya DBS. 235* (AAU). GALLE DISTRICT: Galle, *s. coll. C.P. 1952* in part (PDA). HAMBANTOTA DISTRICT: in clay-sand soil of shrub border on main Yala road past Buttuwa Plain, 23 Jan. 1968, spreading shrub, 3 m tall, corolla yellow, *Comanor 829* (AAU, NY, PDA); growing above normal lagoon water level (dry), Buttuwa Beach area, Karaugaswala, 8–15 m alt., 28 Jan. 1968, shrub 3 m tall, frequent, flowers yellow, mature fruit yellow, *Comanor 883* (AAU, NY, PDA); in dry zone on moist sand near freshwater pond in vegetation characterized by the presence of *Calamus*, Block 2, near Yala, Ruhuna National Park, 20 m alt., 23 June 1967, small tree, flowers yellow, *Mueller-Dombois & Cooray 67062307* (PDA, US); in Plot R. 33, Block I, Rakinawala, Ruhuna National Park, 22 Oct. 1968, 3 m tall shrub with basitonic branching, leaves glabrous, flowers yellow, abundant now, fruit green, *Cooray 68102293R* (LL, PDA); common at Rakinawala, Ruhuna National Park, 18 March 1970, shrub 2.5 m tall, basitonic branching, flowers yellow, collected as voucher for ecologic observations, *Cooray 70031809R* (MO, NY, PDA, US); common in open tall scrub with scattered trees, grass between clumps, Block I, Rakina Wewa near Gonalabbe Lewaya, Ruhuna National Park, 2 m alt., 5 April 1968, tall flat-topped much branched shrub, branches forming flat sprays, flowers bright yellow, *Fosberg 50237* (PDA, US); Yala, sealevel, 13 June 1965, large leaves, "demata", *Lee & Worthington 7103* (PDA); Block I between Yala and Kotabandu Wewa, Ruhuna National Park, 20 m alt., 25 June 1967, straggling shrub, 2–3 m tall, conspicuous opposite branches, complanate stem, grooved on both sides, eaten by elephants, *Mueller-Dombois & Comanor 67062513* (PDA); on sand outside Plot R. 28, Block I, 200 m west of Karaugaswala junction, Ruhuna National Park, 10 Dec. 1967, 3 m tall shrub, voucher for ecological observations, *Mueller-Dombois & Cooray 67121090* (PDA); near rock outcrops, Yala, Jamburagala, 5–7 March 1969, in flower, voucher for primate ecology studies, *Ripley 111* (PDA, US). LOCALITY UNKNOWN: *s. coll. s.n.* (PDA); *Kirmül 226* (M); fruit, "demette ette", *König 197* (L).

Juvenile Form

ANURADHAPURA DISTRICT: Smithsonian Camp, Marai Villu, Wilpattu National Park, 30 June 1969, shrub 3 m tall, fruit green, *Wirawan, Cooray, & Balakrishnan 899* (LL, NY, PDA, US).

3. **Gmelina philippensis** Cham., Linnaea 7: 109 [as "(*asiatica?*) *philippensis*"]. 1832; Jacks. in Hook. f. & Jacks., Ind. Kew. 1: 1040. 1893; Schau. in A. DC., Prod. 11: 679 & 680. 1847; Kurz, For. Fl. Burma 2: 265. 1877; Gamble, Man. Indian Timb., ed. 2, 539. 1902; Gamble, Fl. Pres. Madras 6: 1098. 1924; Cooke, Fl. Pres. Bombay, ed. 2, 2: 505–506. 1958; Backer & Bakh., Fl. Java

2: 606–607. 1965; Burkill, Dict. Econ. Prod. Malay Penins. 1: 1106. 1966. Type: a specimen collected in Luzon, Philippine Islands, no collector designated (B).

Gmelina ? finlaysoniana Wall., Num. List 215. 1832; Schau. in A. DC., Prod. 11: 680. 1847.—*Gmelina finslaysoniana* Wall. ex Kuntze, Rev. Gen. Pl. 2: 507. 1891.

Gmelina asiatica Blanco, Fl. Filip., ed. 1, 492–493. 1837 [not *G. asiatica* Kurz, 1902, nor L., 1753, nor Wall., 1831].—*G. asiatica* Schau. apud Hallier, Meded. Rijks-Herb. 37: 60. 1918.—*G. asiatica* Lour. apud H.J. Lam in Lam & Bakh., Bull. Jard. Bot. Buitenzorg, ser. 3, 3: 70. 1921.

Gmelina hystrix Schult. ex Kurz, J. Asiat. Soc. Bengal 39 (2): 81. 1870.— *G. histryx* Kurz apud Vidal, Phan. Cumong. Philipp. 134. 1885.—*G. hystrix* Kurz ex Kuntze, Rev. Gen. Pl. 2: 507. 1891.—*G. hystris* Schult. apud López-Palacios, Pittieria 6: 17. 1974.

Gmelina bracteata Burck, Ann. Jard. Bot. Buitenzorg 10: 98, Pl. 7, fig. 5 & 6. 1891.

Gmelina finslaysoniana var. *hystrix* Kuntze, Rev. Gen. Pl. 2: 507. 1891.

Gmelina finslaysoniana var. *silvestris* Kuntze, Rev. Gen. Pl. 2: 507. 1891.

Gmelina finslaysoniana var. *viridibracteata* Kuntze, Rev. Gen. Pl. 2: 507. 1891.

Gmelina inermis Naves apud Hallier, Meded. Rijks-Herb. 37: 60. 1918 [not *G. inermis* Blanco, 1837, nor Wight, 1831].

Gmelina philippinensis Cham. apud H.J. Lam, Verbenac. Malay. Arch 222. 1919.—*G. phillippensis* Hall & Gooding, Fls. Islands in Sun 11, 41, 47, & 133. 1966.—*G. philippensis* Cham. & Schlecht. ex Moldenke, Résumé Suppl. 18: 12. 1969.—*G. philippinensis* Cham. & Schlecht. ex Moldenke, Résumé Suppl. 18: 12. 1969.—*G. filipensis* Cham. ex Moldenke, Phytologia 23: 432. 1972.—*G. filippensis* Cham. apud López-Palacios, Pittieria 6: 17. 1974.

Gmelina asiatica var. *philippinensis* (Cham.) Bakh. ex H.J. Lam in Lam & Bakh., Bull. Jard. Bot. Buitenzorg, ser. 3, 3: 70. 1921.

Gmelina finslaysoniana var. *silvestris* f. *colorata* Kuntze ex Moldenke, Phytologia 31: 398. 1975.

Gmelina finslaysoniana var. *silvestris* f. *viridibracteata* Kuntze ex Moldenke, Phytologia 31: 398. 1975.

A moderate-sized or large, dense, attractive, straggling or scandent (if shaded), usually spinose shrub or small tree, to 7 m tall, sometimes prostrate; ultimate branches rather short, divaricate, drooping or subscandent, and forming more or less flattened masses; dwarfed branchlets spinescent, the spines horizontal, short, 0.25–1.5 cm long, or absent (f. *inermis*); bark yellowish, lenticellate; wood white, soft; leaves mostly anisophyllous; petioles 0.5–4 cm long; leaf-blades submembranous, ovate or elliptic to rhomboid-elliptic or obovate, 1.5–10 cm long, 1.5–6 cm wide, apically obtuse or subacute, basally

(and sometimes also apically) cuneate, entire or distantly toothed to slightly
few-lobed, glabrous and shiny above, pale and often glaucous beneath, puberulent only on the larger veins, the intervening spaces covered by many peltate
scales; inflorescence terminal, 10–20 cm long, many-flowered, the cymes
arranged in racemiform clusters in the axils of large foliaceous bracts; bracts
very conspicuous, membranous, broadly oval or ovate to obovate or orbicular and concave, permanently green (f. *viridibracteata*) or yellowish-green
or (in the cultivated f. *colorata*) maroon or purple to red or brownish-red,
sometimes striped or purple-veined, 1.5–4 cm long, 1–3.5 cm wide, apically
mucronate or short-apiculate, shortly ciliate-hairy only along the margins;
flowers pendulous, slightly fragrant, in 1-flowered cymules, easily detached
from the pedicels by day; calyx with 2–4 external glands; corolla bright yellow
or light lemon-yellow, curiously inflated upwards, 4.5–5.5 cm long, externally
moderately densely pubescent or glabrous; the 2 longer stamens often with
gland-tipped hairs; drupes obovoid, pendulous, about 1.2 cm long, yellowish,
smooth, the pericarp soft and watery when mature. Chromosome number:
2n = 38.

D i s t r. Native to the Philippine Islands; also (perhaps introduced) from
India eastward through Thailand, Burma, and Indo-China to Indonesia; rather
widely cultivated for ornament in private gardens and public parks in tropical
Asia, Africa, and America.

U s e s. In the Philippines the juice of the ripe fruit is used in treating
soreness of toes due to excessive and prolonged wetness. In Malaya the
leaves and fruit are pounded with lime and applied to the throat as a poultice in
treating coughs. In Indo-China the juice of the roots is used as a purgative and
in treating overfatigue. Also in Indo-China the extract of the roots (used internally) and of the leaves (used externally) is employed as an excitant, discutient, and in treating diseases of the joints and nerves.

V e r n. Bristly beechbush, Kalulut, Kumbil, Sow-sow, and some 25 other
names are recorded.

N o t e s. The *Jambosa sylvestris* Rumph. and *J. sylvestris parvifolia*
Rumph., often cited as synonyms of this species, actually seem to apply to the
juvenile form of *G. elliptica* Smith.

Gmelina philippensis is sometimes attacked by the fungus, *Meliola clerodendricola* var. *micromera* (Syd.) Hansf.

It is very quick-growing and usually needs severe pruning. It may be propagated by cuttings. The pollen is described in detail by Nair & Rehman
(Bull. Bot. Gard. Lucknow 76: 18. 1962).

S p e c i m e n s E x a m i n e d. KANDY DISTRICT: in outdoor cultivation in Section E, Royal Botanica Garden, Peradeniya, 1550 ft alt., 18 Jan.
1974, shrubby tree, 10 ft tall, numbered "29", corollas yellow, *H.N. & A.L.
Moldenke & Jayasuriya 28140* (AAU, CAI, LL, PDA, US).

18. FARADAYA

F. Muell., Fragm. Phyt. Austral. 5: 21. 1865. Type species: *Faradaya splendida* F. Muell.

Tetrathyranthus A. Gray ex Benth. in Benth. & Hook., Gen. Pl. 2: 1156. 1876.
Schizopremna Baill., Hist. Pl. 11: 119. 1892.
Farradaya Muell. ex Moldenke, Suppl. List Invalid Names 3. 1941.

Open widespreading trees or shrubs, erect or climbing, mostly glabrous throughout or the youngest parts more or less puberulent-pubescent or even tomentose; leaves decussate-opposite or verticillate in 3's, usually glabrous, mostly petiolate, the blades chartaceous or coriaceous, entire, sometimes with basal glands or with stellate scales beneath, the venation rather prominent and distinctive; inflorescence cymose, the cymes usually many-flowered, aggregated in terminal, often large, loosely corymbose panicles or sessile in the leaf-axils; flowers usually rather large and conspicuous; calyx campanulate, mostly coriaceous, closed when immature, but during anthesis split into 2–4 short, valvate, often recurved lobes, the lobes at first coarctate-rostrate, sometimes each 2- or more-toothed; corolla zygomorphic, rather large, usually white and showy, the tube cylindric, straight, exserted, ampliate above, the limb wide-spreading, 4- (or rarely 5-) fid, the lobes imbricate, subequal or the posterior one wider and entire or emarginate and the others subequal and smaller; stamens 4 (or rarely 5), either decidedly or indistinctly didynamous or even not at all didynamous, 2 inserted in the upper part and 2 near the base of the corolla-tube, or sometimes all subequal and all inserted near the apex or near the base of the tube, sometimes long-exserted; filaments short and included or sometimes elongate, often hairy especially basally; anthers ovate-oblong, the 2 thecae parallel; style sunken between the ovary-lobes, elongate, glabrous; stigma subulate, shortly bifid or 2-toothed, sometimes infundibular; ovary composed of two 2-locular carpels, shortly to deeply 4- lobed, at first imperfectly, later completely 4-locular or by abortion 1–3-locular, the locules usually united only to about the middle, 1-ovulate; fruit drupaceous, 4-lobed and 4-locular or by abortion reduced to 1–3 large obovate pyrenes, the exocarp fleshy and succulent, the endocarp hard, 1–4-seeded, the fruit sometimes so deeply lobed as to simulate 2–4 nearly separate 1-seeded pyrenes; seed single in each locule and conforming to it in size and shape.

A genus of about 23 species and infraspecific taxa native to Indonesia, Melanesia, and Polynesia east to the Fiji and Samoan Islands, and south to tropical Australia; several species cultivated for ornament, one very widely so, in tropical regions of both hemispheres. In Ceylon it is known only from cultivation. The genus was originally placed in the Bignoniaceae; the practically gynobasic style indicates close relationship to the Lamiaceae (Labiatae).

KEY TO THE SPECIES

1 Inflorescence lax, the branches glabrate or subglabrate; pedicels to 14 mm long; corolla-lobes to 1.5 cm wide...................................**1. F. splendida**
1 Inflorescence crowded, the branches densely puberulous; pedicels to 3 mm long; corolla-lobes to 5 mm wide..**2. F. papuana**

1. Faradaya splendida F. Muell., Fragm. Phyt. Austral. 5: 21–22. 1865; Hamlyn-Harris & Smith, Mem. Queensland Mus. 5: 1–22. 1916; H.J. Lam, Bot. Jahrb. Syst. 59: 94–95. 1924; H.J. Lam in Bakh. & Lam, Nov. Guinea 14, Bot. 1: 169–170. 1924; Junell, Symb. Bot. Upsal. 4: 109 & 110, fig. 173, & Pl. 6, fig. 3. 1934; Burkill, Dict. Econ. Prod. Malay Penins. 1: 1013. 1966; Corner & Watanabe, Ill. Guide Trop. Pl. 760. 1969. Type: *Dallachy s.n.* from "in nemoribus ad sinum Rockingham's Bay" in Queensland (K).

Farradaya splendida F. Muell. ex Moldenke, Suppl. List Invalid Names 3. 1941 [not *Faradaya splendida* Schum., 1905].

A strong-growing vine or liana or large scrambling and mostly glabrous shrub, to 15 m long, occasionally prostrate, or even a small erect tree when growing in the open; stems pale greenish-brown; branchlets at first minutely puberulent but eventually glabrescent; wood brown, coarse-grained; leaves decussate-opposite, pale or dark green; petioles 1.5–5 cm long, sometimes at first minutely puberulent, eventually glabrous; leaf-blades chartaceous or subcoriaceous, ovate or oblong-elliptic to subrotund, 11–30 cm long, 7–12.5 cm wide, apically acuminate or acute, sometimes subobtuse, entire, basally rounded to truncate or deeply cordate, glabrous on both surfaces except for the minutely puberulent venation beneath, the secondaries 5–7 pairs, with 1–10 glands in (or just below) the axils of the lowest pair beneath, sometimes with some scattered glands on both surfaces; inflorescence axillary and terminal, cymose, mostly lax, glabrous or subglabrous, the upper ones sometimes forming a large panicle; peduncles 2.5–6 cm long; flowers large, showy, fragrant with the odour of *Dianthus caryophyllus*; pedicels 0.3–1.4 cm long; calyx pale green, 1.5–2.5 cm long, usually 2-lobed to about the middle, minutely puberulous, with some large external glands, the lobes acute; corolla white or greenish, 4-lobed, glabrous, the tube slender, infundibular, 2–4 cm long, the limb 4- (or rarely 5-) lobed, occasionally somewhat 2-lipped, with a line of soft hairs or subglabrous, the lobes about 2 cm long, to 15 mm wide; stamens 4 (or sometimes 5), inserted near the base of the corolla-tube, the place of insertion long-pilose, exserted; filaments white, about 6.5 cm long, long-pilose at the base; anthers cream-colour or pale-brown; style white, about 6.5 cm long; stigma shortly bifid; fruit ovoid, usually with 4 (sometimes 1–3 by abortion) basally connate pyrenes, each 1-seeded, the surface glabrous or minutely puberulous, sometimes slightly verruculose.

D i s t r. Native to Australia, New Guinea, and the Aroe and Talaut Islands, widely cultivated for ornament in tropical portions of both hemispheres. *Faradaya papuana* Scheff. and *F. albertisii* F. Muell. are sometimes regarded as conspecific with *F. splendida*, but are probably distinct.

U s e s. The acrid fruit of *F. splendida* is said to be edible. The middle layer of bark is a powerful fish poison, effective and rapid in killing fish and other aquatic animals even when used in great dilution, the active principle being a saponin. The root has been found to contain an alkaloidal substance. The species is a foodplant of the common oak butterfly (*Narathura micale amphis*).

V e r n. Reported from various parts of its range are: Buku, Koie-yan Latára, Mumuni, and Pitutu.

S p e c i m e n s E x a m i n e d. KANDY DISTRICT: near Flower Garden, Royal Botanic Garden, Peradeniya, 6 Nov. 1927, flowers white, *Alston s.n.* (PDA); Section K, Royal Botanic Garden, Peradeniya, March 1896, *s. coll. s.n.* (PDA).

2. Faradaya papuana Scheff., Ann. Jard. Bot. Buitenzorg 1: 42–43. 1876; Schum. & Lauterb., Fl. Deutsch. Schutzgeb. Südsee 525. 1900; Schum. & Lauterb., Nachtr. Fl. Deutsch. Schutzgeb. Südsee 370. 1905; H.J. Lam, Verbenac. Malay. Arch. 234. 1919; Hegnauer, Chemotax. Pfl. 6: 676. 1973. Type: *Teysmann 6773* from near Andaj, New Guinea, probably (BO).

Faradaya splendida Schum. ex Schum. & Lauterb., Nachtr. Fl. Deutsch. Schutzgeb. Südsee 370. 1905 [not *F. splendida* F. Muell., 1865].
Faradaya excellens Schum. ex Moldenke, Phytologia 34: 274. 1976.

A tall-climbing liana, to 25 m long, or large rambling shrub; stem to 2 cm in diameter; branches terete, the youngest ones short-pubescent; leaves decussate-opposite; petioles terete, about 5 cm long, somewhat twisted; leaf-blades elliptic-ovate or broadly ovate, glossy or dull dark-green above, 15–23 cm long, 7–12 cm wide, green beneath, apically obtuse, basally acute or obtuse to truncate or (on wider leaves) subcordate, glabrous on both surfaces when mature, with 4–6 orbicular glands near the larger veins, the secondaries 6–8 pairs, arcuate, the venation dense and prominent beneath; inflorescence branches densely puberulent or short-pubescent, the cymes axillary and terminal, pedunculate, densely many-flowered, crowded, repeatedly trichotomous, much shorter than the subtending leaves; peduncles long or short; pedicels very short, to 3 mm long; bractlets small, subulate; flower-buds white or cream-colour; flowers large, very showy, faintly sweet-scented; calyx large, usually about 1.8 cm long, during anthesis often unilaterally split, later deeply 2-parted; corolla white, the tube infundibular, almost 4 cm long, ampliate at the throat, the limb spreading, the lobes 4 or rarely 5, subequal, about 1.8 cm long, to 5 mm wide, apically rounded to emarginate or bilobed; stamens 4 or rarely 5, inserted slightly above the base of the corolla-tube, exserted; filaments swollen and densely lanate at the base, slender and glabrous above, almost of equal length; anthers versatile, 2-locular, the thecae basally divergent; ovary densely lanate, rather deeply 4-lobed, basally 1-locular, apically 4-locular; style equalling the stamens, apically bifid, the stigmatiferous branches short and equal; fruiting-calyx slightly incrassate; drupes 4 (or often only 1 by abortion), ellipsoid, creamy-white, about 6.5 cm long and 4 cm wide, glabrous, apically obtuse, the pericarp fleshy.

D i s t r. Apparently endemic to New Guinea, sometimes cultivated elsewhere for ornament.

N o t e. The leaves are often insect galled. *Faradaya matthewsii* Merr. of Sabah is sometimes regarded as a synonym of this species, which, in turn, is sometimes united with *F. splendida*.

S p e c i m e n s E x a m i n e d. KANDY DISTRICT: Royal Botanic Garden, Peradeniya, Feb. 1887, *s. coll. s.n.* (PDA).

19. OXERA

Labill., Sert. Austro-calad. 1: 23, Pl. 28. 1824. Type species: *Oxera pulchella* Labill.

Oncoma Spreng. in L., Syst., ed. 16, 4 (2): 11 & 18. 1827.—*Oncosma* Spreng. apud Vieill., Bull. Soc. Linn. Normandie 7: 89. 1863.
Maoutia Montr., Mém. Acad. Roy. Sci. Lyon. 10: 241. 1860 [not *Maoutia* Wedd., 1854].
Borya Montr. ex Beauvis., Gen. Montr. 68. 1901 [not *Borya* Labill., 1804, nor Willd., 1805].

Often scandent mostly glabrous shrubs or woody vines; leaves decussate-opposite or subverticillate, the blades mostly coriaceous or firmly chartaceous, mostly entire; inflorescence corymbose, axillary or terminal, pedunculate, its branches opposite; peduncles nutant or incurved; cymes dichotomous and borne in the upper leaf-axils or producing trichotomous terminal panicles; bracts small or minute, rarely longer than the subtended pedicels; flowers rather large, pedicellate; calyx gamosepalous, varying greatly among the species, narrowly or broadly campanulate, membranous to subcoriaceous, usually deeply 4- (or rarely 5-) fid, the lobes valvate in bud, equal, usually glabrous, rarely glandulose, sometimes the calyx much abbreviated, wide-spreading, coriaceous, the rim only sinuate-dentate; corolla zygomorphic, white or yellowish-white, very variable among the species, the tube infundibular, broadly cylindric or subcampanulate, short and contracted, often ventricose, apically ampliate, straight or more or less incurved, the limb uniform or oblique, 4-fid, sometimes subbilabiate, the lobes subequal or the exterior posterior one or the interior anterior one longer and narrower, erect; stamens didynamous, declinate; the 2 perfect stamens posterior, inserted below the mouth of the corolla-tube, incurved, extending almost to the posterior corolla-lobe; filaments filiform, incurved, more or less exserted, smooth or papillose; anthers ovate or oblong, 2-locular, the thecae parallel, attached below the apex; staminodes 2, anterior, filiform, anantherous, inserted higher in the tube and usually included; disk beneath the ovary thick, fleshy, glandulose; ovary deeply 4-lobed, the lobes parallel or divaricate, free to the base, ovate, obtuse, the ovary at first imperfectly, later completely 4-locular, each locule 1-ovulate; ovules attached laterally above the middle, amphitropous; style filiform, declinate, sunken between the ovary lobes, more or less exserted, the apex obtuse or very shortly bifid, the stigmatiferous branches equal or sub-equal, acute; drupes 4-parted to the base, the pyrenes 4 (or less by abortion), separate to the base, obovoid or oblong, 1-locular, 1-seeded, the exocarp fleshy, the endocarp somewhat indurated, the placenta-bearing lamina inwardly subinvolute; seeds attached near the base, erect or pendulous, the testa membranous and appressed, the embryo conforming to the seed in size and shape, straight, amphitropous, externally rugose; cotyledons grown together beyond the middle, apically distinct or separable; radicle short, inferior.

A complex genus of about 42 species and infraspecific taxa restricted to New Caledonia. One species is widely cultivated for ornament in tropical regions of both hemispheres. It is represented in Ceylon only by the following cultivated species.

The practically gynobasic style indicates a very close relationship with the Lamiaceae (Labiatae).

Oxera pulchella Labill., Sert. Austro-caled. 1: 23–24, Pl. 28. 1824; Schau. in A. DC., Prod. 11: 676. 1847; Guillaumin, Ann. Inst. Bot. Geol. Colon. Marseille 9: 207. 1911; Metcalfe & Chalk, Syst. Anat. Dicot. 1034, fig. 247A. 1950; Graf, Exotica 3: 1482 & 1670. 1963; Menninger, Flowering Vines 336–337, photo 283. 1970. Type: a Labillardiere collection from New Caledonia (P).

Oncoma pulchellum Spreng. in L., Syst., ed. 16, 4 (2): 18. 1827.—*O. pulchella* Spreng. ex Moldenke, Alph. List Invalid Names Suppl. 17. 1947.
Oxera pulchella Dubard ex Moldenke, Prelim. Alph. List Invalid Names 33. 1940.

An arching glabrous shrub or woody vine to 6 m long, often spreading to form a canopy 4 m wide; stems many, tortuous, subterete, verrucose, somewhat ampliate and compressed at the nodes, the young shoots usually arching downwards; leaves decussate-opposite, short-petiolate, mostly borne near the apex of the branches, the blades stiff and leathery, often evergreen, glossy-green, oval-oblong, to 12.5 cm long, entire, apically obtuse, often somewhat keeled along the midrib above; inflorescence profuse, cymose, solitary, axillary toward the base of the branchlets, usually pendent, 2 or 3 times trichotomous; peduncles almost as long as the petioles; bractlets subfoliaceous, lanceolate, diminishing in size upwards; flowers large, showy, long-pedicellate, nutant; calyx conspicuous, chartaceous, somewhat inflated, greenish-white, about 1.2 cm long, 4-parted almost to the base, the lobes oblong, apically subacute; corolla white or whitish, trumpet-shaped, resembling *Digitalis purpurea*, about 5 cm long, ventrally convex, the limb 4-lobed, the lobes subrotund-ovate, apically obtuse, the upper ones pubescent within; stamens long-exserted, equalling the style; fruit composed of 1–4 druplets, yellowish-orange when mature.

D i s t r. A variable species, with 5 varieties already described, all native to New Caledonia. The typical form is often cultivated for ornament in tropical regions in both hemispheres.

V e r n. The only one listed is "Showy oxera".

S p e c i m e n s E x a m i n e d. KANDY DISTRICT: in outdoor cultivation in arbour, Pergola Garden, Royal Botanic Garden, Peradeniya, 18 Jan. 1974, *H.N. & A.L. Moldenke & Jayasuriya 28132* (LL, MOLDENKE, PDA, US); Royal Botanic Garden, Peradeniya, 13 Nov. 1944, flowers white, *Silva 993* (PDA), 13 Dec. 1944, *s. coll. s.n.* (PDA).

20. CLERODENDRUM

Burm. ex L., Gen. Pl., ed. 1, 186. 1737; L., Sp. Pl., ed. 1, 1: 109. 1753; L., Gen. Pl., ed. 5, 285. 1754. Type species: *Clerodendrum infortunatum* L.

Clerodendron Burm., Thes. Zeyl. 66–67, Pl. 29. 1737; Adans., Fam. Pl. 2: 199. 1763 [not *Clerodendron* Hort., 1969].—*Clerodendron* L. ex Westm. in L., Orat. Tellur. Habit. Incr. 59. 1744; L., Gen. Pl., ed. 7, 325. 1767.—*Klerodendron* Adans., Fam. Pl. 2: 12. 1763.—*Clerodendrvm* [L.] ex Retz, Nom. Bot. 155. 1772.—*Clerodendrvm* Scop., Introd. Hist. Nat. 170. 1777.—*Clerodendrvm* L. apud Gaertn., Fruct. 271. 1788.—*Clerodendrum* Ait. ex Moon, Cat. 46. 1824.—*Clerodendrum* L. ex G. Don in Loud., Hort. Brit., ed. 1, 247. 1830.—*Clerodendron* R. Br. ex Meisn., Gen. Pl. 1: 637. 1838.—*Clerodendron* (L.) R. Br. ex Spach, Hist. Nat. Vég. 9: 228. 1840.—*Clerodendron* Auct. ex Pfeiffer, Nom. Bot. 1 (1): 785. 1873.—*Clerodendron* Endl. ex Pfeiffer, Nom. Bot. 1 (1): 785. 1873.—*Clerodendron* Gleditsch ex Pfeiffer, Nom. Bot. 1 (1): 785. 1873.—*Clerodendrum* R. Br. ex Pfeiffer, Nom. Bot. 1 (1): 785. 1873.—*Clesodendron* Peckolt, Ber. Deutsch. Pharm. Ges. 14: 465. 1904.—*Clerodendoron* Wall. ex Kawakami, List Pl. Formos. 84, sphalm. 1910.—*Cherodendron* Lévl. in Fedde, Repert. Spec. Nov. Regni Veg. 11: 298, sphalm. 1912.—*Chlerodendron* Lévl. in Fedde, Repert. Spec. Nov.

Regni Veg. 11: 302, sphalm. 1912.—*Cherodendrum* L. ex H.J. Lam, Bot.
Jahrb. Syst. 59: 28, sphalm. 1924.—*Clorodendrum* Navarro Haydon, Fl.
Com. Puerto Rico [8]. 1936.—*Cleodendron* L. ex Moldenke, Prelim. Alph.
List Invalid Names 18, in syn. 1940.—*Clerodendrom* L. ex Moldenke,
Prelim. List Invalid Names 18, in syn. 1940.—*Cleriodendron* L. ex Mold-
enke, Alph. List Invalid Names 15, in syn. 1942.—*Clerodendron* Balf. ex
Söderberg, Blommer 263. 1954.—*Clerodendrun* Lindl. ex Travassos, Flores
do Brasil 2: 31 & 33. 1955.—*Cleorodendrum* Angely, Fl. Paran. 7: 6,
sphalm. 1957.—*Clerendon* L. ex Moldenke, Résumé 259, in syn. 1959.—
Cleredendrom G. Don ex Espirito Santo, Junt. Invest. Ultramar Est. Ens.
Docum. 104: 41, sphalm. 1963.—*Cleredendron* G. Don ex Espirito Santo,
Junt. Invest. Ultramar Est. Ens. Docum. 104: 80, sphalm. 1963.—*Clerod-
endron* Adans. apud Airy Shaw in Willis, Dict. ed. 7, 255, in syn. 1966.—
Clerodeddrum Gürke ex Richards & Morony, Check List Fl. Mbala 236,
spahlm. 1969.—*Cletodendron* Swamy & Krishnam., J. Bombay Nat. Hist.
Soc. 67: [462], sphalm. 1970.—*Clerodehdron* Kobayashi, Bull. Gov. Forest
Exp. Sta. 226: 214, sphalm. 1970.—*Clerodendrin* Westcott, Pl. Disease
Handb., ed. 3, 499, sphalm. 1971.—*Clerodron* Farnsw., Pharmacog. Titles
9: 115, sphalm. 1974.

Ovieda L., Gen. Pl., ed. 1, 59. 1737; L., Sp. Pl., ed. 1, imp. 1, 2: 637. 1753; L.,
Gen. Pl., ed. 5, 284. 1754 [not *Ovieda* Spreng., 1817].—*Ouieda* L. ex Reichard in L., Gen. Pl., ed. 8, 326. 1778.

Valdia Plum. ex L., Gen. Pl., ed. 1, 59, in syn. 1737; Adans., Fam. Pl. 2: 157.
1763.—*Valdia* Boehm. in Ludw., Defin. Gen. Pl. 39. 1760.—*Valdia* Adans.
ex Rehd., Bibl. Cult. Trees 585, in syn. 1949.

Duglassia Houst. ex L., Gen. Pl., ed. 1, 347. 1737.—*Douglassia* Houst. ex L.,
Philos. Bot. 155. 1751; L., Gen. Pl., ed. 5, 284, in syn. 1754; Adans., Fam.
Pl. 2: 200. 1763 [not *Douglassia* Auct., 1904, nor Durand, 1904, nor Heist.,
1973, nor Lindl., 1829, nor Reichenb., 1828, nor Schreb., 1791].—*Douglas-
sia* Mill., Gard. Dict. Abridg., ed. 4, 1. 1754.—*Duglassia* Amman ex Endl.,
Gen. Pl. 637. 1839.—*Douglassia* Adans. apud Jacks. in Hook. f. & Jacks.,
Ind. Kew., imp. 1, 1: 560, in syn. 1893.—*Douglasia* Mill. ex Post & Kuntze,
Lex. 185, in syn. 1904 [not *Douglasia* Heist., 1904, nor Lindl., 1904, nor
Schreb., 1904].—*Douglasia* Houst. ex Post & Kuntze, Lex. 185, in syn.
1904.—*Duglassia* Adans. ex Moldenke, Résumé 279, in syn. 1959.

Volkameria L., Gen. Pl., ed. 1, 347. 1737; L., Sp. Pl., ed. 1, imp. 1, 2: 637.
1753; L., Gen. Pl., ed. 5, 284. 1754 [not *Volkameria* P. Br., 1756, nor Burm.
f., 1966].—*Volkameria* Willd. ex Moon, Cat. 1: 46. 1824.—*Volkamera* L.
(1737) ex Reichb., Conspect. Reg. Veg. 1: 117. 1828 [not *Volkamera* Burm.,
1768, nor P. Br., 1904, nor Heist.-Fabr., 1759, nor L. (1735) ex Post &
Kuntze, 1904, nor P. & K., 1966].—*Volkameria* "L. etc. corr. Reichenb."
ex Post & Kuntze, Lex. 590, in syn. 1904.—*Bolkameria* L. ex Moldenke,
Prelim. Alph. List Invalid Names 7, in syn. 1940.

Ligustroides L. ex Kuntze, Rev. Gen. Pl. 2: 505, in syn. 1891.

Siphonanthemum Amman, Acta Acad. Sci. Imp. Petrop. 1736: 213–215. 1741; L., Gen. Pl., ed. 5, 47, in syn. 1754.

Siphonanthus L., Gen. Pl., ed. 2, 526. 1742; L., Sp. Pl., ed. 1, imp. 1, 1: 109. 1753; L., Gen. Pl., ed. 5, 47. 1754 [not *Siphonanthus* Schreb., 1858].— *Siphonanthvs* L. ex Reichard in L., Gen. Pl., ed. 8, 65. 1778.—*Siphonantus* St. Hil., Expos. 1: 304. 1805.—*Siphonanthus* Schau. ex Buek, Gen. Sp. Syn. Candoll. 3: 419. 1858.—*Siphonantha* L. apud Benth. in Benth. & Hook. f., Gen. Pl. 2 (2): 1155, in syn. 1876.

Cryptanthus Osbeck, Dagb. Ostind. Resa 215. 1757 [not *Cryptanthus* Nutt., 1849, nor Otto & Dietr., 1836].

Peragu Rheede ex Adans., Fam. Pl. 2: 199, 540, & 589, in syn. 1763.

Pinnakola Hermann ex Adans., Fam. Pl. 2: 199, in syn. 1763.

Paliuroaffinis Sloane ex Adans., Fam. Pl. 2: 200, in syn. 1763.

Marurang Rumph. ex Adans., Fam. Pl. 2: 226 & 575. 1763.—*Marurang* Adans. ex Airy Shaw in Willis, Dict. ed. 7, 699, in syn. 1966.—*Mararungia* Scop. ex Airy Shaw in Willis, Dict., ed. 7, 695, in syn. 1966.—*Mararungia* Rumph. ex Moldenke, Résumé Suppl. 14: 9, in syn. 1966.

Bellevalia Scop., Introd. Hist. Nat. 198. 1777 [not *Bellevalia* Delile, 1836, nor Lepyr., 1808, nor Montrouz., 1901, nor Roem. & Schult., 1819].

Montalbania Neck., Elem. 1: 273. 1790.

Volkmannia Jacq., Pl. Rar. Hort. Schoenbr. 3: 48, Pl. 338. 1798 [not *Volkmannia* Sternb., 1825].

Agricolaea Schrank, Denkschr. Köningl. Akad. Wiss. München 1808 (1): 98. 1809.—*Agricola* Schrank. apud Meisn., Gen. Pl. 1: 637, in syn. 1838.

Torreya Spreng., Neue Endeck. 2: 121. 1821 [not *Torreya* Arn., 1838, nor Croom, 1843, nor Eaton, 1829, nor Raf., 1818 & 1819].

Cornacchinia Savi, Mem. Mat. Fis. Soc. Ital. Sci. Modena, Pt. Mem. Fis. 21: 184, Pl. 7. 1837 [not *Cornacchinia* Endl., 1841].

Egena Raf., Fl. Tellur. 2: 85. 1837.

Rotheca Raf., Fl. Tellur. 4: 69. 1838.

Patulix Raf., Good Book 61. 1840.

Cyclonema Hochst., Flora 25 (1): 225. 1842.

Spironema Hochst., Flora 25 (1): 226. 1842 [not *Spironema* Lindl., 1840, nor Raf., 1836].

Cyrtostemma Kunze, Bot. Zeit. 1: 272. 1843 [not *Cyrtostemma* Spach, 1841, nor (Mert. & Koch) Spach, 1973].

Cleianthus Lour. ex Gomes, Mem. Acad. Ci. Lisboa, Cl. Sci. Mor. Pol. Bel.-Let., ser. 2, 4 (1): 28. 1868.

Siphobaea Baill., Hist. Pl. 10: 106. 1888.—*Siphoboea* Baill. apud Durand & Jacks., Ind. Kew. Suppl. 1, imp. 1, 400. 1906.

Megalosiphon Ekman ex Moldenke, Prelim. Alph. List Invalid Names 32, in syn. 1940.

Woody plants, mostly trees or shrubs, sometimes woody vines, rarely with underground stems, occasionally herbaceous perennials, usually unarmed or rarely with the petiole-base spinescent, glabrous or variously pubescent; leaves simple, decussate-opposite or whorled, rarely scattered, entire or variously dentate, deciduous, exstipulate; inflorescence cymose, the cymes mostly loose-flowered, sometimes dense and subcapitate, pedunculate in the upper leaf-axils, paniculate at the apex of the branchlets, or densely aggregate in terminal corymbs or heads, the flowers rarely solitary, zygomorphic, often large and showy; calyx the same colour as the corolla or contrastingly red, white, or green, campanulate or rarely tubular, truncate to 5-toothed or 5-fid, often accrescent, spreading and subtending the fruit or enclosing it, glabrous or variously pubescent; corolla mostly white, blue, violet, or red, hypocrateriform, gamopetalous, the tube narrowly cylindric, straight or incurved, sometimes more or less ampliate at the mouth or by the stamen insertion, often elongate, more rarely only slightly exceeding the calyx, the limb spreading or reflexed in anthesis, 5-parted, the lobes subequal or the posterior (exterior) pairs slightly shorter and the anterior (interior) one larger, sometimes concave; stamens 4 (or 5), didynamous, inserted in the corolla-tube, usually long-exserted, involute in bud, perfect, alternate with the corolla-lobes; anthers ovate or oblong, 2-locular, with parallel thecae, opening by longitudinal slits; pistil 1, compound, 2-carpellary; style terminal, elongate, shortly and acutely 2-fid apically, the branches stigmatiferous; ovary imperfectly 4-locular, each locule 1-ovulate, the ovules high-lateral, hemianatropous; fruit drupaceous, globose or obovoid, often 4-sulcate and sub-4-lobed, the exocarp more or less fleshy, the endocarp bony or crustaceous, smooth or variously rugose, separating on maturity into 4 pyrenes or these sometimes cohering in pairs; seeds oblong, without endosperm. Chromosome number: $x = 12$? or 23; $2x = 24, 30, 48, 52, 60, 108$, or 184.

The largest genus in the family, very complex, consisting of about 584 specific and infraspecific taxa, natives of tropical and subtropical regions, most abundant in Asia and Africa, poorly represented in the Americas except in cultivation and by naturalization. A few species extend into temperate zones; six species of fossil forms are known from the Tertiary of Europe and Africa. *Cyclonema* Hochst. may prove worthy of separation as a distinct genus. *Tetrathyranthus* A. Gray, often included in the synonymy of *Clerodendrum*, actually belongs to that of *Faradaya* F. Muell.

Clerodendrum is represented in Ceylon by at least three native and seven cultivated and naturalized species and several infraspecific taxa.

KEY TO THE SPECIES AND INFRASPECIFIC TAXA

1 Leaf-blades densely covered beneath with glistening golden scales
  2 Leaf-blades mostly deeply 3–7-lobed...........................**1. C. paniculatum**

2 Leaf-blades merely dentate.....................................**2. C. kaempferi**
1 Leaf-blades without squamose glands beneath, or, if any, these obscured by the pubescence, sometimes glandular-punctate
 3 Corolla-tube distinctly zygomorphic, the limb plainly bilabiate, the tube curvate, swollen; fruit not splitting into 4 separate pyrenes at maturity
  4 Calyx-rim during anthesis truncate or shallowly dentate. .**3. C. serratum** var. **serratum**
  4 Calyx-rim during anthesis deeply dentate or lobed........**C. serratum** var. **dentatum**
 3 Corolla-tube practically actinomorphic, the limb actinomorphic or very weakly zygomorphic, the tube usually almost straight, slender; fruit usually splitting into 4 separate pyrenes at maturity
  5 Leaves mostly or often whorled
   6 Leaf-blades coarsely serrate-dentate or incised-pinnatifid......................
....**4. C. incisum** var. **macrosiphon**
   6 Leaf-blades normally entire or subentire
    7 Leaves in whorls of 3–6, the blades 8.5–23 cm long; corolla-tube 7.5–12 cm long. .
....**5. C. indicum**
    7 Leaves opposite, approximate, or ternate, the blades 2.5–9 cm long; corolla-tube 0.4–1.1 cm long...**6. C. heterophyllum**
  5 Leaves normally all decussate-opposite
   8 Plants normally scandent
    9 Inflorescence mostly cauliflorous or arising from the rhizome....................
....**7. C. schweinfurthii** var. **bakeri**
    9 Inflorescence borne only on aerial branches or branchlets
     10 Corolla bright red to scarlet or crimson, rarely yellow
      11 Calyx in anthesis split to the base, white....................**8. C. thomsonae**
      11 Calyx in anthesis not split to the base, reddish
       12 Leaf-blades leathery, glossy; petioles only 1.5–2 cm long; peduncles to 2 cm long...**9. C. splendens**
       12 Leaf-blades herbaceous, not glossy; petioles over 2 cm long; peduncles often over 5 cm long..**10. C. umbellatum**
     10 Corolla yellowish-white......................................**11. C. wallichii**
   8 Plants usually erect shrubs or trees
    13 Calyx during anthesis 1.5–2.5 cm long, tubular; corolla-tube 8.5–10.2 cm long....
....**12. C. minahassae**
    13 Calyx during anthesis smaller, campanulate or cupuliform; corolla-tube smaller
     14 Corolla crimson or scarlet............**13. C. speciosissimum** f. **speciosissimum**
     14 Corolla white, yellow, or pink
      15 Leaf-blades glabrous or subglabrous beneath
       16 Leaf-blades entire, mostly elliptic; petioles 1–6.5 cm long
        17 Cymes 3-flowered; coastal shrubs
         18 Leaf-blades broadly elliptic, to 9 cm long and 7 cm wide, short-acuminate apically..**14. C. inerme** f. **inerme**
         18 Leaf-blades narrowly elliptic, 2–4 cm long and 1–2 cm wide, acute or obtuse to rounded apically......... ....**C. inerme** f. **parvifolium**
        17 Cymes many-flowered; not primarily coastal
         19 Petioles to 6.5 cm long; leaf-blades to 11 cm long and 6 cm wide, mostly acuminate apically; cymes open......................**15. C. floribundum**
         19 Petioles about 1 cm long; leaf-blades to 8 cm long and 4.5 cm wide, mostly acute apically; cymes dense..............................**16. C. glabrum**
       16 Leaf-blades coarsely dentate, broadly ovate, to 15 cm long and 14 cm wide; petioles to 11 cm long..........................**17. C. lindleyi** f. **albiflorum**

15 Leaf-blades variously pubescent beneath
  20 Leaf-blades mostly entire...**18. C. infortunatum**
  20 Leaf-blades mostly more or less sinuate or irregularly dentate
    21 Leaf-blades small, mostly rhomboid or deltoid, 1.7–6.8 cm long and 1.2–6 cm wide;
      petioles 5–22 mm long...**19. C. phlomidis**
    21 Leaf-blades and petioles larger, the blades not rhomboid-deltoid
      22 Corollas regularly "doubled"....................**20. C. philippinum f. multiplex**
      22 Corollas not "doubled"
        23 Conspicuous discoid glands on calyx, persistent foliaceous bracts, and leaf-
        blades; calyx deeply lobed, the lobes 7–10 mm long and to 5 mm wide..........
        ....**21. C. viscosum**
        23 Discoid glands absent or inconspicuous; bracts early deciduous; calyx merely
        toothed, the teeth about 1 mm long and wide.........**C. speciosissimum f. album**

1. **Clerodendrum paniculatum** L., Mant. 1: 90. 1767; Schau. in A. DC., Prod.
11: 657 & 668. 1847; Clarke in Hook. f., Fl. Br. Ind. 4: 593. 1885; Alston in
Trimen, Handb. Fl. Ceylon 6: 232 & 233. 1931; Crevost & Petelot, Bull. Econ.
Indo-chin. 37: 1295. 1934; Alston, Kandy Fl. 64. 1938; MacMillan, Trop.
Plant. & Gard., ed. 5, 104 & 105. 1944; Abeywick., Ceylon J. Sci., Biol. Sci.
2: 218. 1959; Burkill, Dict. Econ. Prod. Malay Penins. 1: 589, 590, & 593.
1966; Gunawardena, Gen. Sp. Pl. Zeyl. 148. 1968; Fonseka & Vinasithamby,
Prov. List Local Names Fl. Pl. Ceylon 67. 1971; Moldenke in Woodson &
Schery, Ann. Missouri. Bot. Gard. 60: 139–140, fig. 15. 1973. Type: *Herb.*
Linnaeus 810/5 from India (LINN).

Clerodendrvm paniculatum Retz., Nom. Bot. 155. 1772.—*Clerodendron pani-*
    culatum L. ex Edwards, Bot. Reg. 5: Pl. 406. 1819.—*Clerodendron paniculata*
    L. ex Matsum., Ind. Pl. Jap. 2 (2): 532. 1912.—*Clerodendrum paniculata*
    Perry, Fls. World 304 & 313. 1972.—*Clerodendron paniculatus* L. ex Mol-
    denke, Phytologia 26: 371, in syn. 1973.
Volkameria angulata Lour., Fl. Cochinch., ed. 1, 2: 389. 1790.
Caprifolium paniculatum Noronha, Verh. Batav. Genootsch. Kunsten 5: 9.
    1790.
Clerodendrum pyramidale Andr., Bot. Repos. 10: Pl. 628. 1810.—*Cleroden-*
    dron pyramidale Andr. ex Jacks. in Hook. f. & Jacks., Ind. Kew., imp. 1,
    1: 561. 1893.
Clerodendrum splendidum Wall. in Griff., Notul. 4: 169. 1854.—*Clerodendron*
    splendidum Wall., Num. List [49], no. 1803, hyponym. 1829; Schau. in A.
    DC., Prod. 11: 668, in syn. 1847.—*Clerodendrum splendedum* Wall. ex Liu,
    Ill. Nat. & Introd. Lign. Pl. Taiwan 2: 1217, sphalm. 1962.
Cleianthus coccineus Lour. ex Gomes, Mem. Acad. Ci Lisboa, Cl. Sci. Mor.
    Pol. Bel.-Let., ser. 2, 4 (1): 28. 1868.

    Bushy perennial herb or erect shrub, often simple or subsimple, to 3 m tall,
often woody only at the base; stems stout, medullose or hollow, obtusely
tetragonal, usually deeply sulcate in drying, minutely pulverulent-puberulent

or glabrate, the nodes with a broad band of tomentose hairs; leaves decussate-opposite, gradually smaller upwards; petioles 1.2–3.5 cm long, minutely pulverulent-puberulent or glabrate; leaf-blades thinly chartaceous or membranous, ovate, 4–40 cm long, 7–38 cm wide, basally cordate, 3–7-lobed, or the uppermost often entire and basally hastate [var. *diversifolium* (Vahl) Clarke], the lobes triangular-ovate, apically acute or apiculate, variable in size, wilting rapidly, the margins remotely apiculate-denticulate to crenate-dentate or entire, bright green and usually shiny above, lighter and dull beneath, pulverulent and minutely strigillose above or glabrate, densely squamulose with orbicular peltate golden scales and punctate beneath, glabrous between the scales or pubescent only on the venation, the central lobe mostly ovate and large, the others much smaller and triangular; inflorescence axillary and terminal, the axillary cymes mostly confined to the uppermost leaf-axils, the cymes long-pedunculate, 9–13 cm long and 3–7 cm wide, many-flowered, building up often large and thyrsoid terminal panicles to 45 cm long and wide, 1–4 times dichotomous, many-flowered, composed of 4–16 pairs of cymes, the ultimate divisions often racemiform, the branches divaricate-ascending, conspicuously bracteate, minutely pulverulent-puberulent or glabrate throughout but often tomentose at the sympodial nodes; peduncles 1.5–12 cm long, mostly reddish; pedicels rose-colour, almost filiform, 4–15 mm long; foliaceous bracts large, a pair subtending each of the larger pairs of inflorescence-branches, ovate-elliptic, entire or obscurely 3-lobed, similar to the leaves in other respects but smaller; bractlets and prophylla linear, 1–10 mm long, puberulent; flowers slightly odorous, red in bud; calyx red or orange-red, campanulate, 3–5 mm long, short-pubescent, divided to near the base, the segments erect and spreading; corolla hypocrateriform, orange-red to scarlet, rarely white (f. *albiflorum* Moldenke), short-hairy, the tube slender, 1.2–2 cm long, the lobes of the limb 7–8 mm long, separated in the throat by white streaks, the posterior pair shorter and narrower than the others; filaments exserted 2.5–3.5 cm during anthesis; fruit drupaceous, greenish-blue to black.

D i s t r. A spectacularly showy plant native to southeastern Asia from India, Bangladesh, and the Andaman and Nicobar Islands eastward through Burma, Thailand, and Indo-China to Malaya and Indonesia, north into China and Taiwan. It is very widely cultivated in all warm regions, where it often escapes and becomes naturalized; in greenhouses as specimen plants elsewhere.

E c o l. In Ceylon it tends to become weedy in disturbed areas and is spreading.

U s e s. The flowers are widely used in cut-flower bouquets and by girls as ornaments in the hair. In India it is widely cultivated in rockeries. In Malaya an infusion of the vegetative parts is drunk as a purgative and applied externally to distended abdomens; fed to elephants it is thought to make them more confident and brave. It is one of the plants regularly used as a leafy brush to sprinkle consecrated rice-gruel at weddings, in blessing fishing-stakes, and in the rite of "taking the rice-soul". Both in Malaya and in Sumatra it is regarded by natives in magic as the "chief summoner of the spirits".

V e r n. Among some 25 names recorded in various parts of its range are: Danger-flower, Pagoda-flower and red glorybower (E).

N o t e s. The pollen is described in detail by Nair & Rehman in Bull. Nat. Bot. Gard. Lucknow 76: 14. 1962. The plant is readily propagated by cuttings. The fungus, *Didymella sphaerelloides* Sacc. & Syd., often attacks its leaves.

S p e c i m e n s E x a m i n e d. KURUNEGALA DISTRICT: common in abandoned building area and in large colonies along roadside and adjacent fencerows, Dummalasuriya, low altitude, 25 Jan. 1974, erect subshrubs with subsimple stems, corolla orange-red or deep red, *H.N. & A.L. Moldenke & Jayasuriya 28257* (AAU, ARIZ, CAI, KARACHI, LL, PDA, US). COLOMBO DISTRICT: a weed on waste ground, Divulapitya, 24 Sept. 1969, flowers brick-red, *Amaratunga 1848* (PDA); Moratuwa, 27 Nov. 1970, herb with large erect orange-red panicles, an escape, now a bad weed in moist or wet low country, *Amaratunga 2138* (PDA); Kadawata on the Colombo to Kandy road, 5 July 1971, a fast-spreading weed in Colombo District, peduncles, calyx, and base of corolla-tube reddish-orange, corolla orange, throat reddish-orange, filaments reddish-orange, *Amaratunga 2291* (PDA); large colony in shade along roadside, Katana, 4 miles east of Kochikade, 16 Jan. 1974, subshrub about 5 ft tall, leaves wilting easily, corollas scarlet or scarlet-red, *H.N. & A.L. Moldenke, Jayasuriya, & Sumithraarachchi 28120* (AAU, ARIZ, CAI, KARACHI, LL, MO, PDA, US). KANDY DISTRICT: Royal Botanic Garden, Peradeniya, 4 April 1917, *s. coll. 125/49* (PDA); a commonly cultivated shrub growing wild in large groups along roadside, highway A. 5 between Kandy and Nuwara-Eliya, 10 miles from Kandy, 520 m alt., 28 May 1967, *Mueller-Dombois 67052802* (US); in Fernery, Royal Botanic Garden, Peradeniya, 3 July 1913, *J.M. Silva s.n.* (PDA); roadside shrub, Kadugannawa, 6 Sept. 1974, flowers red, *Sumithraarachchi DBS. 422* (AAU, ARIZ, CAI, LACROSSE, LL, LSU, US). KEGALLE DISTRICT: Ruwanwella, 27 Aug. 1963, peduncles red, calyx red, petals orange-red with deeper orange-red toward the centre, *Amaratunga 712* (PDA); frequent on stream bank at forest margin, Kitulgala, 60 miles east of Colombo, 600 m alt., 25 April 1970, shrubs 3 m tall, large panicles of red flowers, *Gould 13588* (US); locally abundant on grassy slopes shaded by tropical forest among rubber plantation, Watura, about 3 miles south of Kegalle, 21 April 1968, tall herb 1 m tall, flowers deep-orange, *Koyama 13553* (NY, PDA); in extensive naturalized colony in waste land, Karawanella, low altitude, 12 Feb. 1974, herbaceous perennials or low subshrubs, 4 ft tall, corollas scarlet, *H.N. & A.L. Moldenke, Jayasuriya, & Dassanayake 28333* (ARIZ, CAI, LL, PDA, US). RATNAPURA DIS-

TRICT: abundantly naturalized in large colonies in roadside vegetation, Galahiteya, low altitude, 12 Feb. 1974, low herbaceous perennial or suffrutescent, corollas orange-red, *H.N. & A.L. Moldenke, Jayasuriya, & Dassanayake 28335* (AAU, MO, PDA, US).

2. **Clerodendrum kaempferi** (Jacq.) Sieb. ex Steud., Nom. Bot., ed. 1, 208. 1821; Steud., Verh. Batav. Genootsch. Kuntzen 12: 31 ["51"] [as *"Clerodendron"*]. 1830; Schau. in A. DC., Prod. 11: 657, 674, & 669. 1847; Clarke in Hook. f., Fl. Br. Ind. 4: 593. 1885; Brandis, Indian Trees 508. 1906; Haines, Bot. Bihar & Orissa 4: 720–722. 1922; Bor & Raizada, Some Beautiful Ind. Climb. 148–149, fig. 93. 1954; Cooke, Fl. Pres. Bombay, ed. 2, 2: 513–514. 1958; Burkill, Dict. Econ. Prod. Malay Penins. 1: 590 & 594. 1966. Type: a plant from Mauritius cultivated in the Schönbrunn garden in Vienna, now probably destroyed.

Volkameria kaempferi Jacq., Collect. 3: 207–209. 1789.—*V. kaempferiana* Jacq., Ic. Pl. Rar. 3: Pl. 500. 1792.—*V. kaempferi* Willd. apud Edwards, Bot. Reg. 8: Pl. 649. 1822.—*Volkameria koemferi* Lam., Enc. 8: 689. 1808.
Clerodendrum squamatum Vahl, Symb. Bot. 2: 74. 1791.—*Clerodendron squamatum* Vahl ex Spreng. in L., Syst. ed. 16, 2: 759. 1825.—*Clerodendron squammatum* Vahl apud Pynaert, Rev. Hort. Belge Etrangere 22: 284 & 287, sphalm. 1896.—*Clerodendron squamatum* Cham. ex Diels, Fl. Cent.-China 550. 1902 [not *C. squamatum* H.J. Lam, 1923, nor Neal & Metzger, 1934, nor Rock, 1934].
Volkameria foliis cordatis, pubescentibus, denticulatis; paniculâ terminali, divaricata; pedunculis coloratis Willd. ex Lam., Enc. 8: 689, in syn. 1808.
Volkameria cordatis, subrotundis, villosulis; floribus paniculatis, caule erecto Jacq. ex Lam., Enc. 8: 689, in syn. 1808.
Volkameria coccinea Loisel.-Desl., Herb. Amt. 8: Pl. 519. 1827.—*V. coccinea* Herb. ex D. Dietr., Syn. Pl. 3: 616, in syn. 1843.
Clerodendron dentatum (Roxb.) Wall., Num. List [49], no. 1799 [as *C. dentatum* Roxb.]. 1829.—*Clerodendron dentatum* Wall. apud Voigt, Hort. Suburb. Calc. 466. 1845.—*Clerodendron dentata* Roxb. ex Petelot, Pl. Méd. Camb. Laos & Vietn. 2: 255. 1954.
Volkameria dentata Roxb., Hort. Beng. 46, hyponym. 1814; Roxb., Fl. Ind. 3: 61. 1832.
Clerodendron coccineum D. Dietr., Syn. Pl. 3: 616. 1843.—*Clerodendron coccineum* Hort. Morr. ex Voss in Vilm., Blumengärt. 1: 832, in syn. 1895.
Clerodendron speciosissimum Hort. Angl. ex Schau. in A. DC., Prod. 11: 672, in syn. 1847 [not *C. speciosissimum* Paxt., 1837, nor Van Geert, 1836].—*Clerodendron speciosissimum* Hort. ex Moldenke, Phytologia 31, 396, in syn. 1975.
Clerodendron illustre N.E. Br., Gard. Chron. 56 [ser. 2, 22]: 424. 1884.

Clerodendron squamatum var. *typicum* H.J. Lam, Verbenac. Malay. Arch. 303.
1919.
Clerodendron kaempferi Sieb. apud Jacks. in Hook. f. & Jacks., Ind. Kew.,
imp. 1, 2: 1276. 1895 [not *C. kaempferi* Fisch. ex Morr., 1845, nor Steud.,
1948].—*Clerodendron kaempferi* (Jacq.) Steud. ex Moldenke, Suppl. List In-
valid Names 2, in syn. 1941.—*Clerodendron kaempferi* (Jack) Sieb ex Tingle,
Check List Hong Kong Pl. 38, sphalm. 1967.—*Clerodendrum kaempferi*
Sieb. ex Moldenke, Résumé Suppl. 15: 19, in syn. 1967; Alexander, Hong
Kong Shrubs 28. 1971 [not *C. kaempferi* Fisch., 1821].
Clerodendrum infortunatum Lour. [in part] apud Merr., Trans. Amer. Philos.
Soc. 24 (2): 337, in syn. 1935 [not *C. infortunata* L., 1753, nor *C. infortunatum* Auct., 1955, nor Blume, 1967, nor Dennst., 1959, nor Gaertn., 1965,
nor Miq., 1968, nor Vent., 1821, nor Willd., 1976].—*Clerodendron infortunatum* Lour. ex Moldenke, Prelim. Alph. List Invalid Names 20, in syn.
1940 [not *C. infortunatum* Auct., 1963, nor Blume, 1947, nor Gaertn., 1788,
nor Lam., 1947, nor Lindl., 1918, nor Schau., 1918, nor F.-Vill., 1882, nor
Walp., 1843, nor Wight, 1850, nor Willd., 1976].

Small semi-woody shrub or treelet, to 3 m tall; branches rather stoutish,
medullose or hollow, very obtusely tetragonal, often deeply sulcate between
the angles in drying, minutely and obscurely strigillose-puberulent or glabrate
(except for the nodes); nodes annulate with a narrow band of long multicellular villous hairs; principal internodes 1.8–4.5 cm long; leaves decussate-
opposite, large; petioles stout, 1.6–24.5 cm long, pulverulent-puberulent, the
lowest 1 cm on the largest ones usually collapsing quickly in wilting; leaf-blades
thin-membranous, dark- or deep-green and shiny above, much paler beneath,
broadly ovate or obcordate, 5.9–21.5 cm long, 5–18.3 cm wide, apically
abruptly acute or very shortly acuminate, subentire or repand to denticulate
along the margins, basally deeply cordate with the lobes often overlapping,
very sparsely strigillose or glabrous above, minutely pulverulent and densely
squamulose beneath with glistening golden scales; inflorescence terminal
or a pair of cymes also axillary in the uppermost leaf-axils; terminal panicle
dense and showy, 2–34 cm long, 15–18 cm wide, composed of 9–14 pairs of
ascending, many-flowered, rather short-stipitate cymes, with short sympodia;
peduncles stoutish, 4.5–6 cm long, minutely puberulent or glabrate, often
deeply sulcate (along with the sympodia) in drying; pedicels slender, 5–15
mm long, puberulent; bracts foliaceous, ovate or spatulate, long-stipitate, to
2.5 cm long and 2 cm wide; bractlets linear or oblong, 5–15 mm long, to 2
mm wide, puberulent; flowers fragrant; calyx campanulate, 5–8 mm long,
rather widely spreading and loose, deeply 5-parted to 1/2 or 2/3 its length,
the lobes ovate or lanceolate, apically acute, externally puberulent; corolla
hypocrateriform, red to scarlet or vermilion, rarely white [var. *album* (P'ei)
Moldenke] or salmon-pink (f. *salmoneum* Moldenke), the tube about twice as

long as the calyx, 1–1.5 cm long, very slender, externally obscurely puberulent, the lobes 3–5 mm long, dorsally puberulent; stamens long-exserted, circinately curvate in bud, the filaments about 4 cm long during anthesis; fruiting-calyx patelliform, rather fleshy, blue, glabrous, the lobes lanceolate, 10–12 mm long, 3–5 mm wide, strongly reflexed in age; fruit red or blue to bluish-black, 6–13 mm in diameter, shorter than the mature calyx; seeds black. Chromosome number: 2n = 52, 60, or 92.

D i s t r. This very handsome species is native from India including the Andaman Islands to southern China, Hainan, and Taiwan, southward and eastward into Malaya and Indonesia.

U s e s. It is widely cultivated for ornament in many tropical and subtropical countries in both hemispheres and in greenhouses as a specimen plant elsewhere. It spreads rapidly by underground stems and may be propagated by seeds or cuttings. In Vietnam an infusion is drunk as a tea in treating consumption. In Indonesia the infusion in vinegar is used in treating gonorrhoea; the foliage is chewed in treating bloody stool and the juice is used as a lotion. In Malaya it is used in native magic for "summoning the forest spirits".

V e r n. Some 25 names are recorded from various parts of its range, including: Bugyini, Petka, Pangil pangil and Tookiri.

N o t e. The *Clerodendron leveillei* Fedde and *C. scopiferum* Miq., often included in the synonymy of *C. kaempferi*, are now regarded as distinct taxa by me, while *C. speciosissimum* Paxt. is *C. speciosissimum* Van Geert and *C. darranii* Lévl., *C. kaempferi* Fisch, and *Volkameria japonica*, also often regarded as cospecific with *C. kaempferi* (Jacq.) Sieb., actually are synonyms of *C. japonicum* (Thunb.) Sweet, a very similar species with its calyx in anthesis 10–15 mm long. *Clerodendrum squamatum* var. *urticifolium* Hook. f. is regarded by me as a separate species, *C. urticifolium* (Roxb.) Wall.

S p e c i m e n s E x a m i n e d. KANDY DISTRICT: Royal Botanic Garden, Peradeniya, June 1887, *s. coll. s.n.* (PDA); in outdoor cultivation, Students' Garden, Royal Botanic Garden, Peradeniya, 1550 ft alt., 18 Jan. 1974, shrub 6 ft tall, corollas scarlet, *H.N. & A.L. Moldenke & Jayasuriya 28161* (LL, PDA, US). MATALE DISTRICT: gregarious herbs in damp roadside patch, Ukuwela, 19 Sept. 1974, 2–5 ft tall, golden leaf under-surface glabrous, flowers bright red, *Sumithraarachchi DBS. 509* (AAU, ARIZ, CAI, LACROSSE, LL, NY, US, WIS). NUWARA ELIYA DISTRICT: in outdoor cultivation, Farr Inn, Horton Plains, 7000 ft alt., 29 Jan. 1974, *H.N. & A.L. Moldenke, Jayasuriya, & Sumithraarachchi 28172* (US).

3. **Clerodendrum serratum** (L.) Moon, Cat. 1: 46. 1824. var. **serratum** Schau. in A. DC., Prod. 11: 657, 664, 674, & 675. 1847; Thw., Enum. Pl. Zeyl. 243. 1861; Trimen, Cat. 69. 1885; Clarke in Hook. f., Fl. Br. Ind. 4: 592. 1885; Watt, Dict. Econ. Prod. India 2: 374. 1889; Trimen, Handb. Fl. Ceylon

3: 360. 1895; Gamble, Man. Indian Timb., ed. 2, 543. 1902; Brandis, Indian Trees 508. 1906; Willis, Cat. 69. 1911; Heyne, Nutt. Pl. Ned. Ind. 4: 121. 1918; Gamble, Fl. Pres. Madras 6: 1099 & 1150. 1924; Alston, Kandy Fl. 64, fig. 346. 1938; Abeywick., Ceylon J. Sci., Biol. Sci. 2: 218. 1959; Burkill, Dict. Econ. Prod. Malay Penins. 1: 593–594. 1966; Gunawardena, Gen. Sp. Pl. Zeyl. 148. 1968; Fonseka & Vinasithamby, Prov. List Local Names Fl. Pl. Ceylon 13, 43, & 95. 1971; Vivekanandan, Sri Lanka Forester, ser. 2, 11: 82, 126, 143, & 145. 1974. Type: *Herb. Linnaeus 809/5* from India (LINN).

Tsjéru téka Rheede, Hort. Mal. 4: 61, pl. 29. 1683.—*Tsjeron theka* Ray, Hist. Pl. 2: 1501. 1693.

Arbor zeylanica fortunata quibusdam Petiv., Mus. 870. 1695.

Téka crispa Commelin, Fl. Mal. 66. 1696.

Planta fortunata, pinna zeylonensibus Hermann, Mus. Zeyl. 59. 1717.

Volkameria serrata L., Mant. 1: 90. 1767.—*V. serrata* Roxb. ex Moldenke, Résumé 393, in syn. 1959.

Frutex flore perlato, fructu rotundo Kleinhof ex Burm. f., Fl. Ind. 137, in syn. 1768.

Caprifolium ovatum Noronha, Verh. Batav. Genootsch. Kunsten 5: 71. 1790.

Clerodendron grandiflorum Salisb., Prod. Stirp. 108. 1795 [not *C. grandiflorum* Gürke, 1893, nor (Hook.) Schau., 1847].

Volkameria foliis lato-lanceolatis, serratis, subsessilibus L. ex Lam., Enc. 8: 690, in syn. 1808.

Clerodendrum macrophyllum Sims in Curtis, Bot. Mag. 52: pl. 2536. 1825 [not *C. macrophyllum* Hook., 1915, nor Blume, 1825].—*Clerodendron macrophyllum* Sims apud Walp., Rep. 4: 114. 1845.—*Clerodendron macrophyllum* Hort. ex Schau. in A. DC., Prod. 11: 664, in syn. 1847.

Clerodendron serratum (L.) Spreng. in L., Syst. ed. 16, 2: 758. 1825.—*Clerodendrum serratum* (L.) D. Don, Prod. Fl. Nepal. 103. 1825.—*Clerodendrum serratum* (L.) Blume, Bijdr. 810. 1826.—*Clerodendron serratum* Wall. ex Schau. in A. DC., Prod. 11: 664, in syn. 1847.—*Clerodendron serratum* Spreng. apud Jacks. in Hook. f. & Jacks., Ind. Kew., imp. 1, 1: 561. 1893.—*Clerodendrum serratum* Spreng. apud H. Hall., Meded. Rijks-Herb. 37: 77. 1918.—*Clerodendron serratum* Blume ex Moldenke, Prelim. Alph. List Invalid Names 21, in syn. 1940.—*Clerodendrum serratum* (L.) Spreng. ex Moldenke, Prelim. Alph. List Invalid Names 23, in syn. 1940.—*Clerodendrum serratum* (L.) Murr. ex Razi, Poona Univ. J. 1 (2): 47. 1952.—*Clerodendron serratum* L. ex Moldenke, Résumé Suppl. 11: 6, in syn. 1964.—*Clerodendrum serratum* Moon ex Rao & Sastry, Bull. Bot. Surv. India 6: 164. 1964.

Clerodendrum ternifolia D. Don, Prod. Fl. Nepal. 103. 1825 [not *Clerodendron ternifolium* Baker, 1883, nor *Clerodendrum ternifolium* H.B.K., 1817].—*Clerodendron ternifolium* D. Don ex Walp., Rep. 4: 107. 1845.—*Cleroden-*

dron ternifolium G. Don ex Moldenke, Prelim. Alph. List Invalid Names 22, in syn. 1940.

Volkameria herbacea Roxb., Hort. Beng. 46, hyponym. 1814; Roxb., Fl. Ind. 3: 64. 1832.

Clerodendron herbaceum (Roxb.) Wall., Num. List 50 ["49"], no. 1815. 1829. —*Clerodendron herbaceum* Wall. apud Jacks. in Hook. f. & Jacks., Ind. Kew., imp. 1, 1: 561, in syn. 1893.

Clerodendron ornatum Wall., Num. List [49], no. 1811. 1829.

Rotheca bicolor Raf., Fl. Tellur. 4: 69. 1838.

Rotheca ternifolia Raf., Fl. Tellur. 4: 69. 1838.

Clerodendrum trifoliatum Steud., Nom. Bot., ed. 2, 1: 383. 1840.—*Clerodendron trifoliatum* Steud. apud Jacks. in Hook. f. & Jacks., Ind. Kew., imp. 1, 1: 562. 1893.

Clerodendron javanense Walp., Rep. 4: 332. 1848.—*Clerodendron javense* Walp. ex Moldenke, Prelim. Alph. List Invalid Names 20, in syn. 1940.

Cyclonema serratum (L.) Hassk., Pl. Jav. Rar. 489–490. 1848.—*Cyclonema serratum* Hassk. apud Jacks. in Hook. f. & Jacks., Ind. Kew., imp. 1, 1: 679. 1893.

Clerodendron cuneatum Turcz., Bull. Soc. Imp. Naturlistes Moscou 36 (3): 221. 1863 [not *C. cuneatum* Gürke, 1900].

Clerodendron serratum var. *ornatum* (Wall.) Kurz, For. Fl. Burma 2: 267. 1877.

Clerodendron serratum var. *wallichii* f. *psilocalyx* H.J. Lam, Verbenac. Malay. Arch. 268. 1919.

Clerodendron serratum var. *wallichii* f. *puberulum* H.J. Lam, Verbenac. Malay. Arch. 269. 1919.

Clerodendron formosum Hort. ex Moldenke, Prelim. Alph. List Invalid Names 19, in syn. 1940.

Clerodendron hoffmannseggianum Klotzsch ex Moldenke, Prelim. Alph. List Invalid Names 20, in syn. 1940.

Volkameria pyramidata Royen ex Moldenke, Prelim. Alph. List Invalid Names 54, in syn. 1940.

Volkameria sessilifolia Heyne ex Moldenke, Prelim. Alph. List Invalid Names 54, in syn. 1940.

Volkameria stricta Roxb. ex Moldenke, Prelim. Alph. List Invalid Names 54, in syn. 1940.

Clerodendron serrulatum Spreng. ex Razi, Poona Univ. J. 1 (2): 47. 1952.— *Clerodendrum serrulatum* Spreng. ex Moldenke, Résumé Suppl. 11: 6, in syn. 1964.

Clerodendron fortunatum Burm. ex Moldenke, Résumé Suppl. 3: 30, in syn. 1962 [not *C. fortunatum* Blanco, 1837, nor Blume, 1844, nor Buch.-Ham., 1831, nor L., 1756, nor Sessé & Moc., 1894, nor Wall., 1885].

Caryopteris serrata (L.) Moon ex Moldenke, Phytologia 23: 428, in syn. 1972.

Herbaceous perennial or subshrub, shrub,or small treelet, 1–4 m tall; stems and branches (if any) relatively stout, purplish or buff in colour, obtusely or subacutely tetragonal, densely furfuraceous when young, becoming merely puberulent or even subglabrate in age, rarely densely incanous-tomentose (var. *pubescens* Moldenke), often somewhat sulcate in drying, often simple and wand-like; nodes not annulate; principal internodes usually elongate, 3.5–10.5 cm long; leaves decussate-opposite or ternate, subsessile or distinctly short-petiolate (var. *wallichii* Clarke); petioles 3–12 mm long, puberulent; leaf-blades thin-chartaceous or submembranous, dark-green (often brunnescent in drying) above, lighter beneath, usually elliptic, occasionally ellipticobovate or obovate (var. *obovatum* Moldenke) to obovate-oblong or almost oblong (var. *nepalense* Moldenke), 7–22 cm long, 3.1–8 cm wide, apically acute or short-acuminate, marginally serrate with acute teeth on the upper 1/2 or 2/3 or merely denticulate-serrulate, basally acute or subcuneate, rarely amplexicaul (var. *amplexifolium* Moldenke), minutely and obscurely strigillose-pulverulent or glabrate above, usually minutely pulverulent-punctate or glabrate beneath, more rarely scattered-pilose above and more densely so beneath (var. *pilosum* Moldenke), densely velutinous on both surfaces (var. *velutinum* Moldenke), or densely pilose above and densely white-tomentose beneath (var. *pubescens* Moldenke); inflorescence terminal and racemose, sometimes large and pyramidal-thyrsoid (var. *wallichii* Clarke), as well as axillary and cymose, usually conspicuously bracteate (especially in var. *wallichii*) and bracteolate, sometimes contracted and dense and more or less branching at the base only in age, at other times conspicuously paniculate-branched even in the early stages of anthesis with very numerous divergent branches of which the lower may be 5–7 cm long and the upper proportionately shorter (var. *wallichii*), usually purplish-pink puberulence throughout; cymes abbreviated, 3–5 cm long, about 3 cm wide; racemes slender, 13–23 cm long, 2.5–4.5 cm wide, densely congested, many-flowered, composed of many opposite crowded cymules, very densely bracteate and bracteolate, erect or nutant; peduncles stout, similar to the apex of the stem in all respects, 1.5–7.5 cm long, mostly (with the rachis and inflorescence-branches) densely puberulous, rarely velutinous (var. *velutinum*) or incanous-tomentose (var. *pubescens*) or even glabrous (var. *glabrescens* Moldenke), often bluish when young, pale green in age; pedicels slender or stoutish, 1–4 mm long, mostly densely puberulent, rarely velutinous (var. *velutinum*) or incanous-tomentose (var. *pubescens*) or even glabrous (var. *glabrescens*); bracts very numerous and conspicuous (epecially in var. *wallichii*), usually confined to the rachis, rather broad, elliptic, to 4 cm long and 2 cm wide, the upper ones much smaller, foliaceous, sessile or subsessile, serrate or entire; bractlets oblong, varying from elliptic or narrow-elliptic to linear or lanceolate, numerous and conspicuous, 5–15 mm long, acuminate at both ends, bluish when young, pale green in age, mostly puberulent, rarely velutinous, tomentose, or glabrous (in vars.); prophylla linear; calyx campanulate, bluish when young, pale green in age, about 4 mm long, mostly puberulent, varying to glabrous or velutinous in vars., the rim usually shallowly repand-dentate, varying to subtruncate and entire (var. *wallichii*) or deeply dentate (var. *dentatum*); corolla decidedly zygomorphic, conspicuous and showy, usually more or less blue, violet, or purple, occasionally pinkish-white or creamy-white (f. *lacteum* Moldenke), the tube cylindric, curvate, swollen, 5–9 mm long, usually twice as long as the calyx, apically oblique, hairy within at the stamen insertion, the limb plainly 2-lipped, unequally 5-lobed, about 2.5 cm wide, the posterior lobes usually erect, flat or hooded, elliptic, spreading, apically obtuse, about 9 mm long, usually dark blue with white streaks basally, lateral lobes usually pale blue or pale lavender, lower (anterior) lobe deflexed, concave, about 1.5 cm long, usually about twice the length of the tube, usually dark purple or dark violet to lilac, sometimes the lower lobe pale blue or bright violet and the others white or tinged mauve; stamens 4 or 5, exserted; filaments 2–2.5 cm long, decidedly curved, blue, densely hairy basally; anthers white; style and ovary glabrous; fruiting-calyx cupuliform, somewhat accrescent; fruit drupaceous, subglobose or broadly obovoid, 6–9 mm long, somewhat succulent, deeply 2–4-lobed, at first glossy emerald-green, finally dark purple or black, not splitting into 4 nutlets at maturity; seeds 1 per lobe or often 1–3 aborted. Chromosome number: $n = 24$.

D i s t r. This species, the only representative of the subgenus [or separate genus] *Cyclonema* in this area, is widely distributed from Pakistan, India, Ceylon, and Burma north into southern and central China and eastward through Thailand, Indo-China, and Malaya to Indonesia. It occurs also in Mauritius, Madagascar, and South Africa, but is probably only introduced there. It is cultivated for ornament in various parts of Europe and tropical Asia. It has been found fossilized in Lower Pliocene formations in France. At least ten infraspecific taxa are recognized, some of which have their most pronounced characteristics noted in the above description, only one of which (besides the typical variety) has definitely been recognized in Ceylon.

U s e s. The species has been found to contain a saponin with anti-allergic and anti-histaminic properties, as well as D-mannitol (in the root bark), an important excipient and diluent in pharmacy, used for boron identification, in renal function testing, as an irrigating fluid in prostatic surgery, and as a vasodilator for cardiac insufficiency. In industry mannitol is used in the manufacture of artificial resins, plasticizers, and electrolytic condensers for radios. The flowers are eaten in Malaya during childbirth. The roots are used in the treatment of febrile, bronchial, and catarrhal afflictions; boiled in water with ginger and coriander they are used in cases of nausea. The roots are also employed to hasten fermentation of rice-beer and against snakebites. The leaves, boiled in oil, are used in applications for ophthalmia, and, when tender, are eaten as a vegetable. The seeds are slightly aperient or laxative; boiled in buttermilk they are used in the treatment of dropsy. The young flowers are also sometimes eaten as greens.

V e r n. Kan-henda, Ken-henda (S); Chiru-dekku, Chiru-tekku, Chiry-tekku, Kandu-parangi, Ratamadakki, Siri-tekku (T). There are also some 75 other names reported from other parts of its range.

N o t e s. The Burmese specimens with broader leaf-blades, of thinner texture, the panicles less mealy to almost glabrous, more lax, and the bracts less numerous and early deciduous are sometimes regarded as var. *ornatum* (Wall.) Kurz.

The leaves of *C. serratum* are often attacked by the fungus, *Podosporium penicillium* var. *clerodendri* Sacc.

The following names are often included in the synonymy of typical *C. serratum*, but actually belong elsewhere. *Clerodendron divaricatum* Jack, *C. farinosum* Wall., *C. farinosum* (Roxb.) Wall., *C. wallichianum* Royle, *C. javense* Walp., *C. javanense* Walp., *C. javanicum* Walp., *C. serratum* var. *javanicum* (Walp.) Hochr., and *C. serratum* var. *wallichianum* Royle more properly are synonyms of *Clerodendrum serratum* var. *wallichii* Clarke; *Volkameria obovata* Roxb. and *Clerodendron obovatum* (Roxb.) Walp. belong to *Clerodendrum obovatum* (Roxb.) Walp.; *Volkameria farinosa* Roxb., *Clerodendron farinosum* (Roxb.) Walp., and *C. venosum* Wall. belong to *Clerodendrum venosum* Wall.; and *Clerodendron spicatum* Thunb. is *Orthosiphon spiralis* (Lour.) Merr., a mint.

The pollen of *C. serratum* is described in detail by Nair & Rehman in Bull. Bot. Gard. Lucknow 76: 16–17, fig. 21 & pl. 2 (9) (1962) and by Nair, Pollen Gr. West. Himal. Pl. 35 (1965).

S p e c i m e n s E x a m i n e d. KANDY DISTRICT: on damp embankment sides of roadside stream by culvert 25/10, Hunnasgiriya, 660 m alt., 10 Feb. 1972, flowers conspicuous, corolla pale blue, *Cramer 3615* (US); common along borders of jungle close to Kadugannawa main road, Kadugannawa, 500 m alt., 28 Aug. 1972, shrub 3 m tall, flowers blue, conspicuous, *Cramer 3841* (US); Kadugannawa, *Gardner s.n. [C.P. 1951]* (LE, PDA, W); on steep roadside banks at margin of forest east of Madugoda, 27 miles from Kandy, 1700 ft alt., 2 April 1969, subshrub 2–3 m tall, leaves opposite or sometimes in whorls of 3's, corolla-limb 2.5 cm across, posterior lobe erect, hooded, dark blue with white streams near base, lateral lobes pale-blue, filaments 2 cm long, anthers exserted, white, *Grierson 1138* (PDA, US); near radio station, Hantane, above Peradeniya, 11 July 1970, shrub 5 ft tall, flowers blue, *Meijer 295* (PDA, US); in outdoor cultivation, Students' Garden, Royal Botanic Garden, Peradeniya, 18 Jan. 1974, shrub 6 ft tall, *H.N. & A.L. Moldenke & Jayasuriya 28155* (PDA, US); abundant on steep road shoulders and banks at edge of jungle at milepost 24/14 four miles east of Hunnasgiriya, 19 Jan. 1974, mostly fruits only, *H.N. & A.L. Moldenke, Jayasuriya, & Sumi-*

thraarachchi 28184 (AAU, ARIZ, CAI, KARACHI, LL, PDA, US); on steep
bank at edge of jungle 4 miles east of Madugoda, 2500 ft alt., 19 Jan. 1974,
H.N. & A.L. Moldenke, Jayasuriya, & Sumithraarachchi 28187 (US); on steep
roadbanks at milepost 18/14 south of Kandy on the Nuwara-Eliya road,
2000 ft alt., 30 Jan. 1974, *H.N. & A.L. Moldenke, Jayasuriya, & Sumithraarachchi 28311* (AAU, CAI, KARACHI, LL, PDA, US); in disturbed burned
dry patana grassland on slope with reddish-brown loam 1/2 mile upslope
from University Circuit Bungalow, Peradeniya, 900 m alt., 31 Oct. 1967,
Mueller-Dombois & Cooray 67103121 (PDA, US); at 25/11 milepost on the
Kandy to Mahiyangane road, 18 Oct. 1973, *Waas 210* (US); in patana grass
on banks, Dekanda, Kadugannawa, 1800 ft alt., 28 May 1939, flowers blue,
Worthington 336 (PDA); common on patana edges and banks, Madulkelle,
3000 ft alt., 13 Sept. 1948, flowers blue, *Worthington 4100* (PDA). MATALE
DISTRICT: roadside along the Matale to Illukkumbura road, 3 July 1974,
shrubs, flowers blue, *Sumithraarachchi DBS. 403* (LL). NUWARA ELIYA
DISTRICT: Rikiligaskade, 17 June 1965, shrubs, corolla with posterior lateral
lobes pale-blue, anterior one dark bluish-purple, "ken-henda", *Amaratunga
880* (PDA); at edge of jungle, Rambode, 3240 ft alt., 28 Jan. 1974, leaves
only, *H.N. & A.L. Moldenke, Jayasuriya, & Sumithraarachchi 28267* (AAU,
PDA, US). KEGALLE DISTRICT: scattered on edge of disturbed jungle
area, hillside around rock faces above railroad tracks 1/2 mile west of Kadugannawa between tunnels 10 and 11, 500 m alt., 5 Sept. 1969, plants growing
6 ft tall, stems fleshy, leaves fleshy, *Grupe 217* (PDA, US); Alagalla rock,
1000 m alt., 8 May 1971, 5 m tall, hardly branched, flowers light violet, labellum dark violet, *Kostermans 24039* (AAU, PDA, US). BADULLA DIS-
TRICT: in shade along stream at 6th milepost behind the pine nursery,
Madawelagama, 2000 ft alt., 15 Oct. 1971, 1 m tall herb with green fruit, *Balakrishnan & Jayasuriya NBK. 821* (PDA, US). LOCALITY UNKNOWN:
s. coll. C.P. 696 (PDA); *Wawra 1184* (W).

var. **dentatum** H.J. Lam, Verbenac. Malay. Arch. 269–270 [as "*Clerodendron*"]. 1919. Type: *J.D. Hooker s.n.*, from Sikkim, 4000–5000 ft
altitude (L).

Clerodendron serratum var. *dentatum* f. *psilocalyx* H.J. Lam, Verbenac. Malay.
   Arch. 270. 1919.
Clerodendron serratum var. *dentatum* f. *puberulum* H.J. Lam, Verbenac.
   Malay. Arch. 270. 1919.

   This variety differs from the typical form of the species chiefly in having
the calyx during anthesis mostly deeply 5-dentate or 5-lobed with deltoid
subacute lobes.
   The plant is a shrub or subshrub, 1.5–3 m tall; stems weak, numerous,

often simple or only obscurely branched, leafy to the base, basally thickened and lenticellate; leaves often in 3's or 4's, the blades mostly deeply dentate, the teeth apically abrupt and often subsetiferous, 3–5 mm long; panicles conspicuous, often lilac-tinged throughout; rachis often dull-maroon; calyx to 7 mm long, glabrous or subglabrous to puberulent (f. *puberulum* H.J. Lam); corollas various in colour, blue or dark bluish-purple to violet, pinkish, lilac, or mauve, often partly or all cream-colour or white, the tube about 6 mm long, the lateral lobes about 6 mm long, the middle (lowest) lobe about 9 mm long, usually darker (or tinged lilac if the others are white).

This rather poorly defined variety appears to range from India to Indonesia and is sometimes cultivated for ornament.

V e r n. Singoegoe and Singugu are recorded from Indonesia.

S p e c i m e n s E x a m i n e d. KANDY DISTRICT: occasional on grassy hillslope close to culvert 33/5 on the Ramboda to Nuwara-Eliya road, Pusselawa, 720 m alt., 28 Oct. 1971, shrub, stems to 1.5 m tall, thickened and lenticellate below, panicle conspicuous, flowers purplish-blue, *Cramer 3446* (US); about 9 miles northeast of Hunnasgiriya near milepost 29/21 on the road to Mahiyangane, 810 m alt., 14 Nov. 1974, shrub 3 m tall with weak wood, upper 4 corolla-lobes light-blue, lower lobe dark blue, rachis dull maroon, *Davidse & Jayasuriya 8417* (LL); abundant along roadsides and on roadcut banks, Medamahanuwara, 1700 ft alt., 19 Jan. 1974, low shrubs with simple or obscurely branched stems leafy to the ground, *H.N. & A.L. Moldenke, Jayasuriya & Sumithraarachchi 28181* (AAU, ARIZ, CAI, KARACHI, LL, MO, PDA, US); abundant on steep roadbanks and edge of forest, sixth hairpin bend, Mahiyangane, 1800 ft alt., 19 Jan. 1974, 6–10 ft subshrubs with mostly simple stems, upper petals varying to white, *H.N. & A.L. Moldenke, Jayasuriya, & Sumithraarachchi 28191* (AAU, ARIZ, CAI, KARACHI, LL, PDA, US). MATALE DISTRICT: common on gravelly slope beside the Rattota to Illukkumbra road, Rattota, about 1000 m alt., 4 March 1977, shrub about 2 m tall, panicles conspicuous, corolla-limb white, the anterior lobe pale blue, *Cramer 4862* (NY); common in sunny wet patana grassland near milepost 27 on the Rattota to Illukkumbura road, 715 m alt., 4 Oct. 1971, erect shrub 2 m tall, corollas white and blue, fruit green, black when ripe, *Jayasuriya 263* (PDA, US); abundant on steep roadside banks and edge of forest, Alawatugoda, 800 ft alt., 23 Jan. 1974, simple-stemmed subshrubs, 6 ft tall, *H.N. & A.L. Moldenke & Jayasuriya 28204* (LL, MOLDENKE, PDA, US); Iriagama, 1572 ft alt., 5 July 1930, flowers dark bluish-purple, *J.M. Silva 178* (NY); roadside on Matale to Illukkumbura road, 3 July 1974, shrubs, flowers blue, *Sumithraarachchi DBS. 403* (LACROSSE, LL); in open places among grass, Midlands, Rattota, 800 metres altitude, 12 Nov. 1972, inflorescence purple, petals bluish-violet, *Tirvengadum, Dassanayake, & Jayasuriya 5* (PDA, US). NUWARA ELIYA DISTRICT: in clumps on the patana at culvert 20/5 on the road from Kandy to Maturata, 12 July 1972, woody shrub to 2 m tall, the labellum darker than the 4 other petals, light-violet, *Maxwell 1000* (PDA, US). MONERAGALA DISTRICT: in secondary forest at mile-post 9/4 on the Passara to Moneragala road, Badalkumbura, 11 June 1974, 2.5 m tall shrub with bluish flowers, *Waas 693* (US). LOCALITY UN-KNOWN: *s. coll. s.n.* (US).

4. Clerodendrum incisum Klotzsch in Peters, Reise Mossamb. Bot. 1: 257 [as *"Clerodendron"*]. 1862. var. **macrosiphon** (Hook. f.) Baker ex Lam & Bakh., Bull. Jard. Bot. Buitenzorg, ser. 3, 3: 80. 1921; Gürke in Engler, Pfl. Ost-Afr. C: 340. 1895; Baker in Thiselt.-Dyer, Fl. Trop. Africa 5: 308. 1900; Woodrow, Gard. Trop., ed. 6, 438. 1910; Chittenden, Dict. Gard. 505. 1956; Willam. & Schub., Agr. Res. Serv. U.S. Dept. Agr. Tech. Bull. 1234: 236. 1961; Harler, Gard. Plains, ed. 4, 159. 1962; MacMillan, Trop. Plant. & Gard., ed. 5, 104. 1962; Sharma & Mukhop., J. Genet. 58: 359, 360, 362, 374, 379, & 381, pl. 9, fig. 6. 1963; Good, Geogr. Fl. Pl. 202. 1964; Backer & Bakh., Fl. Java 2: 607. 1965; Sen & Naskar, Bull. Bot. Surv. India 7: 40. 1965; Burkill, Dict. Econ. Prod. Malay Penins. 1: 589. 1966; Hore & Bose, Bull. Bot. Surv. India 10: 165 & 167–170. 1968; Corner & Watanabe, Ill. Guide Trop. Pl. 754. 1969; Roy & Bose, Hort. Sci. 1 (2): 39–44. 1969. Type: a specimen cultivated at the Royal Botanic Gardens, Kew, from seed originally collected by Sir John Kirk at Usaramo, Tanzania, in 1881 (K).

Clerodendron macrosiphon Hook. f. in Curtis, Bot. Mag. 39: pl. 6695. 1883 [not *C. macrosiphon* (Baker) Pieper, 1928].—*Clerodendron macrosiphon* Hook. ex Moldenke, Résumé Suppl. 11: 6, in syn. 1964.—*Clerodendrum macrosiphon* Hook. ex Moldenke, Phytologia 23: 430, in syn. 1972.

An erect bush, shrub, or undershrub, 0.5–2 m tall, strongly branched; young branches slender, grey, subtetragonal, somewhat densely and shortly pilose-pubescent or spreading-puberulent (glabrous in var. *incisum*); nodes not annullate; leaves decussate-opposite or ternate, usually with small ones in their axils; petioles very slender, 2–15 mm long or even subobsolete, densely short-pubescent; leaf-blades chartaceous, uniformly dark green on both surfaces, brunnescent or nigrescent in drying, narrowly elliptic or oblanceolate to oblong-lanceolate or oblong-obovate, 3–12.5 cm long, 1–5 cm wide, apically acute to long-acuminate, basally tapering or long-acuminate, marginally entire (on smaller leaves) or (on larger leaves, often on the same plant) with 2–8 coarse, widely divergent, and acute teeth near the middle (the actual number of teeth often not the same on both sides), very minutely strigillose-puberulent above, more densely puberulent (especially on the larger venation) beneath; secondaries mostly 5–8 per side, arcuate-ascending, usually not ex-tending directly into the teeth; inflorescence axillary and terminal, cymose, the cymes subcapitate or corymbose, small, few- or profusely many-flowered, crowded, short-pedunculate; flowers extremely large and showy, short-pedicellate or subsessile; peduncles very short and sparsely short-pubescent or obsolete; pedicels rather stoutish, 3–5 mm long, puberulent; bractlets and prophylla small, linear-setaceous, sparsely short-pubescent or puberulent; flower-buds with a deflexed apex, comma-shaped; calyx 5–6 mm long, split to about 1/3 its length, somewhat pilose-pubescent (glabrous in var. *incisum*); corolla very large and showy, expanding in the evening and dropping off the next morning, white or yellowish-white, brightly shiny, tubular, 10–13 cm long, circinnate in bud, unrolling and elongating rapidly, the tube 7–11.5 cm long, externally somewhat thinly glandular-pilose or- pubescent (glabrous in var. *incisum*), the limb about 3 cm wide, shallowly 5-lobed, all the lobes often directed forward, the median one longest; stamens red or pink to purple, 6–7 cm long; fruiting-calyx coriaceous, campanulate, about 5 mm long and wide, glabrate, nitidulous, venose with prominent veins, the rim sharply 5-lobed with narrowly triangular and spreading lobes; fruit drupaceous, obovate, about 7 mm long and 9 mm wide, dark purple when ripe, conspicuously 4-lobed, but usually only 2-seeded, nigrescent in drying. Chromosome number: 2n=30.

D i s t r. A native of Tanzania, this plant is now widely cultivated for ornament outdoors in tropical Asia and America and in greenhouses in Europe and the United States. It is easily propagated by cuttings. Dwarfing may be induced with an appreciable reduction in shoot length and the production of more flowers by application of Cycocel dust or foliar spray. The species is quite variable and other natural varieties are known from Somalia and Madagascar.

V e r n. Glorybower.

N o t e. It is sometimes attacked by the fungus, *Meliola cookeana* var. *viticis* Hansf.

S p e c i m e n s E x a m i n e d. KANDY DISTRICT: Royal Botanic Garden, Peradeniya, July 1889, *s. coll. s.n.* (PDA); in outdoor cultivation in Students' Garden, Royal Botanic Garden, Peradeniya, 1550 ft alt., 18 Jan. 1974, shrub 4 ft tall from severely pruned-back stump, corollas creamy-white, *H.N. & A.L. Moldenke & Jayasuriya 28156* (LL, MOLDENKE, PDA, US). COLOMBO DISTRICT: on roadside, Ja-Ela-Gampha, 6 Sept. 1962, shrub, flowers white, stamens purple, *Amaratunga 344* (PDA); Minuwangoda, 5 June 1967, shrub, *Amaratunga 1318* (PDA).

5. Clerodendrum indicum (L.) Kuntze, Rev. Gen. Pl. 2: 506 [as "*Clerodendron*"]. 1891; Moon, Cat. 1: 46. 1821; Thw., Enum. Pl. Zeyl. 2: 243. 1839; Schau. in A. DC., Prod. 11: 670–672. 1847; Dymock, Veg. Mat. Med. W. Ind. 497. 1884; Clarke in Hook. f., Fl. Br. Ind. 4: 595. 1885; Trimen, Cat. 69. 1885;

Trimen, Handb. Fl. Ceylon 3: 361. 1895; Willis, Cat. 143. 1911; Alston in Tri-
men, Handb. Fl. Ceylon 6: 232 & 233. 1931; Alston, Kandy Fl. 64. 1938;
Sastri, Wealth India 2 (R): 231-232. 1950; Bor & Raizada, Some Beautiful Ind.
Climb. 143-145, fig. 90. 1954; Cooke, Fl. Pres. Bombay, ed. 2, 2: 514. 1958;
Abeywick., Ceylon J. Sci., Biol. Sci. 2: 218. 1959; Burkill, Dict. Econ. Prod.
Malay Penins. 1: 592. 1966; Gunawardena, Gen. & Sp. Pl. Zeyl. 148. 1968;
Fonseka & Vinasithamby, Prov. List Local Names Fl. Pl. Ceylon 5. 1971.
Type: Amman, Stirp. Rar. Imp. Ruth. pl. 15. 1739.

Lysimachia indica Bondt, Hist. Nat. Med. Ind. Orient. 159-160 [as "*Lysima-
chio indico*"]. 1658.
Siphonanthus indica L., Sp. Pl., ed. 1, imp. 1, 1: 109. 1753.—*Siphonanthvs
indica* Raeusch., Nom. Bot., ed. 3, 36. 1797.—*Siphonanthus indica* Willd. ex
Schau. in A. DC., Prod. 11: 670, in syn. 1847.—*Siphonanthus indicus* L. ex
Liogier, Rhodora 67: 350, in syn. 1965.
Ovieda mitis L., Sp. Pl., ed. 2, 2: 889. 1763.—*O. mitis* Burm. ex Scop., Introd.
Hist. Nat. 171. 1777.—*O. mitis* Burm. f. ex Alston in Trimen, Handb. Fl.
Ceylon 6: 232-233, in syn. 1931.
Ovieda inermis Burm. f., Fl. Ind. 136, pl. 43, fig. 1. 1768.—*O. inermis* Jacks.
apud Lam & Bakh., Bull. Jard. Bot. Buitenzorg ser. 3, 3: 85, in syn. 1921.
Montalbania Neck., Elem. 1: 273. 1790.
Siphonanthus angustifolia Willd. in L., Sp. Pl., ed. 4, 1 (2): 606. 1797.
Clerodendron siphonanthus R. Br. in Ait., Hort. Kew., ed. 2, 4: 65. 1812.—
Clerodendrum siphonanthus R. Br. ex Wood, Amer. Bot. & Flor. Add. 1877:
488. 1877.—*Clerodendron siphonantus* R. Br. ex Christoph., Bernice P.
Bishop Mus. Bull. 128: 194. 1935.—*Clerodendron sipho* Langlois ex Mol-
denke, Prelim. Alph. List Invalid Names 21, in syn. 1940.—*Clerodendron
syphonanthus* R. Br. ex Moldenke, Prelim. Alph. List Invalid Names 22, in
syn. 1940.—*Clerodendron siphonanthus* (R. Br.). Clarke ex Sastri, Wealth
India 2 (R): 231, in syn. 1950.—*Clerodendron siphonanthus* Ait. ex Sharma
& Mukhop., J. Genet. 58: 359. 1963.—*Clerodendron shiphonanthus* Bose,
Handb. Shrubs 42 & 123. 1965.—*Clerodendron siphonatus* R. Br. ex Singh,
Sydowia 25: 230 & 231, sphalm. 1972.
Clerodendron longicolle G.F.W. Mey., Prim. Fl. Esseq. 217. 1818 [not *Clerod-
endron longicollis* Borgesen & Paulsen, 1959].
Ovieda verticillata Roxb. ex D. Don, Prod. Fl. Nepal. 102. 1825.
Clerodendron verticillatum (Roxb.) D. Don, Prod. Fl. Nepal. 102. 1825.—
Clerodendron verticillatum Don ex Clarke in Hook. f., Fl. Br. Ind. 4: 595,
in syn. 1885.
Clerodendron angustifolium (Willd.) Hassk., Cat. Pl. Bogor. Cult. 136. 1844.
Clerodendron fortunatum Blume ex Hassk., Cat. Pl. Bogor. Cult. 136, in syn.
1844 [not *Clerodendron fortunatum* Blanco, 1837, nor Buch.-Ham., 1831,
nor Burm., 1962, nor L., 1756, nor Sessé & Moc., 1894, nor Wall., 1885].

Clerodendron mite (L.) Vatke, Linnaea 43: 537. 1882 [not *Clerodendron mite* Vahl, 1931].—*Clerodendron mite* Vatke apud Jacks. in Hook. f. & Jacks., Ind. Kew., imp. 1, 1: 561. 1893.—*Clerodendron mite* (Burm.) Vatke ex Moldenke, Alph. List Invalid Names Suppl. 1: 6, in syn. 1947.—*Clerodendron mite* (Burm. f.) Merr. ex Moldenke, Résumé Suppl. 3: 30, in syn. 1962.

Clerodendron indicum (L.) Kuntze, Rev. Gen. Pl. 2: 506. 1891.—*Clerodendron indicum* Kuntze apud Durand & Jacks., Ind. Kew. Suppl. 1, imp. 1, 101, in syn. 1901.—*Clerodendron indica* (L.) Druce, Bot. Exch. Club Soc. Brit. Isles 3: 416. 1914.—*Clerodendron indicum* (Willd.) Kuntze ex Datta, Handb. Syst. Bot. 182. 1965.—*Cleorodendrum indicum* (L.) Kuntze ex R.R. Rao, Stud. Fl. Pl. Mysore Dist. 2: 748, sphalm. 1973.—*Clerodendrum indicum* Kuntze ex J.F. Morton, 500 Fl. S. Fla. 54. 1974.

Volkameria longicollis G.F. Mey. ex Moldenke, Prelim. Alph. List Invalid Names 53, in syn. 1940 [not *V. longicollis* Petit-Thouars, 1950].

Ovieda siphonanthus Roxb. ex Moldenke, Prelim. Alph. List Invalid Names 33, in syn. 1940.

Virgate soft-wooded shrub or low treelet, to 3 m tall, suffrutescent undershrub or even herbaceous, stoloniferous, of rapid growth; stems usually very straight or arching, mostly unbranched, hollow; branches, when present, very stout, hollow, obtusely tetragonal, the larger ones 8–10-sulcate, subglabrate; nodes (except the younger ones) annulate, occasionally marked with a band of pubescence; principal internodes mostly elongate, 2.5–10 cm long; leaves approximate, opposite, or verticillate in whorls of 3–6, sessile or subsessile; petioles (if present) stout, 3–8 mm long, glabrous, often striate; leaf-blades membranous or thin-chartaceous, mostly very fragile when dry, linear-lanceolate or oblong to narrow-elliptic, varying to oblanceolate, 7.5–23 cm long, 0.7–5.5 cm wide, apically mostly acute or acuminate, sometimes subobtuse, entire [or more or less toothed in f. *semiserratum* (Wall.) Moldenke], basally gradually attenuate to acute, glabrous on both surfaces, sparsely punctate beneath; midrib stout, very prominent beneath; secondaries slender, 7–10 per side, short, arcuate-ascending, prominulous beneath, arcuately joined a few mm from the margins; vein and veinlet reticulation very sparse, obscure above, not at all prominulous beneath; inflorescence axillary and terminal, abundant, the axillary cymes opposite and solitary or whorled, usually supra-axillary, 4–6 cm long, 3–7-flowered, lax, widely divaricate; terminal panicle thyrsoid, to 45 cm long or longer, to 25 cm wide, very showy, usually much elongate and lax, composed of 3–12 whorls of cymes, glabrous throughout, often more or less continuous with the many axillary cymes borne in the upper leaf-axils; peduncles and sympodia similar to the stems or branches in size, shape, texture, colour, and glabrescence, but slightly more slender; bracts foliaceous, resembling the leaves in all respects but smaller, usually numerous, caducous; bractlets broadly linear, very numerous, reddish when young, 5–15 mm long, 2–3 mm wide, glabrous; prophylla linear, 1–6 mm long; pedicels 0.5–2 cm long, glabrous; calyx green or red, very broadly campanulate, thick-textured, glabrous or subglabrous, its tube 5–7 mm long, its rim deeply 5-lobed to or below the middle, the lobes subcoriaceous, wide-spreading, ovate, 6–10 mm long, basally 4–9 mm wide, apically acute or subacute; corolla hypocrateriform or infundibular, mostly white or whitish to cream-colour, varying to pinkish-white or yellow, very showy, not fragrant, closing in the forenoon, its tube very long and slender, 7.5–14 cm long, 1.5–2 mm wide, glabrous or patently glandular-hairy, curvate, the limb 1.5–2.5 cm wide, the lobes oblong or ovate-oblong to obovate, 8–15 mm long, apically obtuse, eventually strongly reflexed; stamens long-exserted; filaments slender, purple, glabrous; anthers oblong, 2.5–3 mm long, purple, the thecae parallel; style long, slender, purple; stigmatic branches short, rather thick; ovary obtuse, glabrous; fruiting-calyx accrescent, fleshy, bright-red or brown-red to purple, to 3 cm in diameter; fruit shiny green when immature, becoming blue-black or reddish-black, 1–1.3 cm in diameter, normally 4-sulcate and 4-lobed (or 1–3-lobed by abortion), the fleshy exocarp mostly dark-blue, fetid; pyrenes 1–4, 1-seeded, rounded except for a slight flattening on the inner surface, about 1 cm long and 6 mm wide, smooth, the endocarp crustaceous. Chromosome number: $n=15$; $2n=40$, 48, or 52.

D i s t r. This species is native from India and Nepal eastward to Burma, Malaya, and Indo-China, north to southern China, and is widely cultivated in warm countries of both hemispheres; naturalized in Madagascar, Indonesia, and from the southern United States through the West Indies to the Guianas. It spreads quickly from cultivation by stolons.

U s e s. The plant is slightly bitter and astringent and contains an alkaloid. In Asia it is sometimes used as a substitute for opium, often gathered and smoked with tobacco. It yields a resin employed in Burma in the treatment of syphilitic rheumatism. In India the leaves are often eaten raw as a veget-able, while the juice from the vegetative parts is used with "ghee" in cases of skin diseases like herpetic eruptions and pemphigus. The resin is used as an insect repellant in preserving clothes. The pounded root is said to be useful (taken with ginger) in treating asthma, coughs, and other pulmonary com-plaints, as well as against scrofulous affections. In Java it is the pounded leaves that are used to cure asthma. In India it is used in the form of ghees, powders, or enemas in treating abdominal tumours; also in the same country against puerperal fever, atrophy, emaciation, cachexy, gravel, excessive thirst, cholera, blindness, consumption, dry coughs, and bronchitis. In some locali-ties pieces of the wood are made into necklaces and worn around the neck as a charm against various ailments. In New Caledonia the leaves are used as a tonic and vermifuge.

430   VERBENACEAE

V e r n. Balaya (S); among some 40 other common names in various parts
of its range are: Bhargi, Bead-flower, Indian glorybower, Tube-flower, Turk's-
head and Turk's-turban.

N o t e. The leaves of *C. indicum* are often attacked by the fungus, *Cer-
coseptoria clerodendri* Pargi & Singh.

S p e c i m e n s E x a m i n e d. COLOMBO DISTRICT: Mirigama, 2
Aug. 1969, flowers off-white, anthers purple, style purple, *Amaratunga 1751*
(PDA); Mrs. Dorothy Fernando's, Barnes place, Colombo, 20 Oct. 1949,
flowers greenish-white, anthers purple, style purple, *s. coll. s.n.* (PDA); coast,
Colombo, 26 May 1949, *Worthington 4206* (PDA). KANDY DISTRICT:
roadside weed, Peradeniya, Oct. 1882, *s. coll. s.n.* (PDA); in outdoor cultivation in Students' Garden, Royal Botanic Garden, Peradeniya, 1550 ft alt.,
28 Jan. 1974, simple unbranched shrubs 6 ft tall, stems hollow, leaves whorled, *H.N. & A.L. Moldenke & Jayasuriya 28169* (US). MATALE DISTRICT:
in outdoor cultivation at Guest House, Dambulla, 400 ft alt., 23 Jan. 1974,
simple stems about 8 ft tall, leaves whorled, corolla cream-colour, *H.N. & A.L.
Moldenke & Jayasuriya 28219* (PDA, US). KEGALLE DISTRICT: a weed
near railroad station, Ambepussa, 23 Aug. 1968, flowers greenish-white, anthers and style purple, *Amaratunga 1628* (PDA). TRINCOMALEE DIS-
TRICT: near hot wells, Kanniyai, 24 June 1975, gregarious shrub, terminal
flowers [i.e., fruiting-calyxes!] crimson, *D.B. & D. Sumithraarachchi DBS. 846*
(US). GALLE DISTRICT: in marsh on coconut estate, Ambalangoda, 19 Oct.
1971, shrub 1.5 m tall, flowers white, calyx green, *Balakrishnan NBK. 939*
(NY, PDA, US); waste land on coconut estate, Ambalangoda, 19 Oct. 1971,
flowers with pink calyx, *Balakrishnan NBK. 940* (PDA, US).

6. Clerodendrum heterophyllum (Poir.) R. Br. in Ait., Hort. Kew., ed. 2, 5:
464. 1812; G. Don in Loud., Hort. Brit., ed. 3, 247. 1839; Schau. in A. DC.,
Prod. 11: 657 & 660. 1847; Baker, Fl. Maurit. 254. 1877; Parker, Forest Fl.
Punjab, ed. 2, 403. 1924; Moldenke in Humbert, Fl. Madag. 174: 237. 1966.
Type: *Herb. Desfontaines s.n.*, from Ile d'France [= Mauritius] (P).

Volkameria heterophylla Poir. in Lam., Enc. 8: 687. 1808.—*V. heterophylla*
    Vent. ex Steud., Nom. Bot., ed. 1, 889. 1821.
Volkameria angustifolia Andr., Bot. Repos. 9: pl. 554. 1808 [not *V. angusti-
    folia* Poir., 1808].
*Volkameria foliis ovatis, lanceolatis, seu lineari-lanceolatis, integerrimis; fructo
    globoso* Vent. ex Lam., Enc. 8: 687, in syn. 1808.
Clerodendrum heterophyllum Ait. ex Steud., Nom. Bot., ed. 1, 207. 1821.—
    Clerodendron heterophyllum R. Br. ex Spreng. in L., Syst., ed. 16, 2: 758.
    1825.—*Clerodendron heterophyllum* [R. Br.] in Ait. apud Jacks. in Hook. f.
    & Jacks., Ind. Kew., imp. 1, 1: 561. 1893.—*Clerodendrum heterophyllum*
    (Poit.) R. Br. ex Moldenke, Alph. List Invalid Names 21, sphalm. 1942.—

Clerodendron heterophyllum Ait. ex Terrac., Trav. Lab. Matiere Med.
Ecole Super. Pharm. Paris 33 (3): 101. 1947.
Clerodendrum lanceolatum Wall., Num. List 87, no. 1790c, hyponym. 1831.—
    Clerodendron lanceolatum Wall. ex Moldenke, Fifth Summ. 2: 971, in syn.
    1971 [not *Clerodendron lanceolatum* N.E. Br., 1959, nor Gürke, 1893].
Clerodendrum ligustrinum Wall., Num. List 87, no. 1790c, hyponym. 1831.—
    Clerodendron ligustrinum Wall. ex Moldenke, Fifth Summ. 2: 971, in syn.
    1971 [not *Clerodendron ligustrinum* R. Br., 1847, nor (Jacq.) Roem. &
    Schult., 1940, nor (Jacq.) R. Br., 1812].
Clerodendrum mauritanicum Schum. ex Moldenke, Prelim. Alph. List Invalid
    Names 23, in syn. 1940.

Low shrub or small tree; branches quite twiggy, slender, grey, subterete
or obscurely tetragonal, densely cinereous-puberulent, glabrescent in age,
often prominently lenticellate; branchlets and twigs very slender, abbreviated,
grey or buff, acutely tetragonal, densely cinereous-puberulent; nodes often
more or less partially annulate, those on larger branchlets marked with
corky sterigmata 0.5–1.5 mm long; principal internodes greatly abbreviated
and only 1–9 mm long on the twigs, to 8.5 cm long on the larger branches;
leaf-scars mostly elevated and conspicuously divergent, circular, corky-mar-
gined, not recurved nor spinescent; leaves decussate-opposite, approximate,
or even ternate, often scattered, very numerous and crowded; petioles varying
from slender to filiform, 3–15 mm long, very minutely puberulent or subglabrate, not at all ampliate at the base; leaf-blades submembranous or very
thin-chartaceous, rather uniformly bright green on both surfaces or slightly
lighter beneath, more or less brunnescent in drying, elliptic or lanceolate-
elliptic, 1.1–9 cm long, 1–3.6 cm wide (or less than 1 cm wide in f. *angustifolium* Moldenke), apically acute or short-acuminate or rarely blunt,
marginally entire or with 1 or 2 blunt lobe-like teeth above the middle or
repand-dentate with widely separated blunt appressed teeth, basally acute or
acuminate to cuneate, glabrate or subglabrate and densely punctate on both
surfaces or very lightly pulverulent-puberulent on both surfaces when immature; inflorescence axillary, but aggregate near the tips of the twigs and appearing as though terminal, cymose, usually corymbiform, 3–5 cm long, 4–6
cm wide, very lax, the cymes numerous, close together, decussate-opposite,
mostly 2–4 cm long and few-flowered, very loosely flowered, simple or 1 or
2 times dichotomous with a terminal flower in the centre of each dichotomy,
densely greyish-puberulent throughout; peduncles very slender or filiform, 1–2
cm long, densely puberulent like the twigs; pedicels very slender or filiform,
elongate, 3–19 mm long, densely cinereous-puberulent; bracts absent; bractlets and prophylla inconspicuous, linear-subulate or setaceous, caducous,
minute, 1–3 mm long, puberulent; calyx campanulate, brunnescent in drying,
2–3 mm long and wide, very sparsely scattered-puberulous, its rim truncate

and entire or subentire (or distinctly toothed in var. *baueri* Moldenke); corolla white, hypocrateriform, its tube narrow-cylindric, 4–11 mm long, usually minutely pulverulent-puberulent on the outside, hardly ampliate except at the extreme apex, the limb about 1 cm in diameter, the 5 lobes subequal, 4–6 mm long, apically obtuse; stamens and style exserted 1 cm or more from the corolla-mouth, the style surpassing the stamens; fruiting-calyx slightly incrassate, cupuliform, to about 5 mm long and 10 mm wide, glabrescent, mostly irregularly split to the base when the fruit is ripe; fruit drupaceous, subglobose, nigrescent in drying, about 7 mm long and wide, glabrous, deeply sulcate.

D i s t r. This species is native to the Mascarene Islands, but is cultivated in many places in India, Europe, and South Africa, mostly as a specimen plant. In Australia it is widely used as a hedge. In Ceylon it appears to exist as yet only in cultivation.

V e r n. Among 8 recorded names are: Bois chenilles, Bois cabris, Bois de bouc, and Various-leaved clerodendron.

N o t e. The pollen is described in detail by Nair & Rehman in Bull. Bot. Gard. Lucknow 76: 16 (1962).

S p e c i m e n s E x a m i n e d. KANDY DISTRICT: cultivated, Royal Botanic Garden, Peradeniya, *s. coll. s.n.* (PDA).

7. **Clerodendrum schweinfurthii** Gürke, Bot. Jahrb. Syst. 18: 177 [as "*Clerodendron*"]. 1893 var. **bakeri** (Gürke) Thomas, Gatt. Clerod. 71. 1936; Baker in Thiselt.-Dyer, Fl. Trop. Africa 5: 293 & 296. 1900; DeWild., Bull. Jard. Bot. Etat. 7: 165. 1920; Hutchins. & Dalz., Fl. W. Trop. Africa 26 (1): 273. 1931; Roberty, Pet. Fl. Ouest-Afr. 179. 1954; Chittenden, Gard. Dict. 505. 1956; Jaeger & Moldenke, Phytologia 30: 389 & 393. 1975. Type: *H.H. Johnston s.n.* from banks of the river below Stanley Pool, Zaire (BM).

Clerodendron congense Baker, Kew Bull. 1892: 127. 1892 [not *Clerodendron congense* Engl., 1887].
Clerodendron bakeri Gürke, Bot. Jahrb. Syst. 18: 175. 1893.

Low shrub, to about 1.5 m tall, often branched from the base, the branches erect or ascending, simple or few-branched, the branchlets glabrous; leaves decussate-opposite, early deciduous from the lower portions of the stems and branches; petioles short; leaf-blades membranous, uniformly green on both surfaces, oblong to elliptic or obovate, 10–15 cm long, apically cuspidate, marginally rather irregularly sharp-serrate with antrorse teeth, basally deltoid or somewhat rounded, glabrous on both surfaces; inflorescence cauliflorous, on the main stems and lower leafless parts of the branches, in dense, long-pedunculate, globose, many-flowered heads, sweetly fragrant; calyx campanulate, about 4 mm long, glabrous, lobed almost to the middle, the lobes ovate, rather shorter than the oblong tube; corolla hypocrateriform, white, its tube elongate, 3–3.6 cm long, externally glabrous, the limb 4-lobed, the lobes obovate, subequal, about 4 mm long; stamens 1.2–2 cm long.

D i s t r. A native of tropical Africa from Sierra Leone, Ivory Coast, and the Cameroons to Zaire and Uganda; occasionally cultivated for ornament, usually as a specimen plant, in some parts of Europe, the United States, and elsewhere. In Ceylon it is known thus far only from cultivated material.

N o t e. *Clerodendrum schweinfurthii* is a polymorphic and variable taxon and the present variety is only one of four that have been described.

S p e c i m e n s E x a m i n e d. KANDY DISTRICT: Royal Botanic Garden, Peradeniya, 6 July 1917, *s. coll. 125/49* (PDA); in outdoor cultivation in Students' Garden, Royal Botanic Garden, Peradeniya, 1550 ft alt., 18 Jan. 1974, sprouts from severely pruned-back stump about 4 feet tall, *H.N. & A.L. Moldenke & Jayasuriya 28158* (US), low subshrubs numbered 26.67 from Zambia, *H.N. & A.L. Moldenke & Jayasuriya 28135* (PDA, US); Royal Botanic Garden, Peradeniya, 14 May 1918, *J.M. Silva s.n.* (PDA).

8. Clerodendrum thomsonae Balf. f., Edinburgh New Philos. J., ser. 2, 15: 233–235. pl. 2 [as "*Clerodendron*"]. 1862; Hook. in Curtis, Bot. Mag. 88: pl. 5313. 1862; Balf. f., Trans. Bot. Soc. Edinburgh 7: 265–266 & 580–581, pl. 7 & 14. 1863; Baker in Thiselt.-Dyer, Fl. Trop. Africa 5: 303. 1900; Merr., Fl. Manila 401 & 402. 1912; Haines, Bot. Bihar & Orissa 4: 720. 1922; Gamble, Fl. Pres. Madras 6: 1100. 1924; Thomas, Gatt. Clerod. 60. 1936; Alston, Kandy Fl. 64. 1938; Bor & Raizada, Some Beautiful Indian Climb. 145–146, fig. 91. 1954; Cooke, Fl. Pres. Bombay, ed. 2, 2: 514. 1958; Huber in Hutchins. & Dalz., Fl. W. Trop. Africa, ed. 2, 2: 442. fig. 307. 1963; Henderson, Malay. Wild Fls. Dicot. 385. 1974. Type: Specimen collected in December, 1861 from a living plant at the Edinburgh Botanical Garden sent by the Rev. W.C. Thomson from Old Calabar, Southern Nigeria, in 1861, and named in honour of his wife, (E).

Clerodendron thomsoniae Dombrain, Fl. Mag. (London) 4: pl. 255. 1865.—*Clerodendrum thompsoni* Barton in Novak, Pict. Enc. Pl. & Fls. 405, fig. 804. 1866.—*Clerodendron thompsoni* Baines, Garden 11: 406. 1877.—*Clerodendrum thomsonianum* Ball. ex Edgeworth, Pollen, ed. 1, 76 & 94, pl. 6, fig. 101. 1877.—*Clerodendron thompsoni* Balf. ex Scott in Solered., Syst. Anat. Dicot. 1: 631. 1908.—*Clerodendron thomsonae* Balf. ex Kawakami, List Pl. Formos. 84. 1910.—*Clerodendron thompsonae* Balf. ex N.L. Britton, Fl. Bermuda 318. 1918.—*Cherodendron thomsonae* Balf. f. ex H.J. Lam, Bot. Jahrb. Syst. 59: 28, sphalm. 1924.—*Clerodendron thomsonea* Schwencke, Zytol. Untersuch. Verbenac. 7 & 19. 1931.—*Clorodendrum thompsonae* Navarro Haydon, Fl. Com. Puerto Rico [8], sphalm. 1936.—*Clerodendron thompsoneae* Balf. ex Moldenke, Prelim. Alph. List Invalid Names 22, in syn. 1940.—*Clerodendron thompsonii* Balf. ex Moldenke, Prelim. Alph. List Invalid Names 22, in syn. 1940.—*Clerodendron thomsonii* Balf. ex Moldenke, Prelim. Alph. List Invalid Names 22, in syn. 1940.—*Clerodendron thompsoni* Hort. ex Moldenke, Suppl. List Invalid Names 2, in syn. 1941.— *Clerodendron thomsonae* Hook. ex Moldenke, Suppl. List Invalid Names 2, in syn. 1941.—*Clerodendron thomasonae* Balt. ex Matuda, Amer. Midl. Naturalist 44: 675, sphalm. 1950.—*Clerodendrum thompsonae* Balf. ex Soukup, Biota 4: 175. 1962.—*Clerodendrum thomsoniae* Balf. ex Menninger, Seaside Pl. 158, pl. 231. 1964.—*Clerodendron thomasei* Harrison, Know Your Trees 57, pl. 150. 1965.—*Clerodendrum thompsoniae* Balf. ex Elliovson, Compl. Gard. Book South. Hemisph., ed. 6, 16, 160, & 235. 1970.—*Clerodendrum thomsonsoniae* Balf. f. ex Encke & Buchh. in Zender, Handwörterb. Pflanzennam., ed. 10, 180. 1972.

Clerodendron thomsoniae var. *balfourii* Jacks. ex Dombrain, Fl. Mag. (London) 4: pl. 255. 1865.—*Clerodendron thompsoni* var. *balfouri* Dombrain, Fl. Mag. (London) 8: pl. 432. 1869.—*Clerodendron thompsoni* var. *balfourianum* Hort. ex Moldenke, Résumé 270, in syn. 1959.—*Clerodendron thompsonae balfourii* Harler, Gard. Plains, ed. 4, 23. 1962.—*Clerodendrum* "*thompsonae C. balfouri*" D'Arcy, Rhodora 69: 438. 1967.

Clerodendron balfouri Dombrain, Fl. Mag. (London) 8: pl. 432. 1869.—*Clerodendron balfourii* Hort. ex E.G. Britton, Addisonia 6: 39. 1921.—*Clerodendron balfourianum* Massart *et al.*, Miss. Biol. Belg. Brés. 1922–23, 1: fig. 52. 1929.—*Clerodendron balfonia* Hort. ex Moldenke, Prelim. Alph. List Invalid Names 18, in syn. 1940.—*Clerodendron balfourae* Hort. ex Moldenke, Prelim. Alph. List Invalid Names 18, in syn. 1940.—*Clerodendron balfouriae* Hort. ex Moldenke, Prelim. Alph. List Invalid Names 18, in syn. 1940.—*Clerodendron balfouriana* Hort. ex Moldenke, Prelim. Alph. List Invalid Names 18, in syn. 1940.—*Clerodendrum balfouri* Hort. ex Moldenke, Suppl. List Invalid Names 2, in syn. 1941.

Clerodendron calycosum Bauman ex Moldenke, Résumé 261, in syn. 1959 [not *C. calycosum* Son, 1959].

High-climbing herbaceous or woody vine or liana, to 7 m long or more, rarely a low shrub 2–2.5 m tall; branchlets slender, greyish, obtusely tetragonal, glabrate; twigs slender, brown or purplish, densely puberulent; leaf-scars often large and circular, borne on prominent sterigmata about 1 mm long, corky; nodes not annulate; principal internodes 1.3–9 cm long; leaves decussate-opposite; petioles slender, 8–35 mm long, minutely puberulent with purplish hairs; leaf-blades thin-chartaceous or membranous, dark-green above, lighter beneath, often nigrescent in drying, elliptic or elliptic-ovate, 6–14.5 cm long, 3–7 cm wide, apically short-acuminate, marginally entire, basally rounded or subacute, glabrate on both surfaces or slightly pulverulent along the larger venation; inflorescence axillary, cymose, abundant near the apex of the twigs; cymes solitary, opposite, spreading, 5–9 cm long, 4–8.5 cm wide, loosely flowered; peduncles slender, 2.6–6.5 cm long, densely puberulent; pedicels very slender, 7–16 mm long, puberulent; large bracts none; bractlets and prophylla linear, 2–11 mm long, to 1 mm wide, or subulate, puberulent; calyx pale yellowish-green, changing to cream-colour and then pure white during anthesis, fading to yellow or pink, or the calyx reddish [f. *speciosum* (Teijsm. & Binn.) Voss], more or less pentagonal during anthesis, 1.8–2 cm long, puberulent, deeply 4-fid to 4/5th the length, the lobes broadly ovate, 8–10 mm wide, apically acute or short-acuminate; corolla hypocrateriform, varying from deep rose [f. *speciosum*], dark red, deep red, or bright red to cardinal red, scarlet, or crimson, its tube very slender, about 2.5 cm long, the lobes of the limb wide-spreading or reflexed, 6–10 mm long, 3.5–4 mm wide; stamens long-exserted; fruiting-calyx faded rose-colour; fruit drupaceous, glossy-black externally, with a brilliant red aril uniting the 4 pyrenes, Chromosome number: $2n = 42, 46, 48,$ or 50.

D i s t r. This is a west tropical African species native from Senegambia to Zaire, now cultivated for ornament almost throughout the world, outdoors in tropical and subtropical regions, in greenhouses elsewhere. It is widely escaped and naturalized in tropical countries of both hemispheres. The especially floriferous cultivated form is often known as var. *delectum* Bailey and a form with the leaves variegated by blotches of yellowish-white is var. *variegatum* Bailey.

U s e s. In Guiana the leaves and flowers of *C. thomsonae* are pounded and then applied to cuts and bruises. In west Africa magic powers are attributed to the plant. It contains both tannin and a saponin. It is easily propagated by layering.

V e r n. Among the over 50 names recorded are: Bleeding heart, glorybower, Danish-flag, Magic-flower, Southern bleedingheart, Thomson glorybower and White bleedingheart.

S p e c i m e n s E x a m i n e d. KANDY DISTRICT: cultivated, Royal, Botanic Garden, Peradeniya, May 1887, *s. coll. s.n.* (PDA), 6 July 1917, *s. coll. 125/49* (PDA).

9. Clerodendrum splendens G. Don ex James, Edinburgh New Philos. J. 11: 349. 1824; Paxt., Paxton's Mag. Bot. 9: 103. 1842; Schau. in A. DC., Prod. 11: 662 & 672. 1847; Hook. f. & Benth. in Hook., Niger Fl. 486. 1849; Baker in Thiselt.-Dyer, Fl. Trop. Africa 5: 300–301. 1900; DeWild., Ann. Mus. Congo, ser. 5, 3: 137. 1909; DeWild., Bull. Jard. Bot. Etat 7: 175. 1920; Hutchins. & Dalz., Fl. W. Trop. Africa 273. 1931; Thomas, Gatt. Clerod. 56–58. 1936; Maheshwari, Fl. Delhi 284. 1963; Burkill, Dict. Econ. Prod. Malay Penins. 1: 589. 1966; Jaeger & Moldenke, Phytologia 30: 395–397 & 406. 1975. Type: *G. Don s.n.* from Sierra Leone (BM).

Clerodendron aurantium G. Don, Edinburgh New Philos. J. 11: 349. 1824.—
   Clerodendrum aurantium G. Don ex Thomas, Gatt. Clerod. 57, in syn.
   1936.
Clerodendron speciosum Hort. ex Carrière, Rev. Hort. 1873: 471. 1873 [not *C.
   speciosum* Dombrain, 1869].
Clerodendron rollissoni Hort. ex Carrière, Rev. Hort. 1873: 471, in syn. 1873.
Clerodendron speciosum var. *rollissoni* Hort. ex Carrière, Rev. Hort. 1873:
   471, in syn. 1873.
Clerodendron splendens Hort. ex Baines, Garden (London) 11: 404. 1877.—
   Clerodendron splendens G. Don apud Jacks. in Hook. f. & Jacks., Ind.
   Kew., imp. 1, 1: 562. 1893.—*Cleredendrom splendens* G. Don ex Espirito
   Santo, Junt. Invest. Ultramar Est. Ens. & Docum. 104: 41, sphalm. 1963.—
   Cleredendron splendens G. Don ex Espirito Santo, Junt. Invest. Ultramar
   Est. Ens. & Docum. 104: 80, sphalm. 1963.—*Clerodendron splendens* Hehl.
   ex Malaviya, Proc. Indian Acad. Sci., ser. B, 58: 351, sphalm. 1963.—
   Clerodendron splendens Gaertn. ex Shah, Canad. J. Bot. 46: [169]. 1968.—
   Clerodendron splendens (Thunb.) G. Don ex Backer & Bakh., Fl. Java 3:
   657. 1968.
Siphonanthus splendens (G. Don) Hiern, Cat. Afr. Pl. Welw. 4: 841. 1900.—
   S. splendens Hiern apud Thiselt.-Dyer, Ind. Kew. Suppl. 2: 172. 1904.
Siphonanthus splendens var. *bakeri* Hiern, Cat. Afr. Pl. Welw. 4: 841–842.
   1900.

   Shrub or twining woody vine, usually scrambling or climbing to 5 m over
other vegetation; branchlets slender, more or less acutely tetragonal, brownish, finely pubescent or very minutely puberulent with appressed brownish
hairs; nodes not annulate; principal internodes 3–7 cm long; leaves decussate-opposite or approximate; petioles slender, 8–20 mm long, minutely
puberulent like the branchlets, sometimes spinescent basally [var. *giletti*
(DeWild. & Durand) Thomas]; leaf-blades thin-membranous or subchartaceous, dark green and rather shiny above, paler and bright green beneath, elliptic or elliptic-ovate to ovate-oblong, oblong-orbicular, suborbicular, or even
narrowly lanceolate, 5–18 cm long, 3–8 cm wide, apically acuminate,
marginally entire or undulate, basally cordate, varying (in var. *giletti*) to
subtruncate, rounded, or acute, glabrous on both surfaces or (in var. *puberulentum* Moldenke) minutely puberulent or (in var. *pubescens* Moldenke)
pubescent beneath, sparsely subimpressed-punctate beneath and basally
with patelliform extra-floral nectaries; inflorescence in corymbose cymes,
supra-axillary and terminal, showy, 7–11 cm long, 6–8 cm wide, brachiate, many-flowered, usually dense, often only a few at or near the apex
of the branchlets, usually minutely puberulent throughout; peduncles relatively stoutish, 1.5–3.5 cm long, brownish, densely puberulent; pedicels
very slender, 3–10 mm long, mostly densely puberulent; foliaceous bracts

none; bractlets and prophylla narrow-lanceolate to linear or linear-subulate, 1–5 mm long or less; calyx elongate-campanulate, about 1 cm long, glabrate or subglabrate, sometimes decidedly puberulent (in vars. *puberulentum & pubescens*), divided to about 1/2 its length, the 4 or 5 lobes broadly triangular, apically long-acuminate (or to 7 mm long, narrow basally and long-caudate-attenuate apically in var. *longicuspe* Moldenke); corolla hypocrateriform, showy and conspicuous, externally subglabrous, deep-red to crimson, the tube very slender, about 2 cm long, the lobes oblong-elliptic, 1–1.5 cm long, 6–7 mm wide, rounded apically, circinate in bud; stamens exserted about 3 cm from the corolla-mouth; filaments yellow or pink, glabrous; anthers basally attached, narrow-elliptic, bluish; fruiting-calyx accrescent, red; drupe black, shiny; seeds black, enclosed in an orange pulp. Chromosome number: 2n = 46.

D i s t r. This is an extremely beautiful species, native of western and central Africa from Mali and Sénégal to Angola, Zaire, and Tanzania; now rather widely cultivated for ornament in various warm parts of Asia, Africa, Australia, and the West Indies and as a specimen plant in Europe and North America. In Ceylon it is known thus far only from cultivation, but tends to spread rapidly and escape.

U s e s. In Africa the leaves, as well as a lotion made from them, are applied to bruises and sores; in Ghana dried powdered leaves are applied to blisters caused by burns. In Zaire a black dye is made from the leaves, and in Nigeria they are the source of a magic potion.

V e r n. Eight names have been recorded for the typical form of this species in Africa, including; Adabi and Geakoi.

N o t e. The pollen is described by Nair & Rehman in Bull. Bot. Gard. Lucknow 76: 15 (1962).

S p e c i m e n s   E x a m i n e d. KANDY DISTRICT: Royal Botanic Garden, Peradeniya, April 1887, *s. coll. 14* (PDA); in outdoor cultivation on arbour in Pergola Garden and in Students' Garden, Royal Botanic Garden, Peradeniya, 1550 ft alt., 18 Jan. 1974, plant climbing, corollas scarlet, *H.N. & A.L. Moldenke & Jayasuriya 28133* (AAU, CAI, LL, PDA, US).

10. Clerodendrum umbellatum Poir. in Lam., Enc. 5: 166. 1804; Schau. in A. DC., Prod. 11: 662 & 673. 1847; Thw. Enum. Pl. Zeyl. 243. 1861; Baker in Thiselt.-Dyer, Fl. Trop. Africa 5: 304. 1900; DeWild., Ann. Mus. Congo, ser. 5, 3: 136. 1909; DeWild., Bull. Jard. Bot. Etat. 7: 173. 1920; Hutchins. & Dalz., Fl. W. Trop. Africa 2 (1): 273. 1931; Thomas, Gatt. Clerod. 58. 1936. Type: *Smeathman s.n.* from west Africa (P).

Clerodendrum scandens Beauv., Fl. Oware & Benin 2: 6–7, pl. 62. 1810.—*Clerodendron scandens* Beauv. apud Schau. in A. DC., Prod. 11: 662. 1847 [not *Clerodendron scandens* (L. f.) Druce, 1917].—*Clerodendron scandens*

Schau. ex Voss in Vilm., Blumengärt. 1: 830, in syn. 1895.—*Clerodendoron scandens* Gledhill, Check List Fl. Pl. Sierra Leone 30, sphalm. 1962.— *Clerodendron scandens* Poir. ex Corner & Watanabe, Ill. Guide Trop. Pl. 757. 1969.

Clerodendrum hirsutum G. Don, Edinburgh New Philos. J. 11: 349. 1824.— *Clerodendron hirsutum* G. Don apud Schau. in A. DC., Prod. 11: 673. 1847 [not *Clerodendron hirsutum* Pears., 1901, nor (Hochst.) H. H. W. Pearson, 1900].—*Clerodendron hirsutum* D. Don ex Moldenke, Phytologia 36: 41, in syn. 1977.

Clerodendrum simplex G. Don, Edinburgh New Philos. J. 11: 349. 1824.— *Clerodendron simplex* G. Don apud Schau. in A. DC., Prod. 11: 673. 1847.—*Clerodendron simplex* S. Don ex Schum., Justs Bot. Jahresber. 28 (1): 496, sphalm. 1902.

Clerodendrum unbellatum var. *umbellatum* Poir. ex Lewalle, Bull. Jard. Bot. Etat. 42: [231]. 1972.

A high-climbing vine to 6 m tall or a woody, weakly scandent, rambling, or clambering shrub, rarely small and suberect, 0.4–1.5 m tall, with decumbent branches [var. *centrale* (A. Chev.) Moldenke]; stems and branches rather slender, obtusely tetragonal, often several m long, densely brownish-puberulent or short-pubescent, less so in age; branchlets and twigs slender, brownish, acutely tetragonal, finely or densely puberulent with very minute appressed brownish hairs; nodes not annulate; principal internodes 1.5–7.5 cm long; leaf-scars often large and prominently raised; leaves decussate-opposite or rarely approximate; petioles rather slender, 0.3–8 cm long, caniculate above, densely puberulent or short-pubescent with minute appressed purplish hairs; leaf-blades thin-chartaceous or membranous, rarely somewhat thicker, bright-green on both surfaces or dark green above and somewhat lighter beneath, mostly brunnescent in drying, shiny, ovate or elliptic-ovate to elliptic or oblong, 3.5–20 cm long, 2.3–12.1 cm wide, apically short-acuminate (or sometimes merely acute on smaller leaves) or rarely caudate, marginally entire, basally obtuse or rounded to subcordate or cordate, glabrate on both surfaces and impressed-punctate beneath or rather sparsely puberulent above with scattered hairs and much more densely puberulent or finely pubescent beneath, sometimes coarsely pubescent on both surfaces [var. *asperifolium* (Thomas) Moldenke] or even tomentose on both surfaces [var. *gossweileri* Cavaco], sometimes the pubescent lower surface with many glistening golden glands [var. *congense* (Engl.) Moldenke]; inflorescence axillary or supra-axillary, cymose, aggregated into a terminal panicle at the branch tips, the individual cymes lax, few-flowered, or several times brachiate with the ultimate branches bearing many distinctly alternate long-pedicellate flowers, 4–11 cm long, 3–9 cm wide, the terminal panicles ample, loosely or densely many-flowered in subumbelloid fashion, divaricate or sometimes bifurcate, to 30 cm long and 24 cm wide; peduncles slender, 2.5–6 cm long, densely puberulent or short-pubescent (as are also the inflorescence-branches) with very minute appressed brownish or purplish hairs; pedicels very slender and wiry, elongate, 5–15 mm long, often longer than the calyx, densely puberulent; a few foliaceous bracts occasionally present, large, narrow-elliptic, to 2 cm long and 5 mm wide, stipitate, puberulent on both surfaces, caducous; bractlets and prophylla linear, filiform, or setaceous, 1–5 mm long, puberulent; flowers showy, fragrant; calyx green to yellowish-green below, cream-colour or white above during anthesis, sometimes turning pale-pink, cupuliform, 7–13 mm long, finely pubescent or tomentose [var. *gossweileri*], the tube campanulate, the limb deeply cleft into 5 lobes, the lobes ovate or lanceolate, usually about 1 cm long, as long as or longer than the tube, whitish, apically acute; corolla hypocrateriform, mostly white with a pinkish or reddish throat, varying to pink, rose, or mauve or (in the cultivated form) red or dark red to scarlet or crimson, the tube 13–22 mm long, puberulous or subglabrate and with many glistening golden glands [var. *congense*], the lobes 5, obovate, subequal, about 8 mm long, shorter than the tube, apically acute; stamens long-exserted, 2.5–3.8 cm long; filaments purple; anthers yellow; fruiting-calyx red or rose-purple to violet or purple; drupes magenta or bluish-black, separating into 4 pyrenes at maturity. Chromosome number: $2n = 24$ or 48.

D i s t r. This is a rather perplexing and apparently variable species native from Mali, Sénégal, and Ghana to Zaire, Kenya, Tanzania, and Angola, widely cultivated in both hemispheres and naturalized in Florida, the West Indies, Brazil, India, Malaya, the Philippines, Indonesia, and elsewhere.

U s e s. *Clerodendrum umbellatum* is widely employed in native medicines in west Africa. The leaves yield a black dye. A leaf decoction is used to treat stomach-ache and the plant is employed in treating cases of rheumatism. The bitter leaves and leaf-juice are used medicinally in Sierra Leone. The leaf-pulp is employed as an enema to hasten the expulsion of the placenta in childbirth. In cases of snakebite in the Ivory Coast the juice of the crushed leaves along with a plaster made from the leaf-pulp are placed on open wounds.

V e r n. Among the 25 names recorded from various parts of its range are: Bleeding-heart, Broken heart, Coração de Jesus, Glory-bower, Lagrima de Miranda and Ursulina.

N o t e s. In Africa collectors mostly describe its corollas as white, but the commonly cultivated form usually has scarlet corollas. The cultivated form is usually referred to as *C. speciosum* Teijsm. & Binn., but according to the colour illustration of that taxon given by Lemaire in Ill. Hort. 16: pl. 593 (1869) this seems to be nothing more than a colour form of *C. thomsonae* Balf. f. [*C. thomsonae* f. *speciosum* (Teijsm. & Binn.) Voss] and not a hybrid between *C. thomsonae* and *C. splendens* G. Don. Still, it is very possible that the scarlet-flowered cultivated plant does represent a hybrid of some sort and deserves nomenclatural recognition. More genetic research is clearly indicated here. Possibly the two chromosomal counts recorded are correlated with the corolla colour. The leaves of this plant are sometimes attacked by the parasitic fungi, *Meliola clerodendri* Hans. and *M. clerodendricola* P. Henn.

Specimens Examined. KANDY DISTRICT: Royal Botanic Garden, Peradeniya, April 1887, *s. coll. s.n.* (PDA); Ibid, 6 July 1918, *s. coll. s.n.* (PDA); in outdoor cultivation in Rock Garden, Royal Botanic Garden, Peradeniya, 1550 ft alt., 18 Jan. 1974, corolla magenta, calyx dull-magenta, *H.N. & A.L. Moldenke & Jayasuriya 28174* (LL, PDA, US). RATNAPURA DISTRICT: isolated plant in outdoor cultivation on arbor, Pelwadiya, low altitude, 12 February 1974, climbing vine, calyx white, corolla scarlet, *H.N. & A.L. Moldenke, Dassanayake, & Jayasuriya 28343* (PDA, US); persistent after cultivation or escaped in waste ground of abandoned lot, Pelwadiya, low altitude, 12 Feb. 1974, calyx and fruit purple, *H. N. & A. L. Moldenke, Dassanayake, & Jayasuriya 28345* (KARACHI, LL, PDA, US).

11. Clerodendrum wallichii Merr., J. Arnold Arbor. 23: 220 [as *"Clerodendron"*]. 1952; Schau. in A. DC., Prod. 11: 663. 1847; Clarke in Hook. f., Fl. Br. Ind. 4: 591. 1885; Gamble, Man. Indian Timb., ed. 2, 543. 1902; Brandis, Indian Trees 508. 1906; MacMillan, Trop. Plant. & Gard., ed. 4, 104 & 514. 1935; Alston, Kandy Fl. 64. 1938; Bor & Raizada, Some Beautiful Indian Climb. 152–153, fig. 96. 1954; Cooke, Fl. Pres. Bombay, ed. 2, 2: 513. 1958; Prain, Bengal Pl., ed. 2, 2: 623. 1963; Backer & Bakh., Fl. Java 2: 611. 1965; Burkill, Dict. Econ. Prod. Malay Penins. 1: 589 & 594. 1966; Raizada, Indian Forester 94: 437 & 455. 1968. Type: *Wallich 1793* from Silut [=Sylhet, Bangladesh] in the British East India Company Herbarium (K).

Clerodendron nutans Wall., Num. List [49], no. 1793, hyponym. 1829; Wall. ex D. Don, Prod. Fl. Nepal 103 [as *"Clerodendrum"*]. 1825 [not *Clerodendron nutans* Jack, 1820].—*Clerodendron nutans* "Wall. ex Don" apud Bor & Raizada, Some Beautiful Indian Climb. 152. 1954.—*Clerodendron mitans* Wall. ex Moldenke, Résumé 267, in syn. 1959.—*Clerodendron nutans* D. Don ex Backer & Bakh., Fl. Java 2: 611, in syn. 1965.

Clerodendron laevifolium H.J. Lam apud Lam & Bakh., Bull. Jard. Bot. Buitenzorg, ser. 3, 3: 81, in syn. 1921 [not *Clerodendron laevifolium* Bakh., 1947, nor Decaisne, 1942, nor *Clerodendrum laevifolium* Blume, 1826].

Volkameria cernua Shepherd ex Moldenke, Prelim. Alph. List Invalid Names 53, in syn. 1940.

Volkameria pendula Wall. ex Moldenke, Prelim. Alph. List Invalid Names 53, in syn. 1940.

Clerodendron wallichii Merr., J. Arnold Arbor. 33: 220. 1952.

Bush, subshrub, or slender shrub, to 3 m tall; stems or branches usually simple and arching, sometimes more or less flexuous or brachiate near the apex, grey-brown, acutely tetragonal and usually very shortly 4-margined on the angles, glabrate (except for the nodes), often half-prostrate and shrubby only at the base; nodes annulate with a ring of hirsute hairs, sometimes obscurely puberulent just above and below the annulation; principal internodes 2–6 cm long; leaves decussate-opposite or ternate; petioles rather slender, 7–10 mm long, glabrate; leaf-blades very thin-chartaceous or membranous, rather dark green and shiny on both surfaces or somewhat lighter beneath, very narrowly oblong, oblong-lanceolate, or lanceolate to oblong-oblanceolate or obovate, 7.5–28 cm long, 1.4–4 cm wide, apically rather long-acuminate or caudate, marginally entire but usually more or less undulate, basally acute or subcuneate, glabrate on both surfaces, more or less punctate beneath; inflorescence terminal, paniculate, nutant, 10–53 cm long, 6–14 cm wide, loosely many-flowered, composed of 7–9 pairs of opposite, divaricate cymes, glabrate and usually nigrescent throughout in drying, the lowermost cymes usually borne in the axils of the uppermost leaves, each cyme 1–5-flowered; peduncles slender, glabrate, 1.9–5.8 cm long; sympodia and inflorescence-branches slender and usually elongate; pedicels very slender, 4–10 mm long, glabrate; bracts usually numerous, mostly large and foliaceous, a pair subtending each pair of cymes, similar to the leaves in all respects but rapidly diminishing in size as the apex of the inflorescence is approached; bractlets and prophylla linear or setaceous, 1–4 mm long, glabrate; calyx ventricose, 5-angled, varying from dark red or reddish to dark purple or brownish, about 8 mm long, 5-fid to about the middle, the lobes oval, wide-spreading, apically rather acute; corolla hypocrateriform, white or whitish to greenish-white or cream-colour, its tube infundibular, about 1 1/2 times the length of the calyx, usually about 1.5 cm long, very lightly farinaceous externally, the lobes obovate, widely separated, reflexed, about equalling the tube in length; stamens lightly tinted with pink or blue, protruding 2.5–4 cm beyond the corollamouth, ascending; style shorter than the filaments; fruiting-calyx accrescent, stellately spreading, red, about equalling the black drupes in length. Chromosome number: $2n = 52$.

D i s t r. This handsome species is native from Himalayan India, Pakistan, Bhutan, and Sikkim to Burma and Indo-China, south to the Nicobar Islands and north to southern China. It is widely cultivated in all tropical and semi-tropical countries and in greenhouses elsewhere. It has escaped and become naturalized in parts of the West Indies and Venezuela. It is employed in the manufacture of wreaths in the Samoan Islands.

V e r n. Among the 25 recorded names in various parts of its range are: Canastilla, Fire-bush, Martinica, Misteriosa, Nodding tube-flower, Ramo de novias, Santa Alda and Unting unting.

S p e c i m e n s   E x a m i n e d. KURUNEGALA DISTRICT: in outdoor cultivation by Rest House, Kurunegala, 300 ft alt., 16 Jan. 1974, shrubs 8 ft tall, corolla white, *H.N. & A.L. Moldenke, Jayasuriya, & Sumithraarachchi 28129* (LL, PDA, US). KANDY DISTRICT: Royal Botanic Garden, Peradeniya, May 1887, *s. coll. s.n.* (PDA); ibid., 17 July 1900, *s. coll. s.n.* (PDA).

12. Clerodendrum minahassae Teijsm. & Binn., Natuurk. Tijdschr. Ned.-Indie 25: 490 [as "*Clerodendron*"]. 1863; Merr., Fl. Manila 401 & 402. 1912; Heyne, Nutt. Pl. Ned.-Ind., ed. 1, 4: 121. 1917; Hallier, Meded. Rijks-Herb. 37: 76. 1918; H.J. Lam, Verbenac. Malay. Arch. 314–315. 1919; MacMillan, Trop. Plant. Gard., ed. 5, 104 & 105. 1943; Backer & Bakh., Fl. Java 2: 608. 1965; Burkill, Dict. Econ. Prod. Malay Penins. 1: 589 & 590. 1966; Corner & Watanabe, Ill. Guide Trop. Pl. 755. 1969; Menninger, Colour Sky 35 & [166], pl. 132. 1975. Type: Based on *Teijsmann 5298, 5774,* and *5868* from Celebes, Indonesia (BO).

Clerodendron infortunatum F.-Vill., Nov. App. 161. 1882 [not *Clerodendron infortunatum* Auct., 1963, nor Blume, 1947, nor Gaertn., 1788, nor Lam., 1942, nor Lindl., 1918, nor Lour., 1793, nor Schau., 1918, nor Walp., 1843, nor Wight, 1850, nor *Clerodendrum infortunata* L., 1753, nor *Clerodendrum infortunatum* Auct., 1955, nor Blume, 1907, nor Dennst., 1959, nor Gaertn., 1965, nor Lour., 1935, nor Miq., 1968, nor Vent., 1821, nor Willd., 1976].

Siphobaea commersoni Baill., Hist. Pl. 10: 106. 1888.—*Siphoboea commersonii* Baill. apud Durand & Jacks., Ind. Kew. Suppl. 1, imp. 1, 400. 1906.—*Siphobaea commersonii* Baill. ex Moldenke, Fifth. Summ. 2: 621, in syn. 1971.

Clerodendron minahassae Teijsm. & Binn., Natuurk. Tijdschr. Ned. Indie 25: 490. 1863.—*Clerodendron minahassae* Merr., Bur. Govt. Labs. Philipp. Bull. 35: 62, in syn. 1915.—*Clerodendron minahassae* Miq. ex Moldenke, Résumé Suppl. 3: 30, in syn. 1962.—*Clerodendron minahassae* Teijsm. ex Malaviya, Proc. Indian Acad. Sci., ser. B, 352. 1963.—*Clerodendrum minnahassee* Buswell ex Moldenke, Alph. List Invalid Names Suppl. 1: 7, in syn. 1947.—*Clerodendrom minahassae* Teijsm. & Binn. ex Menninger, 1960 Price List Fl. Trees [3], sphalm. 1960.—*Clerodendrum minhassae* Teijsm. & Binn. ex Menninger, Fl. Trees World 282, sphalm. 1962.

Clerodendron minahassae var. *typicum* H. J. Lam, Verbenac. Malay. Arch. 315. 1919.

Clerodendron calycinum Zipp. ex H.J. Lam, Verbenac. Malay. Arch. 315, in syn. 1919.

Clerodendron minahassae var. *hypocum* H.J. Lam, in herb.

A shrub, 1–3 m tall, or a small tree to 6 m tall; trunk to 7.5 cm in diameter; bark pale grey; branchlets slender or stoutish, medullose, very obtusely tetragonal, glabrate, often shiny, lenticellate; nodes not annulate; principal internodes 2–7 cm long; leaves decussate-opposite; petioles slender, 0.5–7.5 cm long, very minutely and obscurely puberulent or subglabrate; leaf-blades chartaceous, dark- or bright-green above, slightly lighter beneath, elliptic or oblong to ovate-oblong, 7.5–27.5 cm long, 3–13 cm wide, apically attenuate-acute or short-acuminate, marginally entire, basally obtuse or rounded (rarely subacute) to truncate or subcordate, minutely pulverulent on both surfaces, especially along the larger venation; inflorescence cymose, the cymes 1-many-flowered, aggregated into an abbreviated few- to many-flowered terminal panicle, 5–12 cm long (not including the corollas during anthesis) and 4.5–5 cm wide; peduncles and sympodia short, minutely pulverulent-puberulent or glabrate; pedicels stout, 0.8–2.5 cm long, minutely pulverulent or glabrate; foliaceous bracts none; bractlets and prophylla inconspicuous, linear-subulate, 1–3 mm long, puberulent; flowers with a spicy fragrance, very large; calyx in bud filled with water, during anthesis fleshy, green or yellowish-green, tubular, 1.5–2.5 cm long or (in var. *brevitubulosum* H.J. Lam) 2.5–3.5 cm long or (in var. *grandicalyx* Moldenke) to 4 cm long, 8–10 mm wide, incised less than 1/2 its length, apically often red or reddish, glabrous or short-pubescent externally; corolla very long, hypocrateriform, the tube narrow-cylindric, creamy- or yellowish-white or light yellow, glabrous, 5–8.5 cm long (in var. *brevitubulosum*) or 8.5–10.2 cm long (in var. *minahassae*) or even to 11 cm long (in var. *grandicalyx*), the lobes white or streaked with pink, 2.5–4 cm long, to 1.3 cm wide; filaments and style white or else pink or purple and becoming whitish basally; fruiting-calyx fleshy, accrescent, maroon to red or blood-red, the sharply acute or acuminate lobes becoming widely divaricate in stellate fashion, often to 5 cm across; drupes blue-green to torquoise-blue or purple. Chromosome number: 2n = 52.

D i s t r. This very variable species is native to the Philippine Islands and Indonesia; also known from Singapore and in cultivation in many parts of tropical Asia, the Hawaiian Islands, Florida, the West Indies, and (in greenhouses) Europe.

U s e s. The leaves of this species are used as "greens" in parts of Indonesia. In the Philippines it is regarded as medicinal and used in the treatment of stomach-ache.

V e r n. Among some 25 vernacular names reported for *C. minahassae* are: Fairchild's clerodendrum, Ku-ku and Sunkol.

N o t e s. It propagates readily from seeds or cuttings. The pollen has been described in detail by Nair & Rehman in Bull. Bot. Gard. Lucknow 76: 15 (1962).

The leaves are sometimes attacked by the parasitic fungi, *Meliola clerodendricola* P. Henn. and *Puccinia erebis* Syd.

The names, *Clerodendron fortunatum* Blanco and *C. blancoi* Naves are often placed in the synonymy of the typical form of *C. minahassae*, but actually belong in that of var. *brevitubulosum*, while *Volkameria grandiflora* Blanco, also sometimes placed here, is a synonym of *C. macrostegium* Schau.

S p e c i m e n s E x a m i n e d. KANDY DISTRICT: severely pruned-back stump cultivated in the Students' Garden, Royal Botanic Garden, Peradeniya, 1550 ft alt., 18 Jan. 1974, sprouts 5 ft tall, *H.N. & A.L. Moldenke & Jayasuriya 28168* (US); cultivated, University of Sri Lanka Botany Department gardens, Peradeniya, 1600 ft alt., 12 Dec. 1973, 8–12 ft tall, flowers white, *D.B. & B. Sumithraarachchi DBS. 78* (US); Royal Botanic Garden, Peradeniya, Feb. 1888, *s. coll. s.n.* (PDA).

13. Clerodendrum speciosissimum Van. Geert ex Morren, Hort. Belge 3: 322–323, pl. 68 [as *"Clerodendron"*]. 1836. f. **speciosissimum**. Schau. in A. DC., Prod. 11: 666–667. 1847; H. Hallier, Meded. Rijks-Herb. 37: 80. 1918; H.J. Lam, Verbenac. Malay. Arch. 300–302. 1919; Junell, Symb. Bot. Upsal. 4: 101–209. 1934; Bailey, Man. Cult. Pl., ed. 2, 845. 1949; Encke, Pareys Blumengärt., ed. 2, 447–448. 1960; Graf, Exotica 3: 1480. 1963; Backer & Bakh., Fl. Java 2: 612. 1965; Encke, Schönst. Kalt & Warmhauspfl. 394. 1968; Corner & Watanabe, Ill. Guide Trop. Pl. 754. 1969; B.C. Stone, Micronesica 6: 505. 1970. Type: a Morren collection taken from material given him by Baron Taffin from the Van Geert garden at Ghent, Belgium, August 1835, originally from "des Indes" (BR).

Clerodendron speciosissimum Van Geert ex Morren, Hort. Belge 3: 322. 1836 [not *Clerodendron speciosissimum* Hort., 1975, nor Hort. Angl., 1847].—*Clerodendron speciosissimum* Paxt., Bot. Mag. 3: 217 & 271. 1837.—*Clerodendron speciosissimum* Van Beert ex Bowden, Amer. J. Bot. 32: 195, sphalm. 1945.—*Clerodendron speciosissimus* Everett, Readers Digest Compl. Book Gard. 422, sphalm. 1966.—*Clerodendrum speciosissimum* "Van Geert ex Morren" apud C.D. Adams, Fl. Pl. Pamaic. 636 & 809. 1972.—*Clerodendrum speciosissima* Beames & Key, ABC Indoor Pl. 55, fig. 71, sphalm. 1973.—*Clerodendron speciosissimum* "Van Geer ex Morren", in herb.

Clerodendron fallax Lindl., Bot. Reg. 30: 19. 1844.—*Clerodendrum fallax* Hassk. ex H. Hallier, Meded. Rijks-Herb. 37: 80, in syn. 1918.—*Clerodendron fallax* Schau. ex Moldenke, Résumé 263, in syn. 1959.—*Clerodendrum fallax* Hort. ex Encke & Buchheim in Zander, Handwörterb. Pflanzennam., ed. 10, 180. 1972.

Clerodendron fallax var. *superbum* Ayres in Moore & Ayres, Mag. Bot. 1: 101. 1850.

Clerodendron pulchrum Fawc. in Forbes, Nat. Wand. East. Arch. 514. 1885.

Clerodendron infortunatum Bot. Reg. ex Voss in Vilm., Blumengärt. 1: 831, in syn. 1895 [not *Clerodendron infortunatum* Auct., 1963, nor Blume, 1918,

nor F.-Vill., 1882, nor Gaertn., 1885, nor Lam., 1947, nor Lour., 1793, nor
Schau., 1847, nor Walp., 1843, nor Wight, 1850].—*Clerodendrum infortunatum* Lindl. ex H. Hallier, Meded. Rijks-Herb. 37: 80, in syn. 1918.

Clerodendron infortunatum var. *splendens* Voss in Vilm., Blumengärt. 1: 831.
1895.

Clerodendron greyi Baker in Thiselt.-Dyer, Fl. Trop. Africa 5: 308. 1900.

Clerodendron buchanani var. *fallax* (Lindl.) Bakh., Bull. Jard. Bot. Buitenzorg,
ser. 3, 3: 92. 1921.—*Clerodendrum buchanani* var. *fallax* (Lindl.) Bakh. ex
Moldenke, Résumé 140 *et seq.* 1959.

Clerodendron squamatum Rock apud O. Degener, Fl. Hawaii. fam. 315 sub
Clerodendrum fallax, in syn. 1934 [not *Clerodendrum squamatum* Vahl,
1791].—*Clerodendron squamatum* Neal & Metzger apud O. Degener, Fl.
Hawaii. Fam. 315 sub *Clerodendrum fallax*, in syn. 1934.

Clerodendron foliosa Hort. ex Moldenke, Prelim. Alph. List Invalid Names 19,
in syn. 1940.

Clerodendron calycosum Son ex Moldenke, Résumé 261, in syn. 1959.

Clerodendron devoniense Harvey ex Moldenke, Résumé 262, in syn. 1959.

Clerodendron rojo Hargreaves, Trop. Bloss. Fla. 29. 1960.

Spreading shrub, to 4 m tall, branching from the base; branches many,
erect, sending out underground runners; branchlets usually rather medullose
or hollow, grey or brownish, obtusely tetragonal, often deeply sulcate between the angles in drying, very densely short-pubescent; nodes annulate;
principal internodes 1.5–7.5 cm long; leaves decussate-opposite; petioles often
rather stout, 1.4–21 cm long, densely short-pubescent with cinereous or fulvous hairs like the branchlets; leaf-blades membranous, dark-green above,
lighter beneath, broadly ovate or ovate-rotund, 10–35 cm long, 8.5–26
cm wide, apically very abruptly and broadly acute (rarely sharply acute
or even short-acuminate), marginally entire or more or less irregularly
repand-denticulate, basally cordate, more or less short-pubescent above with
rather sparse whitish multicellular hairs, densely or more rarely sparsely
short-pubescent beneath with cinereous or brownish multicellular hairs,
often marked with scattered black glandular disks along the midrib and
secondaries beneath; midrib stout but usually decidedly narrower basally
than the apex of the stout petiole; inflorescence terminal, paniculate, the
panicle very lax and loosely many-flowered, 15–45 cm long, 14–25 cm wide,
composed of 5–13 decussate-opposite pairs of greatly divaricate cymes, often
conspicuously bracteate, floriferous only at the apex; peduncles continuous
with the branchlets and exactly similar in texture and pubescence, 5–7 cm
long, stout; sympodia densely short-pubescent like the peduncles; pedicels
slender or stout, 5–9 mm long, densely puberulent with brownish hairs; bracts
large and foliaceous, often several pairs, subtending the peduncles and inflorescence-branches, similar to the leaves in all respects but smaller or else

more triangular-ovate and apically more sharply acute; bractlets linear, 3–5 mm long, puberulent; prophylla minute, setaceous; flowers very showy; calyx campanulate, thick-textured, red, 5–9 mm long, 3–4 mm wide, appressed-pubescent or puberulent, the 5 lobes ovate or triangular-ovate to deltoid, about 3 mm long, spreading, apically long-acuminate; corolla hypocrateriform, varying from red or bright-red to scarlet, bright-scarlet, or vermilion, its tube slender, 2–2.5 cm long, about 3–4 times as long as the calyx, the limb wide-spreading, the lobes obovate, 1.5–1.8 cm long, about 7 mm wide; stamens and pistil exserted about 3 cm from the corolla-mouth, the stamens about 4–6 cm long and the style 6–7 cm long; fruiting-calyx patelliform, bright-red, about 1 cm wide, firm, puberulent; drupes bright-red or scarlet, turning black in drying, depressed-quadrangular, about 5 mm long and 7 mm wide, deeply 4-lobed and -sulcate, separating into 4 distinct pyrenes on maturity. Chromosome number: $2n = 48$.

D i s t r. A widely distributed species in Pacific Oceanica from the Caroline Islands and Indonesia eastward to Niue, Tahiti, Rarotonga, and the Marquesas Islands; widely cultivated in southern United States, Europe, and tropical portions of Central and South America, Asia, and Africa.

U s e s. The buds and roots of *C. speciosissimum* are employed in the Hawaiian Islands to relieve constipation.

V e r n. Among some 36 recorded common names are: Coral, Coral haitiano, Java glorybean, Pagoda-flowers, red-honeysuckle, Santo Domingo and Scarlet clerodendron.

N o t e s. It has been very widely confused in literature and herbaria with related species. The *Clerodendrum blumeanum* Schau. often included in its synonymy, is actually a synonym of *C. buchanani* (Roxb.) Walp., while *C. horsfieldii* Miq. seems to be a distinct and valid species; *Clerodendron speciosissimum* f. *macrocalyx* Bakh. is a synonym of *Clerodendrum hettae* H. Hallier. The *Petasites agrestis* Rumpf, often placed in the synonymy of *Clerodendrum speciosissimum*, is definitely a synonym of *C. viscosum* Vent. instead, as can plainly be seen from the splendid illustration of it in Rumpf, Herb. Amboin. 4: 108, pl. 49 (1760). The leaves are often attacked by the fungus, *Meliola clerodendricola* P. Henn.

S p e c i m e n s   E x a m i n e d. KANDY DISTRICT: Royal Botanic Garden, Peradeniya, Dec. 1887, *s. coll. s.n.* (PDA).

f. **album** Moldenke, Phytologia 4: 51–52. 1952. Type: *Bakhuizen 3608* from Java (BO).

Clerodendron infortunatum albiflorum Teijsm. ex Moldenke, Résumé 265, in
    syn. 1959 [not *Clerodendron infortunatum* var. *albiflorum* Hassk., 1855].
Clerodendron fallax f. *fl. albo* Hort. ex Moldenke, Phytologia 28: 454, in

syn. 1974.—*Clerodendron fallax* f. *albiflorum* Hort. ex Moldenke, Phytologia 28: 455, in syn. 1974.

This form differs from the typical form in having white corollas.

The form occurs sporadically with the typical form. In Ceylon it is known thus far only from cultivation, but, like the typical form, it tends to escape and become naturalized very easily.

Specimens Examined. KANDY DISTRICT: Royal Botanic Garden, Peradeniya, June 1887, *s. coll. s.n.* (PDA).

14. Clerodendrum inerme (L.) Gaertn., Fruct. 1: 271, pl. 75. 1788 f. **inerme.** L., Fl. Zeyl. 231. 1747; Burm., Fl. Ind. 136–137. 1768; Burm., Fl. Malab. 6. 1769; Moon, Cat. 1: 46. 1821; Schau. in A. DC., Prod. 11: 660. 1847; Thw., Enum. Pl. Zeyl. 243. 1861; Gamble, Man. Indian Timb. 299. 1881; Dymock, Veg. Mat. Med. W. India 747. 1884; Clarke in Hook. f., Fl. Br. Ind. 4: 589 & 596. 1885; Trimen, Cat. 69. 1885; Watt, Dict. Econ. Prod. India 2: 372. 1889; Trimen, Handb. Fl. Ceylon 3: 359–360. 1895; Brandis, Indian Trees 507. 1906; Willis, Cat. 69. 1911; Heyne, Nutt. Pl. Ned. Ind. 4: 120–121. 1917; H. Hallier, Meded. Rijks-Herb. 37: 61. 1918; H.J. Lam, Verbenac. Malay. Arch. 251–255. 1919; H.J. Lam, Bot. Jahrb. Syst. 59: 95. 1924; Alston in Trimen, Handb. Fl. Ceylon 6: 232 & 233. 1931; Cooke, Fl. Pres. Bombay, ed. 2, 2: 511. 1958; Abeywick., Ceylon J. Sci., Biol. Sci. 2: 218. 1959; Prain, Bengal Pl., ed. 2, 2: 623. 1963; Backer & Bakh., Fl. Java 2: 608. 1965; Ohwi, Fl. Jap. 765. 1965; Burkill, Dict. Econ. Prod. Malay Penins. 1: 592–593. 1966; Arulchelvam, Ceyl. Forester, ser. 2, 8: 83, 86, & 91. 1968; Gunawardena, Gen. & Sp. Pl. Zeyl. 148. 1968; Corner & Watanabe, Ill. Guide Trop. Pl. 755. 1969; Stone, Micronesica 6: 504–505. 1970; Fonseka & Vinasithamby, Prov. List Local Names Fl. Pl. Ceylon 72, 82, 83, 97, & 98. 1971; Vivekanandan, Sri Lanka Forester, ser. 2, 11: 82, 138, & 144. 1974. Type: *Herb. Linnaeus 809/3* (LINN).

Niir-notsjill & *Nir-notsjil* Rheede, Hort. Mal. 5: 97, pl. 49. 1685.—*Niir notsjil* Ray, Hist. Pl. 2: 1573. 1693.—*Nir notsjil* Rheede ex Burm. f., Fl. Ind. 136, in syn. 1768.—*Nir notsiit* Rheede ex Lam., Enc. 8: 688, in syn. 1808.—*Nir-notsjit* Rheede apud Walp., Rep. 4: 112, in syn. 1844.

Baccifera malab. fructu oblongo, tetracocco, calyculato Ray, Hist. Pl. 2: 1573. 1688.

Periclymeno similis arbor myrtifolia maderaspatana Plukenet, Almagest. Bot. 287, pl. 211, fig. 4. 1696.—*Periclymeni similis myrtifolia arbor maderaspatensis* Plukenet, Amalth. Bot. 167. 1705.—*Peryclimeni similis, myrtifolia arbor, maderaspatensis* Plukenet ex Lam., Enc. 8: 688, in syn. 1808.

Jasmini flore frutex philippensis, foliis floribusque fere ternis Petiv., Gazophyl. 67, pl. 42, fig. 7. 1702.—*Jasminum flore frutex philippensis, foliis floribusque fere ternis* Petiv. apud Burm., Fl. Ind. 137, in syn. 1768.—*Jasmini flore, frutex philippensis, foliis floribus fere ternis* Petiv. ex Lam., Enc. 8: 688, in syn. 1808.

Jasminum glanduliferum foetidum, zeylanicum Burm., Thes. Zeyl. 127. 1737.— *Jasminum glandiferum foetidum zeylanicum* Burm. ex Burm. f., Fl. Ind. 136, in syn. 1768.

Jasminum litoreum Rumpf, Herb. Amboin. 5: 86, pl. 46. 1747.—*Jasminum littoreum* Rumpf ex Burm. f., Fl. Ind. 136, in syn. 1768.

Volkameria inermis L., Fl. Zeyl. 231. 1747; L., Sp., Pl., ed. 1, imp. 1, 2: 637. 1753 [not *V. inermis* Blanco, 1837, nor Reinw., 1849, nor Sessé & Moc., 1976].—*V. inermis* Willd. ex R. Br. in Ait., Hort. Kew., ed. 2, 4: 65, in syn. 1812.—*V. inermis* L. f. ex Schau. in A. DC., Prod. 11: 657, in syn. 1847.— *V. inermis* Lour. ex Maxim., Bull. Acad. Imp. Sci. Saint-Pétersbourg 32: 83, in syn. 1887.—*V. inermia* L. ex Moldenke, Résumé 392, in syn. 1959.

Ghuraenda Hermann ex L., Fl. Zeyl. 104, in syn. 1748.

Catesbaea ? javanica Osbeck, Dagbok Ostind. Resa 92. 1757.

Frutex sylvestris, flore albo, Antralia moegri javanis Kleinhof ex Burm. f., Fl. Ind. 136, in syn. 1768.

Serouni laut seu Jasminum sylvestre Kleinhof ex Burm., Fl. Ind. 137, in syn. 1768.

Volkameria commersonii Poir. in Lam., Enc. 8: 688. 1808.

Volkameria foliis ovatis, integerrimis, nitidis; pedunculis calycibus glabris Willd. ex Lam., Enc. 8: 688, in syn. 1808.

Volkameria ramis inermibus L. ex Lam., Enc. 8: 688, in syn. 1808.

Volkameria inermis, foliis ovatis, integerrimis, corymbo trichotomo; ramis teretibus, apice subpubescentibus Lam., Enc. 8: 688. 1808.

Clerodendrum inerme R. Br. in Ait., Hort. Kew., ed. 2, 4: 65. 1812.—*Clerodendron inerme* R. Br. ex Spreng. in L., Syst. ed. 16, 2: 788. 1825.—*Clerodendron inerme* Gaertn. ex Watt, Dict. Econ. Prod. India 2: 372. 1889. —*Clerodendron inerne* Woodrow, Gard. Trop., ed. 6, 437, sphalm. 1910. —*Clerodendron inerme* Auct. ex Merr., Philipp. J. Sci. 7: 245, in syn. 1912. —*Clerodendron inerme* W.F. Wight apud Merr., Philipp. J. Sci. 9: 135, in syn. 1914.—*Cherodendron inerme* (L.) Gaertn. ex H.J. Lam, Bot. Jahrb. Syst. 59: 28, sphalm. 1924.—*Clerodendrum inermi* Farnsworth, Pharmacog. Titles 6 (11): v, sphalm. 1932.—*Clerodendron inermis* L. ex Moldenke, Prelim. Alph. List Invalid Names 20, in syn. 1940.—*Clerodendron inerme* Naud. ex Moldenke, Alph. List Invalid Names 18, in syn. 1942.—*Clerodendrum inerme* Gaertn. ex Merr., Chron. Bot. 10: 256. 1946.—*Clerodendron enermis* Gaertn. ex Moldenke, Résumé Suppl. 1: 16, in syn. 1959.—*Clerodendrum inerme* sensu auct. Japon. ex Ohwi, Fl. Jap. 765, in syn. 1965.— *Clerodendrum inerme* (L. f.) Gaertn. ex Santapau, Bull. Bot. Surv. India 8: 38. 1967.—*Clerodendron enerme* Joshi, Biores. Ind. 4: 4601, sphalm. 1968. —*Clerodendron inerme* Benth. ex Moldenke, Phytologia 34: 273, in syn. 1976.—*Clereodendeon inerme* (L.) Gaertn., in herb.—*Clerodendrom inerme*

1946, 15 ft tall, *Worthington 1859* (PDA); Jungle edge, Dolosbage, 3200 ft alt., 9 June 1946, 15 ft tall, flowering profusely, *Worthington 1860* (PDA). MATALE DISTRICT: Yatawatte, 26 June 1965, shrub, flowers white, "gaspinna" Sinhala, *Amaratunga 901* (PDA); roadside by cardamom plantation, in semi-sun, milepost 29/13 on the Rattota to Ilukkumbura road, 800 m alt., 4 Oct. 1971, erect shrub 3.5 m tall, sepals dark maroon, persistent, fruit black, *Jayasuriya 265* (PDA, US); common low shrubs at edge of jungle, Palapatwela, 600 ft alt., 28 Jan. 1974, corollas white, *H.N. & A.L. Moldenke & Jayasuriya 28208* (AAU, ARIZ, CAI, KARACHI, LL, MO, PDA, US). KEGALLE DISTRICT: on bank of streams on the Kegalle to Bulathkohupitiya road, 11 Aug. 1962, calyx red, berry black, *Amaratunga 294* (PDA); scattered on road shoulders, along fencerows, and in roadside shrubbery, Pussella, low altitude, 12 Feb. 1974, corolla pure-white, *H.N. & A.L. Moldenke, Jayasuriya, & Dassanayake 28336* (AAU, ARIZ, CAI, KARACHI, LL, MO, PDA, US). RATNAPURA DISTRICT: apparently rare on wooded banks at bridge over Perry river near road to Adam's Peak, 350–400 m alt., 7 March 1973, branching shrub on cliff, flowers white, conspicuous red bracts in fruiting stage, leaves cordate, acuminate, *Bernardi 14138* (US); 9 miles southwest into Sinharaja forest from Weddagala, about 80°24′ E. 6°24′ N., 300–460 m alt., 23 Feb. 1977, shrub 3 m tall, flowers white, calyx enlarged and red, *B. & K. Bremer 894* (PDA, S, US); roadside, southern escarpment above Pinnawala, on the Balangoda road, 1000 m alt., 19 March 1968, tree 4 metres tall, bracts red, flowers tetramerous, corolla salverform, *Comanor 1101* (AAU, NY, PDA); common small tree on Adam's Peak trail northeast of Carney, 900–1350 m alt., 23 Nov. 1974, flowers white, *Davidse & Sumithraarachchi 8767* (LL); 5 miles southeast of Pelmadulla along Highway A. 18 to Hambantota, 120 m alt., 24 Nov. 1974, shrub 2 m tall, corollas white, *Davidse & Sumithraarachchi 8783* (LL, US); occasional on disturbed ground along recently opened logging road in tall rainforest, 5 miles southwest of Weddagala, in the Sinharaja forest, 29 Oct. 1976, dense shrub 3–4 m tall, flowers white, fruit black, with carmine accrescent calyx, *Fosberg 56584* (LL); very common on road out of Sinharaja forest, south of Weddagala, 28 June 1972, flowers white, fruit with red bract, *Maxwell, Hepper, & Fernando 971* (MO, NY, PDA, US); Route A. 4 en route to Beluhuloya at milepost 109, 11 Sept. 1969, fruit calyxes bright red, *Read 2262* (LL); in primary forest edge, I.B.P. plot, Sri-Palabaddala, 29 Sep. 1973, shrub 1.5 m tall, red flowers, *Waas 12* (US); by roadside in secondary forest, base of Karawita Kanda, 1 Oct. 1973, shrub 1.5 m tall, *Waas 37* (LL, US); by stream edge in high primary forest, Sri-Palabaddala, Mapalana-ella, 19 Feb. 1974, tree 5 m tall, *Waas 430* (US). BADULLA DISTRICT: Badulla, 4000 ft alt., 1 Sept. 1955, *Palmer & Worthington 1634* (PDA). MONERAGALA DISTRICT: Bibile, 16 July 1924, *Silva s.n.* (PDA). GALLE DISTRICT: on side of jeep track in forest, Kanneliya forest, 200 ft alt., 6 April 1970, small

herb with purple flowers [error!], *Balakrishnan NBK 271* (PDA, US); Hiniduma, 1 km on road to Neluwa, 50 m alt., erect shrub, 1 m tall, leaves yam-
like, membranaceous, corymbs terminal, flowers white, "pinna", *Bernardi
15406* (US); common along shady roadside close to stream, Kottawa, sea-
level, 1 Sept. 1967, shrub about 1 m tall, flowers white, corolla-tube with
white strigose hairs, calyx and pedicels green at first, later becoming scarlet
at fruiting time, drupes subglobose, black, glabrous and shiny, *Cramer 2480*
(MOLDENKE); common in dense shade and along disturbed edge of road,
along Forestry Department logging road 2.3 miles east of turnoff 3 miles
north of Udugama on the road to Hiniduma, 250 m alt., 3 Aug. 1968, small
branching tree or shrub, *Theobald & Grupe 2380* (PDA, US); on the Galle to
Matara road, Aug. 1854, *s. coll. C.P. 2894* in part (BR, LE, NY, PDA),
April 1856, *s. coll. C.P. 2894* in part (PDA). MATARA DISTRICT: Ura-
pola, 17 Aug. 1969, small shrub, flowers white, calyx red, *Amaratunga 1782*
(PDA). LOCALITY UNKNOWN: "gas-pinna" Sinhala, *s. coll. s.n.* (PDA);
"pine-ette" Sinhala, *König s.n.* (L); 1831, *s. coll. s.n.* (K, MOLDENKE, NY);
Burman 66 (M), *s. coll. 148* (L), *Fraser 62* (US), *Gardner 62* (DS), *Herb.
Linnaeus 810/1* (LINN, MOLDENKE photo, NY photo), *Herb. Wight s.n.*
(PDA), *Herb. Zeyl. Hort. Amst. 98* (L), *Walker 1325* (K, LE, NY).

19. Clerodendrum phlomidis L. f., Suppl. Pl. 292. 1781; Moon, Cat. 46.
1821; Schau. in A. DC., Prod. 11: 657 & 663. 1847; Thw., Enum. Pl. Zeyl.,
imp. 1, 2: 243. 1861; Clarke in Hook. f., Fl. Br. Ind. 4: 590. 1885; Trimen,
Cat. 69. 1885; Watt, Dict. Econ. Prod. India 2: 374. 1889; Trimen, Handb.
Fl. Ceylon 3: 360. 1895; Willis, Cat. 69. 1911; Alston in Trimen, Handb. Fl.
Ceylon 6: 232 & 233. 1931; Abeywick., Ceylon J. Sci., Biol.-Sci. 2: 218. 1959;
Burkill, Dict. Econ. Prod. Malay Penins. 1: 589. 1966; Gunawardena, Gen.
Sp. Pl. Zeyl. 148. 1968; Fonseka & Vinasithamby, Prov. List Local Names
Fl. Pl. Ceylon 24, 88, & 95. 1971; Vivekanandan, Sri Lanka Forester, ser. 2,
11: 82 & 145. 1974. Type: *König s.n.* from India, *Herb. Linnaeus 810/3*
(LINN).

Volkameria multiflora Burm. f., Fl. Ind. 137, pl. 45, fig. 1. 1768.—*V. multiflora*
    Burm. apud Pers., Sp. Pl. 3: 365, in syn. 1819.
Planta javanica, flore irregulari Garcin. ex Burm. f., Fl. Ind. 137, in syn.
    1768.
Clerodendrum phlomoides Willd., Enum. Pl. Hort. Berol. 2: 659. 1809; Hartw.,
    Hort. Carlsr. 80. 1825.—*Clerodendron phlomoides* Vahl ex K.C. Gmel.,
    Hort. Mag. Duc. Bad. Carlsr. 72. 1811 [not *Clerodendron phlomoides*
    Hort., 1893].—*Clerodendrum phlomoides* Vahl apud Pers., Sp. Pl. 3: 365.
    1819.—*Clerodendrum phlomoides* L. f. apud Steud., Nom. Bot., ed. 1, 207.
    1821.—*Clerodendron phlomoides* L. f. apud Voight, Hort. Suburb. Calc.
    465. 1845.—*Clerodendron phlomoides* L. apud Schau. in A. DC., Prod. 11:

663. 1847; Atchison, J. Linn. Soc. Bot. 8: 70. 1865.—*Clerodendrum phlomoides* L. apud Trimen, J. Ceylon Branch Roy. Asiat. Soc. 9: 69. 1885.— *Clerodendron phlomoides* L. f. apud Clarke in Hook. f., Fl. Br. Ind. 4: 590. 1885.—*Clerodendron phlomoides* Willd. apud Gamble, Fl. Pres. Madras 6: 1099. 1924.—*Clerodendron phlomoidis* Puri, Indian Forest Ecol. 1: 263. 1960.—*Clerodendrum phlomoedes* L. apud Gupta & Marlange, Trav. Sect. Sci. Techn. Inst. Franç. Pond. Hors. 36 (1): 77, 113, & 129. 1961.—*Clerodendrum phlomoidis* L. f. apud Jain & Tarafder, Econ. Bot. 24: 294. 1970. —*Clerodendrum phlomoids* L. apud Korr, Biol. Abstr. 53: 8133, sphalm. 1972.
Clerodendrum phlomitis Vahl apud Desf., Tabl. Écol. Bot., ed. 2, 64. 1815.— *Clerodendron phlomidis* L. f. apud Trimen, Handb. Fl. Ceylon 3: 360. 1895.—*Clerodendron phlomidis* Trimen ex Gamble, Man. Indian. Timb., ed. 2, 543, in syn. 1902.—*Clerodendron phlomides* L. apud Malaviya, Proc. Indian Acad. Sci. B. 58: 351. 1963.—*Clerodendron phlomidis* L. apud Meher-Homji, Trop. Ecol. 6: 162. 1965.—*Clerodendrum phlomides* L. f. apud Rao & Kumari, Bull. Bot. Surv. India 9: 107. 1967.—*Clerodendrum plomides* Farnsworth, Pharmacog. Titles 8 (8): vi, sphalm. 1973.
Clerodendron multiflorum Burm. ex Kuntze, Rev. Gen. Pl. 2: 506. 1891 [not *Clerodendrum multiflorum* G. Don, 1824].—*Clerodendrum multiflorum* (Burm. f.) Kuntze ex Rao & Sastry, Bull. Bot. Surv. India 6: 281. 1964.

Large shrub or small tree, 5–9 m tall; wood grey, hard, close-grained; bark light-brown, fissured, with dull-white lenticels; branches and branchlets medium-slender, light-grey, twiggy, obtusely tetragonal or subterete, densely pubescent or puberulent with cinereous hairs throughout; twigs very slender, often elongate, otherwise similar to the branchlets in all respects; nodes not annulate; leaf-scars comparatively small, circular, with slightly but sharply raised margins; principal internodes usually 2–4.5 cm long; leaves decussate-opposite, numerous, small; petioles very slender, 5–22 mm long, densely short-pubescent or puberulent; leaf-blades rather thick when fresh, membranous, thin, and fragile when dry, rather uniformly green on both surfaces or slightly lighter beneath, ovate or subrhomboid to rhomboid or deltoid, 1.7–6.8 cm long, 1.2–6 cm wide, apically acute or short-acuminate (rarely obtuse), marginally sinuate or coarsely and irregularly crenate-serrate from the widest part to below the apex (the upper 1/3 and base usually entire) or completely entire, basally acute or subcuneate, irregularly puberulent on both surfaces or glabrescent in age; inflorescence axillary and terminal, cymose, the axillary cymes usually crowded in the uppermost leaf-axils, forming what appears to be a large, rounded, terminal panicle, the individual cymes divaricate, 4–9 cm long and 3–6 cm wide, dichotomous or once or twice trichotomous, usually 3–12-flowered, lax, conspicuously bracteose, sparsely or densely incanous-puberulent or short-pubescent throughout; peduncles 1.5–2.2 cm long; pedicels 4–12 mm long; bracts foliaceous, lanceolate or obovate-lanceolate to ovate, 12–20 mm long, 3–13 mm wide, apically acute; bractlets numerous, narrow-elliptic, 4–9 mm long, 2–4 mm wide, acute at both ends, sparsely pilose especially along the margins; calyx 8–12 mm long, 5-lobed to about half its length, rigid, pubescent or glabrescent, enlarged in fruit, the lobes ovate, apically acutely acuminate, venose; corolla hypocrateriform, mostly white or yellowish-white, varying to red [f. *rubrum* (Roxb.) Moldenke], the tube sometimes pinkish or light rose-pink to pinkish-violet externally and white inside, slender, 2–2.5 cm long, slightly puberulent externally and glabrous inside, the lobes 5, subequal, elliptic, 7–8 mm long, apically obtuse, venose; filaments much exserted, slightly pubescent; style slender; stigma bifid; ovary glabrous; fruit green when immature, black when ripe, broadly obovoid, 6–12 mm long and wide, wrinkled, apically depressed, splitting into 4 pyrenes when mature; endocarp crustaceous; seeds oblong, white. Chromosome number: 2 n=48, 52.

D i s t r. *Clerodendrum phlomidis* is native in southern Asia from the northwestern Himalayas and Pakistan to India and Ceylon. It is cultivated as a hedge plant in many parts of India and for ornament, mostly as a specimen plant, in various parts of Europe, Egypt, Mauritius, and Malaya. Some material, however, distributed as "*Clerodendron phlomoides* Hort." is a composite, *Montanoa arborescens* C. Koch. It should also be noted that "*Clerodendron phlomoides* f. *luxurians* Horsf." is a synonym of *Clerodendrum calamitosum* L., a closely related species not known from Ceylon.

U s e s. Its leaves and stems have been found to contain β- and γ-sitosterols, ceryl alcohol, palmitic and cerotic acids, D-mannitol, and the -B-D glucoside of β-sitosterol. In India the plant is used medicinally for post-natal complaints in women, dyspepsia, stomach-ache, colic, cholera, dysentery, and anthrax. It is fed to cattle to treat diarrhoea, worms, and swollen stomach. The extracted juice of the leaves is used as an alterative in the treatment of syphilis. The leaves are rubbed over the body in cases of dropsy, while the juice of the leaves, flowers, and fruit is used on swellings and body sores. The flowers are also cooked in some curries. The roots are supposed to have alterative properties and are used as a bitter tonic given during convalescence from measles.

V e r n. Gas-pinna, Wadang (S); Talu-dala, Vadamadakki, Vata madakki, Vatamadakki (T); also about 30 other names are known from India and elsewhere in its range.

N o t e s. The flowers of this species are often galled by a gall-wasp, *Paracopium cingalense*, and more or less proliferated. Insects are said to feed on the very young green drupes. The pollen is described by Nair & Rehman in Bull. Bot. Gard. Lucknow 76: 15 (1962).

The nomenclature of *Clerodendrum phlomidis* is much involved, with authors about evenly divided between those adopting *"phlomidis"* (or a variant thereof) and those adopting *"phlomoides"* (or a variant thereof), probably chiefly because of the Index Kewensis' unjustified "correcting" of the original epithet used by the younger Linnaeus.

In regions where there is a dry season this shrub or tree looks almost "naked" during that time of the year, with only a very few terminal leaves on the branches.

S p e c i m e n s   E x a m i n e d. MANNAR DISTRICT: Mantai, Feb. 1890, small tree, *s. coll. s.n.* (PDA). POLONNARUWA DISTRICT: between Topawewa and the Mahaweliganga, 29 March 1905, *Willis s.n.* (PDA). KANDY DISTRICT: in outdoor cultivation in Students' Garden, Royal Botanic Garden, Peradeniya, 1550 ft alt., 18 Jan. 1974, sprouts from roots and new shoots from severely pruned-back stump, *H.N. & A.L. Moldenke & Jayasuriya 28162* (US). BATTICALOA DISTRICT: Batticaloa, *Gardner s.n.* [*C.P. 1950*] (BM, PDA). HAMBANTOTA DISTRICT: abundant on seashore, Kirinda, Dec. 1882, flowers light rose-pink, *s. coll. s.n.* (PDA); roadsides, Kirindi Oya, south of Tissamaharama, 13 Aug. 1932, "wadang" Sinhala, *Simpson 9961* (PDA); in forest scrub, Ruhuna National Park, Block 1, Andunoruwa Tank, 16 Nov. 1968, tree-like shrub, 5 m tall, bark fissured, flowers pinkish-violet outside, white inside, fruit green, voucher collected for ecological observations, *Wirawan 714* (MOLDENKE, PDA, US). LOCALITY UNKNOWN: cultivated, Feb. 1881, *"W.F." s.n.* (BM).

20. Clerodendrum philippinum Schau. in A. DC., Prod. 11: 667 [as *"Clerodendron"*]. 1847. f. **multiplex** (Sweet) Moldenke, Phytologia 41: 10. 1978; Schau. in A. DC., Prod. 11: 666 & 667. 1847; H.J. Lam, Verbenac. Malay. Arch. 259–260 & 318. 1919; Alston in Trimen, Handb. Fl. Ceylon 6: 232–233. 1931; Alston, Kandy Fl. 64. 1938; Abeywick., Ceylon J. Sci., Biol. Sci. 2: 218. 1959; Gunawardena, Gen. & Sp. Pl. Zeyl. 148. 1968; Howard & Powell, Taxon 17: 53–55. 1968; Moldenke in Woodson, Schery, *et al.*, Ann. Missouri Bot. Gard. 60: 141. 1973; Vivekanandan, Sri Lanka Forester, ser. 2, 11: 82 & 145. 1974. Type: *Cuming 1096* from the Philippine Islands (GH lectotype).

Volkmannia japonica Jacq., Hort. Schoenbr. 3: 48, pl. 338. 1798 [not *Clerodendrum japonicum* (Thunb.) Sweet, 1827].
Agricolaea fragrans Schrank, Denkschr. Königl. Akad. Wiss. München 1: 98. 1808.—*Agricola fragrans* Schrank apud Pételot, Arch. Rech. Agron. Cambodge Laos Vietnam 18: 253. 1953.
Clerodendrum fragrans Willd., Enum. Hort. Berol. 2: 659. 1809.—*Clerodendron fragrans* Vent. apud K.C. Gmel., Hort. Mag. Duc. Bad. Carlsr. 72. 1811.—*Clerodendrum fragrans* Ait., Hort., Kew. 4: 63. 1812.—*Clerodendron fragrans* Willd. apud Spach, Hist. Nat. Veg. Phan. 9: 228, in syn. 1840.— *Clerodendron flagrans* Willd. apud Dupuis, Nouv. Fl. Usuel. & Méd. 2: 311,

D i s t r. The origin of this taxon has been lost in prehistory, but most probably occurred in China and/or southern tropical Asia. It is now widespread not only throughout tropical Asia, but also in Pacific Oceanica and the warm portions of Africa and the Americas. It is widely cultivated for ornament outdoors in gardens and hedges in almost all warm countries and in greenhouses as a specimen plant elsewhere, and tends to escape very readily and become "weedy" in suitable climates.

U s e s. In Cambodia flowering branches of this plant are offered in Buddhist temples and in Sumatra the plant figures in ceremonial magic. In the West Indies the flowers are boiled and the resulting infusion is used to alleviate headaches. In Malaya the plant is employed externally either in a decoction to treat rheumatism and ague or mixed with other substances for treating skin diseases. In Vietnam the juice of pounded leaves is used in a decoction to treat gleet or blennorrhoea or, diluted in cold water, as a bath for children afflicted with boils.

V e r n. Sennaimallihay (T); also Bocamellia, Camelia, Cashmere-bouquet, Flor de muerta, Honolulu-rose, Hortensia, Losa, Mil flor, Nassau-rose, Spanish-jasmine, and some 50 others in various parts of its extensive range.

N o t e s. The nomenclature of the taxon is very confused. Howard & Powell (1968) claim that the very widely used and most suitable name, C. fragrans var. pleniflorum, cannot be used under the present Code of Botanical Nomenclature. They have selected the Clerodendron philippinum of Schauer (1847) as the name to be adopted. Unfortunately, Schauer's original description of the taxon asserts that the leaf-blades are entire or only remotely serrate, the corollas scarcely twice the length of the calyx-tube, the stamens and pistil long-exserted (and therefore obviously present in unmodified form), and the fruit baccate. These characters do not match well those of the present taxon where the leaves are almost always coarsely dentate or even sublobed, stamens and pistil are modified into supernumerary petals, and fruit is not produced. If the lectotype which they have designated, Cuming 1096 in the Gray Herbarium, truly does represent the present taxon, then it would appear that, regardless of the original description, the doubled-flowered form of the species becomes the nomenclaturally typical variety and the form with only the normal number of petals and the long-exserted genitalia will have to take on the designation of var. f. philippinum and the form with only a few "single" flowers scattered among many of the "doubled" ones becomes f. subfertile Moldenke. On the other hand, if it is argued that the single-flowered fertile form described by Schauer is the nomenclaturally typical variety, then the doubled-flowered form must be called C. philippinum f. multiplex (Sweet) Moldenke. Experts whom I have consulted favour the latter view, here adopted.

The present taxon has been widely confused with the distinct but closely related C. bungei Steud., C. lindleyi Decaisne, and C. yunnanense Hu. It would also appear that the *Volkameria fragrans* Vent. (1804), *Clerodendrum fragrans* Ait. (1812), *Clerodendrum fragrans* Hort. ex Vent. apud Maheshwari (1975), and *C. coronaria* Hort. ex Bailey (1924) belong in the synonymy of *C. philippinum* var. *simplex* [= *C. philippinum* f. *philippinum*] rather than to f. *multiplex* found in Ceylon. *Clerodendrum philippinum* f. *corymbosum* (Lam & Bakh.) Moldenke, with corymbose inflorescences, is now known as *C. riedelii* Oliv.

Clerodendrum philippinum suckers profusely, will grow in shade as well as in full sun, and is especially valuable horticulturally because it will grow in poor soil and in out-of-the-way-corners. It is sometimes attacked by the fungus, *Aecidium clerodendri fragrantis* Yen.

S p e c i m e n s   E x a m i n e d. KALUTARA DISTRICT: cultivated in garden of main house, St. Vincent's Home, sealevel, 20 May 1970, stems to 1.5 m, flowers mauvish-white, stem and leaves have a musky odour, *Cramer 2982* (PDA, US). KANDY DISTRICT: Peradeniya, 11 May 1963, calyx brownish-red, petals white, *Amaratunga 613* (PDA); a common weed in moist regions at midcountry elevations, Galagedera, on the Kandy to Kurunegala road, 29 July 1971, calyx purplish-red, petals white with a very pale tinge of purple toward their margins, *Amaratunga 2313* (PDA); Royal Botanic Garden, Peradeniya, April 1887, *s. coll. s.n.* (PDA); near waterfalls, Dara Oya, 1 Oct. 1970, *Kundu & Balakrishnan 151* (US); large colony on road shoulders, Galagedera, 500 ft alt., 16 Jan. 1974, *H.N. & A.L. Moldenke, Jayasuriya, & Sumithraarachchi 28130* (ARIZ, CAI, KARACHI, LL, MO, PDA, SRGH, US). MATALE DISTRICT: abundant shrubs at jungle edge, Alawatugoda, 800 ft alt., 23 Jan. 1974, *H.N. & A.L. Moldenke & Jayasuriya 28206* (AAU, LL, PDA, US). LOCALITY UNKNOWN: 1572 ft alt., flowers pinkish-white, *Silva 152* (NY).

21. Clerodendrum viscosum Vent., Jard. Malm. 1: 25, pl. 25. 1803; Schau. in A. DC., Prod. 11: 667. 1847; Matsum. & Hayata, J. Coll. Sci. Imp. Univ. Tokyo 22: 302. 1906; H.J. Lam, Verbenac. Malay. Arch. 285. 1919; Kanehira, Formosan Trees, ed. 2, 648. 1936; Pételot, Pl. Méd. Camb. Laos & Vietn. 2: 253 & 4: 99. 1954; Santapau, Bull. Bot. Surv. India 3: 14. 1961; Backer & Bakh., Fl. Java 2: 611. 1965; Patel, Fl. Melghat. 268. 1968. Type: cultivated specimen from Malmaison garden (P).

Marurang Rumpf, Herb. Amboin. 4: 108. 1750.
Petasites agrestis Rumpf, Herb. Amboin. 4: 108, pl. 49. 1750.
Clerodendrum infortunatum Lour., Fl. Cochinch., ed. 1, 2: 387–388 [in part]. 1790 [not *Clerodendrum infortunata* L., 1753, nor *Clerodendron infortunatum* Gaertn., 1788].—*Clerodendrum infortunatum* Willd. ex Pers., Sp. Pl. 3: 365. 1819.—*Clerodendrum infortunatum* Vent. apud Steud., Nom. Bot., ed. 1, 207, in syn. 1821.—*Clerodendron infortunatum* Schau. apud H. Hallier, Meded. Rijks-Herb. 37: 63, in syn. 1918.—*Clerodendrum infortunatum*

Blume apud H. Hallier, Meded. Rijks-Herb. 37: 64, in textu. 1918.—*Clerodendron infortunatum* Lour. (in part) ex Moldenke, Alph. List Invalid Names 20, in syn. 1940.—*Clerodendrum infortunatum* Auct. ex Santapau, J. Bombay Nat. Hist. Soc. 53: 16, in syn. 1955.—*Clerodendron infortunatum* Auct. ex Legris, Trav. Sect. Sci. Techn. Inst. Franç. Pond. Hors 6: 561, in syn. 1963.

Clerodendrum viscosum Pers., Sp. Pl. 3: 365. 1819.—*Clerodendrum viscosum* Willd. apud Hartw., Hort. Carlsr. 80. 1825.—*Clerodendron viscosum* Vent. apud Schau. in A. DC., Prod. 11: 667, in syn. 1847.—*Clerodendrum viscosum* Kuntze ex Santapau, Excerpta Bot. Sect. A, Taxon. 5: 565. 1962.

Volkameria laurifolia Hort. ex Steud., Nom. Bot., ed. 1, 207 & 890, in syn. 1821.

Clerodendrum cordatum D. Don, Prod. Fl. Nepal 103. 1825.

Volkameria infortunata Roxb., Fl. Ind. 3: 59. 1832.

Clerodendron pubescens Wall. ex Walp., Nov. Actorum Acad. Caes. Leop.-Carol German Nat. Cur. 19, Suppl. 1: 380. 1843.

Clerodendron haematocalyx Hance in Walp., Ann. Bot. Syst. 3: 238. 1853.—*Clerodendron naematocalyx* Hance ex Moldenke, Résumé Suppl. 13: 8, in syn. 1966.

Clerodendron affine Griff. (in part), Not. Pl. Asiat. 4: 170. 1854.

Clerodendron castaneifolium Klotsch ex Garcke, Reise Pr. Wald. Bot. 102, pl. 65. 1863.

Weak erect shrub, large stout undershrub, or erect tree, 0.5–3 m tall, bitter and fetid throughout; bark grey and corky or the outer bark green, the inner white, quickly turning brown; sapwood white; heartwood dark-brown; branchlets medium-slender, obtusely tetragonal, densely appressed-villous with antrorse flavescent hairs on young growth, becoming more sparsely so or even only sparsely appressed-pubescent in age, the young portions often red or purplish-red; nodes not annulate; principal internodes 1.5–11.5 cm long; leaves decussate-opposite or approximate; leaf-buds very densely villous; petioles slender, 2–19 cm long, densely (or in age more sparsely) villous with appressed flavescent hairs; mature leaf-blades thin-chartaceous, thicker and more firm in age, somewhat lighter green beneath, elliptic or broadly elliptic to ovate or elongate-ovate, 6–25 cm long, 3.5–20 cm wide, apically acute or short-acuminate, basally acute or obtuse, broadly cuneate, subcordate, or more usually cordate, marginally more or less denticulate or serrate, varying to coarsely exsculptate or few-dentate, rarely only sinuate or entire [var. *nilagirense* H. Hallier] or minutely serrulate [var. *helferi* Moldenke], rather sparsely villous-pubescent on both surfaces, more densely so on the larger venation and beneath with patent to appressed short or long antrorse brownish hairs (bulbous-based on the upper surface) or only sparsely pilose [in var. *helferi*]; inflorescence terminal, pedunculate, 10–25 cm long and wide, pyramidal,

densely villous throughout with flavescent or sordid hairs, composed of several, opposite, stipitate, ascending or divaricate, mostly rather few-flowered
cymes, lax; peduncles red or purplish-red, 1–6 cm long; bracts foliaceous,
resembling the leaves but much smaller and very densely villous, elliptic,
stipitate, usually bright-red; bractlets and prophylla linear, often obscured by
the pubescence; pedicles red or purplish-red; flowers strongly sweet-scented at
night; calyx bright-green during anthesis, 9–16 mm long, 5-cleft, or the lobes
red, to 10 mm long; corolla white or with purplish-pink or dull-purple at the
mouth of the tube, often with rose markings externally [or even entirely magenta to red in f. *rubrum* Moldenke], pubescent, the tube 2 cm long, cylindric,
usually externally pinkish, often surpassing the calyx and twice as long as its
tube, the segments 6–15 mm long; stamens purplish, 1.5–3 mm long; anthers
green or eventually deep-purple to black; fruiting-calyx much enlarged, deep-
red or maroon edged with purple to entirely red-purple, cupular-patelliform,
1.5–2 cm long, the lobes lanceolate, deep-red, leathery; fruit at first green,
bluish-black or black when mature, globose, about 0.8 cm in diameter, fleshy,
shiny, composed of 4 (or 1–3 by abortion) pyrenes, enclosed in the accrescent
fruiting-calyx. Chromosome number: $2x = 48$.

D i s t r. This widely misunderstood species is native from Pakistan and
Nepal through northern India, Burma, and Thailand, north into southern
China and Hainan island, and east to the Philippine Islands, Sumatra, Java,
and Sarawak; naturalized in Brazil; often cultivated for ornament or as a
specimen plant.

U s e s. The young leaves are considered edible in Thailand, while the
roots, bark, and flowers are used in local medicine in India as a remedy for
skin diseases.

V e r n. Bharit, Juthur, Karu, Tangkai daeng and others in various parts
of its range.

N o t e s. The *Clerodendrum canescens* Wall., often included in the synonymy of *C. viscosum*, actually is a very distinct separate species, while *C.
petasites* (Lour.) Meeuse is a synonym of the very different *C. petasites* (Lour.)
S. Moore. According to Merrill [Trans. Amer. Philos. Soc. 24 (2): 337. 1935]
part of the *Clerodendrum infortunatum* of Loureiro (1790) belongs to *C. viscosum* and a part to the very different *C. kaempferi* (Jacq.) Sieb. Schauer (1847)
regarded *C. viscosum* as a synonym of *C. infortunatum* L., as did Lam (1919)
and many other authors. It is closely related and very similar to this and to
C. villosum Blume. In *C. infortunatum* the corolla-tube is 3 or 4 times as long
as the calyx-tube, the leaves are entire, and the calyx-lobes have a prominent
midrib. In *C. viscosum* the corolla-tube is about twice as long as the calyx-
tube, not at all or but slightly glandular, the calyx-lobes without prominent
midrib, and the plant is northern in distribution, the leaf-blades distinctly
dentate (or subentire in var. *nilagirense*). In *C. villosum* the corolla-tube is

about as long as or only slightly longer than the calyx and is densely glandular, the leaves are entire, and the plant is southern in distribution. *Clerodendrum viscosum* can usually be distinguished from *C. infortunatum* by its large denticulate-serrate leaves, larger and very sweet-scented flowers, the corolla-segments pink at their base, and the calyx-segments less acuminate. *Clerodendrum villosum*, with which *C. viscosum* has also been widely confused, especially in India, has, according to Clarke (1885) its leaves slightly more silky rather than rough-villous, the inflorescence more softly hairy and not red, the calyx 1/3 inch long, divided rather more than half way to the base, the segments more usually glandular, and the corolla smaller.

It should be noted that the *Petasites agrestis* and *Marurang* of Rumpf (1750) are very plainly *Clerodendrum viscosum*, as can be seen from the splendid illustration given by Rumpf. His plant was from Malabar, not from Ceylon; *C. infortunatum* L., to which his names are often referred, was from Ceylon. Meeuse regards *C. petasites* (Lour.) A. Meeuse as the correct name for *C. viscosum*, and in this he is followed by some modern authors, but Merrill has clearly shown in manuscript notes in the New York herbarium that Loureiro's plant represents a very different taxon.

Specimens Examined. KANDY DISTRICT: Royal Botanic Garden, Peradeniya, 15 Sept. 1926, flowers white, calyx red, *Alston 586* (PDA); Royal Botanic Garden, Peradeniya, March 1884, *s. coll. 14* (PDA); Governor's Garden, Kandy, 23 May, 1926, calyx red, "berry" [=drupe] black, *s. coll. s.n.* (PDA).

21. HOLMSKIOLDIA

Retz., Obs. 6: 31. 1791. Type species: *Holmskioldia sanguinea* Retz.

Hastingia König ex. Smith, Exot. Bot. 2: 41, Pl. 80. 1806 [not *Hastingia* König ex Endl., 1966].—*Hastingia* Smith apud Reichb., Conspect. Reg. Veg. 1: 117. 1828.—*Hastingsia* König apud H. Hallier, Meded. Rijks-Herb. 37: 84. 1918 [not *Hastingsia* S. Wats., 1879].—*Hastingsia* Smith ex Moldenke, Prelim. Alph. List Invalid Names 26. 1940.—*Hastingsia* P. & K. apud Airy Shaw in Willis, Dict., ed. 7, 522. 1966.
Platunium Juss., Ann. Mus. Natl. Hist. Nat. 7: 76. 1806.—*Platinium* Juss. apud De Wild., Ic. Select. Hort. Then. 4: Pl. 159. 1903.—*Platunum* Juss. apud Dalla Torre & Harms, Gen. Siphonog. 433. 1904.—*Platumium* Juss. ex Moldenke, Suppl. List Invalid Names 6. 1941.
Holmskidia Dumort., Anal. Fam. Pl. 22. 1829.—*Holmskjöldia* Retz. ex Kuntze, Rev. Gen. Pl. 2: 508. 1891.—*Holmskjoeldia* Retz. ex H.J. Lam in Lam & Bakh., Bull. Jard. Bot. Buitenzorg, ser. 3, 3: 96. 1921.—*Holmskjoldia* Retz. ex Porsch, Jahrb. Wiss. Bot. 63: 565, 577, 584, & 656–669, fig. 4–13. 1923.—*Homskioldia* Navarro Hayden, Fl. Com. Puerto Rico [15]. 1936.

—*Holmskiöldia* Retz. apud Pittier, Cat. Pl. Venez. 2: 330. 1947.—*Holmshioldia* Helfer ex Moldenke, Alph. List Invalid Names Suppl. 1: 10. 1947.— *Homdkioldia* Fourn., Imp. Tree Fam. Costa Rica 13. 1966.—*Homoskioldia* Retz. apud Misra, Bull. Bot. Surv. India 12: 136. 1970.—*Holmskiodia* Anon., Commonw. Mycol. Inst. Index Fungi 3: 823. 1972.

Glabrous or incanous-pubescent shrubs or trees, unarmed or armed with small axillary spines; branches often elongate and more or less clambering, obtusely and often obscurely tetragonal; leaves decussate-opposite, petiolate, deciduous, entire or dentate, exstipulate; inflorescence cymose, axillary and short-pedunculate or crowded at the apex of the branchlets in terminal fashion; bracts often small, deciduous; calyx gamosepalous, with a very short tube, membranous, broadly expanded from a short urceolate base, often highly coloured, very much accrescent in age, entire or very broad and more or less 5-lobed, often very venose; corolla gamopetalous, zygomorphic, its tube cylindric, incurved, slightly ampliate upwards, its limb oblique, spreading, shortly 5-parted, the lobes short, unequal, the 2 posterior ones exterior in bud, the 2 lateral ones smaller, the anterior one largest; stamens 4, didynamous, inserted on the corolla-tube at or below the middle, exserted; anthers ovate, the 2 thecae parallel; pistil one, composed of two 2-locular carpels; ovary very obtuse and entire or obscurely 4-lobed, 4-locular, the cells 1-ovulate; ovules lateral, solitary, subpendulous, affixed in the upper anterior angle of the locule; style exserted, very shortly and acutely bifid at the apex; fruiting-calyx much enlarged, wide-spreading, patelliform or rotate, often brightly coloured, often 2 cm or more in width, almost enclosing the fruit at its contracted base; fruit drupaceous, obovoid, truncate or shortly 4-lobed at the apex, usually more or less enclosed in the urceolate base of the persistent calyx-tube, the exocarp often somewhat juicy, the mesocarp thin, the endocarp hard, splitting into 1–4 nutlets or bony pyrenes; seeds oblong, exalbuminous, the testa membranous.

A genus of about 19 species and subspecific taxa native to southern Asia, southeastern Africa, and Madagascar, reaching its greatest development in Madagascar; one species widely cultivated and often escaped and naturalized in both the East and West Indies and elsewhere; 2 species are known from the Eocene, Miocene, and Oligocene of North America. In Ceylon it is represented only by the following cultivated species.

Holmskioldia sanguinea Retz., Obs. 6: 31–32. 1791; Schau. in A. DC., Prod. 11: 696–697. 1847; Clarke in Hook. f., Fl. Br. Ind. 4: 596. 1885; Campbell & Watt, Descrip. Cat. Econ. Prod. Chota Nagpur 26. 1886; Watt, Dict. Econ. Prod. India 4: 260. 1890; Collett, Fl. Siml. 380–381. 1902; Parker, Forest Fl. Punjab, ed. 2, 403. 1924; Osmaston, Forest Fl. Kumaon 409. 1927; Junell, Symb. Bot. Upsal. 4: 110–111, Pl. 6, fig. 2. 1934; L.H. Bailey, Man. Cult. Pl., ed. 2, 842. 1949; Bor & Raizada, Some Beaut. Ind. Climb. 142–143. 1954; Cooke, Fl. Pres. Bombay, ed. 2, 2: 518. 1958; Abeywick., Ceylon J. Sci., Biol. Sci. 2: 218. 1959; Sastri, Wealth India 5: 108–109, fig. 67. 1959; Graf, Exotica 3: 1479 & 1630. 1963; Backer & Bakh., Fl. Java 2: 612. 1965; Burkill, Dict. Econ. Prod. Malay Penins. 1: 1200. 1966; Pal & Krishnam., Fl. Shrubs 59–60. 1967; Menninger, Fl. Vines 43, 334, & 336. Pl. 280. 1970; Alexander, Hong Kong Shrubs 49. 1971. Type: None designated, but described on material "Habitat in vallibus Bengaliae".

Hastingia coccinea Smith., Exot. Bot. 2: 41–42, Pl. 80. 1806.—*Hastingia coccinea* König ex Roxb., Fl. Ind., ed. 2, 3: 65–66. 1832.—*Hastingsia coccinea* König apud H. Hallier, Meded. Rijks-Herb. 37: 84. 1918.—*Hastingsia coccinea* Smith ex Moldenke, Prelim. Alph. List Invalid Names 26. 1940.—*Hastingsia coriacea* Wall. ex Moldenke, Prelim. Alph. List Invalid Names 26. 1940.
Platunium rubrum Juss., Ann. Mus. Nat. Hist. Nat. 7: 76. 1806.—*Platinium rubrum* Juss. apud De Wild., Ic. Select. Hort. Then. 4: Pl. 159. 1903.—*Platumium rubrum* Juss. ex Moldenke, Suppl. List Invalid Names 7. 1941.
Holmskioldia rubra Pers., Syn. Pl. 2: 144. 1807.
Hastingia augusta König ex Lindl., Bot. Reg. 9: Pl. 692. 1823.—*H. angusta* König apud DeWild., Ic. Select. Hort. Then. 4: Pl. 159. 1903.
Holmskioldia scandens Sweet, Hort. Brit., ed. 1, 323. 1826.
Hastingia scandens Roxb., Hort. Beng. [95]. 1814; Roxb., Fl. Ind. ed. 2, 3: 66. 1832.
Holmskioldia sancuinea Retz. apud De Wild., Ic. Select. Hort. Then. 4: Pl. 159. 1903.—*Holmskoldia sanguinea* Woodrow, Gard. Trop., ed. 6, 442. 1910.—*Holmskjoeldia sanguinea* Retz. apud H.J. Lam, Verbenac. Malay. Arch. 321. 1919.—*Holmskjoldia sanguinea* Retz. ex Porsch, Jahrb. Wiss. Bot. 63: 656–669, fig. 4–13. 1923.—*Homoskioldia sanguinea* Retz. apud Misra, Bull. Bot. Surv. India 12: 136. 1970.
Holmskioldia coccinea Retz. ex Moldenke, Prelim. Alph. List Invalid Names 27. 1940.

Straggling shrub or small tree, 3–10 m tall, rarely scandent; stems solitary or several; branches elongate, often starting at the base of the plant, tetragonal, brachiate-divaricate, glabrescent, often verrucose-lenticellate, the lowest often procumbent; branchlets and twigs fine, rather acutely teragonal, more or less densely and softly short-pubescent on the younger parts, becoming glabrescent in age; wood light red, moderately hard, weighing 43 lb cubic foot; nodes more or less obscurely annulate; petioles very slender, 8–30 mm long, usually not 1/4 the length of the blade, canaliculate above, lightly and softly short-pubescent; leaf-blades membranous or thin-chartaceous, bright green, ovate, 3–12 cm long, 1.5–8.5 cm wide, apically rather long-acuminate or caudate (the acumination 1–1.5 cm long), entire or subentire to (usually) lightly crenate-serrate with appressed often very shortly apiculate teeth, basally truncate or subtruncate to rounded or even subcordate, slightly prolonged into the petiole, glabrate above, lightly short-pubescent on the venation beneath and conspicuously gland-dotted or squamellate, often also more or less impressed-punctate above; inflorescence much abbreviated, to 5 cm long, paniculate, axillary, subequalling or somewhat surpassing the subtending petiole and loose, or terminal and then more dense and subracemiform, composed of 2–6 opposite cymules, the cymules 3-flowered or reduced to a single, long-pedicellate central flower and 2 sterile lateral bractlets; peduncles very short and slender, mostly less than 5 mm long, scattered-pilosulous or glabrous; pedicels slender, 2–10 mm long, scattered-pilosulous or glabrous; foliaceous bracts often present in the terminal inflorescences, 5–20 mm long, 4–9 mm wide, ovate or elliptic, glabrescent; bractlets minute; calyx shallowly cupuliform or rotate, 1/3 to 1/4 as long as the corolla, mostly orange or red (yellow in f. *citrina*), radiately reticulate-venose, the primary veins ending in minute apiculations, persistent, glabrous externally, lightly scattered-pilosulous or puberulous internally; corolla tubular, brick-red or scarlet to orange or red-brown (yellow in f. *citrina*), 1.5–2.5 cm long, the tube 1.5–1.7 cm long, curvate, externally minutely pilosulous, the limb short, oblique, 2-lipped, the lobes apically acutish or rounded, the 4 upper ones very short, the lower one declinate, more than twice as long; stamens attached in the throat or at about the middle of the corolla-tube, slightly longer than the tube, declinate; anthers oval, white; style slender, about 2 cm long, as long as the stamens and parallel with them; ovary glabrous, 4-celled, with one ovule per locule; fruiting-calyx rotate, greatly expanded, circular, nearly flattened, 1.5–2.5 cm in diameter, basally minutely pulverulent-puberulent or glabrous throughout, conspicuously reticulate-venose; fruit globose, brown; often verrucose. Chromosome number: 2n = 32.

D i s t r. This species is apparently native to the subtropical Himalayan region of Pakistan and India, but has been widely introduced and naturalized throughout southern Asia, Mauritius, Indonesia, and the West Indies.

U s e s. It is widely cultivated for ornament in tropical and subtropical parts of both hemispheres and under glass elsewhere.

V e r n. Some 30 names are listed, including: Chinese-hatplant, Chinese-hats, Chinese-umbrellas, Cup-and-saucer plant, Mandarin's-hat, Parasol-flower, and Sombrero-flower.

N o t e s. The gynoecium anatomy is discussed by Junell (1934) and the pollen characters by Nair & Rehman (Bull. Lucknow Natl. Bot. Gard. 76: 18. 1962) and by Sharma & Mukhopodhyay (J. Genet. 58: 359, 369–370, & 383, Pl. 11, fig. 40 & 41. 1963). It flowers practically all through the year and should be pruned closely after flowering peaks. It may be propagated by seeds, cuttings, or layering. The foliage is extensively eaten by sheep and goats. The flowers are favourites of hummingbirds in the Americas and by similar birds elsewhere.

S p e c i m e n s E x a m i n e d. KANDY DISTRICT: in outdoor cultivation, Pergola Garden and in the border of entrance roadway, Royal Botanic Garden, Peradeniya, 1550 ft alt., 18 Jan. 1974, shrubs about 7 ft tall, calyx and corolla orange-red, *H.N. & A.L. Moldenke & Jayasuriya 28134* (AAU, CAI, LL, PDA, US); cultivated in hedge, Rajawatte, Peradeniya, 9 Jan. 1974, *Sumithraarachchi 12* (PDA).

22. GLOSSOCARYA

Wall., Num. List [47]. 1829; Griff., Calcutta J. Nat. Hist. 3: 366. 1843. Type species: *Glossocarya mollis* Wall.

Glossocaryum Smitinand ex Moldenke, Phytologia 34: 274. 1976.

Mostly pubescent or grey-tomentose, scandent or subscandent shrubs; leaves opposite, short-petiolate, the blades mostly ovate or obovate to subrotund and entire; cymes dichotomous, closely many-flowered, usually in a large, dense, terminal, corymbose panicle; flowers small, numerous, often sessile; bracts small or minute or some of the lowermost sometimes foliaceous; calyx campanulate or tubular-campanulate, hardly at all accrescent, the limb spreading and 5-toothed, the teeth mostly broad-based; corolla mostly hypocrateriform or infundibular, the tube narrow-cylindric, the limb subbilabiate, 5-lobed or 5-fid, the 2 posterior lobes exterior and connate slightly higher, the 3 anterior ones subequal and flat or the middle interior (lower) one slightly larger and rather concave; stamens 4 (rarely 5), didynamous, inserted in the corolla-throat, long-exserted; filaments usually very long; anthers ovate or ovate-oblong, the thecae parallel, attached above the middle by a rather inconspicuous connective; style filiform, apically bifid, the branches subulate and apically stigmatiferous; ovary imperfectly 4-loculate, 4-ovulate; fruit capsular, oblong, somewhat widened apically, exserted from the fruiting calyx, 4-valvate, substipitate, the valves narrowly obovoid, their margins from above or slightly below the middle inflexed or involute, placentiferous, each holding one seed by its inflexed margin, dehiscing from the base or from below the middle, freeing a persistent, naked, central column, forming 1-seeded pyrenes which are extended basally in a short or linear wing; seeds oblong, erect, exalbuminous.

A small genus of 12 species and infraspecific taxa from Burma and Thailand east to Indo-China and Malaya, southwest to Ceylon, and south to Australia and the Great Barrier Reef; one species occasionally cultivated. In Ceylon represented only by a single species, *G. scandens*.

KEY TO THE FORMS

1 Leaf-blades pilose or puberulent beneath only on the venation, eventually glabrous.....
....f. **scandens**
1 Leaf-blades permanently densely pubescent on the entire lower surface....f. **pubescens**

Glossocarya scandens (L. f.) Trimen, Cat. 69. 1885. f. **scandens**. Moon, Cat. 1: 46. 1824; Schau. in A. DC., Prod. 11: 657 & 662. 1847; Thw., Enum. Pl. Zeyl. 243. 1861; Trimen, Cat. 69. 1885; Trimen, Handb. Fl. Ceylon 3: 361–362, Pl. 73. 1895; Gamble, Man. Indian Timb., ed. 2, 544–545. 1902; Willis, Cat. 69. 1911; Junell, Symb. Bot. Upsal. 4: 119 & 120. 1934; Abeywick., Ceylon J. Sci., Biol. Sci. 2: 218. 1959; Gunawardena, Gen. & Sp. Pl. Zeyl. 148. 1968. Type: *König s.n.* in *Herb. Linnaeus 809/6* from "circa flumen magnum Monesi-moti-kandel" in Ceylon, collected in 1777 (LINN).

Volkameria scandens L. f., Suppl. Pl. 292. 1781.
Volkameria foliis petiolatis, cordatis, ovatis, integerrimis; panicula corymbosa, terminali; ramulis dichotomis L. f. ex Lam., Enc. 8: 691, in syn. 1808.
Clerodendron linnaei Thw., Enum. Pl. Zeyl. 243. 1864.
Glossocarya linnaei (Thw.) Benth. ex Clarke in Hook. f., Fl. Br. Ind. 4: 598. 1885.—*G. linnaei* Clarke ex Moldenke, Phytologia 28: 458. 1974.
Glossocarya scandens (L. f.) Moon ex Moldenke, Prelim. Alph. List Invalid Names 54. 1940.
Clerodendron scandens (L. f.) Druce, Rep. Bot. Exch. Club 4: 615. 1917.

A straggling subscandent shrub or woody vine; branches divaricate, to 6 m long, the younger ones subterete, finely pilose-pubescent, sometimes converted into short, rigid, horizontal spines; bark pale, smooth; leaves decussate-opposite; petioles 4–6 mm long; leaf-blades ovate or obovate to obovate-rotund, 5–10 cm long, to 4 cm wide, apically acute or apiculate, entire, basally subcordate, pilosulous above when young, paler beneath and minutely glandular-punctate, pilose especially on the venation, glabrescent when mature, the venation finely reticulate; panicles terminal, corymbiform, compact, foliose, to 8 cm wide, incanous-pilose or grey-tomentose; peduncles rather long, axillary, divaricate, stiff, pubescent; bracts elliptic or oblong, about 8 mm long, apically acute, pubescent, sometimes the lower ones foliaceous; flowers sessile or nearly so, the pedicels almost obsolete; calyx hypocrateriform, to 3 mm long in anthesis, externally finely pubescent, the rim shortly 5-dentate, the teeth shallow or broadly triangular, apically rounded or acute; corolla white, externally pilose or strigose, the tube 6–8 mm long, slender, the limb 10 mm wide, the lobes oblong, 3–4 mm long, apically obtuse, the lower one slightly longer; filaments greatly elongate, about 2.5 cm long; style a little longer than the stamens; fruiting-calyx about 4 mm wide; capsule clavate-oblong, 6–9 mm long, 4 mm wide, blue when mature, apically very blunt, externally finely grey-strigose or tomentose; seeds linear-oblong.

D i s t r. Endemic to Ceylon and there rather rare in the forests of the dry region; cultivated in Mauritius.

V e r n. None reported.

S p e c i m e n s   E x a m i n e d. PUTTALAM DISTRICT: near Puttalam, July 1883, *s. coll. s.n.* (PDA). ANURADHAPURA DISTRICT: Kalawewa, February 1888, *s. coll. s.n.* (PDA); Anuradhapura, Aug. 1885, *s. coll. s.n.* (PDA). POLONNARUWA DISTRICT: in primary forest edge of Amban-ganga, Thunmodera, 7 June 1974, flowers white, *Waas 598* (LL, MOLDEN-KE, US). AMPARAI DISTRICT: locally common in thicket in low swampy ground, Waragoda Ara, 1 mile north of Panama, 26 Nov. 1970, vine-like shrub tangled in shrubs, flowers white, *Fosberg & Sachet 52923* (MOLDEN-KE, NY, US); along road near bridge on the river, Kalmunai, on the east coast, low altitude, 30 May 1971, climber, flowers white, *Kostermans 24327* (US). BATTICALOA DISTRICT: at 3rd milepost on the Batticaloa to Kal-kudah road, 11 Oct. 1970, *Kundu & Balakrishnan 187* (US); in dry zone on Rukam Tank bund, 150 ft alt., 12 June 1951, *Worthington 5297* (PDA); Naval Aru, March 1858, *s. coll. C.P. 1948* in part (PDA). HAMBANTOTA DIST-RICT: in open scrub forest with scattered tall trees on clay flat, bottom of abandoned irrigation tank, Andunoruwa Wewa, Ruhuna National Park, 3–5 m alt., 3 April 1968, liana, fruit green, turning blue, *Fosberg & Mueller-Dom-bois 50142* (MOLDENKE). PRECISE LOCALITY UNKNOWN: along large stream, "Monesi-moti-kandal", *König s.n.* (BM), *77 [Herb. Linnaeus 809/6]* (LINN); *s. coll. s.n.* (NY).

f. **pubescens** (Moldenke) Moldenke, Phytologia 38: 498. 1978. Type: *Jaya-suriya 2038* from Ceylon (see below) (NY).

Glossocarya scandens var. *pubescens* Moldenke, Phytologia 36: 437–438. 1977.

This form differs from the typical form of the species in having the lower leaf-surfaces permanently and densely pubescent.

S p e c i m e n s   E x a m i n e d. AMPARAI DISTRICT: in jungle beside rock outcrop, vicinity of Naval Aru, 6 miles south of Pottuvil, low altitude, 3 May 1975, scandent shrub, *Jayasuriya 2031* (LL, PDA, US); beside rock outcrops south of Komari bridge, north of Pottuvil, low altitude, 4 May 1975, very scandent shrub, branches to 6 m, corollas pure white, *Jayasuriya 2038* (AAU isotype, LL isotype, NY, holotype, PDA isotype, US isotype). BATTI-CALOA DISTRICT: on rock outcrop, vicinity of Rukam tank, low altitude, 7 May 1975, scandent shrub, *Jayasuriya 2108* (AAU, PDA, US). COLOMBO DISTRICT: Negombo, 1854, *s. coll. C.P. 1948* in part (BO, PDA). HAM-BANTOTA DISTRICT: rare on woody and shrubby hillside, 9 km beyond Tissamaharama, on the way to Kataragama, in the Yala region, 150 m alt., 9 March 1973, scandent, flowers in white corymbs, *Bernardi 14182* (US).

23. CARYOPTERIS

Bunge, Nov. Gen. Sp. Chin. Mongh. 27. 1835. Type species: *Caryopteris mongholica* Bunge.

Barbula Lour., Fl. Cochinch., ed. 1, 2: 366–367. 1790 [not *Barbula* Hedw., 1782].

Callipeltis Bunge ex Lindl., Nat. Syst. Bot., ed. 2, 278. 1836 [not *Callipeltis* Stev., 1829].

Mastacanthus Endl., Gen. Pl. 638. 1838.

Cariopteris Bunge apud Franch., Nouv. Arch. Mus. Hist. Nat. ser. 2, 6: 111. 1883.—*Carpyopteris* Bunge apud Parsa, Fl. Iran 4 (1): 535. 1949.—*Caryopteria* Grindal, Everyday Gard. India, ed. 16, 183. 1960.

Pseudocaryopteris Briq. ex Iljin, Acad. Sci. Bot. Inst. Dept. Repr. Mat. Hist. Fl. Veg. U.S.S.R. 3: 216. 1958.

Mostly bushes or shrubs, rarely small trees or subherbaceous, erect or rambling, often very fragrant, glabrous or incanous-tomentose; leaves decussate-opposite or ternate, deciduous, mostly short-petiolate, the blades entire or variously dentate, mostly apically acuminate, often minutely glandular-punctate with glistening yellow glands and more or less pubescent beneath; inflorescence cymose, the flowers borne in small, dense, often subcapitate, many-flowered, sessile, axillary cymes or sometimes forming narrow terminal corymbs, panicles, or thyrsi with opposite branching; pedicels short or obsolete; bracts small or minute; bracteoles none; calyx gamosepalous, campanulate, deeply 5-parted, the segments subequal, triangular or lanceolate; corolla zygomorphic, hypocrateriform or tubular, bilabiate, usually blue or violet to rose, rarely white, the tube cylindric, short, the limb spreading, 5-lobed, usually with 4 lobes subequal, ovate to oblong or obovate, flat, and spreading, the fifth lobe (anterior) interior in bud, longer, erect, concave or cucullate, with its margin fimbriate or crisped, sometimes the 2 posterior lobes smaller and the anterior 3 longer, the central one longest and laciniate; stamens 4, didynamous, inserted below the throat of the corolla-tube, exserted, the anterior ones longer; filaments filiform or basally thickened; anthers introrse, the 2 thecae at first parallel, later divaricate, attached apically, dehiscing by longitudinal slits, the connective inconspicuous; ovary imperfectly 4-locular, 2 locules divided in half by false partitions, with 2 parietal placentas, 2 ovules laterally attached on each and separated from each other by the false partitions, ascending, semianatropous; style filiform, elongate, exserted, often surpassing and curving above the anthers; stigma shortly and unequally bifid, the branches subulate; fruiting-calyx slightly enlarged and accrescent; fruit a very small, globose, dry capsule, enclosed by and smaller than the persistent calyx, separating into 4 concave valves with incurved margins, each valve with one seed, the valves separating basally forming 1-seeded dorsally compressed and unequally carinate or winged pyrenes (nutlets); seed oblong, erect, exalbuminous, the embryo fleshy, the radicle inferior.

A genus of about 25 specific and infraspecific taxa falling into two quite distinct subgenera, one of northern temperate and the other of southern tropical distribution. Native from China, Mongolia, and Japan south to the Himalayan region of Pakistan, Tibet, Nepal, Bhutan, and India, east to northern Burma and Thailand. Several species are rather widely cultivated for ornament in both hemispheres. In Ceylon represented only by the following species.

Caryopteris odorata (Hamilton) B.L. Rob., Proc. Amer. Acad. Arts 51: 531. 1916; Clarke in Hook. f., Fl. Br. Ind. 4: 597. 1885; Watt, Dict. Econ. Prod. India 2: 206. 1889; Gamble, Man. Indian Timb., ed. 2, 544. 1902; Collett, Fl. Siml. 381, fig. 121. 1902; Brandis, Indian Trees 512. 1906; Haines, Bot. Bihar & Orissa 4: 723. 1922; Junell, Symb. Bot. Upsal. 4: 115. 1934; Sastri, Wealth India 2 (R): 90. 1950; Parker, For. Fl. Punjab, ed. 3, 576. 1956; Maheshwari, Fl. Delhi 280. 1963. Type: *Roxburgh s.n.* from Bengal, probably in the East India Company herbarium (K).

Volkameria odorata [Hamilton] ex Roxb., Hort. Beng. 46. 1814.—*V. odorata* Roxb. ex Clarke in Hook. f., Fl. Br. Ind. 4: 597. 1885.—*V. odorata* [Buch.-Ham.] Roxb. apud Jacks. in Hook. f. & Jacks., Ind. Kew. 2: 1219. 1895.
Clerodendron odoratum Buch.-Ham. ex D. Don, Prod. Fl. Nepal. 102. 1825.—*C. odoratum* D. Don ex Schau. in A. DC., Prod. 11: 625. 1847.—*C. odoratum* (Hamilton) D. Don ex B.L. Rob., Proc. Amer. Acad. Arts 51: 531. 1916.
Clerodendrum helianthifolium Wall. ex G. Don in Loud., Hort. Brit., ed. 1, 247. 1830.—*Clerodendron helianthemifolium* Wall. ex Steud., Nom. Bot. Phan. 2: 383. 1840.
Clerodendron gulmasta Hamilton ex Wall., Num. List 87. 1831.
Caryopteris wallichiana Schau. in A. DC., Prod. 11: 625. 1847.—*C. wallichianum* Schau. ex MacMillan, Trop. Pl. Gard., ed. 5, 104. 1943.—*Caryopteria wallichiana* Grindal, Everyday Gard. India, ed. 16, 183. 1960.

Small or rather large spreading or straggling shrubs, usually rather bushy, erect or suberect, 1–5 m tall, *Buddleia*-like in general appearance, often evergreen, mostly nearly glabrous when mature, more or less canescent-pubescent when young; stems reddish; branches tetragonal, ascending, the young shoots greyish-pubescent or -subtomentose, eventually glabrescent, annulate at the nodes; bark thin, grey, papery, peeling off in vertical strips; wood dark grey, moderately hard, with the scent of *Prunus avium* wood; leaves decussate-opposite, short-petiolate, odorous when crushed; petioles 6–14 mm long; leaf-blades elliptic or oblong-lanceolate to lanceolate, 3–10 cm long, 1–3.5 cm wide, apically acuminate, basally cuneate, crenate-serrate along the margins or entire (var. *integrifolia*), canescent-puberulent or cinereous-pubescent (var. *integrifolia*); cymes axillary, short and dense, or mostly aggregated in narrow terminal thyrsi, 5–12.5 cm long, 2–3 cm wide, incanous-pubescent throughout, glandulose; bracts linear, 2–2.5 mm long, or minute, apically acute, pubescent; peduncles dark purple; flowers with a sweet fragrance, sometimes faint; calyx campanulate, 2–4 mm long, persistent, externally pubescent, deeply 5- (rarely 6-) fid to below the middle, the segments triangular; corolla bilabiate, varying from blue, blue-violet, or bluish-purple to light violet, light mauve, purplish, lavender, or lilac, sometimes yellow in the throat, sometimes with some white or purplish-white lobes, or all white (f. *albiflora*), the tube 8–12 mm long, glandulose, the limb spreading, 1.2–2 cm wide, 5-lobed, the 4 upper lobes oblong, subequal, about 6 mm long, apically rounded, the 5th (lower) lobe slightly larger, nearly 8 mm long, broader, mostly darker blue and apically notched or obcordate; stamens 4, didynamous, slightly exserted from the corolla-tube but shorter than the pistil; style long-exserted; stigma bifid; ovary imperfectly 4-locular; fruiting-calyx divided to the middle, the segments lanceolate, erect, to 6 mm long, each usually 3-ribbed; capsule nearly dry, dark blue or bluish, globose, 4–6 mm long and wide, closely pubescent, somewhat 4-lobed, ultimately separating into 4 concave valves, each winged along one margin and bearing one seed. Chromosome number: 2n=40.

D i s t r. Native from northern Pakistan, Nepal, Bhutan, Sikkim, and northern India to Thailand, north to southern China; cultivated for ornament in southern Asia, Egypt, Rhodesia, and elsewhere.

U s e s. The wood of this species is used for making walking-sticks and canes in India. The shrub is planted as a hedge around gardens and in parks for its profuse sweet-smelling flowers and dense foliage. It may be propagated by cuttings, but may be severely injured or killed by severe frosts.

V e r n. Among some 15 names recorded from various parts of its range are: Chingari, Karui, Malet, Moháni, Moni, and Shechin. In English members of the genus are usually called: Bluebeard.

N o t e s. In addition to varieties based on leaf-margin and corolla-colour, there are cultivated in India a stiffly erect and a gracefully spreading variety. The pollen morphology is described by Erdtman (Svensk Bot. Tidskr. 39: 283–284. 1945) and by Nair & Rehman (Bull. Bot. Gard. Lucknow 76: 21. 1962).

S p e c i m e n s E x a m i n e d. KANDY DISTRICT: herbaceous grounds, Royal Botanic Garden, Peradeniya, April 1888, *s. coll. 125/49* (PDA); Students' Garden, Royal Botanic Garden, Peradeniya, 6 feet tall, *s. coll. s.n.* (PDA).

24. HYMENOPYRAMIS

Wall., Num. List [25], no. 774, hyponym. 1829; Griff., Calcutta J. Nat. Hist. 3: 365. 1843. Type species: *Hymenopyramis brachiata* Wall.

Hymenolepis Craib ex Moldenke, Résumé Suppl. 3: 32, in syn. 1962 [not *Hymenolepis* Cass., 1817, nor Kaulff., 1824].

Hymenospyranis Wall. ex Moldenke, Phytologia 23: 432, in syn. 1972.—*Hymenofyramus* Wall. ex Moldenke, Phytologia 23: 432, in syn. 1972.

Subscandent shrubs or small trees; branches elongate, the younger parts often more or less canescent-pubescent; leaves opposite, decussate, simple, the blades mostly membranous or chartaceous, entire; inflorescence axillary and terminal, cymose, the cymes mostly loosely many-flowered, mostly aggregated in pyramidal terminal panicles; flowers mostly very small; bracts usually small or even minute; calyx gamosepalous, mostly quite small, 4-dentate or shortly 4-fid; corolla gamopetalous, zygomorphic, subinfundibular or somewhat hypocrateriform, the tube cylindric, usually short, about equalling the calyx, apically widened into the throat, the limb obliquely spreading, 4-parted, the lobes slightly unequal or subequal, the anterior one inside in bud, the others usually longer; stamens 4, inserted in the throat of the corolla, subequal, exserted; anthers ovate, erect, bilocular, the thecae parallel, dehiscing by longitudinal slits; ovary bilocular, each locule imperfectly again 2-locular and 2-ovulate, the ovules laterally attached below the apex; style elongate, capillary, exserted; stigma bifid; fruiting-calyx utricular, greatly expanded, membranous-hyaline, reticulate, inflated, broadly or shortly alate, the apex often closed; capsule small, globose, included by the utricle, 4-valved, the valves deciduous, crustaceous, often externally villosulous, the placentae usually cohering in a 4-alate central axile column or finally separating from each other, the margins inflexed and seed-bearing; seeds attached below the apex, pendulous, 3-angled, exalbuminous, the testa rather thick, the radicle inferior.

A small genus of about eight specific and infraspecific taxa found from north and central India and Upper Burma to Thailand and Indo-China; one species sometimes cultivated as a specimen plant. In Ceylon represented only by the following species.

Hymenopyramis brachiata Wall., Num. List [25], no. 774, hyponym. 1829; Griff., Calcutta J. Nat. Hist. 3: 365. 1843; Voigt, Hort. Suburb. Calc. 472. 1845; Schau. in A. DC., Prod. 11: 626. 1847; Bocq., Rev. Verbenac. 113, Pl. 11, fig. 1–10. 1863; Kurz, For. Fl. Burma 2: 258. 1877; Clarke in Hook. f., Fl. Br. Ind. 4: 598. 1885; Gamble, Man. Indian Timb., ed. 2, 545. 1902; Brandis, Indian Trees 505. 1906; Junell, Symb. Bot. Upsal 4: 95 & 98, fig. 149 & 150. 1934. Type: *Wallich Herb.* 774 from Tuong Dong, along the Myitnga River, tributary of the Irawaddy, Pegu, Upper Burma, collected in 1826, East India Company Herbarium (K).

Hymenospyranis brachiata Wall. ex Moldenke, Phytologia 23: 432. 1972.

A large scandent or rambling deciduous shrub, about 3 m tall, or rarely a small tree, 4–6 m tall; leaves decussate-opposite, short-petiolate; petioles about 8 mm long; leaf-blades ovate, about 9 cm long and 1.5 cm wide, apically acuminate, entire, basally obtuse or rhomboid, glabrate above when mature, grey-pubescent or -tomentose beneath; terminal panicles to 30 cm long and 20 cm wide, leafy below, grey-tomentose throughout; calyx about 1 mm long during anthesis; corolla white or cream-colour to greenish, about 3 mm long, externally pubescent; utricle ovoid, 8–13 mm wide, ventricose, acutely 4-alate, the mouth very small to minute; capsule 3–4 mm long, completely enclosed by the utricle, fulvous-hirsute.

D i s t r. This species is apparently widely cultivated (and perhaps native) in northern and central India and certainly native from Upper Burma and Thailand to Indo-China; occasionally cultivated as a specimen plant in Ceylon, Java, England, and perhaps elsewhere.

V e r n. The only ones reported are: Chintheletneve and Konkang from India.

S p e c i m e n s   E x a m i n e d. KANDY DISTRICT: South Garden, Royal Botanic Garden, Peradeniya, 15 July 1902, creeping shrub, *s. coll. s.n.* (PDA), in Section K, Feb. 1898, climbing shrub, *s. coll. s.n.* (PDA); cultivated, Royal Botanic Garden, Peradeniya, 27 June 1904, *Hallier C. 246* (HBG); LOCALITY UNKNOWN: *s. coll. 125/54* (PDA).

ZINGIBERACEAE

(by B.L. Burtt and R.M. Smith*)

Lindley, Key Struct. Phys. Syst. Bot. 69. 1835. Type: *Zingiber* Boehm.

Rhizomatous herbs; rhizome usually fleshy, sympodial, each element terminating in a leafy or flowering shoot. Leaf shoots with few to many blades, either arranged spirally and with tubular sheaths (*Costus*) or distichously arranged, the sheaths then usually open on the side opposite the lamina (sheaths closed in *Zingiber cylindricum*). Inflorescence occasionally surrounded by sterile bracts, terminal on the leafy shoot or borne directly on the rhizome at the base of a leafy shoot or remote from it. Flowers solitary in the axils of bracts or in cincinni, with or without bracteoles (secondary bracts**). Calyx tubular, often unilaterally split. Corolla tube slender, often exceeding the calyx, divided into 3 subequal lobes. Labellum (anterior staminode) adnate at the base to the corolla tube, almost always the most conspicuous feature of the flower. Lateral staminodes usually present, either as conspicuous petaloid structures or small subulate teeth. Fertile stamen one only; anther more or less sessile or with a distinct filament, thecae separated, parallel or divergent, dorsal connective sometimes developing into an appendage (anther-crest). Style linear, held between the anther-thecae; stigma usually expanded. Ovary inferior, unilocular with parietal placentation or trilocular, or incompletely so, with placentation axile. Epigynous glands ("stylodes") forming erect outgrowths on top of the ovary (Zingiberoideae), in Costoideae replaced by 2 septal nectary glands which arise towards the top of the ovary. Fruit a dehiscent capsule or fleshy berry. Seeds arillate.

Over 40 genera and about 1,000 species; the Zingiberoideae occur mainly in the tropics of the Old World with some representatives in the New World tropics and subtropical Asia. The Costoideae is poorly represented in the Old World.

Twelve genera, including three probably found only in cultivation, occur in Sri Lanka. Of 36 species 12 may be endemic. The Zingiberaceae are most abundant in lowland and midmontane primary forest, less so in secondary forest. They are rarely encountered in the dry zones.

*Royal Botanic Garden, Edinburgh.

**The convenient and widely used term 'bracteole' is used throughout to refer to all bracts arising on the cincinnus.

Zingiberaceae is of considerable importance as a spice family and includes ginger (*Zingiber officinale*), turmeric (*Curcuma longa*) and cardamom (*Elettaria cardamomum*). Several species, notably *Zingiber zerumbet, Costus speciosus, Curcuma zedoaria* and *C. aromatica,* are used medicinally.

The vernacular names given below are as in Trimen, with additions culled from *A Provisional Index to the Local Names of the Flowering Plants of Ceylon* by R.N. de Fonseka & S. Vinasithamby, 1971.

K. Schumann's account in Das Pflanzenreich (1904) is the most recent treatment of the family as a whole. It is unsatisfactory in many ways and the work of Valeton, dealing mainly with the Zingiberaceae of Java, and Holttum's account of the family in the Malay Peninsula, both based largely on living plants, show the inevitable deficiencies of a herbarium investigation such as that of K. Schumann (see Valeton, Bull. Inst. Bot. Buitenzorg 20: 1–99. 1904; Bull. Jard. Bot. Buitenzorg ser. 2, 27: 1–167. 1918; l.c. ser. 3, 3: 128–179. 1921; and Holttum, Gard. Bull. Singapore 13: 1–249. 1950).

Current studies on the family include those of Burtt & Smith (Notes Roy. Bot. Gard. Edinburgh 1972→). Much of this work has been concerned with the enormous difficulties of nomenclature and typification with which the family abounds. The problem of the typification of *Curcuma longa* was one of those that had to be resolved before this flora account could be finalized (Burtt, Notes Roy. Bot. Gard. Edinburgh 35: 209–215. 1977).

Remarkably little herbarium material of Zingiberaceae has been collected from Sri Lanka since the time of Thwaites and a number of species are known only from the type material, which is often inadequate.

Zingiberaceae may be divided into the following subfamilies and tribes, all of which have representatives in Sri Lanka.

KEY TO THE SUBFAMILIES AND TRIBES

1 Leaves spirally arranged; sheaths and ligules tubular; lateral staminodes and external epigynous glands absent, but septal nectary glands present; aromatic oil cells absent.... ....Subfam. **Costoideae**
1 Leaves distichous; sheaths open on side opposite lamina (except in *Zingiber cylindricum*); lateral staminodes present (either petaloid or small subulate teeth on either side at the base of the lip); epigynous glands present (in the Sri Lankan species); aromatic oil cells present...Subfam. **Zingiberoideae**
  2 Ovary unilocular with parietal placentation; anther long exerted on an arched ascending filament...tribe **Globbeae**
  2 Ovary trilocular with axile placentation, or unilocular with basal or free columnar placenta
    3 Style exserted well beyond the anther tip; the elongated anther-crest wrapped around the style; plane of distichy of leaves parallel to the rhizome........tribe **Zingibereae**
    3 Style not far exserted beyond anther tip; anther-crest, if present, never wrapped round style; plane of distichy of leaves parallel or transverse to rhizome
      4 Distichy of leaves parallel to rhizome; lateral staminodes petaloid, free from labellum .... tribe **Hedychieae**

4 Distichy of leaves transverse to rhizome; lateral staminodes represented by small teeth at the base of the labellum or 0.....................................tribe **Alpineae**

KEY TO THE GENERA

1 Leaves spirally arranged; sheaths tubular, lateral staminodes, epigynous glands and aromatic oil cells absent...**1. Costus**
1 Leaves distichously arranged, sheaths usually open on one side; lateral staminodes often present, as petaloid outgrowths or teeth at base of lip, more rarely absent; epigynous glands and aromatic oil-cells always present
  2 Style exserted well beyond anther-thecae and enfolded in long anther-crest, giving beaked appearance to anther...**2. Zingiber**
  2 Style not exserted much beyond anther-thecae; anther-crest, if present, flat
    3 Bracts of the inflorescence adnate to each other, or to axis in lower part, forming a pouch; anther versatile, spurred basally.............................**4. Curcuma**
    3 Bracts free to base; anther never truly versatile, not spurred basally
      4 Bracts of the inflorescence distichous and inflorescence laterally compressed.......
      ....**6. Boesenbergia***
      4 Bracts of the inflorescence spirally arranged
        5 Inflorescence terminal on a leafy stem
          6 Filament long, anther exserted
            7 Filament strongly curved in upper part, style often becoming separated from it and forming a bow-string across the curvature; ovary unilocular; flowers under 3 cm long, often replaced by bulbils...............................**3. Globba**
            7 Filament only slightly curved, if at all; ovary trilocular; flowers at least 7 cm long, never replaced by bulbils...............................**5. Hedychium**
          6 Filament short, anther included
            8 Bracts 2–3 cm long, well spaced on main axis....................**11. Elettaria**
            8 Bracts 0 or minute, if over 2 cm long then inflorescence congested....**8. Alpinia**
        5 Inflorescence basal or arising from long rhizomes
          9 Inflorescence arising near the base of a leaf frond
          10 Staminodes large, petaloid; leaves all basal...................**7. Kaempferia***
          10 Staminodes small or absent, leaf-frond well developed
            11 Bracts subtending solitary flowers
              12 Inflorescence with an involucre of pink sterile bracts; filament and base of labellum forming a short tube above insertion of the petals.....**9. Nicolaia***
              12 Inflorescence without sterile bracts; filament not forming a tube with base of labellum...**10. Amomum**
            11 Bracts subtending cincinni (or rarely outermost bracts subtending a solitary flower)...**8. Alpinia**
        9 Inflorescence arising from wandering rhizomes
          13 Anther not crested; flowers in cincinni.........................**11. Elettaria**
          13 Anther crested; flowers solitary in axils of bracts
            14 Anther-crest very large, more or less equalling labellum; flower resupinate; leaf-frond very short (i.e. leaves appearing basal)..........**12. Cyphostigma**
            14 Anther-crest much smaller than labellum; leaves forming an erect frond......
            ....**10. Amomum**

*Non-native genera.

1. COSTUS

L., Sp. Pl. 1: 2. 1753; L., Gen. Pl. ed. 5. 2. 1754; Baker in Hook. f., Fl. Br. Ind. 6: 249. 1892; Schum. in Pflanzenr. Zing. 378. 1904. Type species: *Costus arabicus* L.

Stems branched or unbranched, stout, leafy. Leaves spirally arranged; sheath tubular, its apex forming a short ligule across the base of the blade. Inflorescence dense, terminal on a leafy shoot (in Sri Lankan plants) or on a short leafless shoot. Bracts usually broad and overlapping, each subtending 1 or 2 flowers. Bracteoles non-tubular (in the Asian species). Calyx tubular, more or less 3-lobed. Corolla-tube longer or shorter than calyx, divided into 3 subequal lobes. Labellum showy, lateral staminodes 0. Stamen with a broad petaloid filament, anther-thecae placed in centre or at least well below apex. Ovary trilocular, with 2 septal glands near the apex.

About 70 species, poorly represented in Asia, 40 native to the New World, c. 25 occurring in Africa.

KEY TO THE SPECIES

1 Upper surface of leaves marked with bands of light and dark green; corolla tube twice the length of the calyx...**1. C. malortieanus**
1 Upper surface of leaves unmarked; corolla tube about the same length as the calyx....
....**2. C. speciosus**

1. Costus malortieanus Wendl., Hamburger Garten-Blumenzeitung 19: 30. 1863; Maas, Fl. Neotrop. Monogr. 8: 72. 1972. Type: Costa Rica, *Wendland*.

Up to 1 m tall. Leaves shortly petiolate, to 20 × 10 cm, obovate, apiculate at the apex, cuneate basally, pubescent, upper surface patterned with bands of light and dark green; ligule 1 mm; sheaths reddish, hirsute. Inflorescence 4–9 cm long, ovoid. Bracts reddish-green, up to 4 × 4 cm, broadly ovate, obtuse, glabrous. Bracteole reddish, open to the base, up to 2 cm long, glabrous. Calyx to 1 cm long, shallowly lobed. Corolla yellow; tube about twice the length of the calyx; lobes narrowly obovate. Labellum yellow, up to 6 × 5 cm, obovate, lateral lobes striped dark red. Stamen white, tinged purple, to 5 cm long, narrowly elliptic. Capsule ellipsoid, glabrous.

D i s t r. Nicaragua and Costa Rica.

E c o l. Cultivated in most tropical countries, probably on account of the attractive leaves. The Lankan specimen was growing in shade, on the roadside edge of a forested gulley near a village.

S p e c i m e n E x a m i n e d. RATNAPURA DISTRICT: Ratnapura to Gilimale, *Burtt 6801* (PDA, E).

2. Costus speciosus (Koenig) Smith, Trans. Linn. Soc. London 1: 249. 1791;

Baker in Hook. f., Fl. Br. Ind. 6: 249. 1892; Trimen, Handb. Fl. Ceylon 4: 246. 1898. Type: Malaya, *Koenig*, Specimen lost.
Banksea speciosa Koenig in Retz., Obs. 3: 75. 1783.

Herb 2–3 m tall, becoming much branched. Leaves shortly petiolate or subsessile, up to 30 × 6 cm, oblong-acuminate, silky below, glabrous or adpressed hairy above, base narrowly rounded; ligule truncate, ciliate. Inflorescence 3–5 cm long, more or less globose, but lengthening with age. Bracts to 1.5 cm long, ovate-acute, usually densely but minutely pubescent, green flushed red or bright red, with a narrow fleshy subapical protuberance. Bracteoles 1 cm long, keeled, ciliate on the margins. Calyx c. 2–3 cm, trilobed. Corolla-tube equal to or shorter than the calyx; lobes ovate-acuminate. Labellum 5–8 cm wide, suborbicular, white with a creamy yellow median band, yellow-haired at throat. Stamen up to 5 × 1.5 cm, yellow at apex, hairy on back. Fruit bright red.

D i s t r. Indo-Malesia to New Guinea and Australia, also much cultivated throughout the tropics.
E c o l. Flowers April to October.
U s e s. The rhizome is used medicinally.
V e r n. Tebu, Koltan (S).
I l l u s t r. Jacquin, Ic. Pl. Rar. 1: t. 1. 1781, as *C. arabicus*.
S p e c i m e n s E x a m i n e d. RATNAPURA DISTRICT: Carney, Adam's Peak, *Hepper, Maxwell & Fernando 4528* (US). MONERAGALA DISTRICT: Between Passara & Moneragala near milestone 5, *Grierson 1139* (US). KURUNEGALA DISTRICT: Weudakanda, *Waas 761* (US). GALLE DISTRICT: Kottawa, *Waas 50* (US), ibidem, *Waas & Peeris 536-A* (US).

2. ZINGIBER

Boehmer apud Ludwig, Def. Gen. Pl. 89. 1760, nom. cons.; Benth. & Hook. f., Gen. Pl. 3: 646. 1883; Baker in Hook. f., Fl. Br. Ind. 7: 243. 1892; Schum. in Pflanzenr. Zing. 165. 1904. Type species: *Amomum zingiber* L. (=*Zingiber officinale* Roscoe).

Zingiber Mill., Gard. Dict. abr. ed. 4, 1754, nom. rejic.

Leafy shoots usually many-bladed. Inflorescence borne separately on a leafless peduncle, more rarely terminal on a leafy stem. Bracts usually large, imbricating, each subtending a single flower. Bracteoles open to the base. Calyx tubular. Lateral corolla lobes often joined together partly by their adjacent sides and to the labellum. Lateral staminodes adnate to the labellum thus forming a 3-lobed structure. Filament rather short; anther-connective prolonged into an elongated crest which embraces the curved upper part of the style. Stigma scarcely wider than style, ciliate round margins.

A large genus of perhaps about 100 species, widely distributed throughout tropical Asia. *Z. officinale* is the only species used commonly for flavouring food, but *Z. zerumbet* and *Z. purpureum* have medicinal properties and are cultivated extensively. Only 2 species are native in Sri Lanka.

Zingiber is readily distinguished from all other Zingiberaceae by the elongated curved anther-crest which embraces the upper part of the style.

KEY TO THE SPECIES

1 Leaf sheaths closed; ligule truncate...............................**1. Z. cylindricum**
1 Leaf sheaths open; ligule bilobed or 1.5–3.5 mm long and entire
  2 Labellum unspotted
    3 Ligule less than 5 mm long, bilobed; bracts pubescent............**2. Z. purpureum**
    3 Ligule 1.5–3.5 cm long, entire; bracts more or less glabrous..........**3. Z. zerumbet**
  2 Labellum spotted
    4 Leaves 5–8 cm wide; bracts narrowly lanceolate...................**4. Z. wightianum**
    4 Leaves less than 1.5 cm wide; bracts ovate.......................**5. Z. officinale**

1. Zingiber cylindricum Thw., Enum. Pl. Zeyl. 315. 1861; Baker in Hook. f., Fl. Br. Ind. 6: 247. 1892; Trimen, Handb. Fl. Ceylon 4: 257. 1898. Type: *C.P. 2287* (PDA, K, BM, CGE)—Fig. 1A.

Leaf shoots up to 2 m, rather slender; leaves sessile, up to 16 × 3 (–4.5) cm, lanceolate-acuminate, often with scattered pubescence below, sometimes glabrous; ligule more or less truncate, often pubescent; sheaths usually glabrous, tubular. Inflorescence borne separately from the leaves; peduncle 7–25 cm long, erect, clothed with lanceolate obtuse scales with sparsely pubescent tips; spike up to 10 cm long when fully developed, fusiform or cylindric. Bracts 2–3 × 1.5 cm, becoming smaller towards the apex of the inflorescence, oblong or ovate, margin white, membranous, with a small, usually sparsely pubescent apiculus, green in the young spike, becoming pink-tinged, finally bright red. Bracteoles 2–3 × 0.5–1.3 cm, becoming shorter and narrower in upper flowers, glabrous. Calyx c. 1.2 cm, unilaterally split, more or less truncate. Corolla pale yellow; tube up to 2 cm; dorsal lobe 2 × 0.6 cm, lanceolate-acuminate; lateral lobes narrower. Labellum 3-lobed, 2 cm long, 1.5–2 cm at widest part, midlobe 1–1.5 × 0.5–0.7 cm, oblong, emarginate; lateral lobes (staminodes) 5 × 5 mm, spreading. Anther subsessile, glabrous, 8–9 mm long, thecae parallel; crest more or less equal to the anther in length. Epigynous glands linear, c. 3 mm long. Ovary 4 mm long, pubescent. Capsule subquadrate, up to 1.5 cm in diameter, red; seed black with a white aril.

    D i s t r. Endemic.

    E c o l. Probably quite common in shady situations up to 1500 m. Flowers February to July.

    N o t e. *Z. cylindricum* shows considerable variation in leaf indumentum.

V e r n. Wal-inguru, Arankaha (S).

S p e c i m e n s E x a m i n e d. COLOMBO DISTRICT: Seeduwa, *Jaya-suriya 1245* (PDA, E-spirit only). KURUNEGALA DISTRICT: Weuda-kanda, *Waas 760* (US, E). KANDY DISTRICT: Watawala, *Burtt & Town-send 57* (E). GALLE DISTRICT: Petiduwa, Habaraduwa, *Cramer 3430* (US). LOCALITY UNKNOWN: *s. coll. C.P. 3699* (PDA, K, BM, CGE).

4. Zingiber wightianum Thw., Enum. Pl. Zeyl. 315. 1861; Baker in Hook. f., Fl. Br. Ind. 6: 244. 1892; Trimen, Handb. Fl. Ceylon 4: 257. 1896. Lectotype: *C.P. 2286* (PDA, K, BM, CGE)—**Fig. 1B.**

Zingiber squarrosum auct. non Roxb.; Wight, Ic. Pl. Ind. Or. 6: 16, t. 2004. 1853.

Stem to 2 m high. Leaves sessile or very shortly petiolate; oblong-lanceo-late, 20–35 × 5–8 cm, acuminate, pubescent (at least on midrib) below; ligule up to 5 mm long, membranous, bifid, lobes rather rounded, glabrous or slightly ciliate. Inflorescence ovate or oblong, up to 9 × 6 cm, borne termin-ally on the leafy stem or radically on a 5–8 cm peduncle; peduncle clothed with membranous sheaths. Bracts greenish-red, up to 5 × 1 cm, narrowly lanceolate, acuminate, lightly pubescent. Bracteoles greenish-red, a little shorter than the bracts, obtuse, lightly pubescent. Calyx translucent green with some red markings, c. 2 cm long, unilaterally split to about half way, obscurely 2- or 3-dentate, sparsely pubescent. Corolla-tube yellow-green, 2.5 cm long, pubescent; lobes yellow-orange, 2.5 cm × 0.5–0.8 cm, acuminate. Labellum yellow-orange, heavily patterned deep purple-red, c. 3 cm long, cuneate-obovate with 2 basal lateral lobes (staminodes) 1 × 0.5 cm. Anther al-most sessile, thecae usually just over 1 cm long, the curved, elongate crest about 8 mm long, dark purple-red. Epigynous glands 3–4 mm, linear, free from each other, rarely 3 present. Ovary 5 mm long, lightly pubescent. Fruit red, c. 2 cm long, oblong. Seed black with a white aril.

D i s t r. Fairly common in forests in low country up to 1500 m. Also oc-curs in South India.

E c o l. Flowers February to July.

N o t e. The occurrence of both radical and terminal inflorescences within a species has been noted in other members of the Zingiberaceae. In Sri Lanka, such diversity of habit is also found in *Alpinia abundiflora*.

S p e c i m e n s E x a m i n e d. POLONNARUWA DISTRICT: near Galoya, *Grierson 1030* (US, E); Alutoya, *Jayasuriya, Dassanayake & Bala-subramaniam 679* (PDA, US, E); between Habarana-Alutoya, *Jayasuriya & Townsend 1184* (US, E); Sacred area, *Dittus 70012001* (US). KANDY DIS-TRICT: E. of Madugoda, *Jayasuriya, H.N. & A.L. Moldenke & Sumithraara-chchi 1418* (K). HAMBANTOTA DISTRICT: Ruhuna National Park,

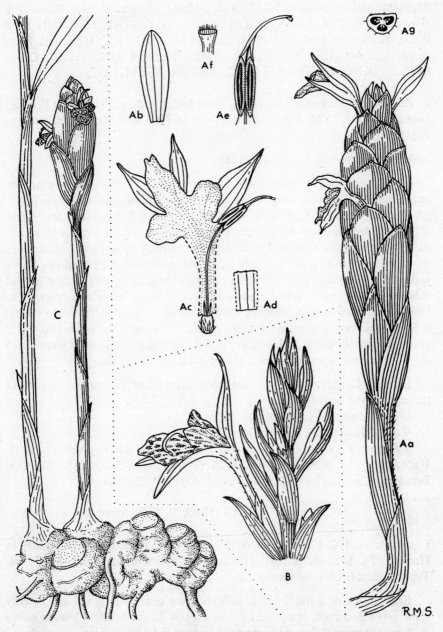

Fig. 1. A, *Zingiber cylindricum* Thw.: Aa, inflorescence × 1; Ab, bracteole × 1; Ac, flower, dissected, × 1; Ad, calyx, dissected, × 1; Ae, anther × 2; Af, stigma, much enlarged; Ag, ovary in T.S. × 2. B, *Z. wightianum* Thw., inflorescence × 1. C, *Z. officinale* Rosc., habit × 1.

Paranatotupola, *Cooray 69120805 R* (K); Menik Ganga, *Mueller-Dombois &
Wirawan 69030714* (US, K). MONERAGALA DISTRICT: 4 miles E of
Bibile, *Fosberg & Sachet 53142* (US). GALLE DISTRICT: Hiniduma Pass,
Bernardi 15448 (US); Mt. Kalubovitiyana, *Bernardi 15485* (US). LOCA-
LITY UNKNOWN: *Thwaites C.P. 2286* (PDA, K, BM, CGE).

5. Zingiber officinale Roscoe, Trans. Linn. Soc. London 8: 348. 1807; Roscoe,
Monandr. t. 83. 1824. Type: No specimen in LINN or Herb. Cliff (BM)—
Fig. 1C.

Amomum zingiber L., Sp. Pl. 1: 1. 1753.

Leafy stems to 2 m. Leaves sessile, up to c. 15 × 1.5 cm, narrowly lanceolate, acuminate, glabrous; ligule 2–4 mm long, membranous, shallowly bilobed. Peduncle up to 25 cm long, erect, clothed with 3–5 cm long lanceolate
sheaths. Inflorescence 4–5 × c. 2 cm, ovoid. Bracts c. 2.5 × 2 cm, green with a
paler membranous margin, the lower ones usually mucronate. Bracteoles
more or less equalling the bracts in length but narrower, membranous. Calyx
just over 1 cm long. Corolla-tube c. 2.5 cm long; lobes dull yellow, dorsal
lobe up to 2 × 1 cm, markedly narrowed at the apex; laterals narrower. Labellum dull dark purple, blotched creamy-yellow; lateral lobes (staminodes)
c. 6 × 4 mm, free almost to the base; median lobe more or less round, 1–1.2
cm wide. Anther-crest dark purple, c. 5–8 mm long. Epigynous glands c. 5
mm, linear, free from each other. Ovary 3 × 2 mm, glabrous.

D i s t r. Country of origin unknown. Cultivated in tropical countries
throughout the world.

U s e s. The root ginger of commerce.

V e r n. Inguru (S); Inji, Shukku (T).

S p e c i m e n s   E x a m i n e d. COLOMBO DISTRICT: Colombo, 1838,
Walker s.n. (E). KANDY DISTRICT: University Botany Dept. Garden,
Peradeniya, *Jayasuriya & Dassanayake 1246* (PDA, E-spirit only).

3. GLOBBA

L., Mant. alt. 170. 1771; Benth. & Hook. f., Gen. Pl. 3: 640. 1883; Baker in
Hook. f., Fl. Br. Ind. 6: 201. 1890; Schum. in Pflanzenr. Zing. 132. 1904.
Type species: *Globba marantina* L.

Erect herbs of slender habit. Inflorescence usually terminal on a leafy
stem, often decurved, sometimes bearing a few sterile bracts. Flowers borne
in few to several-flowered cincinni subtended by bracts, or replaced
by bulbils. Bracteoles open to base. Calyx funnel-shaped, 3-lobed. Corolla
tube slender, well exserted from the calyx; lobes spreading or deflexed. Lateral staminodes attached to corolla-tube at the same level as the corolla

lobes and equalling or exceeding them in length. Labellum connate to the filament in a slender tube about 1 cm above the staminodes, auriculate at the base, the free apical part bilobed. Filament long, slender, curved, with inflexed edges strongly curved in upper part, the style often becoming separated from it and forming a bow-string across the curvature; anther small with parallel thecae which often bear 2 or 4 lateral appendages, crest not or hardly produced. Ovary unilocular, placentation parietal. Fruit a small dehiscent capsule. Seed with a lacerate aril.

About 100 species are recognized, the majority occurring within the northern monsoon area from the eastern Himalayas to Burma, Thailand and Indo-China but also well represented in Malesia.

Globba marantina L., Mant. alt. 170. 1771; Smith, Exot. Bot. 2: 85, t. 103. 1806; Baker in Hook. f., Fl. Br. Ind. 6: 206. 1890. Type: Sheet *45.1* (LINN).

Globba bulbifera Roxb., Asiat. Res. 11: 358. 1810; Thw., Enum. Pl. Zeyl. 315. 1861; Baker in Hook. f., Fl. Br. Ind. 6: 206. 1890; Trimen, Handb. Fl. Ceylon 4: 240. 1898; Fischer in Gamble, Fl. Pres. Madras 3: 1481. 1928. Type: Roxburgh, imperfect sketch, lost?
Globba marantinoides Wight, Ic. Pl. Ind. Or. 6: 15, t. 2001. 1853; Trimen, Cat. 91. 1885. Type: South India, Anamally Forest, *Wight*.

Up to 30 cm tall. Leaves sessile or very shortly petiolate, up to 18 × 5 cm (usually much smaller), oblong to broadly lanceolate, acute at apex, attenuate at the base, minutely puberulous below; ligule short, membranous, white. Inflorescence up to 10 cm long. Bracts lax, 1–2 cm long, broadly ovate, those at the base of the spike at least subtending ovoid bulbils, the remainder subtending few-flowered cincinni. Bracteoles 0.5–1 cm, ovate. Calyx 4–5 mm long, 3–lobed. Corolla yellow; tube c. 1 cm long; lobes ovate, 4 mm long. Lateral staminodes a little longer than the petals. Labellum deeply bifid. Filament to 15 mm; anther with 2 spreading appendages on each side. Capsule oblong, smooth.

D i s t r. Indo-Malesia.

E c o l. Grows in the dry zone.

V e r n. Hinguru-piyali (S); Kechulu-Kalanga (T) (Both names also attributed to *Kaempferia galanga*).

S p e c i m e n s   E x a m i n e d. BATTICALOA DISTRICT: between Ampare & Samanthurai, *s. coll. C.P. 3563* (PDA, K, CGE).

4. CURCUMA

Roxb., Asiat. Res. 11: 329. 1810 nom. cons. prop; Benth. & Hook. f., Gen. Pl. 3: 643. 1883; Baker in Hook. f., Fl. Br. Ind. 6: 209. 1890; Schum., Pflan- zenr. Zing. 99. 1904. Sp. typ. cons. prop.: *Curcuma longa* L.

Rhizome densely fleshy, branched, often with tuber-bearing roots. Leaves basal. Inflorescence terminal on a leafy shoot (i.e. borne in the centre of a leaf tuft) or on a separate shoot and sometimes precocious; spike pedunculate, erect. Bracts joined to each other for about half their length, thus forming pouches, the free ends usually spreading, each subtending a cincinnus of 2–7 flowers; uppermost bracts often larger, differently coloured and sterile forming a coma. Bracteoles open to the base. Calyx tubular, unilaterally split, unequally toothed. Corolla-tube more or less funnel-shaped, limb 3-lobed. Lateral staminodes petaloid, oblong, folded under the dorsal petal. Labellum with a thickened central portion and thinner side lobes which overlap the lateral staminodes. Filament short and broad, constricted at the apex; anther versatile, usually spurred at the base; connective occasionally produced into a small crest. Ovary trilocular. Capsule ellipsoid.

Indo-Malesia to S. Pacific: introduced species elsewhere in the tropics. Perhaps about 40–50 species, with numerous cultivated races.

To maintain *Curcuma* in its current sense it must be attributed to Roxburgh and put on the list of *Nomina generica conservanda*. The original *Curcuma* L. was based on *C. rotunda* L., which is now known as *Boesenbergia rotunda* (L.) Mansf. (see below, gen. no. 6).

KEY TO THE SPECIES

1 Inflorescence with coma of sterile bracts; corolla tube not exserted beyond the bract
  2 Inflorescence central to the leaf tuft and appearing with the leaves; rhizome bright orange within...**1. C. longa**
  2 Inflorescence lateral to the leaf tuft, often appearing before the leaves; rhizome yellow or yellowish-white within
    3 Leaves glabrous below; upper surface with a central purple cloud; bracts densely spotted..**2. C. zedoaria**
    3 Leaves pubescent below; uniformly green; bracts not densely spotted..............
    ....**3. C. aromatica**
1 Inflorescence without a coma of sterile bracts; corolla tube exserted from the bract
  4 Lower bracts spreading; inflorescence up to 15 cm long..............**4. C. albiflora**
  4 Lower bracts ascending; inflorescence 5 cm long or less.............**5. C. oligantha**

1. Curcuma longa L., Sp. Pl. 1: 2. 1753, pro max. parte; Baker in Hook. f., Fl. Br. Ind. 6: 214. 1890; Burtt, Notes Roy. Bot. Gard. Edinburgh 35: 209. 1977. Lectotype: *Manjella Kua* Rheede, Hort. Mal. 11: 21 t. 11. 1692.

Curcuma domestica Val. Bull. Jard. Bot. Buitenzorg 2 ser., 27: 31. 1918; Alston in Trimen Handb. Fl. Ceylon 6: 281. 1931. Type: Malaya, *Koenig*, specimen lost.

Rhizome orange within. Leaf tuft to 1 m; lamina green, up to 50 × 8 cm, lanceolate. Inflorescence 10–15 × 5–7 cm, appearing with the leaves and central to the leaf-tuft. Coma bracts white and green. Fertile bracts green, 5–6 cm long, adnate for less than half their length. Bracteoles up to 3.5 cm long. Corolla white; labellum with a central yellow band.

D i s t r. Cultivated throughout the tropics, not native in Sri Lanka.

U s e s. *C. longa* is the source of commercial turmeric (see The Wealth of India, 2: 402–405. 1950).

V e r n. Kaha (also attributed to *Bixa orellana*), Ath-kaha, Bim-kaha, Rata-kaha (S); Manchal (T).

S p e c i m e n s   E x a m i n e d. COLOMBO DISTRICT: Kalagedihena, *Amaratunga 2127* (PDA, sterile), 1838, *Walker s.n.* (E), *Christison s.n.* (E).

2. Curcuma zedoaria (Christm.) Roscoe, Trans. Linn. Soc. London 8: 354. 1807; Roscoe, Monandr. t. 10. 1825; Baker in Hook. f., Fl. Br. Ind. 6: 210. 1890; Trimen, Handb. Fl. Ceylon 4: 241. 1898; Burtt, Gard. Bull. Singapore 30: 59. 1977. Lectotype: *Kua* Rheede, Hort. Mal. 11: 13 t. 7. 1692—**Fig. 2.**

Amomum zedoaria Christm. in Christm. & Panzer, Linn. Pflanzensyst. 5: 12. 1779; Willd., Sp. Pl. 1: 7. 1797.
Curcuma zerumbet Roxb. Asiat. Res. 11: 332. 1810; Roxb., Pl. Corom. 3: t. 201. 1819; Alston in Trimen, Handb. Fl. Ceylon 6: 28. 1931, Nom. illegit. Type as for *C. zedoaria.*

Rhizome pale yellow-white, smells of camphor; tubers white. Leaf tufts to c. 1 m, of 4–6 leaves; petiole shorter than the lamina, winged; lamina 20–60 × 8–10 cm, oblong or narrowly oblong-lanceolate, acuminate, glabrous with a purple cloud down the centre of the upper surface. Inflorescence c. 10–18 × 6–8 cm, generally appearing before the leaves, produced laterally to the leaf tuft on a 5–15 cm sheath-covered peduncle. Coma bracts whitish at first, soon becoming bright rose-pink or crimson. Fertile bracts up to 5 × 3.5 cm, ovate, tips recurved, pale green with red-tinged margins, densely glandular-spotted, with at least some very short stiff hairs on the upper surface (often confined to the tips); bracts adnate to each other in the lower third. Bracteoles 1.5–2 × 0.5–1 cm, translucent white. Calyx 1–1.5 cm, whitish-green, deeply split dorsally, with 3 small triangular teeth. Corolla white or palest yellow; tube 2.5–3 cm long, funnel-shaped; dorsal lobe 1.3 × 1 cm, broadly triangular, apiculate and with a very faint pink tinge at the apex; lateral lobes narrower, obtuse. Labellum 1.5 cm wide, orbicular, pale yellow, thickened and deep yellow centrally, emarginate, very faintly red-tinged at edges in lower part. Lateral staminodes pale yellow, 1.5 × 1 cm, oblong. Filament c. 5 mm long; anther-thecae c. 7 mm long with incurving spurs. Epigynous glands 3–4 mm long, linear, free from each other. Ovary 4–5 mm, sparsely pubescent. Fruit ovoid, smooth, dehiscing irregularly.

D i s t r. Country of origin unknown. Cultivated and naturalized throughout India and S.E. Asia.

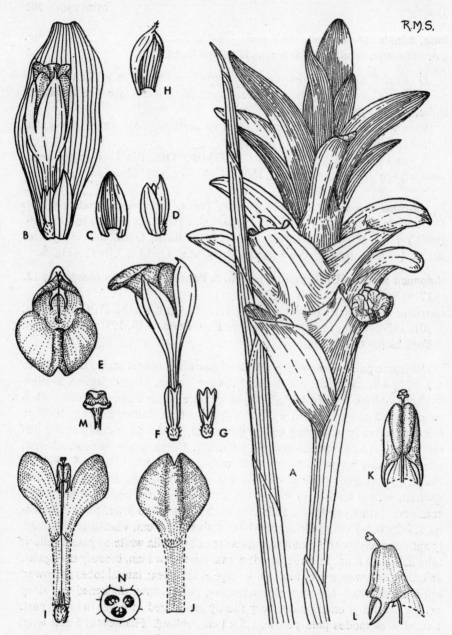

R.M.S.

Fig. 2. *Curcuma zedoaria* (Christm.) Rosc.: A, inflorescence ×1/2; bract, with cincinnus, ×1; C, first bracteole ×1; D, second bracteole, subtending remainder of
cincinnus, ×1; E, flower, from the front, ×1; F, flower, lateral view, ×1; G, calyx,
×1; H, dorsal petal ×1; I, corolla in L.S. showing stamen and lateral staminodes,
petals removed, ×1; J, labellum and corolla tube ×1; K, L, stamen and style ×3;
M, stigma ×6, N, ovary in T.S. ×3.

U s e s. The rhizome is used medicinally and in perfumery.

V e r n. Haran-kaha (also attributed to *C. albiflora*), Kanguni, Naharai (also attributed to *Kaempferia galanga*) (S); Pulan-kizhangu, Kichilick-Kilangu, Manchal, Kichilick-kizhangu (T).

S p e c i m e n s E x a m i n e d. RATNAPURA DISTRICT: Sinharaja, *Burtt 6803* (E); Bopathella Falls, near Kuruwita, Cult. R.B.G. Edinb. C 12867, *Burtt 6815* (E). KANDY DISTRICT: Ambagamuwa, *s. coll. C.P. 3373* (PDA). COLOMBO DISTRICT: Hanwella, *Amaratunga 2283* (PDA). KEGALLE DISTRICT: Arandara on Pindeniya Rd., *Amaratunga 2273* (PDA). GALLE DISTRICT: Pointe de Galle, 1 June, 1860, *Dubuc s.n.* (E); between Nagoda and Wanduramba, *Cooray 69042101* (PDA). LOCALITY UNKNOWN: *Koenig s.n.* (BM); *Brodie s.n.* (E).

3. Curcuma aromatica Salisb., Parad. Lond. t. 96. 1805/6; Thw., Enum. Pl. Zeyl. 316. 1861; Baker in Hook. f., Fl. Br. Ind. 6: 210. 1890; Trimen, Handb. Fl. Ceylon 4: 241. 1898. Type: Cult. *Greville*, no specimen.

Curcuma zedoaria Roxb. Asiat. Res. 11: 332. 1810; Roxb., Fl. Ind. 1: 23. 1820—non (Christm.) Roscoe, 1807.

Rhizome yellow within, aromatic; tubers yellow. Leaf tufts up to over 1 m, 5–7 leaves; petiole often as long as the lamina; lamina 40–70 × 10–14 cm, broadly lanceolate, acuminate, pubescent below. Inflorescence 15–30 × 9 cm, generally appearing before the leaves, produced laterally to the leaf tuft on a c. 5–8 cm sheath-covered peduncle. Coma bracts pink. Fertile bracts up to 6 cm long, tips recurved, pale greenish-white, slightly hairy on upper surface, adnate to each other in lower third. Bracteoles c. 2 cm long, white, lightly pubescent. Calyx about 2 cm long, dorsally split, 3-lobed, lightly pubescent. Corolla pinkish-white, tube just exceeding the calyx; dorsal lobe broadly ovate, arching over the anther, mucronate; lateral lobes narrower, oblong, mucronate. Labellum orbicular, obscurely 3-lobed, deep yellow. Lateral staminodes as long as the corolla lobes. Stamen? Fruit?

D i s t r. Probably wild in India and the E. Himalayas, perhaps native in Sri Lanka; rare.

V e r n. Dadakaha, Walkaha (S); Kasthuri-manjal (also attributed to *Berberis*) (T).

N o t e. No flowers of *C. aromatica* from Sri Lanka have been available for study, and the detail given above is based largely on Trimen. Investigation of fresh or spirit material might indicate important differences between the flowers of *C. aromatica* and *C. zedoaria*, notably in length of corolla tube in relation to the calyx and in shape of the lateral staminodes.

S p e c i m e n s E x a m i n e d. KANDY DISTRICT: near Gampola, *s. coll. C.P. 3705* (PDA); also at K, BM, CGE, LE, s. loc.

4. Curcuma albiflora Thw., Enum. Pl. Zeyl. 316. 1861; Baker in Hook. f., Fl. Br. Ind. 6: 215. 1890; Trimen, Handb. Fl. Ceylon 4: 242. 1898. Type: *C.P. 2737* (PDA, K, BM).

Leaf tuft of 5 (?) leaves, c. 35 cm tall (to tip of uppermost leaf); petioles up to 9 cm long; lamina c. 15 × 7 cm, oblong, acute, rounded at the base, glabrous. Flowering stem produced as the young leaves are developing, lateral to the leaf tuft, or from the centre of the tuft (i.e. terminal). Peduncle up to 12 cm, clothed with one or two sheaths up to 6 cm long, otherwise naked. Inflorescence up to 7 × 6 cm, coma absent. Fertile bracts spreading, 5 × 1.5 cm in lower part of spike, shorter towards apex, lanceolate to oblong-lanceolate, rounded at the apex, glabrous, joined to each other by their bases only. Cincinni few-flowered (2–3?). Bracteoles up to c. 2 × 0.8 cm, lanceolate, rounded at the apex. Calyx 1.3–1.8 cm, obscurely 2–3-lobed, unilaterally split. Corolla white, tube up to 3 cm; lobes oblong, obtuse; dorsal lobe broader than laterals. Labellum tinged yellow, suborbicular, emarginate. Stamen? Fruit?

D i s t r. Endemic, rare.

E c o l. Flowers February to June.

V e r n. Haran-kaha (also attributed to *C. zedoaria*) (S).

I l l u s t r. Bot. Mag. t. 5909. 1871.

S p e c i m e n s   E x a m i n e d. KEGALLE DISTRICT: Kitulgala, 14 March 1950, *Tunnard s.n.* (PDA), ibidem, *Balakrishnan NBK 610* (US, E), ibidem, Forest Reserve across Kelani Ganga, *Robyns 7222* (US). RATNAPURA DISTRICT: Bopathella Falls, near Kuruwita, *Burtt & Jayasuriya 6812* (E), *Thwaites C.P. 2737* (PDA, K, BM)—1 sheet at PDA from Maskeliya—others unlocalized.

5. Curcuma oligantha Trimen, J. Bot. 23: 245. 1885; Trimen, Handb. Fl. Ceylon 4: 242, t. 92. 1898; Baker in Hook. f., Fl. Br. Ind. 6: 215. 1890. Type: Uma Oya, *Trimen s.n.* (PDA).

Flowers produced before, or with the developing leaves from the base of a new leaf shoot. Fully developed leaf tufts c. 12 cm tall (7-leaved?); petioles to 1.5 cm; lamina pale green, mottled with dark green, up to 12 × 3 cm, ovate, acute, rounded or cordate at the base, glabrous. Peduncle c. 5–7 cm, clothed with a few brown membranous sheaths. Inflorescence c. 3–7 cm, narrow, few-flowered, one flower opening at a time. Coma absent. Fertile bracts few (up to 5?), ascending, up to 3 × 0.8 cm, lanceolate, with a lightly pubescent acute apex, joined to each other in lower quarter only. Cincinni probably up to 3-flowered. Bracteoles c. 1.5 × 0.4 cm, more or less triangular, elongated and narrowed at the apex, inner bracteoles smaller. Calyx c. 1.5 cm long, obscurely 2–3-lobed. Corolla white; tube 2.5 cm long, pubescent within; dorsal lobe 2 × 1 cm, ovate with a 2 mm long apiculate apex; lateral lobes smaller, rounded at apex. Lateral staminodes white, c. 1.5 × 0.6 cm, ovate, subacute. Labellum yellow at least centrally, c. 2 × 2 cm, shallowly emarginate, margin undulating. Filament c. 5 mm; anther crestless, c. 3 mm; basal spurs 1.5 mm, pubescent, converging at the tips. Epigynous glands 4 mm long, linear, free from each other. Ovary 3 × 2 mm, pubescent.

D i s t r. Endemic, or perhaps also in South India.

E c o l. In the dry zone. Said by Trimen to be rather common.

S p e c i m e n s   E x a m i n e d. BADULLA DISTRICT: north-west of Badulla, Uma-oya, near the Mahaweli R., Oct. 1884, *Trimen s.n.* (PDA); Hembarawa, *Jayasuriya 405* (PDA, US, E). ANURADHAPURA DISTRICT: Anuradhapura, *s. coll.* (coll. Brodie) *C.P. 3700* (PDA). POLONNARUWA DISTRICT: foot of Gunner's Quoin, 4 miles S. of Mahaweli R., Oct. 1893, *Neville s.n.* (PDA). MATALE DISTRICT: below Lagalla, *s. coll. s.n.* (PDA); Dikpatana, Laggala, *Jayasuriya 1833* (US). JAFFNA DISTRICT: Vadukkoddai, nr Jaffna, 8 Nov. 1951, *Koshy s.n.* (PDA).

5. HEDYCHIUM

Koenig in Retz., Obs. 3: 73. 1783; Benth. & Hook. f., Gen. Pl. 3: 642. 1883; Baker in Hook. f., Fl. Br. Ind. 6: 225. 1892; Schum., in Pflanzenr. Zing. 40. 1904. Type species: *Hedychium coronarium* Koenig.

Up to 2 m tall. Inflorescence terminal on a many-leaved stem. Bracts broad and imbricating, concealing the main rhachis or narrow and enfolding the flowers, each subtending a cincinnus of 2–6 flowers. Bracteoles usually tubular. Calyx tubular. Corolla tube usually exceeding the calyx; lobes long and narrow. Staminodes petaloid, usually as long as corolla lobes but wider. Labellum narrowed at the base, blade conspicuous, almost always bilobed. Filament, with few exceptions, long and slender. Anther-thecae parallel or slightly diverging, free at the base, connective not forming a crest. Ovary trilocular, placentation axile. Capsule globose or oblong. Seed with a lacerate aril.

About 45 species, mainly eastern Himalayan but a few known from South India and Malesia. Doubtfully native in Sri Lanka.

KEY TO THE SPECIES

1 Stamen twice as long as the labellum; flowers red . . . .**1. H. coccineum**
1 Stamen shorter than or only slightly exceeding the labellum; flowers white or yellow
  2 Flowers white, sometimes yellow or yellow-green in centre of labellum only; stamen
    shorter than labellum . . . .**2. H. coronarium**
  2 Flowers yellowish; stamen slightly exceeding the labellum . . . .**3. H. flavescens**

1. Hedychium coccineum [Buch.-Ham. ex] Smith in Rees, Cyclop. 17: 5. 1819;

rima (Wall.) Kuntze.

Gastrochilus Wall., Pl. As. Rar. 1: 22. 1829—non D. Don, 1825.

Leaves usually up to 4, forming a short erect stem. Inflorescence terminal bearing 2-ranked bracts each subtending a single flower. Bracteoles open to the base. Uppermost flower opening first. Corolla lobes more or less equal. Labellum often saccate, entire or sometimes emarginate. Lateral staminodes usually shorter than the petals. Filament about the same length as the anther; thecae parallel, dehiscing by slits or, more rarely, by pores; connective usually produced into a crest. Epigynous glands linear, free. Ovary trilocular or partially so or unilocular. Fruit ellipsoid.

Probably over 40 species, distributed throughout Indo-Malesia.

Boesenbergia rotunda (L.) Mansfield, Kulturpflanze 6: 239. 1958. Type: *Manja-Kua* Rheede, Hort. Mal. 11: t. 10. 1692.

Curcuma rotunda L., Sp. Pl. 1: 2. 1753.
Kaempferia pandurata Roxb., Asiat. Res. 11: 328, t. 2. 1810; Thw., Enum. Pl. Zeyl. 316. 1861; Baker in Hook. f., Fl. Br. Ind. 6: 220. 1890; Trimen, Handb. Fl. Ceylon 4: 243. 1898. Type: Sumatra, no specimen.
Gastrochilus rotundus (L.) Alston in Trimen, Handb. Fl. Ceylon 6: 281. 1931.
Boesenbergia pandurata (Roxb.) Schlechter, Feddes Repert Spec. Nov. Regni Veg. 12: 316. 1913.

Leafy shoot very short, 3–4-leaved; petioles 5–12 cm; lamina up to about 40 × 20 cm, elliptic, acute, slightly hairy on midrib below; ligule c. 5 mm long, of 2 triangular lobes. Inflorescence subsessile, enclosed by the leaf sheaths, densely flowered. Bracts up to 5 cm long, linear-lanceolate. Bracteoles same length as bracts but narrower. Calyx about 2 cm, bifid. Corolla pink; tube exceeding the bracts; lobes c. 1.5 cm, oblong. Lateral staminodes rather shorter and broader than corolla lobes, mottled purple. Labellum about 2.5 × 2 cm, panduriform, apex slightly bilobed. Filament 1 cm long; anther 5 mm, with a short reflexed bilobed crest.

D i s t r. Perhaps native in Java and Sumatra, widely cultivated throughout India and Malaysia.

U s e s. The rhizome is used medicinally in Sri Lanka.

V e r n. Ambakaha (S).

S p e c i m e n   E x a m i n e d. LOCALITY UNKNOWN: *s. coll. C.P. 3702* (PDA).

7. KAEMPFERIA

L., Sp. Pl. 1: 2. 1753; L., & Gen. Pl. ed. 5: 3. 1754; Benth. & Hook. f., Gen.

Pl. 3: 641. 1884; Baker in Hook. f., Fl. Br. Ind. 6: 218. 1890; Schum. in
Pflanzenr. Zing. 64. 1904. Type species: *Kaempferia galanga* L.

Leaves few, stem short or more or less absent. Inflorescence borne terminally on the leafy stem or on a separate branch of the rhizome and not contemporaneous with the leaves. Flowers spirally arranged, borne singly on the
main axis, each in the axil of a bract; bracteole small, bifid, or sometimes
split to the base. Calyx tubular, unilaterally split, shorter than or as long as
the corolla-tube. Corolla lobes more or less equal, spreading or reflexed.
Labellum deeply bilobed, showy. Staminodes petaloid. Anther sessile or
filament very short; thecae parallel, connective prolonged into a distinct
crest. Ovary trilocular.

About 30 species, widely distributed throughout tropical Asia.

KEY TO THE SPECIES

1 Flowers and leaves borne on separate branches of the rhizome and not contemporaneous
....**1. K. rotunda**
1 Flowers borne terminally to leaves.....................................**2. K. galanga**

1. Kaempferia rotunda L., Sp. Pl. 1: 3. 1753; Thw., Enum. Pl. Zeyl. 316. 1861;
Baker in Hook. f., Fl. Br. Ind. 6: 222. 1890; Trimen, Handb. Fl. Ceylon 4: 244.
1898. Type: No specimen at LINN.

Rhizome bearing oblong tubers up to 5 cm long. Leaves few, up to 30 ×
12 cm, oblong-acuminate, purple beneath, mottled green above. Inflorescence
appearing before the leaves, sessile, 4–6 flowered. Bracts imbricating, up to
3.5 cm long, oblong, acute. Bracteoles up to 2.5 cm long, bidentate. Calyx to
6 cm long, unilaterally split. Corolla-tube a little longer than the calyx; lobes
white, of equal length to tube, very narrow. Lateral staminodes white, about
5 cm long, oblong, held erect. Labellum lilac, as long as the staminodes,
deeply divided into 2 suborbicular lobes. Anther-crest longer than the thecae,
divided into 2 (4) lanceolate or subulate segments.

D i s t r. Country of origin uncertain, widely cultivated.
E c o l. Flowers March and April.
V e r n. Yawakenda, Lankenda, Saukenda (S).
I l l u s t r. Bot. Mag. t. 6054. 1873.
S p e c i m e n E x a m i n e d. LOCALITY UNKNOWN: *s. coll. C.P. 3175*
(PDA).

2. Kaempferia galanga L., Sp. Pl. 1: 2. 1753; Baker in Hook. f., Fl. Br. Ind.
6: 219. 1890; Trimen, Handb. Fl. Ceylon 4: 244. 1898. Type: sheet *8.1*
(LINN).

Leaves few, up to 15 × 10 cm, green, often with a narrow reddish edge above, paler below. Inflorescence sessile, of about 12 flowers, enclosed by the imbricating leaf sheaths. Bracts up to 4×1 cm. Bracteoles split to the base (thus each flower appears to have 2 bracteoles), about 3.5 cm long. Calyx 3 cm long. Corolla-tube 4.5–5 cm long; lobes white, 2.5 cm, narrow. Lateral staminodes white, at least 2 cm long, obovate. Labellum slightly broader than long, c. 2.5 cm broad, bilobed in upper two-thirds; lobes white with violet bands in basal half. Anther sessile, crest bilobed, strongly reflexed.

D i s t r. Native in India. Said by Trimen to be cultivated in gardens in Sri Lanka.

V e r n. Hinguru-piyali, Naharai (also attributed to *Curcuma zedoaria*) (S); Kechulu-Kalangu (T).

M a t e r i a l E x a m i n e d. None from Sri Lanka.

8. ALPINIA

Roxb., Asiat. Res. 11: 350. 1810, nom. cons.; Benth. & Hook. f., Gen. Pl. 3: 648. 1884; Baker in Hook. f., Fl. Br. Ind. 6: 252. 1892; Schum. in Pflanzenr. Zing. 308. 1904. Type species: *Alpinia galanga* (L.) Willd.

Catimbium Lest., Ann. Sci. Nat. Bot. 2 Sér. 15: 346. 1841.
Languas Small, Fl. S.E.U.S. ed. 2, 307. 1913.

Leafy shoots up to 12 m tall, more usually 2–4 m, many-bladed. Inflorescence a tightly congested head or a lax raceme or panicle, usually terminal on the leafy shoot, occasionally radical, sometimes with sterile bracts at the base. Fertile bracts subtending a cincinnus of 2–∞ flowers. Bracteoles tubular or non-tubular or absent. Calyx tubular, unilaterally split. Labellum often showy, or small and inconspicuous. Lateral staminodes present as small subulate teeth or lacking. Anther subsessile or with a well developed filament, connective (in the Sri Lankan species) not prolonged into a conspicuous crest. Capsule spherical, rarely elongate.

A large genus of perhaps some 200 species widely distributed throughout Indo-Malesia and S.E. Asia to Queensland. Also occurring in China and Japan. Two species are probably endemic in Sri Lanka.

KEY TO THE SPECIES

1 Inflorescence capitate, surrounded by sterile bracts
  2 Labellum and anther hairy; inflorescence terminal on a leafy stem; entire plant drying rufous brown . . . .**3. A. rufescens**
  2 Labellum and anther glabrous; inflorescence usually on a leafless peduncle separate from the leafy stem, rarely terminal; plant not drying rufous-brown
    3 Bracts, bracteoles and calyx pubescent; labellum without stripes; capsule ovate . . . . . .
. . . .**2. A. fax**

3 Bracts, bracteoles and calyx glabrous; labellum striped; capsule spherical..........
....**1. A. abundiflora**
1 Inflorescence paniculate or racemose, with well spaced cincinni, no sterile bracts present
4 Bracteoles tubular, persistent (splitting with age, but not usually to the base); fruit
black...**4. A. nigra**
4 Bracteoles open to the base, often quickly deciduous; fruit red
5 Inflorescence branched, bracteoles not enfolding the remainder of the several-flowered
cincinnus; labellum with a long claw............................**5. A. galanga**
5 Inflorescence unbranched, bracteoles enfolding the usually 2-flowered cincinnus;
labellum without a claw
6 Leaves glabrous below, margins with well spaced short bristles, lamina not more
than 2.5 cm wide; filament at least twice as long as the anther.......**6. A. calcarata**
6 Leaves pubescent below, margins hairy but lacking short bristles, lamina 7 cm wide
or more; filament more or less equal to the anther in length......**7. A. malaccensis**

1. Alpinia abundiflora Burtt & Smith, Notes Roy. Bot. Gard. Edinburgh 34:
179, fig. 5. 1975. Type: *C.P. 3374* (PDA, K, BM).—**Fig. 3A.**

Elettaria floribunda Thw., Enum. Pl. Zeyl. 319. 1861—non *Alpinia floribunda*
Schum. in Pflanzenr. Zing., 439. 1904.
Amomum floribundum (Thw.) Trimen, Cat. 92. 1885; Trimen, Handb. Fl.
Ceylon 4: 250. 1898—excl. descr.; Baker in Hook. f., Fl. Br. Ind. 6: 233.
1893.
Amomum involucratum auct. non (Thw.) Trimen; Fischer in Gamble, Fl.
Pres. Madras 3: 1487. 1928.

Leafy stem sometimes exceeding 3 m. Leaves usually sessile, occasionally
with petioles up to 2 cm long; lamina up to 60×12 cm (those with distinct
petioles narrower, up to 5.5 cm wide) oblong or narrowly lanceolate, acuminate, glabrous or sometimes lightly pubescent beneath, attenuate at base;
ligule 1.5 cm long, membranous, obtuse, glabrous or lightly pubescent. Inflorescence capitate, truncate or globose, up to 10×10 cm, either separate
from the leafy stem on a leafless, sheath-covered, 20–40 cm peduncle or,
more rarely, terminal on a leaf-shoot; sheaths 15×2 cm, narrowly lanceolate
and often overtopping the inflorescence, forming a showy red involucre.
Sterile bracts red, in 1 or 2 series, c. 3×4 cm, usually mucronate, glabrous.
Fertile bracts glabrous: those at the base of the inflorescence resembling the
sterile bracts and often subtending a single flower and bracteole, those from
the remainder of the inflorescence becoming narrower and longer, averaging
3.5×2 cm and subtending short-stalked glabrous cincinni of up to 7 flowers.
Bracteoles open to the base or tubular, c. 2×1.5 cm when spread out, becoming smaller towards the top of the cincinnus, oblong, lightly 2-keeled,
apiculate; tubular and non-tubular bracteoles may occur within the same
cincinnus. Calyx 1–1.5 cm long, tubular, saccate in upper half, unilaterally
split. Corolla-tube slightly exceeding the calyx or more or less equal to it;
dorsal lobe broadly ovate, 7×5 mm, laterals narrower. Lateral staminodes

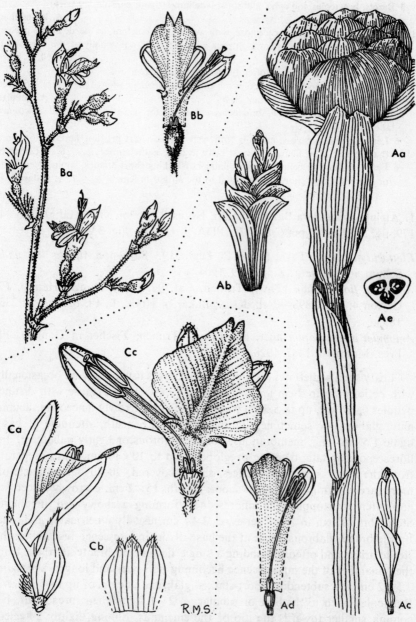

Fig. 3. A, *Alpinia abundiflora* Burtt & Smith: Aa, young inflorescence ×2/3; Ab, cincinnus ×1; Ac, flower ×1; Ad, flower, dissected, ×1; Ae, ovary in T.S. ×4. B, *A. nigra* (Gaertn.) B.L. Burtt: Ba, part of inflorescence ×2/3; Bb, flower, dissected, ×1. C, *A. malaccensis* (Burm. f.) Rosc.: Ca, flower ×1; Cb, calyx, dissected, ×1; Cc, flower, dissected, ×1.

absent. Labellum white, striped pink, c. 1 cm long, obovate, shallowly and often rather unequally 3-lobed. Anther more or less sessile, up to 5 mm long; thecae parallel, or slightly divergent at apex, connective not prolonged into a crest, emarginate. Epigynous glands 3 mm long, free from each other. Ovary c. 4 mm long, glabrous. Capsule (only immature fruit seen) spherical-oblong, thin walled.

D i s t r. Also occurs in South India.

E c o l. Flowers February to November.

N o t e. The inflorescences of *A. abundiflora* and the succeeding species, *A. fax*, are surrounded by an involucre of sterile bracts, thus superficially resembling *Nicolaia* (*Phaeomeria*), but the floral details are quite unlike that genus. Nor should these species remain in *Amomum* where, as far as is known, the bracts usually subtend a single flower and no sterile bracts occur. *A. abundiflora* was originally described as having the inflorescence borne separately from the leafy shoot (as in *Amomum*) but it is now known that terminal inflorescences may occasionally occur. Of particular interest is the character of the bracteoles in *A. abundiflora*; they may be open to the base or, less frequently, tubular, and both kinds may occur within a single cincinnus (see Smith, Notes Roy. Bot. Gard. Edinburgh 34: 179, f. 5. 1975).

Recent collections of *A. abundiflora* show some variation from the type material but probably not sufficient to justify according varietal rank to the plants in question. The type gathering has distinctly petiolate leaves and the upper sheaths of the peduncle do not seem to overtop the more or less globose inflorescence. *Burtt & Townsend 66*, from Kotagala hill, is identical. The majority of the specimens cited below have broader, sessile leaves and markedly flat-topped inflorescences which are overtopped by the peduncle sheaths; in other respects these plants do not differ from the type. Another collection, *Burtt & Townsend 58*, from Watawala, has both sessile and petiolate lamina and a globose inflorescence. Mr. A.H.M. Jayasuriya states, from observations made in the field, that the upper leaves of *A. abundiflora* are always sessile, while those at the base of the frond are nearly so. He has not seen plants with well developed petioles.

S p e c i m e n s E x a m i n e d. NUWARA ELIYA DISTRICT: Horton Plains, track to Kirigalpota, *Grierson 1099* (PDA, E); track between Horton Plains and North Cove, *Townsend 73/164* (K, E); Horton Plains, halfway from Farr Inn to Little World's End, *Read 2042* (US); between Small World's End and Big World's End, *Theobold & Krahulik 2761* (US); past Pattipola on road to Horton Plains, *Mueller-Dombois & Comanor 67070823* (US); hills surrounding Nuwara Eliya, *C.F. & R.J. Beusekom 1411* (US); Hakgala, *Cramer 4112* (E); Hakgala Natural Reserve, approach from Sita Eliya, *Jayasuriya, Sohmer & Eliezer 1374* (US); Kandapola F.R. along loop road, *Jayasuriya, Sohmer & Eliezer 8355* (US). KANDY DISTRICT: forest on E. of Adam's

Specimens Examined. KANDY DISTRICT: Dickoya, *Thwaites C.P. 3732* (PDA, K).

4. Alpinia nigra (Gaertn.) Burtt, Notes Roy. Bot. Gard. Edinburgh 35: 213. 1977. Lectotype: *Cardamomum zeylanicum fructu rotundo nigro, in caulium summitate* Hermann, Parad. Bot. 320. 1689. No specimen in Herb. Hermann (BM)—**Fig. 3B.**

Zingiber nigrum Gaertn., Fruct. 1: 35, t. 12. 1788.
Heritiera allughas Retz., Obs. 6: 17, t. 1. 1791. Type: Ceylon, *Koenig* (LU).
Alpinia allughas (Retz.) Roscoe, Trans. Linn. Soc. London 8: 346. 1807; Baker in Hook. f., Fl. Br. Ind. 6: 253. 1893; Trimen, Handb. Fl. Ceylon 4: 247. 1898.
Languas chinensis (Retz.) Alston in Trimen, Handb. Fl. Ceylon 6: 282. 1931, excl. basionym; see Notes Roy. Bot. Gard. Edinburgh 35: 214. 1977.

Leafy stem to 3 m. Leaves sessile or very shortly petiolate, up to 50 × 15 cm, linear-lanceolate, acuminate, some pubescence on either side of the midrib below, otherwise glabrous; ligule c. 0.5 cm long, rounded, entire, pubescent; sheaths glabrous. Inflorescence paniculate, pubescent, usually rather lax with remote cincinni. Bracts membranous, up to 0.5 cm long (those at the base often much larger), each subtending a cincinnus of up to 4 shortly pedicellate flowers. Bracteoles tubular, membranous, splitting to the base readily. Calyx 0.5–1 cm long, pubescent, 2–3-toothed, unilaterally split. Corolla-tube not exceeding the calyx; lobes 1–1.3 cm long, linear-oblong, pubescent outside, the dorsal lobe wider and cucullate. Labellum clawed, up to 2.5 cm long, limb cuneiform, 3-lobed, the midlobe divided into 2 triangular lobes, lateral lobes rounded. Lateral staminodes reduced to small subulate teeth at the base of the labellum. Stamen shorter than the labellum; filament 0.8–1 cm; anther 5 mm, thecae parallel, no distinct crest produced. Epigynous glands 1–2 mm, free from each other. Ovary 4 × 2 mm, trilocular, densely pubescent. Capsule globose, 2 cm in diameter, black, very brittle, glabrescent; seed black.

Distr. Throughout Indo-Malesia, wild and cultivated, common in Sri Lanka.

Uses. The rhizome is used medicinally.

Vern. Alu-gas, Alan, Keleniya (S); Shittai-rattai (T).

Specimens Examined. LOCALITY UNKNOWN: *s. coll. C.P. 3157* (BM); *McCrae 564* (BM); *Koenig s.n.* (LU); *Koenig s.n.* (BM). *Walker s.n.* (K).

5. Alpinia galanga (L.) Sw., Obs. 2. 1791; Thw., Enum. Pl. Zeyl. 319. 1861; Baker in Hook. f., Fl. Br. Ind. 6: 253. 1892. Type: No specimen at LINN.

Maranta galanga L., Sp. Pl. ed. 2, 3. 1762.

Languas galanga (L.) Stuntz, U.S.D.A. Bur. Pl. Industr. Bull. no. 261: 21. 1912.

Leafy shoots to over 2 m. Leaves up to 60 × 15 cm, oblong-lanceolate, glabrous. Inflorescence terminal, pubescent, up to 30 cm long, with numerous short branches. Bracts up to 2 cm long, usually less, rather membranous, ovate, easily breaking off, each subtending a cincinnus of about 4 or 5 flowers. Bracteoles similar to the bracts but smaller. Calyx up to 1 cm long. Corolla greenish-white; tube slightly exceeding the calyx; lobes c. 1.5 cm long, rounded. Labellum white, veined with lilac, c. 2 cm long, unguiculate in lower half, limb emarginate. Lateral staminodes small, subulate. Filament up to 2 cm long, slender; anther-thecae 5–8 mm, cells parallel, no crest produced. Epigynous glands 3 mm long, fleshy, free from each other. Ovary 2 mm long, glabrous. Capsule 1 cm in diameter, globose, orange-red.

D i s t r. Probably wild in parts of India, Indo-China and Malaysia; cultivated throughout S.E. Asia. Not native in Sri Lanka.

U s e s. The rhizome is used for flavouring and medicinally.

S p e c i m e n E x a m i n e d. LOCALITY UNKNOWN: *Walker 1158* (K).

6. Alpinia calcarata Roscoe, Trans. Linn. Soc. London 8: 347. 1807; Roscoe, Monandr. t. 68. 1824; Baker in Hook. f., Fl. Br. Ind. 6: 254. 1892. Type: Cult. Liverpool, no specimen.

Languas calcarata (Roscoe) Alston in Trimen, Handb. Fl. Ceylon 6: 282. 1931.

Leaf stem rather slender, up to just over 1 m high. Leaves sessile, up to 35 × 2.5 cm, linear-lanceolate, acuminate, narrowing towards the base, glabrous on both surfaces, the margins bearing short bristles at least 1 mm apart, often much more remote; ligule up to 1 cm long, membranous, entire, ciliate. Inflorescence terminal, rather short, up to 10 cm. Bracts absent (or quickly deciduous?). Flowers usually borne in pairs, very shortly pedicellate, each subtended by a non-tubular, membranous, oblong, 1–1.5 cm long quickly deciduous bracteole. Calyx c. 6 mm long, sparsely pubescent, 3-lobed, unilaterally split. Corolla-tube shorter than, or equalling, the calyx, pubescent at the throat within; lobes oblong, 1–1.5 cm long, the dorsal 0.5 cm wide, laterals narrower. Labellum obovate, 2–3 cm long, 1.5–2 cm wide in lower half, apex emarginate, white, lined rose-purple. Lateral staminodes subulate, arising on either side at the base of the labellum. Stamen up to 2 cm long, filament narrow, c. 1.3 cm, anther 5–7 mm, thecae more or less parallel, pubescent, slightly divergent at the apex, no crest formed. Style exserted for c. 2 mm from anther. Ovary sericeous, c. 4 mm long, subglobose. Epigynous glands c. 1.5 cm long, rather thick, dorsally united. Fruit globose, orange-red.

D i s t r. Native of India. Widely cultivated.

V e r n. Katu-kiriya (S).

S p e c i m e n s E x a m i n e d. KURUNEGALA DISTRICT: Dummala-suriya, *Jayasuriya 1191* (PDA, US); Kurunegala—Narammala between 7–8th mile post, *Amaratunga 2239* (PDA). KANDY DISTRICT: Peradeniya, *McCrae 566* (BM, CGE). NUWARA ELIYA DISTRICT: near Pannala, 13 Jan. 1950, *Rhind s.n.* (PDA). LOCALITY UNKNOWN: *Pailett? s.n.* (CGE); *Baker 114* (E); *Walker s.n.* (K).

7. Alpinia malaccensis (Burm. f.) Roscoe, Trans. Linn. Soc. London 8: 345. 1808; Baker in Hook. f., Fl. Br. Ind. 6: 255. 1892; Ramamoorthy in Saldanha & Nicolson, Fl. Hassan Distr. 762. 1976. Type: Rumphius, Herb. Amb. 5: t. 71, fl. 1747.—**Fig. 3C.**

Maranta malaccensis Burm. f., Fl. Ind. 2. 1768.
Alpinia nutans Roscoe var. *β* Thw., Enum. Pl. Zeyl. 320. 1861.
Alpinia nutans Roscoe var. *sericea* Baker in Hook. f., Fl. Br. Ind. 6: 256.
  1892; Trimen, Handb. Fl. Ceylon 4: 248. 1898. Type: Ceylon, *C.P. 3312* (PDA).

Leafy stem robust, to 3 m. Leaves with 3–5 cm rounded pubescent petioles; lamina narrowly lanceolate, acuminate, up to 60 × 7 cm, usually densely pubescent below or pubescence confined to margins and midrib; ligule to 1 cm long, hairy, coriaceous, entire; sheaths shortly pubescent. Inflorescence erect or slightly curved, main axis pubescent. Bracts absent. Cincinni of 2 very shortly pedicellate flowers or reduced to a single flower, stalk 0.5–1.5 cm long, pubescent. Bracteoles white, open to base, 1.5–2 cm long, folded round the bud becoming quickly deciduous as the flower opens, lightly pubescent at apex. Calyx white, 2 cm long, pubescent at least at the apex, shortly 3-lobed and deeply split unilaterally. Corolla white, tube up to 1 cm long, glabrous; lateral lobes 3 × 1 cm, ciliate-margined, dorsal lobe broader, also ciliate. Labellum yellow-orange, heavily lined with scarlet, 3–5 cm long, 3 cm across at widest part, sides incurved, narrowing to an emarginate apex, with 2 papillose fleshy swellings at the base. Lateral staminodes subulate, less than 5 mm long. Filament c. 1 cm long; anther of equal length or longer, thecae parallel, connective not prolonged into a crest. Epigynous glands 5 5 mm long, free from each other. Ovary 5 mm long, pubescent, trilocular. Capsule turning red at length, globose, up to 3 cm in diameter, shortly pubescent.

D i s t r. Malesia.

V e r n. Ran-kiriya, Galangal, Kalu-wala (S); Pera-rattai (T).

I l l u s t r. Bot. Reg. t. 328. 1818.

N o t e. It is difficult to understand why Baker placed this plant as a variety of *A. zerumbet* (*A. nutans*). It may be readily distinguished from that species by the smaller size of the flowers, erect inflorescence, pure white bracteoles and longer petioles. At the British Museum there is a painting of the plant accompanied by a detailed description by Moon, taken from a specimen collected near Kandy; this description accords well with *A. malaccensis*. Thwaites' collections, which typify Baker's variety, are in fruit only and show much less leaf pubescence.

Specimens Examined. COLOMBO or KURUNEGALA DISTRICT: between Negombo & Kurunegala, *s. coll. C.P. 3312* (PDA, K, BM, CGE). KANDY DISTRICT: Hantane, *Burtt & Townsend 53* (PDA, E).

9. NICOLAIA

Horan., Monogr. Scit. 32. 1862; Benth. & Hook. f., Gen. Pl. 3: 644. 1883—sub *Amomum*. Type species: *Nicolaia elatior* (Jack) Horan.

Phaeomeria [Lindl., Nat. Syst. Bot. ed. 2, 446. 1836—nom. inval. ex] Schum. in Pflanzenr. Zing. 261. 1904.

Leafy shoots often very tall, many-bladed. Inflorescence on a separate, elongate, erect, leafless peduncle, surrounded by an involucre of large sterile coloured bracts, the receptacle of the inflorescence almost flat. Fertile bracts rather narrow and thin, each subtending a single flower. Bracteoles tubular. Calyx usually with 3 short teeth, unilaterally split. Corolla-tube shorter than the calyx; lobes held more or less erect. Labellum short, erect, joined at the base to the lower part of the filament, thus forming a short tube above the insertion of the petals, the limb inrolling in a coil as the flower fades. Lateral staminodes 0 or present as rudimentary hairy teeth or bumps. Filament (the free part) short, usually exceeded by the anther which is emarginate at the apex, never crested. Epigynous glands short and fleshy, encircling the style, free to the base on one side. Infructescence rounded or becoming elongated, fruit smooth.

About eight species, all Malesian.

Nicolaia elatior (Jack) Horan., Monogr. Scit. 32. 1862; Burtt & Smith, Notes Roy. Bot. Gard. Edinburgh 31: 210. 1972, which see for full synonymy. Type: Sumatra, *Jack s.n.* (specimen lost?).

Alpinia elatior Jack, Mal. Misc. 2, 7: 2. 1822, reimp. in Hook., J. Bot. 1: 359. 1834.

Leafy shoots to 5 m; petioles to 4 cm; lamina up to 90 × 20 cm, glabrous; ligule shortly bilobed. Peduncle up to 1.5 m, clothed with glabrous, green sheaths. Sterile bracts crimson-pink, 8–12 × 2–3 cm, spreading. Fertile bracts showing a transition from the sterile bracts, becoming much smaller (3–5 cm long) towards the centre of the inflorescence. Bracteoles c. 2 cm long, unilaterally split. Calyx longer than the bracteole, 3-toothed, unilaterally split. Corolla pink. Labellum deep crimson with white or yellow margin. Filament white; anther red. Fruit spherical, 2–2.5 cm in diameter, shortly pubescent.

D i s t r. Probably widely distributed in Malaysia where it is known as the "Torch Ginger". Cultivated throughout the tropics as an ornamental.

U s e s. The young flowers have some culinary merit.

N o t e. *Nicolaia elatior* has been seen in gardens near Kandy and on the roadside from Peradeniya University campus to the wireless station. It is also cultivated in the Royal Botanic Garden. It is included here because its habit may lead to confusion with *Alpinia abundiflora* and *A. fax*. While the structure of the inflorescence is quite different in *Nicolaia*, it is most easily distinguished by the pink sterile bracts; those of *A. abundiflora* and *A. fax* are bright red or red-brown.

10. AMOMUM

Roxb., Fl. Ind. 1: 317. 1820, nom. cons.; Benth. & Hook. f., Gen. Pl. 3: 644. 1883; Baker in Hook. f., Fl. Br. Ind. 6: 233. 1892; Schum. in Pflanzenr. Zing. 222. 1904. Type species: *Amomum subulatum* Roxb.

Leafy shoots c. 1–3 m tall, many-bladed. Inflorescence borne separately near the base of a leafy shoot; peduncle subterranean, or above ground and more or less prostrate. Bracts imbricating, each subtending a single flower. Bracteoles usually tubular (rarely absent). Calyx tubular, sometimes unilaterally split. Corolla-tube never much exceeding calyx, usually shorter; dorsal lobe usually wider than laterals. Labellum conspicuous, often trilobed. Lateral staminodes usually small subulate teeth or 0. Stamen with a well-developed filament, anther-thecae parallel or diverging, connective often produced into a well-developed crest. Ovary trilocular. Fruit often covered with fleshy spines, sometimes winged.

Probably about 90 species distributed from India and China through Malesia to Queensland. Eight are endemic in Sri Lanka.

KEY TO THE SPECIES

1 Inflorescence few-flowered (2–3?); leaves appressed silvery pubescent below; petioles up to 15 cm...**1. A. hypoleucum**
1 Inflorescence many-flowered; leaves, if pubescent below, then not appressed silvery; petioles not exceeding 2.5 cm
  2 Leaf margin callose-denticulate towards tip; anther-crest absent........**2. A. nemorale**
  2 Leaf margin entire, sometimes pubescent, never callose-denticulate; anther-crest always well formed
    3 Leaf margin densely villous below; ligule bearded..............**3. A. benthamianum**
    3 Leaf margin glabrous; ligule glabrous, ciliate or pubescent, never bearded

4 Leaves up to 1.5 cm broad; rhizome spreading....................**4. A. graminifolium**
4 Leaves at least 2.5 cm broad, usually much more; rhizome spreading or not
  5 Bracts and bracteoles quickly deciduous; ligule bifid; capsule 9-ribbed..............
  ....**5. A. pterocarpum**
  5 Bracts not quickly deciduous; ligule entire; capsule probably always echinate
    6 Ligule longer than the petiole; bracts not conspicuously ciliate
      7 Upper part of ligule deciduous; bracteole bilobed; fruit red......................
      ....**6. A. masticatorium**
      7 Upper part of ligule never deciduous; bracteole truncate; fruit dark purple.........
      ....**7. A. echinocarpum**
    6 Ligule consistently shorter than the petiole; bracts ciliate
      8 Inflorescence conspicuously densely fulvo-sericeous when dry, robust, 5–10 × 6 cm; leaves glabrous below...**8. A. fulviceps**
      8 Inflorescence not conspicuously fulvo-sericeous when dry, 3–5 × 2.5–3 cm; leaves with some pubescence beneath or glabrous
        9 Inflorescence subglobose, 2.5 × 3 cm; bracts not conspicuously imbricating........
        ....**9. A. acuminatum**
        9 Inflorescence ovoid to oblong, 3–5 × 2.5–3 cm; bracts imbricating; leaves with some pubescence below................................**10. A. trichostachyum**

1. Amomum hypoleucum Thw., Enum. Pl. Zeyl. 318. 1861; Baker in Hook. f., Fl. Br. Ind. 6: 240. 1892; Trimen, Handb., Fl. Ceylon 4: 254. 1898; Fischer in Gamble, Fl. Pres. Madras 3: 1487. 1928; Ramamoorthy in Saldanha & Nicolson, Fl. Hassan Distr. 764. 1976. Type: *C.P. 3532* (PDA, K, BM).

Rhizome creeping; leafy-shoots to 1.75 m, sheaths loose to base; petioles 2.5–7.5 cm; lamina up to 60 × 11.5 cm when fully developed, often much smaller, oblong-lanceolate, acuminate, appressed pubescent below; ligule short, bilobed; sheaths not tightly clasping. Peduncle 2.5–7.5 cm long, slender. Inflorescence up to 5 cm long, narrow, few (3?)—flowered. Bracts c. 3 cm long, oblong, membranous. Bracteoles non-tubular (?), longer than the bracts, trilobed, the dorsal lobe apiculate. Calyx 3.5 cm long, 3-lobed. Corolla white; tube c. 4.5 cm long; lobes 2.5 cm long, the dorsal lobe 8 mm wide and cucullate-mucronate, the laterals narrower. Labellum stained yellow and pink, 3.5 × 2.3 cm at widest part, blade rounded at apex, narrowing into a 1.5 cm long shaft. Lateral staminodes small, tooth-like. Filament 6 mm long; anther 9 mm, the connective prolonged into a 3 × 8 mm truncate crest. Ovary 5 mm long, sericeous. Capsule globose, 1.5 cm in diameter with 7–8 ridges.

D i s t r. Also occurs in South India. Rare in Sri Lanka.
E c o l. Flowers August to November.
S p e c i m e n s E x a m i n e d. KANDY DISTRICT: Alagalla, *Thwaites C.P. 3532* (PDA, K, BM).

2. Amomum nemorale (Thw.) Trimen, Cat. 92. 1885; Trimen, Handb. Fl. Ceylon 4: 251. 1898; Baker in Hook. f., Fl. Br. Ind. 6: 233. 1892. Type: *C.P. 3703* (PDA, K, BM).

522   ZINGIBERACEAE

Elettaria nemoralis Thw., Enum. Pl. Zeyl. 319. 1861.

Leafy stem 60–120 cm; lamina shortly petiolate (c. 1 cm), 14–30 (?) × 3–5 cm, narrowly lanceolate, acuminate, glabrous, the margins callose-denticulate towards the tip; ligule short, rounded, entire, ciliate. Peduncle 5–7 cm, clothed with broad, loose scales. Inflorescence 2.5–3.5 cm long, subglobose to oblong. Bracts 0.7–1.5 cm long, orbicular or obovate, membranous, lightly pubescent towards the tip. Bracteoles lanceolate. Calyx 1.7 cm long, glabrous. Corolla greenish-white, tube 3.5 cm long; lobes up to 1.2 cm long, oblong, obtuse, subequal. Labellum veined with pink, reniform, 3-lobed, lateral lobes falcately recurved, midlobe smaller and rounded, 2–3-fid. Lateral staminodes? Anther c. 4 mm, thecae glabrous, connective not prolonged into a crest. Ovary pubescent. Capsule smooth, subglobose, c. 1.75 cm in diameter; seeds few, large, enclosed in a white spongy pulp.

D i s t r. Endemic. Not re-collected. The above description, with a few amendments, is based on those of Thwaites and Trimen.

S p e c i m e n s   E x a m i n e d. KALUTARA DISTRICT: Hewesse, Reigam Korale, *Thwaites C.P. 3703* (K).

3. **Amomum benthamianum** Trimen, J. Bot. 23: 266. 1885; Trimen, Handb. Fl. Ceylon 4: 255. 1898; Baker in Hook. f., Fl. Br. Ind. 6: 242. 1892. Type: *C.P. 3864* (K).

Leafy stem 60–120 cm tall, slender. Lamina shortly petiolate (up to 7 mm), 15–25 × 2.5–3.5 cm, linear-lanceolate, caudate-acuminate, minutely puberulous on both surfaces, margins villous; ligule up to 2 cm long, rounded, densely bearded with fulvous hairs. Peduncle 5–8 cm, slender, clothed with short oblong sheaths. Inflorescence 2.5 cm long, globose, main axis velutinous. Bracts c. 1.2 cm long, oblong, acute, membranous, more or less glabrous with tomentose tips. Bracteoles? Calyx 4 mm long, pubescent. Corolla-tube 2.5 cm long, lobes oblong-obtuse. Labellum? Lateral staminodes? Filament 3 mm long; anther 6 mm, thecae pubescent, connective prolonged into a broadly elliptic 3-lobed crest. Ovary 2 mm long. Capsule ovoid, 1.75 × 2 cm, copiously echinate with short curved spines.

D i s t r. Endemic.

N o t e. The type material of this species, which has not been re-collected, is imperfect. The above description is based on that of Trimen and our own observations on Thwaites' specimen in the Kew Herbarium.

S p e c i m e n   E x a m i n e d. KALUTARA DISTRICT: Reigam Korale, *Thwaites C.P. 3864* (K).

4. **Amomum graminifolium** Thw., Enum. Pl. Zeyl. 430. 1864; Baker in Hook. f., Fl. Br. Ind. 6: 238. 1892; Trimen, Handb. Fl. Ceylon 4: 253. 1898. Type: *C.P. 3820* (K, BM, G, CGE).

Leafy stem 1–1.6 m. Leaves shortly petiolate or subsessile; lamina 30–40 × 1.5 cm, linear-lanceolate, acuminate, glabrous; ligule up to 5 mm long, entire, rather truncate, glabrous. Peduncle up to 7 cm long, usually densely fulvous, clothed with membranous, often lightly pubescent, scales up to 1 cm long. Inflorescence ovate or subglobose, up to 5 cm long. Bracts 1–2 cm long, linear-lanceolate, glabrous or sparsely pubescent. Bracteoles tubular, 1 cm long, pubescent. Calyx almost 2 cm long, unilaterally split, minutely 3-lobed, pubescent at apex. Corolla-tube 1.5–2.5 cm long; lateral lobes c. 1.5 × 3 cm, linear-oblong, obtuse; dorsal lobe much wider. Labellum 2 × 1.5 cm, obovate, 4-lobed. Lateral staminodes 0? Filament 1 cm long, slender; anther-thecae 3 mm long, ciliate, divergent at the tips, connective prolonged into a 1.5 cm broad, 0.5 cm long, reniform, undulating crest. Ovary 3 mm long, pubescent.

D i s t r. Endemic.
E c o l. Flowers in May.
S p e c i m e n s E x a m i n e d. RATNAPURA DISTRICT: Sinharaja Forest, *Burtt 6806* (leaves only, E). LOCALITY UNKNOWN: *Thwaites C.P. 3820* (PDA, K, BM, G, CGE).

5. Amomum pterocarpum Thw., Enum. Pl. Zeyl. 317. 1861; Baker in Hook. f., Fl. Br. Ind. 6: 241. 1892; Trimen, Handb. Fl. Ceylon 4: 254. 1898. Type: *C.P. 3021* (PDA, K, BM, G, CGE).—**Fig. 4A.**

Amomum microstephanum Baker in Hook. f., Fl. Br. Ind. 6: 239. 1892.

Leafy stem to 2.5 m; petioles up to 4 cm long or leaves more or less sessile; lamina up to 70 × 15 cm, oblong-lanceolate, acuminate, narrowed and unequal at the base; glabrous except for tip and short pubescence on either side of midrib below (type), or lightly pubescent over entire lower surface; ligule c. 1.5 cm long, membranous, bifid, sheath areolate, glabrous. Peduncle 5–12 cm, ascending, clothed with 2 × 2 cm, broadly ovate, glabrous sheaths. Inflorescence many-flowered. Bracts and bracteoles not examined, presumably very quickly deciduous. Flowers white, on pedicels up to 5 mm long. Calyx 2.5 cm long, saccate, distinctly 3-lobed, the lobes more or less acuminate, each with a very small subapical spur, glabrous. Corolla-tube more or less equalling the calyx; lobes 2.5 cm long; laterals 5 mm wide, lanceolate; dorsal almost twice as wide, cucullate. Labellum white, flushed orange centrally, 3 × 2 cm, including the 6 mm parallel-sided claw, limb ovate-orbicular, pubescent at throat within, a few scattered hairs on limb. Lateral staminodes short, blunt appendages. Filament short, c. 2 mm; anther over 1 cm long, thecae narrow, diverging at the tips, connective prolonged into a 1 cm wide, semilunar, obscurely 3-lobed crest. Epigynous glands c. 6 mm long, linear, free. Ovary rather elongated, c. 6 × 3 mm, very shortly but densely pubescent. Capsule 9-ribbed, ribs winged.

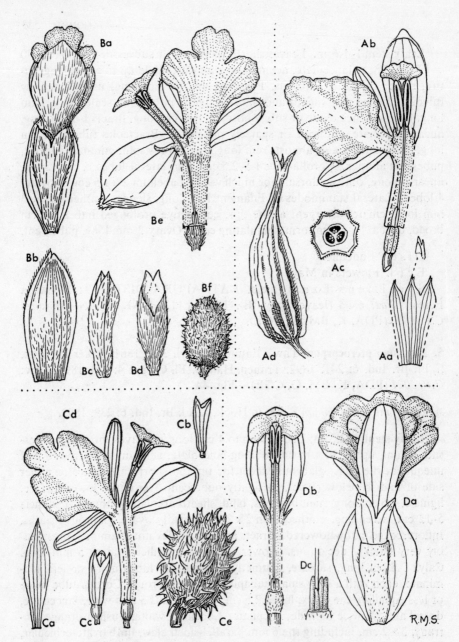

Fig. 4. *A. Amomum pterocarpum* Thw.: Aa, calyx, dissected, ×1; Ab, flower, dissected, ×1; Ac, ovary in T.S. ×3; Ad, capsule ×1. B, *A. fulviceps* Thw.: Ba, flower with bracts ×1; Bb, bract ×1; Bc, bracteole ×1; Bd, calyx ×1; Be, flower, dissected, ×1; Bf, immature capsule ×1. C, *A. masticatorium* Thw.: Ca, bract ×1; Cb, bracteole ×1; Cc, calyx ×1; Cd, flower, dissected, ×1; Ce, capsule ×1. D, *A. echinocarpum* Alston: Da, flower with bracts ×1; Db, flower in L.S., showing stamen and lateral staminodes, ×1; Dc, epigynous glands ×2.

D i s t r. Also occurs in South India.

N o t e. *A. microstephanum*, described from South India, cannot be separated from *A. pterocarpum*.

S p e c i m e n s E x a m i n e d. MONERAGALA DISTRICT: Badalkumbura, *Jayasuriya & Townsend 1190* (PDA, US, E). LOCALITY UNKNOWN: *Thwaites C.P. 3021* (PDA, K, BM, G, CGE).

6. Amomum masticatorium Thw., Enum. Pl. Zeyl. 317. 1861; Baker in Hook. f., Fl. Br. Ind. 6: 238. 1892; Trimen, Handb. Fl. Ceylon 4: 252. 1898. Type: *C.P. 3701* (PDA, K, BM).—**Fig. 4C.**

Leafy stem to 4 m. Leaves subsessile, up to 40 × 5 cm, narrowly lanceolate, caudate-acuminate, glabrous; ligule up to 3 cm long, acute or obtuse, the membranous upper third or half deciduous, ligules from the top of a 'frond' shorter and remaining intact (?). Peduncle 5–7 cm, flexuous, decumbent, clothed with 1–2 cm long, broadly ovate, lightly pubescent, membranous sheaths. Inflorescence globose, up to 5 cm in diameter. Bracts 2 × 1–1.3 cm, obovate, obtuse, pubescent, margins slightly ciliate. Bracteoles tubular, up to 2 cm long, bilobed, glabrous. Calyx c. 3 cm long, trilobed, lobes usually lightly pubescent at their tips. Corolla yellow, tube not exceeding the calyx, glabrous or with some pubescence outside; lateral lobes c. 2 × 0.4 cm, oblong, obtuse, dorsal lobe twice as broad. Labellum yellow, streaked red, 1.5–1.8 cm long, 1–1.5 cm across at widest part, more or less orbicular, narrowed to a short claw at the base, limb 3-lobed, midlobe bifid. Lateral staminodes 3.5–6 mm, linear. Filament c. 8 mm long; anther-thecae 5–6 mm, diverging above, very shortly pubescent at base and apex, the connective prolonged into a 1 cm wide × 0.3 cm long semilunar obscurely 3-lobed crest. Epigynous glands 4 mm long, usually united. Ovary 3 mm long, glabrous, or sometimes shortly and sparsely pubescent. Capsule globose, up to 2 cm across, echinate.

D i s t r. Endemic, said by Trimen to be abundant at Hantane.

U s e s. The aromatic rhizome is chewed with betel.

N o t e. The Laxapana Falls collections differ from the type in having the corolla tube entirely glabrous and the ovary at least sparsely pubescent. The deciduous upper part of the ligule is, however, apparent. This feature, which may be absent in the upper part of the frond, where leaves and ligule are very much smaller, has not been observed in any other species of *Amomum*.

S p e c i m e n s E x a m i n e d. KANDY DISTRICT: Hantane, *Thwaites C.P. 3701* (PDA, K, BM); Laxapana Falls, above Murutenne, *Grierson 1048* (US, E); below Laxapana Falls, *Burtt & Townsend 117* (E); Gannoruwa Hill, *Wirawan 614* (US, K, E).

7. Amomum echinocarpum Alston in Trimen, Handb. Fl. Ceylon 6: 283. 1931. Type: *C.P. 3020* (PDA, K, BM, CGE).—**Fig. 4D.**

Amomum echinatum Thw., Enum. Pl. Zeyl. 316. 1861; Baker in Hook. f., Fl. Br. Ind. 6: 242. 1892; Trimen, Handb. Fl. Ceylon 4: 255. 1898—non Willd.

Up to 4 m high. Leaves sessile, up to 60 × 8 cm but often considerably smaller, narrowly lanceolate, acuminate, rounded at the base, glabrous; ligule up to 2 × 2 cm, truncate, clasping the stem, coriaceous with a membranous margin. Peduncle up to 30 cm, flexuous, covered with imbricating sheaths; sheaths 1.5–3 × c. 1.5 cm, obtuse, coriaceous, glabrous; inflorescence globose, c. 5 × 5 cm. Bracts c. 2.5 × 2 cm, obtuse, pubescent with a thin membranous margin. Bracteoles tubular, 1.5 cm long, truncate, obscurely keeled laterally and lightly pubescent, margin ciliate. Calyx c. 2.5 cm long, slightly saccate, 3-lobed, each lobe with a small subapical spur or swelling, pubescent at the base at least. Corolla-tube more or less equalling the calyx in length, pubescent at the throat within; lobes 2–2.5 cm long, oblong, rounded at apex. Labellum broader than long, up to 3 × 3.5 cm, the claw up to c. 1.5 cm, limb obscurely 3-lobed. Lateral staminodes 2–3 mm, subulate, usually bifid to base. Filament c. 1.5 cm; anther more or less equalling the filament, thecae parallel, pubescent, the connective prolonged into 1 cm wide, obscurely 3-lobed crest. Epigynous glands about 5 mm long, fused. Ovary pubescent, 3–5 × 3 mm. Capsule globose, echinate, spines curved.

D i s t r. Endemic. Common around Kandy.
E c o l. Flowers February to May.
V e r n. Bu-Kiriya (S).
S p e c i m e n s E x a m i n e d. KANDY DISTRICT: jungle behind R.B.G. Peradeniya, *Kostermans 23002* (E); southern slope of Gannoruwa hill, *Jayasuriya 1197* (PDA, US, E); route from Peradeniya to Ratnapura, 5 m S. of Bulatkohupitya, *Burtt 6794* (E). KEGALLE DISTRICT: mile post 64/21 between Ginigathena and Kitulgala, *Read 2190A* (US). LOCALITY UNKNOWN: *s. coll. C.P. 3020* (CGE).

8. Amomum fulviceps Thw., Enum. Pl. Zeyl. 317. 1861; Baker in Hook. f., Fl. Br. Ind. 6: 237. 1892; Trimen, Handb. Fl. Ceylon 4: 252. 1898. Type: *C.P. 3122* (PDA, K, FIR).—**Fig. 4B.**

Phaeomeria fulviceps (Thw.) Schum. in Pflanzenr. Zing. 263. 1904.

Up to over 3 m tall. Petioles up to 1.5 cm long; lamina to 40 × 7 cm, lanceolate, acuminate, abruptly narrowed at the base, entirely glabrous; ligule 1cm long, coriaceous, entire, glabrous. Peduncle up to 11 cm long, clothed with ovate-acute, mucronate, imbricating sheaths, sheaths lightly pubescent at apex. Inflorescence often more or less globose, sometimes ovoid, c. 5 × 7–5 cm, becoming elongated in fruit. Bracts 2–3.5 × 1.5–2 cm, ovate-oblong, conspicuously fulvous hairy. Bracteoles tubular, 1.5–2.5 cm long, bilobed, keeled on the lobes, the keels sometimes extending to the base of the bracteole, light-